MORPHOLOGICAL ANALYSIS OF LAND FORMS

MORPHOLOGICAL ANALYSIS
OF LAND FORMS

A CONTRIBUTION TO PHYSICAL GEOLOGY

BY

PROF. DR.

WALTHER PENCK

TRANSLATED BY

HELLA CZECH, Ph.D. (Vienna)
LECTURER IN THE INSTITUTE OF EDUCATION, UNIVERSITY OF LONDON

AND

KATHARINE CUMMING BOSWELL, B.A., M.Sc. (Lond.)
FORMERLY LECTURER IN THE DEPARTMENT OF GEOGRAPHY,
UNIVERSITY COLLEGE, SOUTHAMPTON
(NOW SOUTHAMPTON UNIVERSITY)

MACMILLAN AND CO., LIMITED
ST. MARTIN'S STREET, LONDON
1953

MACMILLAN AND COMPANY LIMITED
London Bombay Calcutta Madras Melbourne

THE MACMILLAN COMPANY OF CANADA LIMITED
Toronto

ST MARTIN'S PRESS INC
New York

PRINTED IN GREAT BRITAIN

PREFACE

This work of Walther Penck's was published posthumously by his father, the famous geographer Albrecht Penck. The latter's preface points out that for ten years his son had been carrying on his investigations into the course of crustal movements, making use of the earth's surface forms as starting point. In 1921 he termed this method *morphological analysis*. A letter, written in 1922, outlined his plan for a projected work, larger than what he actually accomplished before his early death in 1923.

The first chapters have the titles found in the present book—up to 'Development of Slope'. He wrote '. . . development of the entire slopes and their dependence upon the downcutting of running water . . . I thought of then continuing with erosion by running water. But that will not do, since the work of running water depends not only upon the water, but more especially upon the gradient down which it flows; and the gradient is dependent upon the movement of the earth's crust. If this rises rapidly, the angle of inclination is great (since the area concerned then rises high above its surroundings); if it rises slowly, the angle of inclination is produced slowly, and remains slight. Thus, dealing with erosion, I have already come to the crustal movements which were to be my goal; and so I am compelled, like my predecessors, to go straight from the whole collection of the earth's land forms to the crustal movements, when I have not yet described the way in which those forms are to be observed. That will not do. What is this collection of forms? What does one see in mountains, in Swabia, etc., over the whole world? *Surfaces, denudational slopes*, make up the whole set of land forms. And it is where the surfaces meet downwards in valleys, that the rivers are to be found. Thus what we see is emphatically not the vertical incisions produced by running water, but only slopes which develop upwards, with a definite form, from the eroding rivers, *whilst* these are eroding. In brief: what is seen at the earth's surface is not land forms due to erosion, but merely a relief produced solely by the development of slopes. This slope development, however, is not possible by itself, but presupposes simultaneous downcutting by rivers. The eroding river

v

creates the vertical distance between the height and the valley bottom; denudation, however, creates the slope, the material surface, which actually unites valley bottom with high-lying part. It thus follows that— after the slope development and its dependence upon erosion have been treated—the description of the land forms, i.e. of the relief of the earth's surface, must logically come next. It belongs organically to the investigation of the slopes, and not to that of erosion. There is no need whatever to know how erosion works, how it depends upon the movements of the earth's crust, in order to be able to describe the manner in which slopes are combined into a wealth of land forms, into form associations. This is controlled by laws, as comes out clearly in a presentation kept free from any interpretation. A presentation of the land forms found on the earth is no easy task! It could not be accomplished were there not quite definite relief *types* occurring in quite definite areas of the earth. I have now just finished the treatment of those types which are characteristic of the monotonous continental regions—such as Africa, Australia, etc.— and furthermore of the regions of uplift within those areas (e.g. the type of the German Highlands, with the Scarplands; this type is repeated all over the earth in zones of analogous structure). I am about to contrast these phenomena with what is to be seen in the mountain belts (these are the zones of mountain chains which border the Mediterranean Sea continuing across south and central Asia to the Pacific Ocean, and the analogous belt that surrounds the Pacific Ocean . . .). In this way I shall come to erosion, and after that to crustal movements. It will then be relatively easy and simple, since there is a logical connection: the relief type described, X, signifies a certain thing as regards crustal movement; that is to say, only on a crustal unit of the earth which moves in this quite definite way can that relief type X come into existence. This, therefore, indicates to me what course the crustal movements take. I envisage it in this fashion, and I think of fitting in detailed treatment of definite regions, e.g. the Black Forest—Alb—Alps—certain characteristic forms of Central Asia, of the Andes, etc. This would serve not only as an illustration of how to apply the whole method and the results that can be obtained from it, but also to present a picture of the types of crustal movement and their distribution over the earth. In this culminating chapter, wide and surprising vistas will appear leading towards the *causes* of crustal movement. It is to this fundamental problem of geology that I intend to devote the whole of my labours, possibly to the end of my life.'

Then follows a long account of Walther Penck's life, which is here summarised.

He was born in Vienna on the 30th August, 1888. He developed into a first class mountaineer, his earliest considerable climb being at the age of eight when he accompanied his father on a scientific expedition. Austrian schools provided good training in Natural Science; and he was specially fortunate in having as teacher Paul Pfurtscheller, one of those to whom he dedicated this book. When his father left the University of Vienna for that of Berlin, Walther Penck began his university studies there—to be interrupted by a visit to the United States of America, where he followed further courses whilst his father was delivering lectures. They travelled extensively; and under the guidance of G. K. Gilbert saw the earthquake fissure at San Francisco. The return journey was via Hawaii (where his deep interest in the volcanic phenomena decided the young man to become a geologist), Japan, north China and Siberia. Berlin University was soon exchanged for Heidelberg, as being better suited to the line he wished to pursue. After graduating, he studied further at Vienna.

In 1912 he became geologist to the Dirección General de Minas in Buenos Aires. His mountaineering training stood him in good stead as, with merely the trigonometrical points supplied, he mapped 12,000 sq. kms. in north-west Argentina, and made a reconnaissance across the whole width of the Andes.

While home on leave in 1914, war broke out, and he served for a while with the German army in Alsace. The report made on his first year's work at the southern edge of the Puna de Atacama had meanwhile qualified him for a post in the Department of Geology at Leipzig University. But towards the end of 1915, Turkey being under the influence of the Central Powers (to whom she had allied herself), he was appointed Professor of Mineralogy and Geology at the University of Constantinople (Istambul). In 1916 he investigated the coal deposits of the Dardanelles, as well as visiting the Bithynian Olympus (Ulu Dağ) with a party of students. In 1917 he added to his duties those of a Professorship at the Agricultural College of Halkaly on the Sea of Marmora. But recurrences of malaria, after a visit to the southern coast of Anatolia, made a return to Germany necessary in the summer of 1918; and the conclusion of the war prevented him from getting back to Constantinople. He became an unsalaried teacher (*Privatdozent*), with the title of Professor, at the University of Leipzig, and had a paid lectureship in

Surveying (topographical and geological). He worked at the results of his researches in the Argentine sierras and in Anatolia, and spent a good deal of time tramping the German Highlands with his wife—the Fichtel-gebirge, the Thuringian Heights, the Franconian and Swabian scarp-lands, the Harz and the Erzgebirge, as well as visiting the Eastern Alps.

The value of money became less and less, and his Argentine savings were at an end. It was found later that he endured considerable priva-tion. But he refused more lucrative posts that would have prevented him from continuing his research and preparing for publication the results and his views on them. Conditions were slightly better after the end of 1921 when he recovered some of his property from Turkey. But by then he was already far from well, though he made further expeditions, the last being to check his observations in the Black Forest. On 29 Septem-ber 1923, he died of cancer (in the mouth), leaving a widow and two small sons.

He was only 35. W. Salomon, the professor under whom he had graduated, wrote to his father of the high hopes they had entertained that he would have lived to become one of the world's leading geologists.

In reading the *Morphological Analysis*, it has to be remembered that it is only part of a projected larger work. Nevertheless, he considered this part to be complete, so that Albrecht Penck published it as it stood, without any editing. The author had dedicated his work to Albrecht Penck and Paul Pfurtscheller, his 'two teachers in the art of observing nature'.

A list of Walther Penck's publications will be found on pages 352 ff.

Ten years or so ago a number of American geomorphologists engaged in a co-operative effort to provide a synoptic translation of *Die Morpho-logische Analyse*. Some progress was made; but the project came to a halt, partly because Professor O. D. von Engeln, Cornell University, who was promoting the enterprise, learned of our work on a full translation, and generously suggested that its success would be a happy solution and should have American encouragement.

The object of the translators has been to give as exact a rendering as possible of an important work which it has not been easy for English speaking students to assimilate, on account of its difficult and sometimes obscure style and its use of unfamiliar terminology.

In view of the controversial nature of some of Walther Penck's views, the translators have felt it right to keep very closely to his own wording, even at the cost of some verbosity and repetition. However, summaries of each section have been prepared, and will be found at the end of the book (pp. 355 ff.); so that readers can find relatively quickly the parts which they wish to study in detail in the full text.

The English expressions for the terms coined by W. Penck will be found in the Glossary, as well as other words for which students may wish to know what was in the original.

Our grateful thanks are tendered to various members of University College, Southampton: to the late Professor O. H. T. Rishbeth, whose influence stimulated the desire to understand this book; to his successor as Head of the Department of Geography, Miss F. C. Miller, for encouragement and constructive criticism; and to the staff of other departments for their assistance with doubtful points. We also wish to express gratitude to Professors Alan Wood, A. A. Miller, J. E. Kesseli, P. G. H. Boswell (and through him, Professor Reid), the late Professor J. Sölch and others for kind help over specific difficulties.

We are particularly indebted to the late J. F. N. Green, F.G.S., who spent much time during the last year or so of his life in reading through the whole script (whilst one of us was abroad), making valued comments and suggestions.

Some mistakes may thus have been avoided. For any that remain, responsibility must of course rest with us.

H. CZECH

K. C. BOSWELL

KATHARINE CUMMING BOSWELL
1889–1952

This book was still in the proof stage when, to the deep regret of all concerned with its production, the news was received that Miss Boswell had died of heat stroke at Beni Abbès on September 19th, 1952, while attending the Nineteenth International Congress of Geology in Algiers. The tragedy of her death before she could see her work completed is heightened by the fact that it occurred on a journey into the Sahara, where she was trying to resolve some of the controversial points raised by Penck in his discussion of desert conditions.

CONTENTS

LIST OF PLATES

[   ] = not in Walther Penck's text

CHAPTER I

INTRODUCTION

1. NATURE OF THE PROBLEM

Study of the morphology of the earth's surface has developed as a borderland science linking geology and geography. The reason for this is the knowledge that land forms owe their shape to the processes of destruction which engrave their marks on the solid structure of the earth's crust; and that the properties of this crust decide the details of the sculpturing, as well as the arrangement in space of the individual forms. Its immediate purpose being to explain the origin of the multifarious land forms which appear at the surface of the earth, morphology very soon had a specially close connection with geography; and today, it is considered an integral part of geography proper, the study of the earth's surface, and treated as such[1]. Thus work on morphological problems has been overwhelmingly, though not exclusively, in the hands of geographers; and there has been scarcely any attempt to go beyond the aims prescribed by geography.

The material of morphology, however, contains within itself problems which reach far beyond the limits set by geography, and are neither exhausted nor solved by a genetically based description of the surface forms of the planet. *The significance of these problems lies in the realm of geology*; and their solution seems reserved for general geology, especially physical geology. *The problem is that of crustal movement.*

To see the matter more clearly, we must examine the character of the main and fundamental question of morphological science. However keenly geology and geography may be interested in the solution of this question as to the origin and development of land forms, the problem is neither specifically geological nor geographical, but is of a *physical nature*[2]. This results from the relationship and interdependence of those forces, or sets of forces, which produce the surface configuration of our planet. The destructive processes sculpturing the land, all of them together included in the concept *'exogenetic' forces*, cannot become effective until the earth's crust offers them surfaces of attack, until it is exposed to them. Parts of the crust covered by the sea are as much protected from the sculpturing forces as are those parts of the dry land which are being not destroyed but built up. Here, as there, material is not being removed from the earth's crust, but is being piled up on it in the form of rock strata; no unevennesses, no definite relief, are being created, but any unevenness of the crustal surface is being levelled up as by freshly falling snow. The activity of the destructive forces is limited to those parts of the earth which rise above these zones of deposition. Thus the indispensable prerequisite for attack by exogenetic processes of destruction is the activity of those *endogenetic* forces, originating within the planet, which are responsible for raising individual portions of the crust above sea level, and which, on dry land, raise individual blocks above their surroundings, in general create *upstanding parts*, thus giving rise to the altitudinal form of the earth's surface. Leaving aside endogenetically-caused volcanic accumulation (which attains morphological importance only to a modest extent, is limited to a few localities, and moreover has its further fate determined by that of its substratum), the endogenetic processes consist of *movements of the earth's crust*. In view of our present geological experience, their existence requires no further proof. The fact that we know of no piece of land which has not been once or several times submerged below sea level, is by itself striking evidence. Adequate proof that it is a matter of movement of the solid land and not fluctuations of sea level is this: the displacements of level which are of morphological significance, i.e. those which determine present altitudinal relationships on the earth, have never been of a corresponding amount everywhere on the earth's surface, now or at any other period[3].

The earth's surface is not only a limiting surface between different media, nor merely a surface of section giving the desired information about the structure of the earth's crust; *it is a limiting surface between different forces working in opposition to one another*. Both produce displacements of the rock material: the endogenetic forces displace it by raising parts of the earth's crust above their surroundings, or sinking them below these—at present it does not matter whether the direction of the forces is vertical or otherwise, so long as they lead to vertical displacement of level at the planetary surface; the exogenetic forces displace it by transporting solid material along the earth's surface. In the latter case, the transference usually takes place from higher to lower parts, the motive power always being the force of gravity. The endogenetic transference of material, on the other hand, is independent of the force of gravity. It is manifestly against gravity that magma reaches the crust and even the surface. *On this contrast depends the characteristic of mutual opposition between endogenetic and exogenetic processes.* The conflict goes on at the surface of the crust and it finds its visible expression in the tendency—long recognised—for exogenetic transference of material to lower the projecting parts of the land and to fill in depressions, in short to level, to remove any unevennooooo which the endogenetic processes have created and are still producing on the crustal surface.

Thus the earth's surface is a field of reaction between opposing forces, and the effectiveness of the one depends upon the preceding activity of the other. On all surfaces so conditioned as to be the scene of inter-action between opposing and mutually dependent forces, there is a tendency for a physical equilibrium to become established. This obtains when both forces do the same amount of work in unit time, i.e. when they work at the same rate or have the same intensity. Accordingly, there is equilibrium at the earth's surface when the exogenetic and the endogenetic processes, when uplift and denudation, subsidence and de-position, take place at the same rate; and not only when—as is generally assumed—both processes have died out, and their intensity is conse-quently zero.

The visible results of endogenetic and exogenetic influences at the earth's surface are *forms of denudation* on the one hand, and, on the other, the *correlated deposits** which are formed simultaneously. The two stand in a similar relation to the forces producing them as do the cut surface and the sawdust that are formed when a log is pushed against a rotating circular saw. It is clear that very different forms develop according to whether denudation is acting more slowly than uplift, more quickly, or at the same rate; and so whether the ratio of the intensity of exogenetic to that of endogenetic activity works against the former or in its favour, or whether there is a state of equilibrium. Therefore it is possible to see plainly in the forms of denudation not merely the results of endogenetic and exogenetic transference of material; but even more that they owe their origin and their development to a relationship of forces, *to the ratio of intensity between exogenetic and endogenetic processes.*

The physical character of the morphological problem comes out clearly. The task before us is to find out not only the kind of formative processes, but also the development of the ratio of their intensities with respect to one another. None of the usual geological or specifically morphological methods is sufficient for the solution of this problem. As is now self-evident, it requires the application of the methods of physics.

Which physical methods are concerned, and at what stage in the morphological investigation they not only may, but must, be applied, follows from the nature of the three elements which together form the substance of morphology.

[* See glossary].

2. BASIS, NATURE AND AIM
OF MORPHOLOGICAL ANALYSIS

These three elements are:

1. the exogenetic processes,
2. the endogenetic processes,
3. the products due to both, which may here be collectively called the actual morphological features.

It is well known that *the exogenetic forces* are at work over the whole earth, in all climates. They consist of two processes, the onset and the course of which are fundamentally different. The one has already been characterised elsewhere as a process of preparation: *the reduction* of rock material.* By this is to be understood all the processes which lead to a loosening of the solid rock texture, to disintegration of the rocky crust so that it becomes changed into a mobile form, transportable. Climate and the type of rock are what decide in the first place the nature and the course of the reduction, the rendering the material mobile. The structure of the earth's crust, which determines the world distribution of rock types, is therefore just as important for morphology as the world distribution of different climatic conditions.

Rock reduction alters the composition and texture of the material. It does *not* produce denudational forms. These do not appear until the reduced material has been removed: only when matter has been taken away from a body does it change its shape. Only if its composition and texture are altered does there arise what the mineralogist calls a pseudomorph. *Earth sculpture is due to exogenetic transference of material. The sum total of this constitutes denudation.* Rock reduction is an essential preliminary to its occurrence; the rock material must have acquired a sufficiently mobile condition before there can be transport at all, either of its own accord (spontaneous) or by the aid of some medium. The processes of denudation are, one and all, *gravitational streams*, obeying the law of gravity. Climatic conditions and type of rock influence the details of their further course. Their effects, therefore, are of different magnitudes in areas of differing climatic nature and differing geological make-up; nevertheless—and this must here be stressed in view of widely held misconceptions—they are *not of different types*.

All the processes of denudation have, as gravitational streams, a non-uniform character—which, as will be shown, is in contrast to the processes of reduction. That is their fundamental property. Their commencement, their course of development, take place before our eyes. They can be observed in all their phases, and their systematic investigation

[* *Aufbereitung*. See glossary.]

is thus possible everywhere on the earth, not only qualitatively—as has already been more or less fully done—but quantitatively, a matter which so far has been hardly attempted. Here there is a wide field of inductive research, as yet unworked. And it promises results of as great or even greater importance to morphology than those which that recent branch of knowledge, soil science, has already produced with regard to rock reduction.

All the *actual morphological features* can, like the exogenetic processes, be directly observed, and are thus an object of inductive research. However, their limits must be extended far more widely than is customary. It is by no means enough to determine and to characterise the forms of denudation as they actually appear in their various combinations; the *stratigraphical* relations of the *correlated strata*, formed simultaneously, are of just as great importance. Their thickness and the way in which they are deposited on the top of one another, how they are connected with their surroundings in the vertical and in the horizontal direction, their stratification and especially their facies, reflect both the type of development in the associated area of denudation, and its duration, and they supplement in essential points the history recorded there. The position of this record in the geological time sequence depends entirely upon investigation of the correlated strata and their fossil content. As a rule far too little weight is given to working on this stratigraphical material. Because of this, our knowledge about the actual morphological features is correspondingly scanty. True, we must take into account that these are not, like denudation, for instance, subject to one uniform set of laws; but that they are peculiar to each individual part of the crust which will have undergone a special development of its own. *They are individual in their character*.

This individuality is essentially dependent upon the way in which the activity of the *endogenetic processes*, particularly crustal movements, varies from place to place. Since crustal movements cannot be directly observed—with the exception of earthquakes—information about them is deduced from the effects they have produced. These, however, are to be regarded merely as indications that crustal movements are taking place, and bear much the same relation to them as the shaking of a train does to its forward motion. The passenger, now and then looking out from the window of the moving train, recognises its movement by the jolting and by the shifting landscape visible outside. The geologist recognises crustal movements by earthquakes and by disturbance in the stratification of rocks. The latter shows the earliest time at which the crustal movements took place at the given spot, and the total amount of disturbance produced up to the time of observation. But the conditions of bedding give practically no clue as to what, during the period of movement, was the distribution of the separate effects which add up to this total resulting disturbance; neither do they indicate the intensity of the crustal movement—whether it was rapid or slow—the changes of intensity in successive intervals of time—whether increasing or decreasing, nor the course of the movement—whether continuous or by fits and starts, nor whether it is still continuing or came to an end in times past. Yet all these have often been assumed in a perfectly arbitrary manner.

Crustal movements cannot be observed directly, and no adequate tectonic method is known for ascertaining their characteristics. Thus, in studying land forms, it is not permissible to make definite assumptions as to their course and development, and to base morphogenetic hypotheses upon them. Moreover, it is perfectly clear that of the three elements—endogenetic processes, exogenetic processes, and the actual morphological features—dependent upon one another, in accordance with some definite law, like three quantities in an equation—it is the crustal movements which correspond to the unknown, about which statements can be made only as a final result of the investigation, not as one of the premises. On the other hand, it has been shown that each of the other quantities can be established by observation, completely and with certainty for each individual case. Their dependence upon one another, in conformity with some definite law, has already been recognised, and it will subsequently be further developed. The equation—to continue the simile—permits of an unequivocal solution. *Morphological analysis is this procedure of deducing the course and development of crustal movements from the exogenetic processes and the morphological features.*

The function of this analysis of land forms, and its aim, is therefore *geological, or more exactly, physico-geological.* The first thing to be done is to state clearly and solve the problems of the origin and development of denudational forms. The present book treats this complex of problems as a matter of physical geology, to which it organically belongs in virtue of its nature—as was emphasised at the beginning. Having found the outlines of its solution, we have a base from which to move forward to the ultimate aim of morphological analysis, as indicated above. Far-reaching possibilities open up from this point. As has already been more fully set out elsewhere[2], the analysis of land forms gives totally different information about essential features of crustal movement from that which geologico-tectonic research can find out from the structural characteristics of the earth's crust. The two methods, the morphological one here developed, and the geologico-tectonic, supplement one another; at no point is one a substitute for the other. Only the two together supply that sum of basic facts which affords a prospect of solving the main problem of general geology, *the causes of crustal movements*. This is a matter which does not seem to allow of a solution by any purely tectonic method; and so far any attempt to solve it upon this far too narrow basis has been of no avail.

3. CRITICAL SURVEY OF METHODS
(a) CYCLE OF EROSION

A first attempt in the direction of morphological analysis was the theory of the Cycle of Erosion developed by W. M. Davis[4]. Familiarity with it is here assumed. The cycle theory has, it is true, a purely geographical aim, viz. the systematic description of land forms on a genetic basis, which has been aptly called their 'explanatory description'. Thus there was no direct attempt to discover more about endogenetic processes. Results in this direction have been obtained only by the way, and they were not meant for further use except so far as they were considered to serve the explanatory description[5]. This totally different orientation of the setting of the problem does not in any way alter the importance for morphological analysis of the *principle* of the cycle concept. *That principle is the idea of development*, in its most general sense: a block, somehow uplifted, presents one after another, in systematic sequence, forms of denudation which result from one another; and their configuration depends not only upon the denudation which is progressing in a definite direction, but also—as Davis himself suggested, though merely as a conjecture[6]—upon the character (the intensity) of the uplift.

What has found its way into morphological literature as the cycle of erosion is what Davis expressly defined as a special case of the general principle, one which was particularly suitable to demonstrate and to explain the ordered development of denudational forms. It is postulated that a block is rapidly uplifted; that, during this process, no denudation takes place; but that on the contrary, it sets in only after the completion of the uplift, working upon the block which is from that time forward conceived to be at rest. The forms on this block then pass through successive stages which, with increase of the interval of time since they possessed their supposedly original form, i.e. with increase of developmental age, are characterised by decrease in the gradient of their slopes.

They are arranged in a *series of forms*, which is exclusively the work of denudation and ends with the peneplane*, the peneplain. If a fresh uplift now occurs, the steady development, dependent solely upon the working of denudation, is interrupted; it begins afresh, e.g. the pene-

[* See glossary.]

plane is dissected. A new cycle has begun; the traces of the first are perceived in the uplifted, older forms of denudation. Thus it has become usual to deduce a number of crustal movements, having a discontinuous jerky course, from the arrangement by which more or less sharp breaks of gradient separate less steep forms above from steeper ones below.

It was possible to draw this conclusion, in such a general form, only because the above-mentioned special case, chosen by Davis mainly for didactic reasons and developed in detail on several occasions, is usually taken as the epitome of the cycle of erosion, and is quite generally *applied* in this sense. Both Davis himself[7] and his followers have made and still make the tacit assumption that uplift and denudation are successive processes, whatever part of the earth is being considered; and investigation of the natural forms and their development has been and is being made with the same assumptions as underlie the special case distinguished above. There is, therefore, a contrast between the original formulation of the conception of a cycle of erosion and its application. Davis, in his definition, had in mind the variable conditions not only of denudation, but of the endogenetic processes; in the application—so far as we can see, without exception—use is made only of the special case, with its fixed and definite, but of course arbitrarily chosen, endogenetic assumption. And criticism, with its justified reproach of schematising, is directed against the fact that the followers of the cycle theory have never looked for nor seen anything in the natural forms except the realisation of the special case which Davis had designated as such. Thus even opponents of the American doctrine have taken their stand not against the general principle of the cycle of erosion, but against its application; and they referred merely to the one special case that alone was used[8]. Thus there seems throughout to have been a misunderstanding with regard to the cycle of erosion: its originator meant by it something different from what is generally understood. The way in which the theory is applied, the trend of the criticism it has received, hardly permit any doubt of this. Thus it is necessary to consider more closely the application of the *cycle of erosion* and the criticism directed against it.

As a method, the theory of the cycle of erosion introduces a completely new phase in morphology. Deduction, so far used only within the framework of inductive investigation, or as an excellent method of presentation, has become a means of research. Starting from an actual knowledge of exogenetic processes, the cycle theory attempts to deduce, by a mental process, the land-form stages which are being successively produced on a block that had been uplifted, is at rest, and is subject to denudation. Not only is the order of the morphological stages ascertained by deduction, but also the forms for each stage; and the ideal forms arrived at in this way are compared with the forms found in nature. There are two points in this method which must be considered critically: (*a*) deduction as a means of investigation; and (*b*) the facts on which the assumptions are based.

To begin with, it is obvious that the ideal forms, which are supposed to develop on *a stationary block,* can be deduced successfully only if there are no gaps in our knowledge of the essential characteristics of the denudational processes. Should this pre-requisite not be fulfilled, the deduction is nothing but an attempt to find out from the land forms alone both the endogenetic and the exogenetic conditions to which they owe their origin. It is like trying to solve an equation having three quantities, two of which are unknown; we can expect only doubtful results. The American school may be justifiably reproached with not considering it their next task to eliminate one of the unknown quantities by systematically investigating the processes of denudation all over the world. On the whole, their part in throwing light upon the exogenetic processes has been a very modest one. Yet this is not a decisive blow to the cycle concept. For amongst the 'exogenetic' assumptions made, there is no principle which has not been verified by experience, and criticism by opponents has been unable to show any mistakes in this field[9].

Till very recent times[10], no one has even seriously examined the second or 'endogenetic' assumption of the applied cycle of erosion, namely, uplift and *then* denudation. On the contrary, morphologists of every school have generally started from the same assumption as soon as they came to discuss the problem of the development of land forms. Even the opponents of the American school have done this, and indeed tacitly still do so, even in those cases when they have completely disregarded any endogenetic influence on the forms of denudation, and have done no more than consider how the individual land forms might have arisen purely from the work of denudation: for instance, the way in which they depend upon rock material. Invariably they have started with a given fixed altitude for the crustal segment considered; that is, they have begun by considering uplift already completed and followed by a period of rest.

Thus, up to now, it cannot be said that there has been any really well-grounded criticism directed against the factual assumptions of the cycle of erosion.

The second point was the use of deduction as a method of morphological research—though of course in addition to induction and essentially based upon it. A. Hettner utterly and roundly repudiated the use of this for morphology[11]. However, no such conclusion would be drawn from

Hettner's remarks and his arguments. In these he deals with the concepts of Davis—which he considers are not precisely enough formulated —especially the concept of morphological age; further, he points out that inadequate attention has been paid to the character* of the rock and to the exogenetic processes; and finally he considers the application of the theory to specific cases. At one point only does he touch upon the problem of method, and that is when he levels the reproach against the cycle of erosion that it rests upon inadequate assumptions as to the exogenetic processes. That reproach has already been considered above. But so far as the erosion cycle is concerned, this is only *one* side of the question; for, as has already been shown, it makes further very definite assumptions about the endogenetic processes. Apparently Hettner considers them to be correct and admissible, since he does not examine them also. But the possibility that the deductive method used for the cycle of erosion may be based upon inadequate assumptions does not permit the passing of judgment upon the applicability of deduction itself to the whole sphere of morphological research[12]. In addition, this statement may be made: *In morphology, as in any other branch of knowledge concerned with physical problems, deduction as a means of research is not only permissible, but also imperative; unless we wish to renounce the greatest possible exactitude and completeness in the results, and to exclude our branch of learning from the rank of an exact science, a rank which it both can and should acquire in virtue of the character of the questions with which it deals.* It is merely a matter of finding out where, in the process of investigation, we should resort to the method of deduction; and above all making sure that correct and complete data are then provided for it. The provision of these is, as before, exclusively the domain of inductive observation; it only can accomplish this, the deductive process never. It is by no means the deductive character of the method itself which makes it impossible to go along the American way of applying the cycle of erosion, but the incompleteness and, as will presently be shown, the incorrectness of the assumptions made. Thus opposition to the deductive method as a tool for use in morphological investigation has been unable to do serious harm to the theory of the erosion cycle, and it is not to be expected that it will ever succeed in doing so.

We now turn to the assumption made about endogenetic processes when applying the concept of the cycle of erosion.

(b) Relationship between Endogenetic and Exogenetic Processes

Exogenetic and endogenetic forces begin to act against one another from the moment when uplift exposes a portion of the earth's crust to

[* See p. 19 for what this term comprises; or glossary.]

denudation. So long as uplift is at work, denudation cannot be idle. The resulting surface configuration depends solely upon whether the endogenetic or the exogenetic forces are working the more quickly. Were there no denudation, a block, however slowly it is rising, might in course of time reach any absolute height; and its increase in altitude would be limited solely by the physics of the act of formation, provided that it is inherent in this not to continue indefinitely. It is rather like the way in which an impassable limit has been set to the increase in height of volcanoes by the extinction of volcanic activity, which often comes to an end prematurely, as soon as a certain height has been reached, because lateral effusions replace the summit eruptions. However, it is from the outset that exogenetic breaking-down at the earth's surface works against endogenetic building-up, i.e. denudation works against uplift, in-filling by sediments against subsidence. It is easily to be understood that an actual elevation can come into existence only if uplift does more work in unit time, and so is working more rapidly, than denudation; a hollow appears only when subsidence takes place more quickly than sediment is supplied, than aggradation. *This state of affairs forms the substance of the fundamental law of morphology: the modelling of the earth's surface is determined by the ratio of the intensity of the endogenetic to that of the exogenetic displacement of material*[13].

A brief survey of the earth's surface shows that this ratio very often changes, or has changed, to the prejudice of the exogenetic forces; the accumulation of a volcanic cone is possible only because it takes place more rapidly than the removal by denudation of the accumulated material. Faults can become visible as unlevelled fault scarps, for instance in the zone of the rift valleys of East and Central Africa[14], only when the formation of faults takes place more rapidly than levelling by denudation. Generally speaking, the origin of any outstanding elevation, any mountain mass, is bound up with the assumption that mountain building is more successful, i.e. works more rapidly, than denudation. Thus the varied altitudinal form of the land shows that in many cases the work of denudation is lagging behind the endogenetic displacement of material, here more, there less, or has done so in the past. *The one consistent feature, however, common to every region, is that the activity of exogenetic happenings is subordinate to that of endogenetic processes.* This relationship, most impressively brought to the observer's notice by the different kinds of relief and the different altitudes occurring at the earth's surface, forms the basis of morphological analysis. For if the exogenetic forces are less active than the endogenetic movements, then their effect, the earth's whole set of land forms, must also in its main outlines accommodate itself to whatever law has its visible expression stamped by crustal movement upon the face of our planet. Any change in kind or in intensity which these movements undergo must therefore—as has long been known—leave its traces upon the landscape.

If the intensity of denudation consistently lagged behind that of the endogenetic movement, then in course of time a block rising in such a way could, even in spite of the exogenetic processes, reach any absolute height; though it would of course do so more slowly than if the earth were not subject to denudation. But the relationship is not an unchanging one. For, like all other gravitational streams, the processes of denudation increase in intensity with the gradient, in a definite manner to be discussed later; and the gradient increases with the increase in *vertical distance* between summit and foot of the uplifted portion of the crust. This is true provided the *horizontal distance* between the two points is not at the same time proportionately increased; and, as a rule, it is not. Thus it was possible, even some decades ago, to formulate it as an empirical law, fundamentally correct, that intensity of denudation increases with absolute height, other things being equal. This means a shift in the relationship of the endogenetic to the exogenetic rate of working, in favour of the latter, and an ever closer approximation to physical equilibrium. The actual attainment of the equilibrium could be prevented only where there was no limit to the *increase* in endogenetic movement, so that rising blocks would gain in height indefinitely. The insignificance of the altitudinal modelling of its surface bears witness to how little such conditions obtain on the earth, an insignificance which is not clearly brought out, with distinctness, till comparison is made with the dimensions of the earth as a whole.

The above short survey shows that it is essential, when investigating the origin and development of denudational forms as they appear at the earth's surface, to *ascertain the relationship between the intensity* of the endogenetic and of the exogenetic processes, in short, between uplift and denudation; and it is necessary to follow out how this changes as time goes on. None of the present methods used in morphology brings us nearer to achieving this end; none even attempts to do so. The assumption generally introduced, that uplift and denudation were successive processes, or could at any rate be treated as such, has stood in the way. In this respect the only difference between the cycle theory and its opponents is that Davis made the above assumption in order to provide a specially simple case, of particular use in illustrating the cycle concept; but, at the same time, he kept well in mind[15] the importance of concurrent uplift and denudation. To be sure, this was a notion of which he scarcely ever made use, and his followers never. Those of the other school, no less schematically, start in every case from the same assumption; they, moreover, have occasionally tried to justify the general correctness and permissibility of such a course[16]. It is as if they made use of a device familiar in school physics, which is merely a make shift for presenting in a physically correct manner the resultant of processes acting concurrently. This is a grave mistake in method.

It is permissible to proceed in this way only in the case of *uniform forces* which, in successive units of time, produce effects that remain of equal magnitude. If, in a diagram such as Fig. 1, the co-ordinates *ab* and *bc* represent the effects of simultaneous, uniform forces, the straight line *ac* represents the resultant effect *during* the whole process. In order to ascertain this, it is sufficient to follow the events first from *a* to *b*, then to *c*.

(c) THE DIFFERENTIAL METHOD

It is quite different, however, when forces acting simultaneously are *not uniform*, i.e. are changing their intensities in successive units of time and are therefore doing different amounts of work. To find out the resultant during the whole process, it is here necessary *to follow* the course of Nature *continuously*, as was made possible in physics, where such problems are constantly cropping up, only by the invention of the differential calculus[17]. To make this clear, let us remind ourselves of the problem: to find the trajectory of a missile fired horizontally from a point *a* (Fig. 1). As the effect of the firing, it would reach *b*; but at the same time, under the influence of the force of gravity, it would drop down by the amount *bc*. To find point *c*, which the projectile reaches, it would really be sufficient to follow events first from *a* to *b*, then from *b* to *c*, that is to imagine the effects of the firing and of gravity as coming into play successively. The trajectory, however, has not been found in that way. It lies on a curve of some kind between the initial and final points, between *a* and *c*. To determine it, we must find out how the magnitude of the operating forces alters in successive exceedingly small units of time. This can be done by plotting a diagram of forces for each moment, as in our figure, e.g. ab^1c^1, $a^2b^2c^2$ ... $a^mb^mc^m$, etc., so that the simultaneous effect of the forces is represented by the very minute distances ac^1, a^2c^2 ... a^mc^m, etc., as if they were uniform during these extremely short intervals of time and took place successively. The error thus made becomes infinitesimally small, if the values chosen for the diagram are made infinitesimally minute; and this method, consisting of an infinite number of infinitely small variables, comes infinitely near the *continuous* course of Nature. This becomes clear if in our figure the triangles ab^1c^1, $a^2b^2c^2$, etc., are, as is necessary, made infinitely small; they then disappear completely in the full line *axc*. Since the forces are now changing from moment to moment, the very small distances ab^1, a^2b^2, etc. and b^1c^1, b^2c^2, etc., are thus of different lengths, and so the infinitely small resultants ac^1, a^2c^2, etc., are also of different lengths and at different inclinations. Strung out after one another, they do not form a straight line, but bend in a curve: the trajectory axc which was to be found. *This is the differential method. It is the only way that leads to our goal, which is the exact representation of the resultant of several simultaneous processes that are not acting uniformly during their course.*

The forces which take part in modelling the land do not act uniformly. It has already been shown that this is so for denudation, and it is a matter of course for crustal movements. They begin from the position of rest,

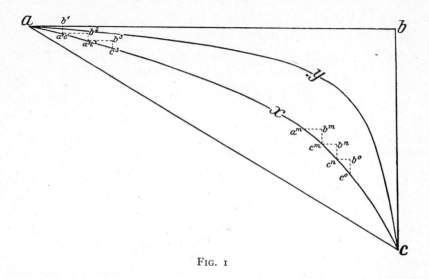

FIG. 1

so they must then be accelerated; and they end with the position of rest, having then suffered deceleration. Whether or not the starting point and the end coincide with a position of absolute rest is of no importance. If indeed we think of the alternation of uplift and subsidence, as has so often, if not as a general rule, taken place on the earth, then the position where subsidence changes to uplift (or vice versa) is the position of rest. *In any case, the movement of the crust is a non-uniform process, which becomes uniform only temporarily during its course, but can never begin uniformly with any definite velocity.* It is not superfluous to stress this obvious factor in view of the often inadequate conceptions which are widespread as to the physics of motion, and even of the fundamental concepts of physics.

To illustrate the position, let us draw a diagram (Fig. 1), in which the

co-ordinates represent the effects of crustal movement (*a b*) and of denudational processes (*b c*). The result of their simultaneous action, the
forms of denudation, then appears in the shape of curves between *a* and
c. Naturally they are all situated within the triangle *abc*; since any
curve drawn outside it, as for example, a curve deviating in convex
fashion downwards from the straight line *a c*, would signify that denudation had begun before subsequent endogenetic action had exposed the
crustal fragment to exogenetic destruction or, in other words, that
denudation was the prerequisite for crustal movement. Within the triangle an infinite number of curves are possible, all of which begin at
point *a* and end at *c*. Each of these curves represents not a single form,
but a *developing series of forms* through which a crustal fragment passes
when it is being uplifted and denuded. It is obvious that all the series of
land forms which can possibly develop on the earth have one common
starting point and one common final form. The former is characterised
by the beginning of uplift and denudation (point *a*), the latter by the
extinction of endogenetic and exogenetic displacements of material
(point *c*). In between lies the endless variety of forms that correspond to
the varying ratio of intensity of exogenetic processes to that of endogenetic ones; and they are arranged on an infinite number of curves, each
of which represents a series of forms peculiar to the surface development of a crustal fragment which has had a particular course of endogenetic development.

Thus we see that land forms are not, as the erosion cycle postulates, a
single developing series, but that they form an infinite number, and that they
are arranged [on the diagram], *not in a line, but on a surface.* This surface
is enclosed by two limiting curves that, at least as regards total dimensions, represent developing series which, on the earth, are *just not pos-*
sible: the straight line *a c*, that is the series of forms arising from the
uniform development of uplift and denudation, and the axes *a b—b c*,
which would be the series of forms that would arise if uplift and denudation succeeded one another. Whether *fragments of the limiting curves* can
be observed as component parts in the development of forms on the
earth, and which fragments might in that way be realised, will have to
be decided by the following investigation.

The relationship of the cycle of erosion (and of methods based upon
similar assumptions) to the complex of problems concerning development of land forms now becomes evident. Point *b* in the diagram represents denudation which sets in only after the completion of uplift; and
the series of forms that arise purely as the work of denudation on a
motionless block is represented by one limb of the limiting curve: the
line *b c*. Its starting point *b* by no means coincides with the point (*a*)

from which all development of forms on the earth begins. The perfectly arbitrary choice of that starting point is clearly shown. But, on the other hand, there also emerges the fact that although the method adopted for the erosion cycle (in its applied form) is incorrect in principle, yet it must nevertheless lead to the discovery of the correct final form common to every one of the series of denudational forms that develop on the earth, provided that the method was logically correct and not based upon faulty exogenetic assumptions. The theory of the cycle of erosion does satisfy both these requisites, as cannot be doubted even by its opponents. Point c in the diagram represents the end-peneplane,* the peneplain, the origin of which was made clear by W. M. Davis, and a little later, independently, by A. Penck, both basing themselves upon detailed inductive observation[18]. One could not, however, in this way deduce a single one among the infinite series of developing land forms which are not only possible but actually exist on the earth in the different parts which have had various endogenetic histories. Almost everything in this field still remains to be done by morphology. Not merely must the investigation start at the beginning of uplift and denudation (point a); it must take into account not only the simultaneous effects of endogenetic and exogenetic action, but above all their variable intensities[19]. *For this one must turn to the methods of physics, and indeed to such as permit a continuous following of the variable quantities, that is, the differential method.* This method not only can, but *must* be used in investigating the interdependence between the *processes of movement* which take part in the modelling of the land. For mass-transport of eroded material depends upon a gradient, the factors producing which are crustal movements; and mass-movement of denuded material depends upon a gradient, the processes producing which arise from the results of erosion†[20].

This leads to the

(d) PRESENT METHOD OF APPROACH

The main stress is laid upon investigating the ways in which denudation works, and the preparatory processes, the aim being to find out if denudation follows laws which are uniformly applicable and what these are. Thus, in the first place, it is a matter of studying those processes of denudation the course of which depends directly upon the *surface gradient* of the crust and therefore indirectly upon its movements. These

[* See glossary.]

[† Translators' note: The author's distinction between erosion along the line of a watercourse and denudation over a whole surface must constantly be borne in mind. This point of difference between German and English-American usage was discussed by W. M. Davis, *Journ. Geol.* XXXVIII (1930), p. 13.]

fall into two categories: (*a*) denudational processes in which the movement is spontaneous*; (*b*) those making use of an agent that is itself in motion (air, water, ice). Now group (*b*) includes also processes which depend only remotely, or not at all, upon the surface gradient, and which do not show any direct connection with crustal movement. Currents in standing water, particularly in the sea, are examples of this, and air currents. In both cases, lines of movement within one and the same medium are caused by *differences of pressure*. They imprint upon the surface of the crust features having no connection with crustal movements, which have but a limited value, or none at all, for discovering these. Hence this book does not treat of ocean currents; and the effects of wind are considered only in so far as they act with and influence other sub-aerial streams that are dependent upon gravity. Their work must be distinguished from endogenetic influences, even though it is restricted to certain parts of the earth, and is of limited importance in these. It is particularly over arid stretches of land, devoid of any continuous cover of vegetation, that wind effects are encountered; and the lowest base level to which they can possibly extend is the surface of any accumulation of water. For arid regions this means, in the first place, the water table. This is so for basins of inland drainage, the visible surface of which forms the base level of erosion for the bordering slopes; and its position is determined—if not exclusively, yet in the main—by climatic conditions and not by those of crustal movement. Wind may here play a considerable part in the modelling of those slopes; not indeed directly, as observation shows, but indirectly through bringing the base level of erosion down to the level of the (dry season) water table.

Minor forms due to wind action appear all over the world, wherever there is an arid portion of surface exposed to the wind, provided weathering has previously done its work. But even apart from these, it is *climate* which primarily conditions the denuding as well as the depositional activity of the wind. Nowhere indeed are the forms which it produces dominant, not even in the regions of its greatest importance; but they are overprinted upon the dominant forms, forms which there too have been created by denudational processes bound up with the surface gradient.

The movement of ice and snow, and the effects produced by them, present similar relationships. True, their movements follow the surface gradients; yet their existence is a response to climatic conditions. It is unsuitable, therefore, to use forms produced by them for the deduction of crustal movements. That their origin has no direct connection with these is at once evident from the character of their level of reference, the

[* See p. 64.]

base levels of erosion below which their sculpturing cannot possibly reach. For glaciers, that level is the melting lower end; for the stretches lying between them, it is the snow-line. The position of the melting tip depends both upon that of the snow-line, determined exclusively by climate, and upon the mass of each individual stream of ice which, other things being equal, increases with the size of the gathering ground. With stable climatic conditions, the influence of crustal movements is to alter the position of the glacier snout and that of the snow-line, not with reference to the base level of running water, e.g. sea-level, but with reference to the glaciated summits or to the original position of the snow-line. Thus, investigation of glacial phenomena can establish to what extent the observed displacements of the snow-line are due to climatic changes or to crustal movements, but no clue is thereby given as to the nature or course of these events. Hence the whole set of phenomena belonging to glacial geology also falls outside the scope of this book.

And finally, an examination of coastal development has no place here. Knowledge is assumed of the processes which are today considered to be modelling the details of sea-coasts, whether by denudation or by deposition, and of how these processes are believed to transform coasts which are neither rising nor sinking. For the problems here treated, the only phenomena of importance are those from which it is possible to deduce vertical movement of the coast-line, with the necessarily associated horizontal displacement, uplift and subsidence of the solid earth, rise and fall of sea-level. In so far as eustatic fluctuations can be successfully excluded, these phenomena supply information as to the occurrence of the crustal movements, the time of their commencement, and their direction (relative to sea-level); but only in a limited degree to their course of development and changes in intensity. In this respect they fall into the same category as the conditions of rock stratification. This does not remove the necessity for a somewhat detailed consideration of the proved oscillations of the coast-line; for this concerns the *oscillations of the base level of erosion for running water*, which—whatever their origin—have the greatest conceivable repercussions on the modelling of the land, the type of denudation and deposition, and the distribution of these.

That the investigation may be directed aright with reference both to matter and place, we are beginning with a short survey of the earth's crust and its structure, this being the stage for all geological and morphological occurrences.

CHAPTER II

THE EARTH'S CRUST

Variations in physical properties, such as capacity for expansion, elasticity, cohesion, etc., and in chemical composition of constituent minerals, make rock susceptible in varying degrees to the chemical and physical influences which prevail at the earth's surface. Such susceptibility is influenced further by the kind of mineral fabric and its strength, the *texture of the rock*, and above all by variations in its *cohesion*. Cohesion depends not only upon the texture but also upon *structure*, a term comprising such phenomena as rock partings along divisional planes (say, bedding or foliation planes), cavity filling, form and extent of pore space, etc., the cement, its nature and strength, diagenesis, and the various stages of metamorphism such as contact effects, impregnation, reconstitution, recrystallisation. The sum total of these properties, together with the details of *rock stratification*, in short, the *character of the rock*,* are responsible for the various degrees of resistance which rocks offer to chemical and mechanical destruction. They vary not only from one case to another; but they also vary from place to place, even when climatic conditions and exposure are identical. Thus, *other things being equal, it is the character of the rock* which proves to be *the determining factor in the detailed sculpturing of denudational forms*. Careful tracing of this *adaptation of form to rock character* is essential for learning how to distinguish its morphological influence from that exerted by endogenetic processes, the crustal movements. The endogenetic conditions that are morphologically significant are twofold: those which are dynamic, the *endogenetic processes*, viz. movement and transference of material, which will not be considered here; and those which are static, the *endogenetic states* resulting from those processes. The latter include the three following elements which should be carefully distinguished: (*a*) the composition of the crust, which consists of many different kinds of rock, (*b*) its structure, which determines the surface distribution and arrangement of the rock types, and (*c*) the altitudinal modelling.

1. COMPOSITION AND STRUCTURE OF THE CRUST

The structure, the internal build, is the sum total of all the stratigraphical relationships[21]. Wherever there are upstanding portions of the

* *Gesteinsverhältnisse.*

land, and these are the only places where observations can be made, two essentially different structural zones can be distinguished in broad outline. These may be called the *substructure* and the *superstructure*. The boundary between them lies at a stratigraphical horizon which varies from place to place, and is nowhere associated with a surface at a definite level.

The characteristic feature of the substructure is folding, in all rocks capable of folding, that is those with parting planes (bedding and foliation) whether original or acquired. At any given temperature there is a definite limit to the capacity for folding possessed by a rock with given properties. If compression has caused this limit to be reached, the rocks become *incompetent*; and from that moment they react to the continued pressure in a different way, viz. by molecular transformation. This is most nearly complete in the deep-seated zones along the lines of folding. Here, as may be seen for example, in the central parts of the Alps or of the Variscan folds, not only are the structural characteristics lost and replaced by others, a discordance disappearing, for instance, and being represented by a tectonic concordance, but the rock itself undergoes complete reconstitution, recrystallisation, and acquires a new mineralogical composition and a new arrangement of the component minerals. It is exclusively in the substructure that such reconstitution phenomena occur; it is here that schistosity and the crystalline schists originate. It is, finally, in the substructure that most of the magmatic injections are to be found, in particular all those huge intrusive bodies showing a granular texture, of which stocks and batholiths are typical.

The substructure is exposed over vast areas of land; everywhere it forms the base, the foundation, upon which other material, wherever this is present, is piled. It may, therefore, be taken as the peripheral part of the earth's crust proper, even though what might be considered as the remains of the planet's hypothetical, original crust, due to its solidification, cannot be seen anywhere, even in this. Rather, according to our present state of knowledge, it is exclusively of reassorted sedimentary material and of igneous rocks that this lower zone consists. The sedimentary material here reassorted was formerly worn off upstanding parts, deposited in depressions, and folded throughout its entire extent, though at different periods. In the deep-seated zones it underwent reconstitution along the lines of folding; but in its peripheral parts the sedimentary properties are more or less clearly preserved. The igneous rocks are partly in the form of intercalations of extrusive material, but are mainly intrusions which must have increased the volume and mass of that shell of the lithosphere concerned. Thus, though they are not the only types, crystalline siliceous rocks are by far the commonest rocks found in the substructure.

Stretches of this substructure are covered by a thin, incomplete mantle of rock, the *superstructure*. It is made up of sediments which show no signs whatever of reconstitution. There are, in addition, extensive volcanic extrusions, and small intrusive bodies of a hypabyssal nature (typically the true laccolith) which penetrate the sedimentary mantle. In the superstructure, clastic material is more common than crystalline; and the chemically stable substances, such as limestone, quartz, hydrated silicate of aluminium, etc., to be traced back to the end-products of weathering, predominate over the chemically unstable silicates.

These striking, but by no means universal, differences in rock texture and composition lead to a general difference in susceptibility to rock reduction in these two structural zones. On the whole, too, they provide different conditions for circulation of water. But what is of greatest significance is the difference found everywhere in the bedding: *the super-structure has no folding*; its tectonic disturbances are restricted to those of a minor degree. Flat bedding is typical of the superstructure; and it alone affords the conditions requisite for the formation of tablelands and scarplands such as are so impressive in south-west Germany.

Now what are the genetic relations between superstructure and substructure? What delimits the one from the other? Nowhere on earth are flat-lying Archaean beds known; everywhere they are folded. But the lower surface of the Palaeozoic by no means coincides with the boundary between superstructure and substructure. It is found instead that all divisions of the geological formations, from the oldest Palaeozoic up to and including the Lower or the Middle Pliocene, are represented in both the substructure and the superstructure: the strata, as individual formations, but never complete in a continuous sequence the same everywhere, occur flat bedded in one part of the world; but on approaching certain belts, these very same strata lose this property: they are folded and so have acquired the characteristics of the substructure. This may be excellently seen by comparing, for example, the unfolded Palaeozoics of the Baltic provinces with those of the same age but within the Armorican-Variscan belt of folding; or the Mesozoics of south-west Germany with the Triassic and Jurassic of the Alps, and the north German Tertiaries with the equivalent formations at the edge of the Alps. The fundamental difference is not the texture or composition of the rocks, but their bedding. *In the one set of regions, rocks of the super-structure transgress over an older folded substratum; in the fold belts, they are, by virtue of their folding, incorporated in the substructure.* The completeness with which this process takes place is seen in the reconstitution of Mesozoic sediments to form schists in certain parts of the Alps or of the Apennines, these sediments being the same as those which, outside the belt of geologically youthful folding, form parts of a scarcely disturbed superstructure. The lower surface of this, i.e. the boundary between it and substructure, is always a *fold-discordance*.

Evidence as to the arrangement of the zones of folding that compose the substructure, and the date of their formation, is afforded not only by their position within the sequence of geological formations, but also by their position on the earth's surface. Those of more remote periods are shown to have just as regular a distribution as the fold belts of geologically recent origin. In the first place, there is an increasing certainty that, on the whole, the folding includes wider areas, the earlier it began. In the Archaean, a period of unknown duration, no part of the crust was exempt from folding. Archaean beds are always folded, wherever they have been examined. This folding certainly did not take place simultaneously all over the earth, but successively both in time and place. As far back as the Upper Silurian and Lower Devonian, there had been a substantial narrowing of the area in which folding recurred. In Eur-Africa, for example, the region folded at that time extended only from the north of Scotland to the central Sudan. A further narrowing had taken place by the Upper Carboniferous—the region of folds then stretched only from southern England to the Sahara south of the Atlas lands; and by the Tertiary we find the occurrence of folding limited to a narrow strip traversing the Mediterranean lands in a winding course. Similar successive narrowings of the folded area have been established for the two Americas, Asia and Australia. It is a universal phenomenon.

Thus, in course of time, these properties of the crust which allow the strata of the superstructure to be compressed and folded, are lost over wider and wider areas. The visible parts of these areas withdrawn from folding, made rigid as it were, are called *continental masses*; and the mantle of sediments, in so far as any were laid down, is preserved with little disturbance to form the superstructure. On account of the zonary narrowing of the fold belts, the base of this is usually at a lower stratigraphical level the further it is from the Mesozoic-Tertiary strip of folding.

The development of the crustal structure is according to law. Up to the present, it has led to contraction, into two narrow belts, of the zones within which folding could originate: one of these, the *Pacific belt*, surrounds the Pacific Ocean; the other, the *Mediterranean belt*, stretches from the Atlantic through the Mediterranean region and south Asia to the Pacific Ocean, where it joins the Pacific belt. These are *zones of instability*, in which we recognise remains of earlier, much more extensive zones that had similar characteristics. Loss of instability cannot be traced to folding. Otherwise those areas in which the superstructure had once been folded to incompetence would thereafter remain stable, so acquiring and retaining the properties of the rigid continental masses. Obviously this is *not* the case. In the Alps, as well as in other young fold mountains, the marks of Permian, Carboniferous, and still older periods of folding are in many places visible in the uncovered basement of folded Mesozoics. Folding does not prevent the recurrence of folding at the same place. *Folding causes whatever material in the superstructure is capable of folding to become incorporated in the substructure, but the crustal instability is in no way removed.* This instability is not just due to the fact that the rock material is capable of being folded, but is the property which the crust possesses of carrying out movements of a special kind; and it does not possess this property outside the zones of instability. The most outstanding feature is that within these zones the earth's crust is able to sink down into deep elongated troughs, troughs within which sediments accumulate throughout geological periods, so that a specially thick superstructure is produced (geosynclines); and later, during and after the folding of this, they rise again, to form mountains. But it must be emphasised that the folding, and the rising of the folded parts with their substratum to form mountains, by no means destroys the ability of the crust to sink again at the same place to form a trough of sedimentation, nor prevents its filling material from being yet again folded. This ability of the superstructure, on reaching a certain thickness, to sink down, to become folded, and to rise as mountain chains, is however lost in course of time to ever wider areas, as may be seen from the way in which crustal structures behave; or, in other words: *the rigid continental masses grow at the expense of the zones of instability.*

It is the conditions in the superstructure which best reflect the differences in nature between stable continental masses and the zones of instability. On the stable blocks, it is, when present, of slight thickness, and has no deep sea formations. Its structural characteristic, flat bedding, is retained even if it has been affected by crustal movement, has suffered tectonic disturbance and has become, on a rising continent, an area of denudation. In the unstable zones it is far otherwise. In narrow subsiding troughs there accumulates a superstructure the thickness of which is to be measured in kilometres, and includes strata having abyssal facies. If involved in crustal movement, it loses its structural characteristics; it becomes folded, and thereafter behaves like any other part of the substructure, the folding of which may go back any distance in time, provided it is not part of what has already become a definitely rigid continental block.

In this way we learn, from the fate of the superstructure, that crustal movements are of a different type in stable and unstable regions. Apart from seismic and magmatic phenomena, to which we shall return in another connection, this difference is reflected particularly in the altitudinal form.

2. THE ALTITUDINAL FORM OF THE EARTH'S CRUST: HOW IT IS BUILT UP

The stable and the unstable regions coincide respectively with the two systems of major land forms. In each, there are elevations and depressions, of a common type and of a common order of magnitude, standing opposed to one another. Continental masses and oceans form the one system. This comprises by far the greater part of the earth's surface, and the second system, arranged in two narrow belts, divides it into three self-contained units. The first of these lies around the North Pole and is formed of North America east of the Cordillera and north of the Antilles, Greenland and the north of Eurasia, including the islands and seas in between. The second is made up of South America east of the Andes, Africa south of the Atlas, the greater part of Antarctica, Australia and India, with the Indian and South Atlantic Oceans. The Pacific Ocean covers the whole of the third. These three areas are unequal in size, this being determined by the course of the two mountain belts mentioned above: the Pacific belt which is firmly welded on to one side of the continental masses whilst on the other it faces the Pacific Ocean; and the Mediterranean belt, the greater part of which is between continental masses lying to the north and south. Where this reaches the sea it, like the Pacific belt, gives rise to a 'strike' coast, called by E. Suess the Pacific type of coast. It may be contrasted with the Atlantic type, which is not formed by zones of recent mountain building, but cuts across them and frequently also across the older structures. However it occasionally runs almost parallel to the latter for thousands of kilometres, as for instance in the case of almost the whole north and east coast of South America as far as La Plata. Just as the Pacific type of coast characterises the mountain belts, so the Atlantic type forms the oceanic boundary of the continental masses. Apart from deep-rooted contrasts of a seismic, and even more of a magmatic nature[23], the form of the land surface is the most obvious indication of this typical arrangement and delimitation which present some of the most difficult problems of geology, and obviously are the result of an extraordinarily long development controlled by definite laws[22] (see p. 33). So far as the oceans and continents are concerned, this surface modelling, in spite of all kinds of differences in detail, is characterised by world-wide uniformity. The simplicity of the ocean floor, which has an average depth of between 4000 and 5000 metres, has been confirmed by all the more recent soundings, and it is not to be expected that a further increase in density of the still wide-meshed network of soundings will invalidate the result of our present knowledge[24]. The form of the continental surface, including the shelf seas, is no different in nature. Steeper slopes, locally with the steepness of precipices, form a link between the simple features of the ocean floor and the gentle relief of the continental platforms. These have, as a rule, no very great relative or absolute height. The steeper slopes, found at the continental margins and more particularly in the mountain belts, are thus features alien to the elevations formed as the continental surface buckled in various ways. Take any part of the crust which has undergone uniform movement, and express as a fraction the ratio between its altitude and its horizontal diameter—that is, its angle of slope, its slope being that of a plane touching the individual heights carved out by denudation. It will be found that the average value of this fraction is far smaller for areas on the continental masses than that which is typical of the narrow elongated elevations occurring in the mountain belts.

The youngest folded structure found in the stable regions is late Palaeozoic. With few exceptions, the upwarpings of the continental surface cut across this structure, thus showing in a direct manner that they are of more recent origin. But even where, as in the upstanding massifs of the Urals or the Appalachians, their extent is determined by the course of the old structure, a wide gap of time separates their origin from that of the folds; the upstanding mountainous feature is a creation of geologically recent date, and has not the least connection with the folding of the strata. They cannot be called 'fold mountains'.

Fold mountains, the characteristic of which is the approximate coincidence of fold structure and mountainous elevation in extent, arrangement and time of origin, occur today only within the two mountain belts, which are the second system of the earth's major forms. In general terms, the raised forms are elongated and comparatively narrow archings of the crust which usually take a curved and even festooned course; sometimes they bend right around deep basins filled by the sea—e.g. the Mediterranean region—or around continental basins of the same type as the Pannonian Basin or that of eastern Turkistan. They are systems of closely ranged chains; and in certain zones, such as Inner Anatolia, Iran, Tibet, Puna de Atacama, etc., their height above the intervening troughs, i.e. the relative height, diminishes, while at the same time the whole system is apparently increasing in average altitude and in width. In these cases, the individual chains may be seen to separate further from one another and even to die out, so that the longitudinal depressions fuse together, thus widening to form high-lying basin-like hollows. These systems of mountain chains are regularly accompanied by zones of sub-

sidence, the marginal deeps, which are more or less their equivalents.
They, too, appear to differ in their nature. One sort, including the deep
sea troughs, are apparently geosynclines of the same type as the Mesozoic sedimentation troughs which were later transformed into lines of
folding. They are usually to be found quite close to them. The Adriatic
Sea, with the Plain of the Po, belongs to this type. As regards gravity
compensation, their behaviour is different from that of the equally elongated regions of subsidence of the Alpine Foreland type[10], which are not
confined to the neighbourhood of the Mesozoic-Tertiary fold zones but,
like the Gran Chaco - Pampa trough, for example, may also occur with
systems of ranges showing no recent folding. Just as the chain mountains
in general tower above the mean height of the continents, so the corresponding marginal deeps, genetically connected with them, sometimes
sink to considerable depths below the general level of the ocean floor.
The earth's greatest altitudes and its greatest depths belong to the
mountain belts; and between these extremes, the elevations above sea-
level and the depressions below it attain a matchless variety of form.

The occurrence of fold mountains, as defined above, where systems of
mountain chains exist, led to the idea that the mountains were due to
'up-folding'. E. Suess in particular set forth this view in his book *The
Face of the Earth*. It was thought that the mere folding of strata could
produce an actual absolute uplift of the rock forming the earth's crust.
In Europe most of the important elevations do characteristically show a
Mesozoic-Tertiary compression of strata, Mesozoic and more recent in
age, so that this concept was a possible one; and the same connection can
also be traced in mountain chains of southern Anatolia, southern Iran,
and on through the Himalayan system to the furthest of the Sunda
Islands.

Yet, for the two Americas, even though analogous features do occur,
to some extent, it is often impossible to maintain a causal relationship:
altitudinal form because of folding.

Opposed to this are two sets of important facts: first of all, we know
from experience that intensity of folding does not correspond with
greater or less development of altitude. Take, for example, the lower surface of the Gosau transgression in the Eastern Alps. Following it out, one
finds that, with a change of facies, it becomes detached from the concordant series of strata which at one time formed the Flysch foreland, and
transgresses along a denudation surface of flattish form very little broken
up by vertical dissection; it passes over belts which are highly folded and,
a little further to the south, even overthrust. Then, in the region of the
inner and most violently disturbed zone of the Calcareous Alps (Ötscher
nappe—Hahn's Tyrolese unit and Juvavian nappe) it comes on to a

moderately dissected mountain land, penetrating its valleys. It seems that pre-Gosau movements had formed the central parts of the Eastern Alps into majestic mountains; but it is by no means certain that any equally severe compression of strata took place there. It seems unlikely that the pre-Gosau hilly country mentioned above, and the peneplane (piedmont flat) of the same age which adjoins it to the north, could have been produced from a mountain region of moderate or perhaps great height during that short period of most vigorous crustal movement between the time when it arose and when it was covered.

Features of the outer ranges of the Dinarids and of the western Taurus are no less impressive. Crossing from inner to outer zones, ever higher horizons beginning with Lower Cretaceous, transgress inwards towards the mountains over a violently folded substratum, along what is generally a perfectly graded peneplane. Each successive zone outwards invariably shows that the transgressing strata were later themselves folded, and then in a similar way covered by younger horizons. There can never have been anything but more or less graded peneplanes at the places where these surfaces of transgression now occur; for outwards (what was then seawards) they end in bedding planes. This is quite apart from the fact that the intervals between the periods when folding began and when the folds were covered in (and these were quite brief, especially in the outer zones) were times of very strong crustal movement which absolutely precluded the formation of end-peneplanes. Exactly the same thing, but extended over the whole area of folding, is found in the zones of Upper Jurassic folding in the Pacific mountain belt and of the slightly younger, pre-Cretaceous phase of Saxonian folding in Central Europe. In both regions, the covering strata transgress on to and over beds which are of Upper Oxfordian age in the Pacific belt, and of Lower Cretaceous in Central Europe; and in both, the surface below them is a perfectly graded land surface, a peneplane, as can easily be verified in the neighbourhood of the Westphalian Cretaceous syncline. In western Argentina the unconformity passes into a bedding plane; it corresponds to the duration of the Lower Oxfordian, i.e. a very brief period and one of tectonic unrest. All the same, the only land form present is a peneplane which cannot under such circumstances have been produced from more vigorous modelling such as mountain country. The position in the district of the Westphalian Cretaceous syncline is analogous, and still clearer. The Cretaceous there transgresses over a peneplane which can be clearly seen both at the edge and also, by means of borings, in the interior; it stretches south-west to north-east, in the direction of the former slope, over the Variscan structure of the Rhine Massif, its early Mesozoic deposits, and the zones of Saxonian folding and faulting. In the same direction, the Cretaceous series from Cenomanian to Valanginian and Wealden is gradually completed downwards, the Jurassic series from Kimmeridgian and Wealden upwards, so that somewhere near Bielefeld the unconformity passes into a bedding plane. This position, too, makes it impossible for there ever to have been any other land forms than this graded peneplane on the folded substratum (see p. 165)[25]. These instances, the number of which could easily be multiplied, show that folding is not always connected with the production of mountain heights; and that a sharp distinction must be made between the folding of strata and the raising of the folded strip.

Again, and more important still, insufficient attention has been paid to the fact that the Mesozoic-Tertiary zones of folding form only a fraction of the mountain belts of the world. These by no means coincide with the fold belts, but reach out far beyond them. Even in the narrow Dinaric-Tauric festoon, and to a greater extent further eastward (inner Armenian-Iranian ranges—Pamir), it becomes clear that the mountain ranges have nothing at all to do with the lines of recent folding. Either they cross them at an acute angle (Anatolia)[26]; or, more commonly, they are parts of the crust having a superstructure not folded at all, or scarcely so, and a substructure folded at some far distant period of earth movement. Here it is quite evident that folding and raising are independent processes, separated in time. The Central Asiatic systems of ranges, often exceeding 6,000 metres in height, which occur north and northeast of the Himalaya zone and stretch to the Behring Sea, as well as the greater part of the Andine ranges of both the Americas, belong to this class of mountains. For a long time it was thought that they were systems of tilted blocks, or long narrow horsts lifted above equally narrow rifts; thus overwhelming importance was assigned to the formation of faults, even though their existence was not always proved, very often not even sought[27].

It has recently been shown that this division into ranges, separated by longitudinal depressions, is the result of undulatory warping which, in certain areas, has affected and is still affecting a peripheral crustal shell, obviously sheared. In their essence, the ranges are anticlines, the troughs synclines. *Broad folding** was the name given to the process[28]. So far as can be seen at the present day, it is regularly accompanied by simultaneous regional arching of the whole block which is being folded. Faults and overthrusts may develop when the broad folding reaches stages of increased intensity. But they are features accompanying movement of a higher order, and are associated with the properties of the material being moved and with the degree of intensity of the movement.

* *Grossfaltung.*

Thus they do not, as has been frequently proved, influence the general character of the movement; this can always be recognised as an undulating or folded arching (mountain arch) of extended phase. There is good foundation for the belief that upfolding is not—as was originally thought[26]—the effect of an extraneous compression, but is an intrusive enlargement of the area affected, and thus consequent upon the entry of magma into the crust[29].

Very often—for dry regions one may say usually—the broad synclines are areas of deposition. It has been shown, for the Andes of north-west Argentina, how arching of the ranges reacts upon the correlated* strata which have accumulated in the synclines, how they are distorted and folded. Analogous phenomena have been found in Anatolia, in the Tien Shan and Persia, in the Sunda Islands and in several other parts of the mountain belts[30]. This may, among other things, account for the difference of opinion as to whether the Island of Celebes is of fold-mountain structure or not. Apparently the champions on the one side considered that the essential feature was the folded Neogene in the broad synclines; whilst the others took it to be the Eocene which is occasionally visible on the broad anticlines and is not folded at all, or scarcely so. Our attention is thus directed to another question, extremely important from the morphological point of view.

3. CONNECTION BETWEEN ALTITUDINAL FORM AND THE STRUCTURE OF THE EARTH'S CRUST

A sharp division in time between folding and up-arching of strata, clearly seen where broad folding has affected mountain belts outside the Mesozoic geosynclines, does not exist along the lines of the Mesozoic-Tertiary folding itself. Here an overlap in time has been established for the origin of individual lines of folding and their elevations as mountains. This, together with the fact that they coincide in space, shows an intimate connection between these different effects of mountain-building forces. In the western Taurus bundles of folded strata and packets of rock slices are combined into single ranges of broad folds which subdivide the raised Tauric arc, producing a regular up and down effect, parallel to its strike. Broad folding, which has produced the system of ranges, is here a continuation of the folding of the strata and outlasts it[26].

In the Alps, too, conditions are similar. Their complicated structure, and the far-reaching dissection into regions of peaks and regions of valleys make it very difficult to find the answer to the problem under consideration; but youthful movements of the type of broad folding

[* See glossary.]

probably did occur, and have been structurally proved for their eastern end[31]. Here, too, broad folding is the process which outlasts the folding of strata and which produces the altitudinal form of the mountain masses; and it is the same in the Andes of north-west Argentina where, also, packets of completed folds have been raised in broad folds. Similar observations have been made in the region of the Mesozoic geosyncline of eastern Mexico, and in the Basin Ranges of North America[32]. The same thing appears very distinctly in eastern Greece and western Asia Minor within the Dinaric-Tauric festoon. Here the late Mesozoic and early Tertiary fold lines play no part whatsoever in building up the altitude of the mountains, but are cut transversely across their strike by the ranges which are typical broad folds[33]. *Thus there are already many indications that broad folding is the process which determines the altitudinal form of the mountain belts. It probably also determined the zones of Mesozoic-Tertiary geosynclines in which the sediments, now visible along the lines of folding, were deposited. For it seems to be generally true that the broad folding continues, as it were, the folding of the strata, and in any case outlasts it; so that its effect—the altitudinal form of the system of ranges—becomes evident when the folding of the strata is approaching the phase of incompetence whereby the material of the superstructure becomes incorporated in the substructure.* Then, as may be seen by inspection, the line of young folds behaves, in respect of the mountain-building processes that are still continuing, like that of any other part of the substructure within the zones of instability[34], however long ago this may have been folded. That is, the line of young folds is included in the broad folding.

Structure and altitudinal form are different effects of crustal movement. The question is to find what structure belongs to any given elevation, or increase in altitude, of a part of the earth's crust. It would, of course, be a mistake to look for connections between, for example, the Variscan fold structure of the Harz and its present altitudinal form. They are due to entirely different acts of formation. The movements which made the Harz into a mountain mass are structurally recorded, not in the old folded substructure but in the superstructure which, deposited at the side and on the top of it, has been dragged and tilted on the one side, and on the north side is pushed over and overthrust. This indicates a definite and essential feature of the crustal movement that produced this effect, viz. its direction. It is, therefore, just like folding in being bound up with the existence of material capable of being folded, in the absence of which it cannot occur, even though the nature and direction of the crustal movement is perfectly adequate. Quite generally, the structural record of any process of endogenetic movement which has produced some upstanding part is associated with the presence of material that can be deformed, i.e. primarily with strata of the superstructure which before the disturbance were deposited at the side and on the top of the portion of crust subjected to the movement. For the tectonic expert, difficulties begin only with the absence of a superstructure in which stratification can record how the crustal movements have operated, i.e. when these movements are indicated merely by the crustal elevations. *Every crustal movement leaves its traces in the superstructure, and the sum total of these makes up the structure of the earth's crust.* Not only does this structure differ from place to place, but also it was produced at very different periods. It is preserved as a disturbance of the bedding; but the other effect of the crustal movement, the altitudinal modelling or the vertical upbuilding, is not durable. Should the movement die out anywhere, denudation removes all the parts that had been left projecting, and the depressions are filled in; the structural features alone remain.

There is thus every reason for the geologist to direct his full attention particularly to those phenomena which *represent the sum total of the actual effects of the crustal movements, effects which are related to one another both in time and in mode of origin, viz. structure* AND *altitudinal form.* Only at such places, and with what has so far received little attention, a more detailed working out of the relations between these two effects, will it be possible to arrive at a well-founded judgment regarding the essential features of the crustal movements and the course of their development.

It is quite obvious that the structure may give no clue as to the course of the movements producing it. Under persistent compression, strata are folded to incompetence. What is then observed is, first, not the cessation of the forces that produced the folding, but the conclusion of the folding, i.e. the fact that the material has become unsuitable for the same reaction to the same forces; and secondly, the total amount of disturbance which has occurred up to the time of observation. Suppose that a set of strata is being tilted by one-sided uplift, e.g. on the flank of an arch, and by similar amounts in similar intervals of time. In due course the tilting increases to a limiting value (vertical position). In such a case, could observations be made at different times during the earth's history, they would convey the picture of different degrees of disturbance, which in every case would give the total amount of disturbance which had been reached up to the time of observation. *The structure is always the sum total of individual effects; and the disturbance is found to be greater, the greater the amount that sum total reaches. With a given intensity of crustal movement, structure is a function of time.*

This does not apply to the altitudinal form, as the following reasoning will show, and as has been directly proved by the observations mentioned above (p. 22 ff.). If a part of the crust, carrying a flat-bedded super-structure over an old-fold substructure, should be arched up, it will at the same time be denuded. It can gain in height only when the uplift acts more quickly than the denudation working against it. Suppose the arch-ing to take place very slowly, so slowly that denudation can work against it with complete success, from the very beginning; the block cannot grow in height even when uplift lasts indefinitely, unless this latter becomes more intense, i.e. quicker. During the course of such long-enduring slow uplift, the superstructure will vanish except for the marginal zones. Here the strata are tilted and upturned, more so the longer the movement lasts; but the altitudinal form remains unaltered and small. It does not increase with time, unlike the degree of disturb-ance of the strata lying above or against the upraised part, and unlike the total amount of denudation and of course the thickness of the cor-related strata. It does increase, however, with the intensity of the crustal movement: *for a given duration of crustal movement, the altitudinal form of the earth's crust is a function of the intensity of uplift.* This is the reverse of the relation for crustal structure.

This fundamental connection brings out most clearly the reciprocal relationship between tectonics and morphology. When the structure is examined, it gives quite different information as to the essential charac-teristics of the crustal movements from that found by examining the alti-tudinal modelling, with its set of land forms. *Tectonic and morphological studies are complementary to each other; the one is not a substitute for the other.*

It cannot be said that in research work generally this clear relationship between the structure and the upbuilding of the earth's crust (altitudinal form) takes the place which its fundamental importance deserves, especi-ally with regard to morphology. As already mentioned, there is frequently lacking that sharp distinction between the dynamic and the static ele-ments in the endogenetic conditions, between causes and effects, which is absolutely essential. Then, above all, the assumption that the alti-tudinal form may be thought of as something given in a completed form, somehow produced in the past by some process of uplift now at an end, prevents the two static endogenetic phenomena from being balanced against one another and correctly appraised as different effects of endo-genetic processes. Finally, reaction against the cycle concept of Davis, who did try to separate the endogenetic conditions correctly according to their nature, has played an equally important part in creating a school of thought which emphasises the morphological significance of the earth's structural character (that of the rocks) to a degree which obviously can no longer be justified.

For the most beautiful structure cannot be expressed morphologically if it is, for example, covered by the sea or reposing deep down in the crust. Before the structure of any portion of the crust can become visible through differential denudation (assuming that there are rocks differing in their powers of resistance) it must first be uplifted and exposed to denudation. Only then can there take place that adaptation of denudational forms to the character of the rock which has been already mentioned. This process does not work quite simply; various other processes depend on it; and we shall see later that so far the most important of these has been completely overlooked. The need for following the process in detail has repeatedly been stressed; yet the scope of morphology would be restricted and meagre, were morphologists to be satisfied with investigating that self-evident process of adaptation, which must of necessity take place wherever denudation occurs. Attention should be drawn primarily, as the main object, to the processes which make denudation possible; the detailed adaptation of forms, dependent on this, should take a secondary place. These processes are the crustal movements which give the earth's surface its altitudinal form, so providing the processes of denudation with the gradient they need. Regarding the structure of the earth's crust, the question must again be put as to whether and how far this can be taken as something finished, something given, amongst the premises for morphological investigation. It turns out to be a question of whether the structures observed are completed, or are undergoing further development whilst denudation is at work in the area where they occur. The answer varies accordingly; and here it is nor wrong, under all circumstances and in every case, as it is for the upbuilding of the crustal altitude, to consider them as completed and to treat their relationship to denudation from that point of view. Uplifted and uncovered parts of the Variscan folds do possess a completed inner structural plan. This does not alter while denudation is wearing it away, nor does denudation receive its impulse to work from *those* crustal movements which once upon a time produced this structure. Rather does this come from the very much later movements that created the upstanding part. The same is true for the Appalachians, with their structure of very regular old-folds. It is this fortunate situation which has played no small part in leading to the detailed elucidation there, by Davis and his pupils, of the adaptation of the drainage net to the given fold structure, with the etching out of this latter.

It is most instructive to compare this with the Swiss Jura, a sedimentary block where the main folding set in during the Pliocene. The surface, consisting of anticlines and synclines, has been denuded to varying extents, the process beginning at least as far back as the Eocene, and continuing since then uninterruptedly and to an ever increasing degree. Here the folds were formed and continued to develop whilst denudation was working on them. On the rising anticlines it found and is still finding endogenetic conditions different from those in the synclines which are relatively sinking. Study of the morphological development of the Swiss Jura, and of the way in which the drainage-net as well as individual land forms have become adapted to the folded structure, can by no means begin by taking that structure as a given element, already completed; but it must take into account that it has been formed and has developed whilst denudation was going on. In the Folded Jura the development of land forms may be expected to depend upon the constantly changing intensity of the endogenetic movements in the same way as it has been shown to do to a greater extent in the area of broad folding[8]. Speaking quite generally, when crustal movements have produced, as it were, images of themselves in the present relief, the structural features of the stratification exhibited in denudation areas cannot all be taken as finally fixed, and so treated in the study of their morphological development. For wherever the characteristic features of the land forms are to any great extent determined in their details by the character of the rock, their *development* is immensely affected by the *further growth* of the structure.

CHAPTER III

REDUCTION OF ROCK MATERIAL*

Only here and there, and for a limited time, do rocks freely exposed at the earth's surface still preserve the characteristics due to their mode of origin, i.e. outcrop with chemical composition and texture unchanged. Instead, there is a zone of altered rock material covering almost every place where material is not being deposited, but is being removed by denudation. These *rock derivatives* form the actual surface of the solid earth. Their thickness varies considerably; on steep rock faces they are absent or reduced to a weathered crust of only a few millimetres; their thickness generally increases as the gradient of the slope lessens, and may reach tens of metres. At the same time the nature of this mantle of altered rock changes; it consists of fragments of more or less fresh rock mixed with substances in which the original properties of the rock material can no longer be recognised. The quantitative ratio of the rock fragments, the rubble, to the products of completely transformed rock is very varied and changes from place to place in a characteristic manner. In just the same way there are regular differences in the chemical nature of the transformed products. Not only can these be referred back to differing degrees of transformation, but they also affect products of the same degree of transformation as found in the various parts of the earth. In spite of all these differences, the substances in question have this in common: their formation is associated with a loosening of rock texture, leading to a complete disintegration into separate particles. We therefore speak of *reduction of the rock material*. The longer the processes of rock transformation are at work, the further this reduction is carried; and it ceases only with the formation of unalterable end-products. Considering their mechanical properties only, they are in a state of the greatest possible incoherence and so possess the greatest possible mobility. *The progressive reduction of rock brings about increasing mobility of the crustal material.*

1. NATURE OF WEATHERING. EXPOSURE

The very fact of the reduction of rock shows that what is exposed is not in a state of equilibrium. This is true not only for the crystalline

* *Aufbereitung.* [See glossary.]

silicate rocks, but also for sediments of every kind. Both owe their chemical and mineralogical composition, their texture and their structure (jointing, foliation, stratification, etc.), not only to the nature of the original material, but just as much to the physical conditions under which they were formed and to the various processes that have occurred at their place of formation. Thus for the origin of igneous rocks, of crystalline schists, and of chemical sediments, there is always a definite critical pressure and temperature; the properties of other sediments, especially their cohesion, depend upon the processes of consolidation included under the term diagensis (cementing by precipitation from circulating solutions, and especially the changing of colloidal constituents into a crystalline form). As regards the sum total of the factors influencing their origin, the rocks are in equilibrium; and they would preserve the characteristics due to this unchanged, were the external conditions to remain unaltered. But these conditions are changed when the rocks come into contact with the atmosphere, and are thereby *exposed* to the forces acting at the visible surface.

Directly and indirectly, these forces depend to an overwhelming extent upon solar radiation. The other factor is found in the chemical properties of the mobile coverings of the earth. Rock is no longer in a state of equilibrium when it has been torn away from the surroundings associated with its formation, and exposed to fluctuating temperatures, varying amounts of moisture, and the chemical action of water, carbonic acid, and various other agents with which it comes into contact. There are in addition the mechanical and chemical effects of the biosphere, particularly of the plant cover. The rock material can no longer exist in the same form, and has to adapt itself to the new external conditions, i.e. a fresh state of equilibrium must be attained. *The process of weathering consists of the physical and chemical changes thus brought about.*

Weathering is, therefore, a phenomenon associated with the adaptation of the material to the physical and chemical conditions prevailing at the earth's surface. *The necessary condition for its occurrence is the exposure of the rock surface to atmospheric conditions; and it cannot continue unless this exposure is preserved.* At first, there is the same degree of exposure at all parts of the surface, independent of gradient. If, however, differences do develop, it is the result of the subsequent phenomena due to reduction of the rock, or else it is the effect of vegetation covering the rock surface. On the whole, the rock is reduced to a greater extent, the greater the area of rock surface freely exposed. Comparing upstanding areas of the same size in ground plan, but of different heights, those of greater altitude have steeper flanks and a greater surface exposed to weathering. Therefore, for the same conditions in respect of rock properties and climate, there is a greater amount of rock reduction and more fresh rock given over to weathering than where the height is less (assuming equal base measurements). This is one of the reasons for what is to be observed all over the earth, the fact that on greater heights with steeper slopes there is more thorough demolition of the rock than on lower elevations with gentler slopes.

It is impossible to overestimate the significance of exposure as influencing denudation, and of the processes at the earth's surface which prepare for it and bring it about. Special attention must therefore be given to tracing the conditions which determine the preservation or, as the case may be, the renewal of exposure.

2. WEATHERING PROCESSES[35] AND THEIR PRODUCTS

The processes which take part in rock reduction fall into three categories: (*a*) physical, (*b*) chemical, (*c*) physico-chemical. In the first group are those of *mechanical weathering*; they bring about mechanical disintegration of the rock without altering the composition of its substance. The second group is that of *chemical weathering*; its effect is the transformation of the substance. Near the visible surface, rock is disintegrated into fragments of various sizes, as a phenomenon accompanying the change into chemically-altered end-products. The *process of solution* belongs to the third group. In many ways it is connected with chemical reactions, and is therefore generally ranked with chemical weathering; but it may attain great independent significance. It also is accompanied by surface disintegration of the soluble rock into fragments. The three processes of destruction do not work separately, but are to be seen acting simultaneously all over the land surface. However, from one region to another, the part which each plays in rock reduction varies in importance.

(*a*) MECHANICAL REDUCTION
Effect of Insolation

All over the world the most conspicuous feature of weathering is the mechanical loosening of the rock fabric. Immediately above the unaltered rock there is always to be found—that is, apart from certain exceptions to be considered later with their causes—a zone essentially composed of rock fragments with the same general composition as the underlying rock (the rubble horizon, or rocky horizon, of the soil profile). Physical and chemical processes share in its formation. Amongst the former, special importance must be attached to the factor chiefly responsible for mechanical weathering, namely, fluctuations in temperature at the rock surface, or *ground temperatures*.

Fluctuations in the temperature lead to fluctuations in the volume of the rock; and in the long run no rock fabric can withstand this. The outer surface of the rock expands and contracts with the changes in temperature more readily than do the interior parts. Thus tensions are set up, and in spite of the smallness of the amount by which the volume varies[36], they cause flakes to split off from the surface. Where rocks are granular and composed of several minerals, differences in their coefficients of expansion also play a part, unequal expansion and contraction effecting disintegration into the grains of the individual minerals.

For this kind of mechanical reduction, the decisive factor is not the absolute magnitude of the temperature differences, but the rapidity with which they occur[37]. The more quickly expansion and contraction follow one another, the greater are the tensions in the rock, and it is these which bring about its disintegration. With slow fluctuations of temperature the material has time to adapt itself; the tensions are in this case small, and insufficient to burst the rock fabric apart. Thus the differences in the air temperature, which are passed on to the ground, matter comparatively little for the disintegration of rocks: the contrasts between summer and winter are of no importance, those between day and night only where they succeed one another rapidly. This is, however, the case in arid belts of the world and in the central parts of continents[38], since here (1) atmospheric moisture and (2) ground moisture are slight or absent altogether. As a rule, moisture in the atmosphere decreases the amount of heat received and that radiated. Thus changes in the ground temperature are slowed down and their range diminished. On the other hand, ground moisture absorbs a large part of the heat supplied to the ground, and on cooling gives it up again but slowly. In this way, the heating and cooling of rocks are very much lessened and slowed down. For these reasons, the fluctuations of ground temperature in the moister climatic regions have scarcely any practical effect on rock reduction. The horizon of stony soil seen there usually owes its origin to other causes.

The ground's greatest and most rapid temperature differences are brought about not by the temperature of the air, but by direct insolation; and in this connection the above mentioned influence of air moisture and ground moisture plays an important part. In arid regions, moreover, the rock surface is bare or covered by only sparse vegetation, and so insolation can act unimpeded. *Weathering due to temperature changes is essentially a consequence of insolation.* It is entirely absent from humid regions with their well-developed plant cover; its main distribution coincides with the arid areas of the world.

Fragmentation of rock by insolation is a phenomenon of the outermost surface. It does not reach even the few metres' depth to which fluctuations of soil temperature are measurable, but is confined to the far thinner peripheral zone in which *rapid* contrasts of temperature make themselves felt. No measurements are available. Also, there is by no means unlimited disintegration of the rock through insolation. The process itself does, indeed, give rise to fragments of all sizes, down to fine and very fine particles such as are also incidentally produced when rocks are broken with a hammer. They are, however, merely a by-product of the destruction brought about by insolation, and their production ends with it. This end is reached when the rock fragments have become so small that there is no longer *any great separation in time* between the reactions of their surface and of their core to changes of temperature, as shown by changes of volume. It thus depends upon (*a*) the rapidity of the temperature changes and (*b*) the rock's conductivity of heat[39]. For good conductors, the disintegrating effect of insolation ceases to be felt whilst the size of grain is larger than for poorer conductors. Rocks of a close-textured type occur as grit among the end-products of such disintegration; complex granular rocks (with different crystalline components, or with a different cementing material between them) are at least broken up into their components.

Insolation rubble is, as regards texture, characterised by a mixture of grains of all possible sizes, and this is so during the whole course of its formation. In the early stages, large fragments predominate, with grit and fine particles little in evidence; when development is advanced, these latter have increased very considerably; and in the final stage, the fine particles are absolutely preponderant over the various grades of grit which represent the smallest size for the granules derived from the various rocks which differ in their power of conducting heat[40].

Frost Weathering

Frost shattering occurs where temperatures are near freezing point and the rocks contain water; and this is perhaps the most powerful factor in mechanical reduction. It is due to the fact that water, as it freezes, expands by one eleventh of its volume. If it is in rock fissures, these are widened and become branched; for the water, which freezes from above downwards, forms a stopper of ice preventing any escape of the water that is lower down in the rock, even if this does solidify with expansion of its volume. The pressure thus exerted is passed on hydrostatically, in all directions, including downwards, by the water that is not yet solidified. Thus the mechanical loosening of the rock fabric extends deep down, past the zone of freezing. But it would be wrong to assume that this effect reaches to absolutely any depth, or on the whole increases in an unlimited manner as frost action progresses downwards. According to P. W. Bridgman's investigations, the shattering effect of freezing is at its maximum at $-22°$ C., when it exerts a maximum pressure of 2050 atmospheres per square centimetre. Below this temperature, the water freezing in a closed vessel, and therefore in rock fissures which are closed above, no longer forms the ordinary kind of ice, expanding in volume, but the modification Ice III, which contracts as it solidifies[41]. This throws light upon the magnitude of the loosening force exerted by frost weathering; but it also shows the limitation of its field of action, since in closed fissures and capillaries the maximum pressure is very soon reached. Even under the most favourable circumstances, frost shattering may come to an end at a few metres' depth.

An essential preliminary to frost weathering is the existence in the rock of hollow spaces, for absorbing water, i.e. an original porosity, or else a fissuring which rocks may acquire secondarily, e.g. from tectonic stresses. The size of grain in frost-produced rubble is generally decided by the density of the network of fissures in the unshattered rock (or by its latent capacity for fissuring). In addition, there are quantities of rock splinters, fine as dust, which have been split off parallel to the surface of the rock by rapid changes of temperature[42].

The region subject to frost weathering lies near the snow-line or beyond it; it is characteristic of the polar zones and the high parts of mountain regions, and also, seasonally, of those temperate lands across which the snow-line moves backwards and forwards once a year. It is absent, of course, from perpetually warm, moist regions, and from arid ones. The rocky horizons of the soils of the temperate zone may be partly caused by frost action, but neither exclusively so, nor everywhere.

Going from the snow-line in the direction of increasing warmth, the period of winter frost becomes shorter and shorter, and frost action occurs less and less frequently. All the same, the rubbly horizon does not seem to disappear in that direction, not even where the effect of insolation is eliminated. Beneath a vegetation cover, the pressure exerted by growing roots (*pressure from roots*) especially by those of the higher plants, has a certain significance for the mechanical loosening of rock into the fissures of which the roots wedge themselves. This is, of course, the case only where the root system reaches down as far as, and below, the bottom of the rocky soil, i.e. where the cover of weathered material is no thicker than the depth of the roots. In considering mechanical weathering, it is easy to overestimate the significance of the vegetation cover. Thus too little weight is often given to the *mechanical reduction (not mechanical weathering) which occurs as a phenomenon that accompanies chemical weathering, and locally solution as well*[43]. Since these processes act along the lines of weakness present in the rocks, such as bedding planes, foliation surfaces, fissures due to contraction, and especially the joint planes which divide all rock up into separate pieces, the parts enclosed by the paths of the chemical weathering, though themselves unattacked, become loosened from the rest of the rock. They are brought out of their places by changes in volume due to chemical alteration, or by fluctuations in volume of the chemically weathered material dependent upon varying amounts of moisture in it (swelling and shrinking of colloids); and they become heaped into the irregular piles characteristic of the rubbly horizon. There is no place in the world entirely free from such mechanical reduction by chemical processes. The region of frost weathering is the most nearly so, and next in order comes that where insolation is the dominant factor. In hot wet regions they are the chief way by which mechanical loosening of rock fragments occurs, and they are the typical way for the temperate zones.

(b) CHEMICAL WEATHERING

Chemical weathering is bound up with the presence of water. This is in part split up into H^+ and OH^- ions and therefore acts as acid or base according to whether the compound attacked consists of a weak acid and a strong base or vice versa. Silicates are affected, first by the action of the acid; later, apparently, by that of the hydroxyl ions, and are split up (hydrolysis). Amongst others, A. D. Cushman and J. Hubbard have shown that, in the weathering of silicates, hydrolysis is far more important than the acids, e.g. carbonic acid, etc.[44], brought to the rock in the water. This, as well as other acids, reacts especially with the bases released from the broken down silicates, thus forming salts, some of which are more readily soluble; what is left remains behind as an ingredient of the *eluvial soils*. The chemical processes generally become more vigorous as the temperature rises, not so much because the salts are then more soluble as because of the greater ionisation of the water, this being about twice as great in the tropics as in the temperate regions. Below 0° C. chemical weathering ceases. Thus it rarely occurs beyond the snow-line; and, though it is by no means entirely absent, it is of even less significance there than in the arid regions of the world, where scarcity or absence of water checks chemical change. Its main field of action lies in temperate lands, especially where there are warm humid conditions giving *equable temperatures*.

Chemical weathering is substantially aided by a plant cover and by bacteria. This is, first, because the excretion of chemically active substances (e.g. acids)[45] occurs wherever the processes of life are being carried on; and further, because a continuous cover of vegetation stores up the water which plays an important part in weathering, giving it up only slowly to the substratum (preservation of moisture in the rock and lengthening of the period during which water acts chemically upon the rock surface); finally, and above all, because the dead parts of plants, as they decay, excrete chemically active substances (such as carbonic acid), as well as themselves changing into what is of the greatest importance for the reactions occurring in the soil, viz. *humic substances*. These are the residues of organic decay, which become mixed with those of organic weathering.

The new knowledge that colloids[46] *form a large part of the products of chemical weathering is of fundamental importance, not only for pedology but very specially for the question of denudation.* This applies not only to the silicic acid set free from silicates, which readily loses its colloidal form, but also to the hydrated oxides of iron and aluminium and to their compounds with silicic acid; the lengthy series of the clays and loams (eluvial) belongs here. They represent the more or less uniform end-products of chemical weathering that result from the very varied types of rock found in the world, and their properties depend in detail upon the climatic conditions under which they were formed. Thus they are occasionally referred to as *climatic soils*[47]. In regions of predominantly chemical weathering, they result from the further reduction of the rocky horizon, when this has not already been removed by denudation; and they then form a characteristic horizon above the rubbly zone, one which becomes poorer in rock fragments from below upwards.

Colloids possess to a high degree the property of taking up water and mineral substances, not in chemical but in mechanical union (adsorption)[48]. By this means they swell, attain an ever increasing mobility and can finally pass into a state similar to that of a solution (sols). On drying up, mobility is again completely lost; clay, to take an example of soil colloids, becomes cohesive, it bakes hard. But this is not the case when, instead of pure water, it was an aqueous solution of salts that had been adsorbed by the colloids; for, as drying proceeded, they became saturated with substances capable of crystallisation. In such a case, the dry colloids of the soil are crumbly, mobile like dry sand or dust, and are not cohesive. These conditions are of the utmost importance to denudation; and it is far from being a matter of indifference whether colloidal components are present or not in the weathered material awaiting transport, and what conditions influence its accumulation or removal.

Salt solutions precipitate the colloids, and thus prevent their being carried away in the form of sols. It is assumed that the effect is produced by the ions, split off from the salts, apposing themselves to the colloidal particles carrying the positive or negative charges, and neutralising these. Flocculation of the colloids from their aqueous solution also takes place when colloids with different charges meet. Because of its extraordinarily wide distribution, limy material plays an important part in the distribution and fate of soil colloids. Precipitated colloids accumulate on limestone, the Mediterranean red earth (terra rossa) being an instance of this[49].

Such precipitation through the agency of salts is rendered more difficult by the *humic substances* which, because they react like acids, used to be called 'humic acids'[50]. They, too, are colloids, but they are not nearly so easily precipitated by electrolytes as are the inorganic colloids. These latter apparently take up (adsorb)[51] greater and greater quantities from the humic materials, and so they finally acquire the same property of slighter sensibility to the precipitating influence of electrolytes. Adsorptively unsaturated, so-called acid, humus not only dissolves certain soil colloids, but also prevents their precipitation. Adsorptively saturated, neutral humus does not possess this property. It does not exist in a dissolved form, but is admixed with the soil colloids, and when soaked with water it has, like them, the property of a high degree of mobility (the well-known smeary pap-like quality of wet loam).

Thus it is very important, in making a critical examination of the processes of denudation and how they work, to know where the humic substances occur. They do not simply coincide in distribution with the earth's vegetation cover; but, according to R. Lang's work, are associated with a definite relationship between mean temperature and moisture, the *rain factor*. This indicates the average amounts of precipitation occurring in a district for each degree Centigrade. Similar numerical ratios are obtained for low temperatures and small amounts of moisture, or for high temperatures and abundant moisture. A certain numerical value of the rain factor marks out the area where humic substances occur, just as other numerical values seem to be characteristic in respect of other quite well-defined soil types. These values of the rain factor mean, in every case, the *optimum conditions* under which, in the most favourable circumstances, that special type of soil comes into existence at a given place, and under which the humic exchanges in the soil take their characteristic course[52]. Chemical weathering goes on to a quite considerable extent throughout the zones extending from the equator to the summer snow-line. Continuous vegetation covers only narrower belts, viz. three strips which are separated by the two arid belts; and for humic weathering the space is narrowed down again within those three strips.

(c) Solution

In regions where there are humic substances, the weathered material becomes poor in inorganic colloids. These, like the soluble salts, are to a large extent carried away; part reaches the rivers and so is lost to the land surface[53]. On the whole, the process is one of solution (leaching). Analogous processes in regions of easily soluble rocks such as gypsum, limestone, dolomite, etc., reach an important independent development wherever the rocks are provided with sufficient moisture. It is not so much the simple solvent effect of chemically pure water as the influence of aqueous solutions which react with the soluble rocks. Another well-known fact of prime morphological importance is the tenfold increase in solubility of limestone in water which contains CO_2; this is brought about by the formation of the readily soluble bicarbonate[54]. If in such water there is even a very minute proportion of carbon dioxide existing in the form of H_2CO_3, this acts as a strong acid on account of its very considerable dissociation into H^+ and HCO_3^- ions, and it can attack even siliceous rocks successfully.

The solution of limestone is thus really dependent upon chemical change. It differs, however, from most of the other hydrochemical reactions in that, on precipitation from the solution the original material, the normal carbonate, is regained. This can be observed wherever carbonic acid is removed from the solution by a rise in temperature or a lowering of the pressure (as when calcareous solutions leave narrow fissures for wider ones), or by biological processes (through plants). It has often been debated whether the phenomena of limestone solution must not be actually absent or at least greatly reduced in the tropics, since the absorption of carbon dioxide by water decreases with rise of temperature (at a pressure of one atmosphere). That is correct. However, carbonic acid is not the only solvent, for humic substances have an analogous and no less extensive action in destroying readily soluble rocks. Credit is due to K. v. Terzagi for having pointed out the extraordinary—and usually very much under-rated—significance of vegetation in the solution of rocks, especially of limestone[55]. In the Limestone Alps, for example, on reaching the upper limit of forest, one becomes aware of how cushions of vegetation are, as it were, sunk into the limestone. There is a widening of all those hair-like cracks of tectonic origin which are close shut in the unaltered rock; and cushions and strings of dead and living vegetation can be seen at the bottom of them. As soon as the gaping cracks and clefts produced by vegetable solution intersect, the rock disintegrates into fragments bounded by smooth surfaces, which generally meet in sharp edges. Before this disintegration occurs, the rock is penetrated in all directions by lapiez-like furrows[56], which bear no relation to the surface gradient. Similar features may be observed in other rocks also (an excellent example is afforded by the granite of the Brocken, Fichtelgebirge, etc.), and in humid regions this is the typical minor land form associated with solution[57].

Exactly the same thing takes place, but to a much greater extent, under a continuous cover of vegetation, and so in forests, and can be seen at the base of uprooted trees. Here the processes are intensified to an extraordinary degree, and they amount to major effects which are not to be found in a similar form outside the forested areas. The discussion of Karst phenomena will bring us back to these conditions.

There is a widespread opinion that no chemical weathering or solution takes place in arid regions, since water is lacking. This is not correct. Even the driest parts of the world receive dew and—though it may be but rarely—precipitation; and by no means all the water evaporates at once. On the contrary, even here part trickles down to the water table which, although very deep down, is present[58]. In this way chemical work (hydrolysis) and solution are effected. The latter is brought about particularly by the salts, such as sodium carbonate, which are dissolved in the scanty circulating waters. This dissolves the silica, alumina, etc., to a considerable extent. Water lingers longer in small hollows than on the surrounding parts. Before it evaporates, it has accomplished its work of destruction and leaves behind it crumbling residues which the wind carries away. So these minute hollows grow in depth and width, and may become the great water holes which play an important part in arid regions and contain reserves of water.* E. Kaiser gives an account of the origin of large basins of interior drainage in the Namib, which arose in a similar way in places where easily attacked Cambrian strata were left in the synclinal cores of the fold structure. The floors of these basins are described as places of intense chemical weathering and solution, and the residues that form here (adsorptively saturated, crumbly colloids together with sand and rubble) are partly removed by the wind[59]. The flanks of the basins, on the other hand, develop in a normal way under the influence of denudational processes that will be discussed later, and they are therefore practically unaffected by the wind. But they can develop only because the basin floors are places where the reduction of rock is going on intensively, and where material is being removed by wind, so that they have been lowered. Similar conditions seem to prevail in the great oases of the Libyan Desert which have generally, but most incorrectly, been held to be major forms of denudation by wind.

If salts are present in greater quantities, they crystallise out on the

* 'Bankwasser'.

rock surface from the concentrated solutions; but within the rock they remain active for a long time and lead to internal rock decay. If the brittle rock core comes into contact with the atmosphere, it may be cleared away, and the chemically unaltered shell, often no thicker than paper, becomes an envelope for cavities widening towards the interior. Such are particularly often to be seen in crystalline rocks, e.g. in the granite of arid and semi-arid regions; and they are called Tafoni in Corsica. The honeycomb-like, differential weathering of sandstones is due to similar causes. Here it is especially the cementing material that is decomposed and dissolved by salt solutions, the loose sand grains being blown away or otherwise removed. The phenomenon, previously taken to be a specific desert formation, has not the least connection with climatic peculiarities, but is bound up with the occurrence of circulating salt solutions of dilute acids. It is excellently shown in the Quader sandstone of Saxon Switzerland or the Bunter sandstone of the Palatinate Forest[60].

3. RATE OF WEATHERING AND DIFFERENTIAL WEATHERING

Any force of given intensity, attacking uniformly all over a surface, achieves greater results in unit time when in a less resistant region than when in more resistant surroundings. The widespread phenomenon of *differential weathering* depends upon this law. Such an attacking force affects by the same amount all places having the same degree of exposure; and its definite, constant intensity is fixed within the limits of areas which have corresponding climatic conditions. With equal exposure, e.g. in places where the rocks are freely exposed, or where they are covered by a deposit of the same kind and thickness—weathered material or a plant cover—the amount of weathering in unit time depends upon the character of the rock. That property of rocks which, other things being equal, determines the rate of weathering is called its resistance to weathering.

RESISTANCE TO WEATHERING

The causes of this are to be found, on the one hand, partly in primary characteristics owing their origin to the way in which the rocks have been formed, and on the other hand, partly in such as have been acquired afterwards. To the first group belong chemical composition, texture, and such primary structures as parting along bedding planes, foliation surfaces and contraction planes; to the second group, the way in which these planes lead from the earth's surface into the interior of rock bodies, which means the attitude of the beds, and more particularly the way in which all rock complexes are disintegrated by mechanical and especially by tectonic stresses into small pieces of varying size by fractures, which either have already formed or are forming a close network of cracks. These, together with the partings due to primary structure and the porosity which is particularly characteristic of clastic rocks, form the *inner surface** of the rocks, which is in communication with the outer surface, the outcrop.

This inner surface is of the greatest importance for all those processes of weathering in which water in any form takes part, since it allows the water to penetrate to the interior of the rock complexes, and so defines the paths of the weathering. The greater the surface of attack, the more weathering can accomplish; the available surface increases, however, with the size of the inner surface[61]. Rocks that are more highly jointed, for example, are—other things being equal—more liable to destruction, either by frost, chemical weathering or solution, than those which are less well jointed. In porous sandstone it can be seen that the cementing material is most decayed where the decomposing solutions could circulate most freely, as where the parts that have retained their porosity remain between former cracks filled in earlier by deposits from solution. These latter stand out as ridges when the weathered particles are removed. In addition, there is the original difference in the chemical composition of the crustal rocks which enables them, at a given place, to offer a different degree of resistance to the chemical agents at work there. For example, crystalline siliceous rocks are obviously far more subject to chemical weathering than sediments which, like quartzite or clay, have a composition that corresponds to the end-products of weathering. But there are also finer differentiations, since, for example, the individual silicates have very different powers of resistance to chemical attack by water or aqueous solutions. In consequence of this, siliceous rocks of varying mineral composition, possess varying powers of resistance to chemical action; just as in the series of the more chemically stable sediments there are differences arising in the same way—always assuming that otherwise the properties, exposure and climatic conditions are similar. There is no need to discuss further the importance of different degrees of rock solubility in the process of solution. Mention has already been made of the fact that breaking up by insolation depends upon the capacity for conduction of heat resulting from the texture and mineral composition of the rock concerned. To supplement this, reference may here be made to the colour of the rock: dark coloured rocks experience a stronger heating effect than light coloured, and so are subject to greater

*[Cf. p. 19—extent of pore space.]

and more rapid fluctuations in volume, and disintegrate more easily, than the latter. In arid regions, furrows are thus often associated with, for example, veins of dark coloured igneous rock.

Resistance to weathering is thus based upon the various properties of rocks. It is different not only for rocks of different composition in the same climate, but also for the same types of rock in different climates. It depends not only upon original characteristics due to the manner of formation, but also upon what the rocks have since undergone. Two things must in particular be considered. On the one hand, there are changes in texture such as occur with diagenesis, bringing about an increase in crystallinity. For example, pure limestone is on that account generally less easily soluble with increasing geological age; because of changes due to infiltration, the porosity becomes less (consolidation of texture), and the degree of crystallinity is increased. On the other hand, there is the cracking due primarily to tectonic stresses. To be able to associate the differences in cracking with specific elastic properties of the rocks, the comparison must be made between those from zones of similar tectonic development. A malm limestone of the Swabian Alb differs as to the extent of its inner surface from an Alpine limestone of the same age and composition, and as regards resistance to weathering is not directly comparable with any other Alpine rocks.

It follows from this that a morphological grouping of rocks, based on their resistance to weathering, is not feasible. Attempts at this are therefore of only doubtful value even when restricted to a definite climatic region[62].

Differential weathering produces effects of two kinds. The indirect one has been already indicated when treating mechanical reduction by chemical weathering. Since this penetrates deep down, especially along the cracks, etc., it loosens solid pieces, bounded by the interior surfaces, from union with the rest of the rock. The same thing happens in the process of solution. Hence solid rock fragments are by no means missing from residual soils, even in regions of exclusively chemical weathering and solution. Rivers everywhere receive weathered material, and it is these fragments in it, and not the dissolved or suspended colloids, which do mechanical work. In those parts of the world where mechanical weathering is practically non-existent, running water owes part of its tools to differential chemical weathering (examples being the rivers of wooded karst or of forested tropical mountains).

The second effect of differential weathering is to make evident the heterogeneity of rocks. It appears in the form of relief, since depressions are related to the zones of weakness, and elevations to the more resistant parts of the rocks. *It is not the absolute values of resistance to weathering which form the criterion, but the relationship of these to one another in neighbouring types of rock, a relationship which varies from place to place.* One and the same dyke of igneous rock may, as is well known, rise like a wall from less resistant surroundings, whilst it becomes a furrow on entering a more resistant type of rock. The *differences in resistance of rocks* to weathering become evident. That is, however, no longer a direct effect of weathering, but a consequence of removal of the reduced rock material. Where there is no such transport, naturally neither the lack of homogeneity in the rock, nor the differential effects of weathering caused by this, can become visible.

Therefore, when rocks can be distinguished in the relief, it means that a greater amount of the one type of rock has been reduced, become capable of removal and been removed in unit time than of another, more resistant to weathering. Hence resistance to weathering can be summed up in the following way: rocks are resistant when the process of reduction takes a comparatively long time to bring them to a form that can be denuded, i.e. one of sufficient mobility; unresistant rocks are those in which this transformation takes place more rapidly, assuming that the conditions of denudation are the same in both cases.

If in unit time just twice as much material, for example, is reduced and removed from one rock as from surrounding more resistant ones, the difference in relief increases as time goes on, since the smallest effects achieved in unit time are always twice as great on the one side of the rock boundary as on the other, and these differences are cumulative. It follows from this that—*under similar conditions of denudation and with a constant difference between the rocks—the adaptation of land form to difference of rock material is a function of time.*

4. UNIFORMITY IN THE PROCESS OF ROCK REDUCTION. THE SOIL PROFILE

Weathering acts over the surface; and, with the same exposure, as well as attacking factors of the same kind and magnitude, that is in a region of uniform climatic conditions, each portion of the surface is affected to an equal degree. Provided the upper surface of the crust were homogeneous, weathering would strike equally deep everywhere; and after the lapse of a definite time there would be a superficial rind of rock with a definite thickness converted into a product of weathering with a definite composition. If, in such a case, pure end-products of weathering have arisen, these form the uppermost horizon of the soil profile. In regions where chemical weathering is predominant, this would be loam or clay of a composition dependent no longer upon the original material, but

D

upon climatic conditions. In a complete soil profile there follows below that a mixture of the end-product with more or less altered rock fragments, which increase in number and size downwards, becoming fresher, whilst the amount of the colloidal end-products decreases. Thus the rubbly horizon develops downwards, then comes the zone of merely loosened parent-rock, and finally that where it is unbroken. This is below the limiting depth to which, up to that time, weathering and the chemical changes connected with it extend; but between the zone of loosening and that of rock rubble there is a lower limit, of special importance to denudation,* where mechanical rearrangement has been completed for particles separated off from the coherent rock mass. In regions where mechanical weathering is predominant, a complete soil profile shows, from below upwards, above the zone of merely loosened rock, mechanically reduced rubble of ever smaller grains, with an increasing admixture of fine to very fine particles.

The horizons of the entire soil profile, as they succeed one another, show increased reduction from below upwards; but naturally they are not sharply marked off. They develop from one another in such a way that loosening pushes further down into the unbroken rock, whilst from the former zone of loosening there develops a rubbly horizon, and from the upper parts of that, the pure end-product. The soil profile grows in depth; and its uppermost horizons, lying exposed at the surface, are always composed of that part of the rock earliest, and so longest, subjected to reduction. Thus, as time goes on, the mass of the reduced material increases and the degree of reduction. These two have a very different significance for denudation. The amount of reduced material produced in unit time determines how much rock can be denuded even under the most favourable given conditions: no more than exactly the amount that has been reduced, i.e. has become loose and mobile. The degree of reduction, on the other hand, affects the onset of denudation and the course of its development at the place considered.

It is not known how long a time is required for any particular rock to become loosened, and then to develop a rubbly zone and finally an horizon of purely end-products. Therefore it is not known how long a period of reduction is needed for soil horizons to develop from one another in the direction of an increasing degree of reduction. All that is certain is that it takes considerably more time for the unmixed end-product to develop from the zone of coarse rubble than for the latter to arise from the zone of loosening. The following statement makes this clear: the task assigned to weathering may be expressed by the frequency of division necessary for cutting the material up into smaller and smaller

* [See pp. 53–54.]

fragments (i.e. by the number of the divisional planes). Thus it is obvious, that the mere loosening of the rock is a far smaller task than the multiple subdivision in the rubbly horizon, and this again is one immeasurably less than the decomposition of the material into colloids or very fine dust, which means an almost infinite multiplication of the process of division. The number of divisional surfaces grows in geometrical progression. If such an ever increasing task were to be performed in consecutive equal periods of time, the intensity of the reducing processes would have to be raised to the power of the number of such periods. But, physical and chemical agents taken together have, on the whole, a constant intensity at a given place[63]. Therefore it follows that, compared with the later phases, the initial stages of rock reduction are actually passed through far more quickly: that it takes a shorter period of reduction to loosen rock than to change the zone of loosening into one of rubble: and that this latter again arises much more rapidly than the end-product develops from it—*always assuming similar exposure. The degree of reduction is not proportional to the duration of the reduction; but, the exposure being the same, decelerates.*

But that does not apply to the *quantity of rock material reduced.* It can easily be seen that equal lengths of time will always be required for reduction to produce, from any given rock, one and the same soil horizon with a similar profile below it. If the whole of the soil cover could be removed from the unaltered rock surface, then weathering would have to work exactly the same length of time at that same spot as on the first occasion in order to produce a similar new cover of soil identical in thickness with the same surface horizon at a similar stage of reduction and with the same sequence of horizons below. The same amount of material has then been reduced as in the first instance. In the same way, for neighbouring places on the earth's surface which have the same type of rock and of climate, weathering needs the same amount of time to reduce similar quantities of rock into a soil cover of corresponding thickness and identical profile development, with the same topmost horizon at a similarly advanced stage of reduction. If this is nearer to the state of completion, the times of formation are correspondingly very much longer, as shown above; if further from completion, they are relatively shorter. But profiles with the same topmost horizon have invariably had equally long periods of formation, provided corresponding processes of reduction are acting on the same types of rock. *This important relationship is what is meant by uniformity in the reduction of rock.* It is a concept of fundamental importance, for it provides perhaps not an absolute yet a relative measure of the intensity of denudation, since it becomes possible to compare the work achieved in the same periods of time by the uniform reduction and by the non-uniform denudation of rocks.

5. UNEQUAL EXPOSURE

The phenomena so far investigated have been those which may be observed at places with similar exposure and similar climate. One condition for unequal exposure has already been considered: the plant cover (pp. 38, 40, 41, 44–45). Where there is a continuous cover it entirely prevents heat weathering (insolation) and checks attack by frost since it protects from cold and possibly also produces physiological heat. On the whole, therefore, it reduces exposure to mechanical weathering. Its behaviour towards chemical weathering is different. Thus the earth's mantle of vegetation is in every case, as has been shown, a factor in increasing the exposure which it is impossible to overestimate. A forest cover is more favourable to chemical weathering and solution than is that of turf or steppe, whilst these again are more favourable than bare spots[64]. This is borne out by the way in which strips of vegetation sink down, sometimes on quite a large scale, into a calcareous subsoil, and the occurrence of doline-like snow holes in the High Calcareous Alps; for this means that, favoured by these conditions, chemical and physico-chemical processes are more effective than, and outpace the physical forces to which the surrounding rock, just because of its bareness, is particularly favourably exposed.

The second factor in unequal exposure is the cover of rubble and soil found at the surface of the earth's crust. It is more difficult to estimate the importance of this since—as will be described in a later chapter—it is only under certain conditions that it is stationary, being usually on the downward move in areas of denudation.

It can easily be seen that an increasing thickness of soil hinders mechanical weathering and eventually stops it, insolation effects ceasing sooner than frost weathering. In this respect it diminishes exposure. But for chemical weathering it is not true to the same extent. Certainly the soil cover does not, like the mantle of vegetation, produce substances which bring about decomposition; but as regards moisture, it behaves somewhat like a sponge. It becomes soaked through with water, taking up more the thicker it is; and it gives off its moisture slowly both upwards and downwards. In times of drought this can be observed: whilst the upper parts of the accumulated soil are drying out, the lower still remain damp for a long time. These conditions affect the rocky substratum. Where a thick cover of soil protects it, chemical weathering is favoured as compared with the bare or less well protected parts of its surface. Now it has been observed that chemical decomposition, i.e. the transformation of the rock-forming minerals into colloidal end-products, does not always stop at the lower limit of the rock loosening, but under especially favourable circumstances it strikes deeper towards the lower limit of weathering, to be discussed later. Then the fragments in the rubbly zone, the loosened rock immediately below that, and the zone lying beneath—which is physically intact and has preserved its original structure—are all transformed into a clayey mass. Occasionally seen in the tropics, it also now and then occurs in our own part of the world, in places where there has locally been great chemical alteration such as in the strata below the Lower Oligocene brown coals of Saxony and elsewhere. Under the influence of bog water, the quartz-porphyry lavas of the Rotliegende have here been kaolinised to far below the zone of loosening. This has happened particularly on the flat floors of those basin-like valleys, between inselberg-like elevations, in which brown coal and clastic Oligocene strata have been laid down, i.e. in areas of deposition. One cannot speak of a 'zone of rubble' here; it is rather a matter of white clays, rearranged derivatives of the kaolinised porphyry, which pass downwards into rock material, unchanged in structure, but completely decomposed (the so-called 'Kapselton'). As the elevations are approached, the lower layers of the Oligocene strata show a distinct, more or less kaolinised horizon of rubble. Outside the Oligocene bog deposits, the soil profile is normal and covered only with thin sediments which transgress over the slopes of those half-buried hills of Lower Oligocene material. Here it can be seen distinctly that the kind of soil profile depends upon the thickness of the overlying material.

There is another phenomenon of the same order. It is obvious that actually the loosened zone of the normal soil profile, once the higher horizons of the complete profile have formed above it, does not penetrate into the interior of the rock at the same rate as it can develop at freely exposed surfaces, though one might have expected it to do so. The loosening does not forge ahead of those higher horizons with its characteristic speed of formation, but eats more and more slowly into the unaltered rock. It follows from what has already been mentioned that under favourable circumstances the transformation of siliceous rock into a colloidal end-product is able to overtake the zone of loosening and may then reach far below it. But above all it shows that the lower limit of the rubbly zone—whatever the profile above may be—is at a slighter depth, which according to my observations does not greatly exceed two metres (apart from material piled up locally above the normal soil profile).

The explanation of this behaviour may be found in the fact that, for a rubble horizon to be developed from the zone of loosening, there must be a rearrangement of the fragments loosened from the solid rock.

Amongst the forces of rearrangement, mention has been made of the pressure of roots, fluctuations in volume of the colloids, freezing and thawing. But as soon as the weight of the overlying mass exceeds a certain value, owing to increasing depth of the soil profile or to accumulation from outside, these forces are insufficient to do their work against the load. The consequence is that the pieces of rock bounded by, for example, joint planes, do indeed, under the influence of progressive weathering, cease to cohere to their surroundings. But they remain in their places, and are ultimately decomposed, unless a limit is put to the profile's growth by 'spontaneous'* migration of the material, or unless heavy material moving downhill penetrates so successfully into the zone of loosening that it dislocates, by lifting or chiselling off, the merely loosened but not yet rearranged pieces of rock.

Thus it follows that a soil cover favours chemical change, and with it the preparation of colloids. Its growth in thickness, however, increasingly hinders the downward extension of the lower limit of the rubble zone even in regions where the weathering is predominantly chemical. And that lower limit has its special importance for denudation, since only exceptionally does it fail to coincide with the lower limit of the profile of reduction[65]. Hence in this case also there results a lessening of the exposure, a deterioration of the conditions making ready for denudation.

Summing up, it may be said that for any kind of mechanical reduction, a soil cover lessens the degree of exposure.

Consequently a portion of the earth's surface with a soil cover of varying thickness has different degrees of exposure so far as the *upper surface of the rock* is concerned, even if all the other conditions—rock properties, climate, vegetation cover—are exactly the same. *The upper surface of the soil cover*, however, is subject to the same exposure. With an arrangement in which the thickness of the soil cover decreases steadily in one direction, so that finally the unaltered rock outcrops—the case most frequently found and the most important—it is on the bare rock that the exposure is greatest, the mechanical reduction and the increase in depth of soil profile most rapid. If further, the inner arrangement is such that, with decreasing soil thickness, lower and lower horizons of the soil profile are displayed at the surface (till the bare unaltered rock is reached), these having experienced only their decreasing degrees of reduction— this again is the commonest and most important occurrence at the earth's surface—the various horizons lying next to one another and with similar exposures develop at their own special rates. On the bare rock, reduction acts most quickly; in the other direction, where a complete soil profile lies

* [See p. 17 and p. 64, line 23.]

beneath the pure end-product of weathering, this process has already terminated at the surface. In other words: *the rock surfaces which have better exposure try to catch up with those less well exposed, not only in the amount of reduced material, but also in its degree of reduction*, assuming all other circumstances to be the same. This fact is of the greatest importance when such unequally exposed surfaces are inclined. It concerns every part of the earth which is subject to denudation (see p. 37).

6. MOBILITY OF REDUCED MATERIAL

That quality of reduced material which is of fundamental importance for denudation is its mobility. It is a question of friction, dependent in the first instance upon cohesion, which is proportionally less, the greater the number of divisional planes which cut up the material into individual small pieces. Mobility, therefore, increases with the degree of reduction, and the superposed horizons of the complete soil profile are of increasing mobility. The concept developed on p. 51 can now be expressed in a form which has a morphological value: *making crustal material mobile is, on the above supposition, a process which goes on in a uniform manner.*

Wherever they may be on the earth's surface, the reduced materials come into contact with water, to a varying extent; and, since they differ in their properties, this has very great importance as regards their mobility. For the rule holds that moisture reduces mobility (increases cohesion) when the dry substance is less cohesive than water, and increases it for substances which in their dry state are more cohesive than water[66]. Reduced material of the first group includes dry fragments, poor in colloids, such as are produced by insolation; the second group comprises all the weathered material of the moist temperate and moist tropical regions with their wide marginal zones, since this is rich in colloids. In the dry state it binds, baked firm. Even small quantities of moisture, however, increase its mobility; and as the amount of water increases, this effect increases at an ever greater rate. The more colloidal matter present—especially if it is clay—the more readily mobile is the material. The *highly mobile end-products of reduction* (pure clays or loams) form the last link in the chain, the initial one being the rocky horizons. However—and this needs to be particularly stressed—since some chemical weathering generally occurs, nowhere is there a complete absence of colloids between the fragments to promote their mobility and lessen friction, even if their amount is more or less insignificant so that any considerable mobility is lacking.

It is otherwise with the products of predominantly mechanical weathering, caused by heat and cold. A small quantity of water increases the cohesion (lessens the mobility); larger amounts of liquid, on the other hand, affect them in the same sense as if the material were rich in colloids. Each rock particle is surrounded by a film of water, the density of which—according to Ehrenberg—increases from the surrounding liquid towards the surface of the particle. This swims as if on a cushion of water, so long as it does not exceed the size of a grain of sand. In this way, fine-grained material when thoroughly soaked may actually become fluid, e.g. quicksand. The mobility of the coarser rubble, when soaked through, is due to its loss of weight in water and to the effect of water in reducing friction. *The magnitude of the friction* depends upon the size and shape of the grains, which are of importance not for the fact of mobility, but only for its degree. Rubble of any kind and of any origin, whether wet or dry, whether mixed with colloids or not, is less mobile the more corners and edges it possesses, the less rounded the fragments.

In the case of frost weathering, a point of special importance is that the products are formed in a region where the water, seasonally abundant, contains—in consequence of its low temperature—a far smaller amount of dissolved salts (electrolytes) than elsewhere. Thus the ever-present colloids are not precipitated. For this reason the water maintains its fluidity undiminished even when only small amounts of it penetrate into the reduced material[67]. It imparts extraordinary mobility to this, as is strikingly illustrated by polar solifluction and the rock-flows of the high-lying regions of Central Asia.

In arid regions, on the other hand, chemical weathering plays a more important part. There is considerable formation of soil colloids. These remain precipitated during the periods when there is moistening, since the water, but rarely present, contains abundant salts in solution. As a rule, however, the colloids are dry, and not cohesive, as in moist climates, but crumbly because of adsorptive saturation with salts. Such soil crumbs augment the mass of fine to very fine particles with which the insolation rubble is mixed from the very beginning, the amount increasing as it develops. They help to reduce friction between the rock fragments, which indeed finally float, as it were, in the fine-grained groundmass. And since that fine material does not adhere to the other components of the rubble, or 'moisten' like water, small amounts of it are sufficient to render a mass of coarse fragments more readily mobile. As, in the course of reduction, the individual grains become smaller and the amount of the fine grains increases, the rubble becomes more mobile. At the end of the series is a highly mobile mixture of grit, sand and dust.

The great inequality in size of the grains, which is characteristic of insolation rubble in all stages of its development, is of decisive importance for its mobility. For the coarser heavy components exert upon the underlying fine grains, by means of their weight, a non-uniform pressure which these endeavour to evade; they succeed in doing so because they lack cohesion, and on inclined surfaces they escape downwards. *The increased mobility of the dry mixtures of rubble produced by mechanical 'heat weathering', as contrasted with material in which the grains are more or less equal in size, depends upon these physical conditions: reduction of friction between the components of the rubble, and unequal pressure exerted by the larger fragments on the fine grains of readily mobile sizes.*

7. WORLD CLIMATIC AND SOIL ZONES

The forces leading to rock reduction depend fundamentally upon conditions of temperature and moisture (precipitation). The arrangement of these at the earth's surface shows a definite pattern: in a general way, mean temperature decreases from the equator polewards, and with absolute height. Humidity does not change in the same direction, but depends upon the general circulation of the atmosphere, the distribution of land and water and, as regards detail, the altitudinal form. Thus there are various parts of the world characterised by relationships of temperature and humidity, different for each part but uniform within it, and these are differentiated as climatic regions. In them, physical and chemical processes take different shares in weathering; as a result there are differences in the reduced material. *It has already been pointed out that this does not involve any difference with regard to that effect of weathering which is the prerequisite for denudation—the mobility of the weathered substances.* All over the earth, weathering of any kind acts in the direction of increased reduction of material, making it increasingly mobile; and the question is merely whether this takes place equally fast in the various climatic regions, or at different rates.

In the demarcation of climatic regions, the decisive factor from the morphological point of view is what happens to the precipitation that falls on the land surface. On these lines, A. Penck distinguishes three major divisions[68]:

(a) *the humid climate* in which precipitation is in excess of evaporation, so that a surplus flows off in permanent rivers;

(b) *the nival climate* in which snowfall is in excess of melting, so that there is transport by glaciers;

(c) *the arid climate* in which evaporation is in excess of precipitation. There are no permanent streams here.

To complete this, there must be added the transference of surface water to the ground water. In a humid climate there is more rain than evaporates or soaks into the ground. The water table lies near the surface and permanent water courses do not give water to it, but take from it. In an arid region there is, on the contrary, less precipitation than evaporation and infiltration. Where there is any ground water at all, its surface is deep down, and water seeps into it from the intermittently flowing streams.

Humid conditions recur in three strips along the earth's surface: round the equator (humid tropical); and, with lower mean temperatures, in the temperate latitudes of both hemispheres (humid temperate). They are interrupted by the arid continental interior regions, and are separated from one another by the two arid belts into which they grade by climatic transitions. Theoretically on either side of the arid belts there are sharp boundaries, the limits of aridity, where evaporation and infiltration just counterbalance precipitation. But they cannot be drawn on the earth's surface any more sharply than can the snow line separating the humid from the nival regions, beyond which more snow is precipitated during the year than is melted. For such boundaries undergo seasonal fluctuations. In the course of a year they advance towards the equator (and descend where the climatic zones are developed as altitudinal belts), and they retreat again polewards (or rise, as the case may be). The regions through which they pass are characterised by seasonally different climates and they belong in part to the intermediate transitional zones between the *completely humid* and the *completely arid* regions.

Neglecting details in the distribution of precipitation—which result from the arrangement of land and water, of highland and lowland—the following is roughly the arrangement found on the earth's surface, starting from the nival regions and going equatorwards: Just outside the ice cover, the day temperature for a large part of the year fluctuates round about o° C. The lower waterlogged layers of the soil remain frozen— according to an old note of Wild's, at a mean annual temperature of − 2° C.[69]—only the upper horizons thawing. That is the *polar zone*, the realm of predominantly mechanical frost weathering. When the snow melts, the reduced material becomes highly mobile, since it is then soaked through with water poor in electrolytes (polar solifluction). On freezing, the mobility is entirely lost.

In the direction of increasing mean annual temperature, frost phenomena become less and less noticeable, chemical and humic weathering more prominent. Reduced material develops, rich in colloids, the end-product being black or brown[70]. It is thoroughly moist at all seasons and so almost always in a state of increased mobility (the rubble as well. See p. 55). This is the *completely humid temperate region*, with precipitation fairly uniformly distributed throughout the year.

This uniformity is lost as the arid belts are approached. In the semi-humid region there is an alternation of wet and dry seasons. In the wet season, chemical weathering is active; but there are spots where, in the dry season, only physical disintegration by heat (insolation) occurs. Reduced substances, rich in colloids, are to be found here too; but they are mobile only in the wet season; when dry, they bake into a coherent mass, and hold fast the other components of the weathered material, rendering them immobile. The end-products are coloured red by iron oxide ('red earth')[71].

Semi-humid regions occur on either side of the arid belts. On the poleward side are the subtropics—with rain in winter, when the sun is at its lowest; on the equatorial side the rainy season is in summer when the sun stands high. This is usually considered as part of the tropics; and the monsoon regions belong to it.

Here, too, red soils, rich in colloids, are typical. They often—but by no means always—consist of hydrated aluminium oxide; this makes its appearance as the end-product of the most far-reaching decomposition leading, under the influence of tropical temperatures and water of high chemical activity, to the loss of the last remnants of the alkalis and silicic acid. The term laterite is now restricted to these soils[72].

Equatorwards of the tropics, the rainy seasons, associated with the highest altitude of the sun, occur twice a year, and merge more or less definitely so as to give very abundant rainfall spread over the year. With this the *completely humid tropical province* is entered. Here conditions for the existence of humus recur, and weathering takes the same course as in the temperate zones. The end-product is yellow earth which is coloured black or brown by humus (black and brown earths)[73]. On account of the perpetual heavy soaking, this colloidal material is constantly in a state of high mobility.

Climatic transitions lead to the *arid belts* (and arid continental interiors) which separate the humid zones. Water and so chemical weathering are by no means entirely absent. In the transitional regions of the *semi-arid province*, they reach considerable importance; yet there is not here, either, sufficient precipitation to feed permanent or periodic streams. Water seeping down to the deep-seated water table is partly—not entirely—drawn back to the surface by capillary processes; and there, on evaporation, deposits the substances which it has dissolved on its way. Efflorescences of readily soluble salts and crusts of the less soluble calcium carbonate, locally also of silica, cement the peripheral soil horizons. In the completely arid region, with its scarcity of soil moisture, these desert crusts become less frequent. In both types of region the ground water is confined to favoured spots, as a rule to the alluvium-filled basins, and it lies very deep down. It is salty, often a concentrated brine from which salts are precipitated locally where the water table comes to the surface (salt lakes). Soil colloids are by no means absent; however, they are mobile not only when they are thoroughly wet but also (as already pointed out) when in the dry state since, because of their adsorptive saturation with salts, they form fine loose crumbs[74]. In the arid belts, it is insolation which determines the prevailing form of rock reduction. Especially in the completely arid region, the rubble formed is as a rule dry and therefore practically always highly mobile. In the semi-arid region this is the condition only during the dry period. In the rainy season there is often considerable soaking of the material and it then becomes still more mobile for *that* reason, the colloids playing no small part in this effect. On the other hand, at the times of transition from dry to moist, and vice versa, the mobility of the material reduced under arid conditions is lessened, for the reasons stated above (p. 56).

Thus the general position is as follows: from the equator to the edge of the ice caps, reduced substances develop which, on account of their own nature and of the climatic conditions under which they were formed, possess the highest possible degree of mobility. *In every climatic region, there are optima for mobility of the material derived from the rocks.* Products of chemical weathering, highly mobile when moist, and becoming bound and immobile when dry, are developed just at those places where moisture is abundant during the course of the year; and it is in exactly such spots, possessing these very favourable conditions, that the material of mechanical weathering which is most mobile when completely dry or thoroughly soaked, is developed.

In addition to this invariable and characteristic feature, which is a fact of the greatest importance from a morphological point of view, there are the various types of soil products which are peculiar to the individual climatic regions. These are termed *climatic soil belts*[75]. Taking into account only the end-products of reduction, such as appear in a climatic region under the most favourable circumstances—and the distribution of these can then, according to R. Lang, be recognised by a definite numerical value of the rain factor—the following soil belts succeed each other in this order from pole to equator:

Frost soils of mechanical disintegration,⎫	nival zone
having the colour of the parent rock ⎭	polar zone
Black raw humus - - - - -	sub-polar transition zone
	(super-humid region)
Black earth (dark-coloured yellow earth) -	temperate humid region
Brown earth (dark-coloured yellow earth) -	transitional
Red earth - - - - - -	semi-humid region

Yellow-grey steppe soils (insolation rubble)	semi-arid region
Insolation rubble the colour of the parent rock - - - - - - -	arid region
Steppe soils - - - - - -	semi-arid region
Red laterite⎫ Red earth ⎬ - - - - - -	semi-humid tropical region
Brown earth (dark-coloured yellow earth) -	transitional
Black earth - - - - - -	humid tropical province
Raw humus - - - - - -	super-humid tropical region

The colour of the soil proves to be a characteristic feature[76]. And if, during the course of the year, different climatic conditions obtain, seasonal variations in colour can be observed in the transitional regions[71]. In the same way the superposition of soil types of different colours can be taken as an indication of climatic changes, and a very sensitive one, for these actual transitional regions[77].

8. LIMITS OF WEATHERING

If the weathered substances remained where they were formed, the land would be covered with an increasingly thick layer of soil, its upper horizons consisting of the unalterable end-product characteristic of each climatic type. The question is to what depth the rock decay could then penetrate.

It has been shown (p. 53) that the lower limit of mechanical reduction, by mechanical and chemical weathering, is to be found at a depth of a few metres. Chemical changes, however, take place below that. They continue down to the level of the ground water. The properties of this are quite different from those of the seepage water reaching it; it is especially poor in oxygen—oxidation processes, therefore, come to an end at this level—and so it is richer in carbon dioxide. In particular, the aeration of the rocks, which is essential for their decomposition, ends at the level of the ground water. And finally, chemical products of whatever kind, precipitated near and below the water table, show that the ground water is saturated with mineral matter. Thus the water table separates two zones in which chemical processes take place in the reverse direction. Below it, is the zone of cementation, the realm of diagenesis; above it is the area in which chemical weathering and solution are at work (zone of oxidation).

If the products of chemical weathering which remain at their place of origin are in the form of stable end-products right down to the water table, then any further transformation, any further reduction, ceases.

The level of the water table is their absolute lower limit. The thickness of such a soil cover, forming undisturbed, would depend solely upon the position of the water table. That is determined first by the climate—in humid regions it is nearer the exposed surface than in arid ones; then by the kind of rock—it is lower down in permeable than in impermeable areas; and finally by the surface relief which is approximately followed by the water table. It lies farther from the surface beneath elevations than beneath depressions. From this it is easy to decide between what limits the thickness varies for an ideal soil cover, developing undisturbed, and also its world distribution. Comparing this with what is actually found to be the case, we gain a most impressive picture of the continuous and far-reaching effect of the denudational processes which everywhere hinder the formation of an ideal soil zone.

9. RELATIONSHIP OF WEATHERING TO DENUDATION

Nowhere in the world does the water table lie immovably fixed, even if the climate and the character of the rock remain unaltered, any more than reduced material anywhere remains at the place where it was formed. For as this moves away—as happens on every inclined land surface, so long as it is not an area of deposition—the exposed surface is continuously lowered, and the level of the water table sinks with it. Wherever denudation is taking place on the earth, the lower limit of weathering is in consequence gradually moving down deeper, i.e. zones of rock, which till then were subject to diagenesis, are now subject to weathering. What is true for the lower limit of weathering naturally applies also to any horizon of the profile above it: the border zone, especially important for denudation, between the horizon of rock loosening and that of the rubble, is under such circumstances also in a position to move downwards and is compelled to do so. *We shall call this process the renewal of exposure.*

RENEWAL OF EXPOSURE

It takes place more rapidly, the greater the quantity of rock material removed from any point in unit time; in other words, the more intense the denudation. *Thus renewal of exposure is a function of the intensity of denudation.* As only loose particles of rock can be carried away, it has also a definite relation to rock reduction, and to the amount of rock reduced in unit time as well as to the degree of reduction. In the one limiting case, the tiny pieces leave the place where they were formed immediately after having been loosened from the body of the rock. This means a rapid renewal of exposure; since each time pieces are removed, only those relatively short intervals of time have been needed which, at a given place, are required for the loosening and detachment of fragments from the parent rock. It is merely the horizon of rock loosening which can be produced, and not any soil horizons of a farther advanced degree of reduction. Bare rock crops out (p. 65). It is the sign of very rapid, very intense denudation. And this means that (a) the rock fragments are removed immediately they have been detached from their connection, and (b) that the horizon of loosening develops at the surface, i.e. with unimpeded exposure, and under such conditions works downwards more actively than any of the other zones in the profile of reduction. Here, therefore, within a definite length of time, a layer of rock of the greatest possible thickness, with the maximum amount of rock material, is reduced and changed into a form just sufficiently mobile for the denudation which follows immediately. Denudation here is intense because great quantities of rock are removed in unit time from their place of origin, not because the material is then rapidly moved on.

In the other limiting case, reduced substances leave their place of origin only after such long intervals of time that, during them, chemically stable end-products have formed as far down as the water table. This is the limiting case for cumulative weathering also. Between these limits, the relation between renewal of exposure and rock reduction gives rise to a continuous series of an infinite number of links from which only one will be taken to illustrate the general conditions. Suppose that, at a certain place, a complete soil profile comes into being, with unaltered rock at the base, the zones of loosening and of rubble above that and the horizon of the pure, very highly mobile end-product at the top, and that this profile just *maintains* itself. Then the removal of the reduced substances from their place of origin (the renewal of exposure) requires just as much time as weathering needs for the production of the highly mobile end-product. Only this moves away: it is prepared afresh to the same amount, and rock destruction reaches down into the rock that was intact. A stationary condition is set up.

The same of course applies to any link whatever in the series, when it is no longer the pure end-product that is formed and maintained at the top of the soil profile, but any horizon of a lesser degree of reduction. However, these are cases of quicker, more intense denudation; for the less the degree of reduction in the zone of soil which is *uppermost* and therefore exposed to the full, the more rapid is the rate of formation, and the greater the quantity of rock which in a given length of time attains the mobility needed for migration, and consequently leaves the place where it originated. *In any case, since on a given gradient a particular degree of mobility is required to make the material unstable and so necessitate its migration, removal of material on that gradient must be related to the length of time needed for the process of reduction to produce the required mobility.*

Two essentially different processes are at work, and they must be sharply distinguished since they have an entirely different significance and their varying mutual relationship leads to entirely different effects: (*a*) *the intensity of the denudation, which is expressed by the quantity of reduced material leaving its place of origin in unit time*, and (*b*) the rate at which the reduced material then moves on, which is expressed as the distance it travels in unit time. It depends upon the kind of denudational conditions and upon the type of material moved, and it will be discussed later.

However, the quantity of rock made available in unit time for removal by denudation, i.e. which has acquired the mobility that, at a given place, renders it unstable and thus necessitates spontaneous movement, is always the result of an equivalent period of reduction (p. 51). *This uniformity in the time of preparation needed to bring reduced material to a definite degree of reduction (mobility) provides a measure for intensity of denudation.* The spontaneous removal of the reduced rock material can, for its maximum rate, take place as fast as its preparation. Only what is available for removal by denudation, what is loose, can be removed, and *spontaneously*, by which is meant the movement of the small pieces from their place of origin of their own accord under the influence of gravity, as contrasted with their forcible detachment from their more or less loosened connections, and their premature[78] removal from their position, e.g. by heavy material moving from above.

If we consider conditions of denudation where there exists, in adjoining areas, a series ranging from pieces of rock only just loosened, through material corresponding to the re-arranged rubble horizon to, finally, highly mobile end-products which are only just being removed from their place of origin, then it is seen that this series corresponds to one of a decreasing rate of denudation. In each case it equals the rate of formation of the respective soil horizons; and—as we have shown—this takes place more slowly the more highly mobile, i.e. the farther reduced, are the products to be formed (p. 51). Consequently, spontaneous denudation can attain the greatest possible intensity where the rock reduction goes on in the most vigorous, most rapid fashion. Other things being equal, this is the case on a freely exposed rock surface. It occurs in the horizon of rock loosening, the deepest zone of the profile of reduction, and the one which—with unreduced exposure—develops most rapidly and advances most quickly towards the interior of the rock (pp. 50–51).

As a rule, bare rock is associated with steep slopes, since it cannot appear without a definite relationship between the two processes (*a*) and (*b*) mentioned on p. 64. If in unit time great quantities of reduced rock material leave their place of origin, implying great intensity of denudation, and if, for some reason or other, they also move away comparatively slowly, then there appears an accumulation, a damming up of the material, and the denudational surface becomes covered with it. *In this way its exposure is decreased, and so the rock reduction at this surface is retarded* (pp. 54–55), *and there necessarily follows a diminution in the intensity of denudation until there is equilibrium between the preparation of material for carrying away and its actual transport.* Bare rock can outcrop only when further rapid removal of the detached rock fragments from their place of origin is followed by rapid further transport.

The immediate consequence of these relations, the proof, as it were, that they are as stated, is a phenomenon governed by law and easily verified in every one of the denudation areas of the world. But so far it has been, in most cases, overlooked: *The distribution of weathered material, and its type, depend upon the inclination of the slopes*[79]. In general, the thickness of the soil cover increases as the steepness of the substratum diminishes. This is to be seen not only where transported material is held up, as at the gentler foot of a slope where increase in thickness is the result of accumulation. It is also true where the sedentary soil profile does not, either in type or mode of formation, appear to be noticeably influenced or altered by material transported from higher up. Not only, however, does the thickness of the layer of soil decrease up the slope, *but the further rule applies that, as slopes become steeper, only the lower horizons of the normal soil profile are developed at the surface.* On the gentler slopes we find, at the top of a thicker soil profile, an horizon which has undergone more thorough reduction, or even one showing the pure end-product; on steeper slopes there is only the rubbly horizon as the uppermost formation of a less developed profile. With further steepening, there appears the scarcely-covered zone of loosening, and finally the bare rock. Where rising slopes are concave, as for instance on the uppermost parts of the German Highlands, almost the whole soil profile may occasionally be crossed as one moves from below upwards[80], the horizon being lower the higher up it outcrops and the steeper the slope. Just as in a soil profile, the horizons are not sharply divided from each other, neither are they in this arrangement where they are next one another at the surface. As slopes become steeper, the soil cover becomes thinner and also poorer in end-products, and its composition shows an increasing proportion of angular pieces of rock. This is true for humid as well as for arid regions.

BLOCK SEAS
[SEAS OF BROKEN ROCK]

These are a conspicuous and widespread feature of the German Highlands. The rules just considered apply to most block seas, which exhibit very clearly the relationships mentioned above. They are accumulations of blocks of stone, frequently of a considerable size; and fine-grained packing material, especially the end-products of weathering, is absent from between their surfaces. Von Łoziński, apparently for that reason, took them to be the result of mechanical weathering, more particularly of the frost weathering which was thought to have prevailed in the extra-glacial regions of Central Europe during the Pleistocene glaciation[81]. B. Högbom, followed by W. Salomon, went a step further, taking the blocks to be Pleistocene rock streams on account of their occasional—not very great—resemblances to the present day block streams found in polar regions. He considered them to have originated, and to have moved, in an analogous manner, but not to be developing any further nowadays[82]. The feature is thus considered as fossil, and as having been conditioned by climate; and Meyer-Harrassowitz drew from it far-reaching conclusions as to the nature of the Pleistocene climate in the extra-glacial region of Central Europe[83].

Obviously, theory and hypothesis have here far outrun observation. In individual cases, there are some features which indicate that the accumulations of blocks have in the main had their origin in the geological past—to place them in the Ice Age or in one of the ice ages is a mere assumption not proved by any observations—but in most cases they can be shown to be developing further and to be moving as much as ever at the present day. It is not possible to generalise from either the one or the other of the two sets of observations. It can only be stated in general terms that the slowly-acting processes of rock reduction, like all the processes taking part in modelling the present land forms, reach far back—often considerably farther than into Pleistocene times; at some places they came to an end at a certain time, having produced this same form; at others, however, they are today still working in the same direction.

A whole series of facts makes it evident that block seas are not a phenomenon due to climatic conditions; and, more especially, that they are not connected with the sphere of mechanical frost weathering. First of all: they occur in regions which were out of the way of any frost action even during the Pleistocene period. For instance, I found them in Uruguay on the steeper slopes of inselbergs of granite, syenite or quartzite which rise above the surrounding country in the southern part of the Brazilian shield. They were again observed at every altitude on serpentine and andesite elevations in north-west and central Asia Minor, here, too, connected with slopes of a definite gradient. *In exactly the same way the block seas of the German Highlands are associated with certain types of rock which show a tendency to break down into more or less coarse blocks, and they occur on slopes of a definite gradient.* If here they were the products of Pleistocene frost weathering, it would be not only a few definite rock types that would have a share in their composition, but all kinds which had the same exposure, since chemical weathering is for the most part excluded from the region of frost weathering. But upon investigating the scree, which is equivalent to the block seas and which has formed near them in districts where the rocks have differing properties, one finds that it shows unmistakable traces of chemical weathering, in every profile and at every horizon. This is more marked in the derivatives of chemically unstable silicate rocks than in the more stable sedimentary ones such as limestone, marl, clay, quartzite, etc., and less marked in the rubble horizon than in the higher horizons of more advanced reduction. Here, even a geologist's experienced eye cannot generally recognise from the formation alone what part chemical weathering has had in the mechanical reduction of the rocks, and what part the frost shattering now attacking them, not to mention a possible part taken by weathering under conditions of Pleistocene cold. Would it be likely that in the German Highlands only granite, basalt here and there, massive basic rocks, Devonian quartzite, certain horizons of the Bunter sandstone, and in some places schists formed by contact metamorphism, should be reduced by frost weathering, while the long series of other types of rock remained unaffected? Or would the derivatives of only the latter have since been further attacked chemically and altered, whilst the above listed rocks of the block seas were preserved unchanged?

We can come to grips with the question only if we replace the interpretation and explanation of what is on the whole a rather small number of observed facts by new and more thorough research. Such was made by O. H. Erdmannsdörfer in the Harz, and finally by me in the Harz, Fichtelgebirge, and Black Forest. Two sets of accumulations of blocks can be distinguished. The one consists of *screes*, accumulations of broken-down fragments which pile up on steep slopes and because of their own movement occasionally spread out and flatten as they extend downwards. Often, but not always, they adjoin a rocky source of supply and they consist of angular fragments, bounded by joints and fracture planes. Examples may be found in the block fields of schist in the Oder valley, of granite in the Bode valley (Harz) as well as the rock seas of Bunter sandstone in the Odenwald and Black Forest. It has been shown that the last named are accumulations of pieces from the resistant upper layers—which only rarely stand out as rocky crags; below these, the more crumbly lower bed is weathered out and gradually washed away, especially where springs emerge, so that the overlying rock masses break off[84].

The second type of block sea is only exceptionally connected with a rocky source of supply. Much more often the source is in the substratum of the actual accumulations of blocks. Moreover, it does not extend over their whole area, but is associated with those parts of the slopes which have a quite definite inclination; whilst the blocks, on account of their downward movement, have often come to rest upon the slopes below, which are considerably less steep.

On the Fichtelgebirge (e.g. at the Kösseine near Waldstein, Fichtelberg, etc.) and in the neighbourhood of the Brocken in the Harz, numerous exposures lay bare the substratum of the block fields of granitic and —in the Fichtelgebirge—diorite blocks. Above coherent fissured rock there can always be found a zone measuring several metres (on the Luisenburg, Fichtelgebirge, 10 metres thick!) in which roundish blocks of solid rock are embedded in a weathered product of far advanced chemical decomposition. The structure is here everywhere preserved intact, the blocks as well as the decomposed material between them still remaining associated with one another in their original positions. (In the case of the Proterobase* of Fichtelberg, the detritus is a loamy end-product; in the case of the granite, it is a fine crumb-like and more or less loamy grit). This structural cohesion is no longer present in the case of the next higher horizon (3–5 metres thick at the Luisenburg). From the loss of structure, from the pulverisation of the more loamy granitic grit and the packing together of the blocks pushed one above the other, it may be recognised that this zone is one of complete rearrangement and of movement. Locally, blocks still in place reach from below into the zone of movement, but otherwise its lower limit is *sharp* though with irregular pockets, like the bed of a river.

G. Klemm (*loc. cit.*[82]) has reported such profiles from the Odenwald also. They are the rule and recur with every kind of variation. It follows from them:

1. that the fragments—particularly those of the typical block seas of granite and of analogous, e.g. basic, igneous masses—have been loosened from the rock fabric not by mechanical but by chemical weathering;

2. that the tendency to form blocks is a specific quality of the rocks concerned; and

[* A special type of diabase found in the Fichtelgebirge, of earlier age than the other diabases there.]

3. that the source of supply of these blocks lies in their own substratum.

Thus they correspond in every respect to an horizon of a normal soil profile of chemical weathering, and have absolutely nothing to do with the effects of 'periglacial' or polar frost[85]. The problem now arises as to what conditions can make acute this tendency to form blocks, so leading to the development of a block field.

Where sufficiently deep exposures prove that the orgin of a block field is of this above-mentioned kind, there is nothing to be seen at its surface of the decomposed sandy detritus, rich in colloidal end-products, which at lower horizons forms a very well developed matrix. Rather, block rests upon block, the material between having been removed, washed away. In gulleys and valley tracks, where running water collects, the rainwash is more thorough and so there is a better development of accumulated blocks that are impoverished in respect of material between them. This is also the case where there are no block seas on the adjoining slopes, so that there can be no accession of fragments occasionally sliding down, or rolling, from them.

Yet even in such valley furrows, the blocks cease to be dominant when gradients become less. Exactly the same thing may be noticed in the far more numerous block fields which develop on slopes away from valley courses. If these pass either upwards or downwards into slopes with a smaller gradient, the blocks are seen to sink more and more into the ground—whether it is wooded or not makes no difference; only their tops poke up here and there, and finally even these disappear. On examination, the soil is found to consist of coarse gritty products of decomposition, mixed with rather small lumps, or of gritty loam in which float larger isolated fragments that disappear when the inclination of the ground is less than 10°. The phenomenon follows this law: with decreasing gradient the block seas disappear; they are replaced at the surface by material in which reduction has gone further, a fine grit more like the end-product of chemical weathering. It is only such material that is, under the given conditions, sufficiently mobile to move away. And even if, here, the granite amongst it disintegrates into blocks (e.g. in the quarries at Plattenstein, Fichtelgebirge), the blocks still have to remain where they were formed, and under such conditions their material becomes transportable only when it has been changed into a mixture of loam, grit, and coarse fragments, or—if the slope of the ground is less, into a mixture of loam and grit, or—finally—into highly mobile loam.

Conversely, block seas are typically displayed where the slope increases (at gradients averaging 15°–30°). The exposed profiles prove that the material is moving: what carries out the movement is the lower layer, a mixture of blocks, grit and loam; the upper layer of accumulated blocks is on the whole passively borne along. The movement of the boulders is indicated here by the trees, at every stage of growth, which have their roots in between them, and are frequently found to be bent and pushed out of position[86]. Increasing steepness of the substratum leads to the transition from block seas to blocky scree, e.g. at the Steinerne Renne in the Harz. The blocks are less and less rounded, turning into broken angular fragments below which is visible the bare rock; no longer is there any higher horizon of the soil profile, no thick zone of chemical weathering.

Thus, in just the same way, typical rock seas of granite are not related to rocky cliffs as screes are to their rock source. This is perfectly clear from an examination of the cliffs which jut out from gentle slopes. Occasionally they are surrounded by a festoon of fragments, corresponding to the normal screes found at the base of precipices; they gradually disintegrate into a heap of rounded blocks, but no block fields or stone rivers adjoin them. Rather do they form islands of blocks in the midst of a countryside where the rock is more highly reduced; and the material from them is incapable of being transported till, like the surrounding granite, it has disintegrated into loamy grit and rubble. Thus on the so-called second terrace of the Bithynian Olympus, all transitions can be found from high projecting cliffs through towerlike piles of rounded blocks and groups of single blocks to rubble heaps, all that remains of former rocky cliffs[87]. Such examples are also widely distributed in the Harz and Fichtelgebirge.

However, a different picture is presented by the cliffs which rise up from the steeper slopes or are superimposed upon their upper margins. They then often appear as a source of supply for block fields, without contributing the main part. When their surroundings consist of the same rock materials disintegrating into blocks, a rather steep slope, even if there are not actual cliffs, will feed a rock sea. If, on the contrary, other kinds of rock are exposed on the hillside, rocks which have no tendency to disintegrate into coarse blocks, then narrow strips made up of blocks lead down from the cliffs—screes drawn out as it were into tails—and make clear what a small contribution is brought by decaying cliffs to a rock sea surrounding them.

SUMMARY

The block seas of granite and kindred formations have here been treated in somewhat greater detail since they bring out clearly the connection, conforming to definite laws, between rock reduction and denudation. Apart from those portions of the transported mass of blocks which have migrated as stone rivers and so have reached the gentler parts of slopes, a process which finds its equivalent in the displacement of scree material, to be discussed later, we find that the block fields correspond to definite horizons in the profiles of reduction, these reaching the surface on certain gradients. On steeper slopes they are replaced by deeper horizons, less reduced; on gentler ones by higher horizons at a more advanced degree of reduction. This arrangement is no longer a simple effect of weathering, but it already shows the influence of denudation. *It proves that at the present day there is spontaneous migration of reduced material*; it further shows that spontaneous denudation is more rapid and more intense on steeper slopes than on gentler ones (p. 64). The preparation of mobile material that can be removed by denudation, as contrasted with denudation itself, seems to be delayed more where the slopes are slight. On steep ones the soil cover is thin and the pieces of rock are removed soon after they have been loosened from the rock fabric; on gentler ones the soil cover is thick, since far-reaching comminution and the making mobile of the material must occur before it is possible for pieces of rock to move away. *From this we can deduce the two fundamental prerequisites for removal by denudation: inclination of the ground and mobility of the material.* The arrangement of the reduced material on the land surface, as illustrated by the seas of granite blocks, shows that, to be able to move away, greater mobility is needed the less the inclination of the substratum; or conversely, *the steeper the slopes, the less the mobility needed for the removal of the material by denudation. For denudation, which acts over the whole surface, the ratio of the inclination of the ground to the mobility of the rock derivatives is the determining factor. Other things being equal, the intensity of denudation increases with the steepness of the slopes* (see p. 65).

Only one link in this relationship can be referred to weathering: rock reduction, i.e. rendering the material mobile. This depends upon the properties of the rock and upon the climate. For a given place, the rock properties determine the amount of rock which can in unit time be brought into a sufficiently mobile form by the reducing processes at work there. Climate determines the kind of reducing processes, and so the type of reduction products and their composition. But it by no means decides the characteristic feature of rock reduction itself, which goes on uniformly over the whole earth, and in all climates, and which is alone relevant for denudation. Everywhere, in all climates, those relationships which give it the greatest possible mobility are found in the conditions under which it is forming. Thus no climatic region provides especially favourable conditions for the production of the mass movement which brings about denudation over the whole surface; and so there is no possibility of different denudational forms, which had a different course of development, arising in different climates, *provided the endogenetic premisses are the same.*

CHAPTER IV

MASS-MOVEMENT

Weathering by itself does not produce any land-forms. It must be emphatically stressed that these arise only when the weathered material leaves the place where it was formed, i.e. by denudation.* *The driving force for this is always the force of gravity*[88], whether the displacement of material along the earth's surface occurs spontaneously or is helped by a moving medium. Of such media, those acting on the earth are air, water and ice. It is only if there is a gradient that they begin to move. Hence their motive power also is the force of gravity, whether the gradient is caused by the inclination of the substratum beneath the medium, or by differences of density within it. The particles make for their goal by the shortest possible path in the direction of the gradient. For that reason, and because of its vastly different but also relatively high mobility (even in the case of ice), the motion of the medium is a continuous flow along definite paths of movement which are demarcated from their surroundings. The morphological efficiency of the moving medium is naturally confined to those paths, and it therefore has a tendency *to be linear*. On land, these dense media, water and ice, show this characteristic most clearly: here their weight forces them against the surface of the solid ground, their movement follows the slope, their path of movement becomes bordered by firm banks, if such were not already present. In these respects, the much lighter and more mobile air behaves differently. The paths of its movement are not bordered by firm banks, they vary in position, and the movement at its base appears not to obey the force of gravity, since wind blows over mountain and valley, rises and falls. Water, however, does the same thing along the irregular floor of a river, and the phenomenon recurs in other gravitational streams. From a physical standpoint we must put currents of air with currents of water; for then the movement and morphological effect at the bottom of the paths of movement within the two media become comparable. In the one case, the river beds form the base; in the other, whole stretches of land. Thus, in respect of the individual slopes composing a landscape, movement of the air is indeed independent of the gradient; and it attacks over

[* The German word *Ahtragung* really means 'carrying away'.]

the whole area, just as water attacks the river bed, or ice the bed of the glacier, over its whole area.

The immediate effect which moving media have on the solid surface of the earth is the removal of solid material loosened from the rock texture, as soon as this comes within the sphere of the paths of movement. Caught in the stream, the rock derivatives appear to be passively carried along by some means of transport, irrespective of possible movements of their own. With A. Penck, then, we speak of *mass-transport*[89]. This is restricted to the paths of moving media. Outside these, there is the spontaneous independent migration of the reduced substances; and indeed this occurs on all slopes where rocks are being reduced, and where the inclination exceeds a minimum amount which observation shows to be removed by only a few degrees from the horizontal. All such movements are here grouped as *mass-movement*[90]. Their combined action produces *denudation of the surface* of the land in the truest sense of the word. The direction of the movement—as contrasted with surface transport by wind—is determined by the gradient of each individual declivity of the terrain.

Only in the case of a vertical rock face could the full force of gravity be put to use in effecting the transport of reduced substances (free fall). Where surfaces are less steeply inclined, the driving force that comes into play is only that component of the acceleration due to gravity which is parallel to the surface of the ground in the direction of the gradient; and it is proportional to the sine of the angle of inclination. It can release a mass-movement and keep it going only when it is able to overcome the resistance opposing it.

1. RESISTANCE TO DENUDATION

This must therefore be taken into account as a very important factor. It is to be understood as the sum of the resistances opposing movement towards grade. For all the processes of denudation are displacements of matter directed towards bringing the material into a position of stable equilibrium. Disturbance of equilibrium is caused by crustal movements which put the rocks into such a position (as regards bedding and altitude) that they cannot permanently maintain themselves there. *Herein lies the relationship between crustal movement and denudation.*

There is no difficulty about setting in motion the disturbed rocks if they possess but slight cohesion and so have mobility, like unconsolidated deposits or wet clay. But most rocks possess greater cohesion, and obtain the requisite mobility only through the process of weathering. *Resistance to denudation accordingly depends in the first place upon the cohesion of the rock.*

COHESION OF ROCKS

Unweathered rock which at the outset possesses little cohesion (i.e. has a great number of divisional planes and consequently great mobility), takes part in mass-movement to just as great an extent as weathered substances which have been produced from a long series of rocks of greater cohesion and have only in that way acquired their mobility[91].

The number of rock types which are already mobile in the unweathered state, or become so when in contact with water, is not great; their distribution is far greater. Not only do the still unconsolidated deposits, as a rule geologically recent, of fluviatile, lacustrine, aeolian, etc., origin, and the clastic uncompacted products of volcanic origin, belong to this class, but above all it is the clayey rocks. The greater the *content of colloidal clay*, the greater, too, is the mobility which becomes effective upon moistening. Since for denudation it is only the mobility of the material which is of decisive importance, there are adaptations of form to unweathered rock types of differing mobility in a manner analogous to those for rocks that have different resistances to weathering. Usually the one is taken for the other, and forms are considered to be the result of differential weathering when this has nothing whatever to do with the matter. An example of this is the 'weathering out' of dykes of igneous rock from marly and clayey sediments. These latter are almost immune to weathering, at any rate incomparably more resistant to it than any igneous rock whatsoever. That 'weathering out' is the result of very unequal resistance to denudation. The clayey rock is resistant to weathering; but when thoroughly wet, it possesses greater mobility than the suceptible igneous rock can, in the same time, acquire through weathering. Therefore, in unit time, more of the former is removed, carried away by denudation, than of the latter[92]. Thus it will not do to deduce—without further investigation—differences in resistance to weathering from the resistance to denudation which becomes morphologically visible in adaptation of form to the character of the rock and depends upon differences in the mobility, originally existing or acquired.

Whilst, in weathered material, the onset of mobility is bound up with the zones of soil which adjoin the surface, in clayey rocks it comes about wherever these come into contact with water. Thorough wetting of clay always means a lessening of cohesion in those rocks of which it forms a part. If it is evenly distributed, say as cement in sandy or calcareous strata, or as multiple intercalations between less mobile rocks, a frequent occurrence in the flysch of the Apennines, Alps, etc., then the whole rock complex becomes mobile when it is wet through; and the mass-movement, as well as the forms of denudation produced, is determined mainly by the properties of the mobile material. But even if a layer of clay is overlain by rocks of totally different nature, with a higher degree of cohesion, these are affected by the results of saturation. If the layer of clay outcrops, and if it has a valleyward dip, then the complex of overlying rocks ceases to be in equilibrium as soon as water renders the clay highly mobile and makes it a 'lubricant', a word that aptly expresses the property of reducing friction possessed by swollen colloids. Under these conditions, the occurrence of mass-movement, and the forms which arise, depend not only upon the properties of the mobile stratum and its bedding, but just as much upon the cohesion of the overlying rocks and their bedding. Rockslides may take place, rocky niches are left walled round by bared joint planes, streams of rock fragments roll down into the valley. These are phenomena of a kind quite foreign to the mobile types of rock; but they are very often brought about by their presence, their properties and their arrangement.

What matters here is not only the way in which the rock was laid down, upon which depends the arrangement of the planes of least cohesion (bedding planes, joint planes, etc.), and so partly also the paths by which percolating water penetrates into the heart of the rock, but in general upon the permeability of the rock to water. This decides, other things being equal, how much of the rain falling upon an area flows off the surface and does mechanical work upon it, how much seeps down and is brought to any clayey rocks which may happen to be present, and which become mobile. In the case of these latter, so far as they outcrop, the effect of great mobility is reinforced by that of the impermeability which renders them highly susceptible to the attack of rainwash as compared with permeable (porous, loose-textured, fissured) types of rock. These conditions account for the extraordinary ease with which the clayey rocks, which can scarcely be attacked at all by weathering, break down and become unstable in response to denudation, a feature which is their special characteristic[93].

Cohesion is the resistance opposing the commencement of mass-movement. The resistance which particularly hinders it throughout its course is friction.

FRICTION

No results are available of any research on its magnitude. It is at any rate very great. Therefore most mass-movement takes place extremely slowly[94], a fact which almost prevents direct observation of it. For the rest, a number of phenomena can easily be traced to friction, and understood from the physical conditions associated with it.

When accumulating masses of rock waste migrate (i.e. not just separ-

ate little pieces of rock), there is friction between the components—
internal friction—and between the moving mass and the substratum over
which it passes—*external friction*. In both cases there is sliding friction
and rolling friction; and as a rule not only hard bodies but also water
and wet colloids take a share in the movement. Now, the conditions
influencing internal friction are these:

(*a*) it increases with the size of the area of contact, and is therefore
less in the case of coarse material than of fine;

(*b*) it increases with the weight (pressure), and is therefore greater in
the lower soil horizons than in higher ones, and on steeper slopes is less
than on gentle ones; and

(*c*) it is greater, the more angular and the less rounded the components
(roughness of grain). The size and shape of grain are influenced by the
properties of the rock, especially in the first stages of reduction; but they
are also influenced by the processes of weathering dominant at the given
place. For instance, under desert insolation-weathering, a sandstone disintegrating into its individual grains provides quite different conditions
for friction from those where the rock is compact and homogeneous,
fracturing along joint planes, even if both are at the same stage of reduction. On the other hand, where there is similarity in the character of the
rocks and in climate, the size of grain diminishes with increased reduction, and the shape becomes more and more rounded. This change can
be traced in any soil profile. The friction is partly caused by the edges
and corners, since they have surfaces which are particularly large in
relation to their volume. This means that they are the places most exposed to attack and so they disappear very rapidly. Thus, as it becomes
further reduced, insolation rubble shows excellently how the pieces of
rock become rounded as they become smaller. A similar effect can be
recognised in the upper horizons of chemically weathered soils where
fragments of rock, if still present, are at least rounded at the edges.
Further, the coarser components mutually wear each other away (attrition), and this plays an essential part in rounding mobile weathered
material, whatever its origin. It indicates that rolling and rotating processes are to the fore during mass-movement.

(*d*) The last important point is that friction is always greater with the
transition from rest to movement than during movement.

It follows that, as a general rule, friction decreases from the bottom of
the soil profile upwards, in the direction of decreasing weight. Therefore, on a given slope, the material above moves more rapidly than that
lying below it, even if both have the same degree of mobility. This has
often been observed directly in streams of homogeneous rocks derived
from landslides, both rockfalls and slumping, and it has been repeatedly

described as a rolling over and over of the material. It is just the same with the slow movements of the reduced material mantling the slopes. As the stilt effect of tree trunks [see p. 109] eloquently proves, the upper horizons here move along more quickly than the lower ones. Not only have they greater mobility, but in particular they have a slighter load to support. The result of this distribution of mobility and friction in the soil profile is that the superficial cover of weathered material does not move equally throughout as a uniform system, but there are different rates for any given slope, so that the upper parts move along what are at that time the horizons lying below them, the topmost parts having the greatest speed, those deepest down going the most slowly. *This type of movement is a rolling over and over, not pushing nor sliding, and its physical analogue is flow*[95].

These differences in friction, caused by unequal load, are particularly well seen where the soil cover is of a different thickness in adjacent areas. Let us first consider uniformly inclined slopes with the soil profile decreasing in thickness upslope, exposing what were lower horizons. The rubble horizon that follows immediately above that of the loosened rock would of itself have the same friction everywhere; but in one case it is at the surface and in another it is loaded with additional material. In the first instance, therefore, there is less frictional resistance to be overcome than in the latter. As a result—other things being equal—the fragments move down more quickly from the higher parts of the slope, where they are freshly exposed at the surface, than from the lower ones where other material is superimposed. *Consequently the degree of exposure is increased, and exposure is renewed more quickly in the former than in the latter case, and this simply means more intense denudation above than below* (see pp. 54 and 65). The effects of this are especially clearly seen wherever there is an intersection of slopes having a mantle of reduced material, which becomes thinner from the base upwards, but is continuous and so naturally moves down not as individual little pieces but as a mass. The slopes do not intersect in sharp ridges, but are flattened near the top, the crests being rounded off.

This feature finds just as full expression in the zones of intersecting slopes where the same arrangement of the soil cover goes hand in hand with an increase in steepness from below upwards. The friction of the material is here reduced, not only because the load decreases upslope as the soil cover becomes thinner, but also because there is a decreasing pressure on the substratum in the same direction. The pressure that influences the magnitude of the friction (the weight of the down-pressing material) acts at right angles to the frictional plane, and becomes less the steeper the inclination. When the perpendicular is reached, i.e. with vertically rising walls, this pressure is nil, and consequently there is no friction to hinder mass-movement[96].

Friction diminishes with increasing steepness of the substratum Therefore there is less resistance to be overcome on steep slopes than on gentle ones; material is more easily set in motion on the former, and less mobility is needed for its migration. This general law of denudation deals with the one condition (treated on p. 65) which affords a universal correlation between the type of soil and the inclination of the slope.

The appearance of *conditions which reduce friction* is of the greatest importance for the whole course of the mass-movement. Attention must be drawn to the following points: Throughout the whole journey, the moving material, whatever its nature, not only undergoes the far-reaching effects of reduction (unless it is already in the form of end-products), but also its grains become smaller by mutual attrition, as well as somewhat rounded. Mobility is constantly increasing as it moves from the region of supply to the place of accumulation, or to the line of the river. Intermixture with fine to very fine particles, and with colloids, increases in the same direction, both these reducing friction in every sort of weathered material, without any exception. Water, generally more abundant in the lower parts of the district than in those higher up, acts in the same way. *Thus the conditions for movement, even on a very slight gradient, are better as the distance from the region of supply increases.* For reducing the friction yet further on these gentle slopes, increasing wetness is an essential factor. This is due to the fact that, other things being equal, infiltration increases with diminishing gradient, whilst there is a decrease in the amount of surface run-off. That such movement does actually occur on very slight gradients is shown by the spreading out of spontaneously moving material (i.e. material not transported by a moving medium), on surfaces with a slope of less than 5°. This can be observed at suitable spots in every climatic zone. Obviously this spreading out takes place even when friction has become so great in the lower horizons of the accumulated material as to prevent any further movement there[97]. The overlying material then gradually moves along over that beneath it.

Thus it may be seen that, on the whole, as one goes downslope, the frictional conditions become less favourable to movement; while the factors reducing friction become more and more pronounced in that same direction. This is of the utmost importance for the net result of the denudation: in this way movement begun on the higher, steeper parts is continued on lower, gentler slopes. And there is no indefinitely growing accumulation of material that has become incapable of movement. The conditions governing friction and its lessening do not indeed lead to a situation in which the more mobile material on the gentler slopes is moving faster than the rubble on steep declivities—next to nothing is known about the rate of the movement—but they do lead to a state such that on the whole, material continues to move downwards so long as the gradient exceeds a minimum value of just under 5°.

These conditions apply to all the climatic regions of the world, as may be easily realised if the factors reducing friction are compared with the conditions producing mobility of the material. The two coincide: their world distribution is the same. *On the whole, there are present at some time or other in every region of the world—other things being equal—optimum conditions which initiate and maintain spontaneous mass-movement, in so far as this depends upon the mobility of the material and its frictional moment.*

Root Systems of Plants

The presence of plant roots, particularly the network belonging to woody plants, is a most important hindrance to the migration of reduced material; and the frequency of its occurrence is second only to that of frictional resistance. It has even been maintained that a continuous cover of forest would entirely prevent the migration of reduced material, since this would be held fast by the root system[98]. But this hypothesis cannot be upheld against the weight of facts. No place on earth is known where the tree limit is associated with an interruption in the conditions of denudation, which would be visibly expressed by a change in the land forms. Not one of the numerous elevations rising above the tree-line has either a break of gradient or any sharp line of demarcation between the forms above it and others of a different shape below. No change whatsoever appears in the land forms when parts of the earth's crust, which are tectonically alike, extend from an unforested climatic zone into one richly wooded. Whether we examine mountain systems like the Andes, cutting across various forest belts, mountain massifs rising above the tree limit, or continental areas of a different tectonic nature, their extensive denudational areas reaching into the most varied climatic regions, some with and some without continuous forest, observation always brings out this one fact: the forest forms a cover the presence or absence of which has no marked influence on the fashioning of the land. This was as true in the past as now. Quite a number of eminences rise from the tropical forest region to above the present snow line; and one is readily convinced, and in an impressive manner, that there is *nowhere* any sharp division, any land-form boundary, to mark the line to which the early Quaternary tree-limit was depressed in the same way as were the other climatic zones. If, however, neither the present nor the former tree limit is associated with a change in the various land forms occurring, or with any break whatsoever in the surface modelling, it cannot be maintained that the denudational processes which actually shape the land are taking any different course beneath a forest cover, or would be brought to an end sooner there than anywhere else.

More particularly, the above hypothesis is utterly at variance with all detailed *observation* on the properties of the reduced substances, on their present migration beneath a continuous forest cover as well as elsewhere, and on the root systems of the plant cover.

Here we can do no more than indicate briefly the essential points. Naturally it is possible to consider the influence of root systems upon the movements of rock derivatives only for such climatic regions as have conditions suitable for a continuous forest cover. These are the humid provinces and adjoining parts of their marginal zones. They are areas in which chemical weathering is predominant, with the formation of colloidal end-products. When thoroughly wet, these could be prevented from moving along an inclined substratum only by sieves of the fineness of animal membranes. That is to say, there cannot generally be a felting of roots dense enough to stop the migration of highly mobile reduced material, so long as the gradient exceeds a minimum value of some few degrees. It could not be done even by a network of grass roots, which is of far finer mesh than that of woody plants. Thus it is quite absurd to speak of movement being brought to a standstill beneath a forest cover, even though the roots may temporarily hold fast the rock fragments of a rubble horizon. These do indeed remain in place until further disintegration has so far diminished their size that they can pass through the meshes of the root network, or until the rootlets, which do not live for ever, die off and rot away, so freeing the fragment which had been held back until another root, occurring below, once more holds it up. In such a case the root system does act more or less like a sieve: the colloidal substances and the comminuted pieces of rock move away, the larger fragments either remain behind or move on at a relatively slower pace according to circumstances. Now and again this can be observed on the steeper slopes where the tree roots are resting almost directly upon the surface of the loosened rock. If observers were satisfied with noticing that such rock fragments were held fast by the root network and took no account of the remaining components of the soil, of the end-products, and especially of the whole formation of the soil profile, the impression would indeed be given that denudation was retarded underneath a forest cover, though not of course that it was entirely stopped. However, wooded regions by no means form an exception to the previously established law (pp. 65, 71) that with increasing steepness of slope the

F

thickness of the soil decreases, and ever deeper soil horizons become exposed at the surface. This shows that the obstacle which the root-net may place in the way of the migration of individual pieces of rubble is far from stopping denudation in general. Obviously its effect is completely counteracted by the greater intensity of chemical reduction and solution. These lead to more rapid formation of colloidal end-products and removal of soluble substances here than outside the wooded area.

It is only roots which can exercise this sieving effect; and it is actually to be observed only on slopes so steep that the root network is fixed into the root horizon as if with grappling irons. On less steeply inclined slopes it is quite different. From artificial sections in forested regions, and more particularly from natural exposures where trees have been blown down by the wind, it is possible by systematic search to get a sufficiently good idea of the soil conditions and of how they are related to *the depths reached by roots*. This is found to be always less than the breadth of the root system; and in areas of denudation it shows, within certain limits, a dependence upon the slope of the soil: *other things being equal, the depth diminishes as the slope of the substratum increases*. On steep declivities, e.g. in the forested parts of the Alps, or on the steep slopes of the German Highlands, the root system spreads a long way out, reaches a depth of only a few decimetres, and rests almost directly upon the living rock. The soil is always thin; in type it corresponds to the lower parts of the rubble horizon which often has very few small pieces, and in that case consists chiefly of coarse fragments, entangled in the roots, and of end-products rich in colloids. Here the pressure of the roots in loosening the rock is everywhere unmistakable.

It is different on the flattish slopes. Here depth of rooting reaches its maximum value, which however has never been found to be more than about one and a half metres. Here, too, the *dense* matting of roots is confined to the upper decimetres, below which the network very rapidly becomes more widely meshed. A sparse curtain of roots reaches beyond, to the layer one to one-and-a-half metres deep. Only isolated strands reach as far down as two metres, and there they have arrived at the zone of loosening. Here the thickness of the soil prevents the rock from being prized apart by the roots. These figures refer to the root systems of tall deciduous and coniferous trees.

The depth to which the roots extend is thus approximately parallel to the local thickness of the soil. In the limiting case, on steep slopes, it is somewhat greater than the depth of the soil; on gentle slopes, on the other hand, it is less; in between are transitional conditions characterised by a diminution in soil thickness and root depth as the substratum becomes more steeply inclined. Observations on the depth of root systems would lead one to conclude it is, at most, on the steeper slopes that the matting of roots retards mass-movement. On the other hand, where there are flattish slopes, it is out of the question to speak of retardation by that means; for root density increases in *that* very direction, from underneath upwards, in which the size of soil grain is diminishing. The mobility of the material is therefore increasing, and the chance that it will be hindered in its migration disappears.

Not only are these conditions applicable to our part of the world, but they have their parallel in the wet tropics where intensity of chemical decomposition, together with the power of growth possessed by vegetation, is so great that even steep slopes, which could give rise to nothing but bare rock faces in the temperate zone, have a thick layer of colloidal end-products for their uppermost horizon of soil, and are forest clad. As K. Sapper has pointed out for tropical Central America, the root system is shallow, about three-quarters of a metre to a metre in depth; and below this, the products of weathering can move along unhindered[99]. Observations by W. Behrmann in New Guinea show to what extent this goes on; he frequently found that the rather thin root mat was no longer connected with the soil, but lying in a cavity. Here there had been migration of the material underneath the cover of vegetation[100].

It is in some other direction that we must seek the effect of a continuous cover of forest upon mass-migration. *Never is it that of checking denudation or of preventing it entirely. This is strikingly proved by the fact that in forested as well as in treeless regions there is to be found a correlation between the steepness of declivities and the arrangement of both the thickness and the type of the soil cover.* Furthermore, in both there are soil profiles where the normal reduced profile of the lower layers is covered over by material of another facies which has come from higher up. Such profiles as these show that there has been specially lively downward movement of the rock derivatives; and this is brought about under a forest cover, and continued, even to the present day, by the same conditions as produce it in unforested districts[101].

2. MOTIVE FORCES CONCERNED IN MASS-MOVEMENT

During the eruption of Vesuvius in 1906, dry avalanches of ashes went down from the margin of the crater over the flanks of the cone[102]. Their restricted area, as well as the short duration and rapidity of the whole course of events, render them particularly suitable for studying the origin, progress, and effects of mass-movement. The material consisted of a loose mixture of volcanic ejecta, lapilli, sand and very fine dust, so that it had exceptional mobility. This, and the lessening of friction due to the considerable amount of heat which these substances possessed, found expression in the liveliness of the downward movement. The material did not, however, set off on its downward journey immediately it had been deposited on the mountain side, although there was a slope; movement did not begin until the deposit of tuff had acquired a certain thickness. Once in motion, the material did not come to rest till it had reached the foot of the cone, where there is a very rapid decrease in gradient. This course of events shows very clearly that the force of gravity is the prime cause of the movement, and keeps it going so long as the gravity component, which diminishes as the slope becomes less, is sufficient to overcome the resistance of friction. It was, however, inadequate to release the movement, i.e. to overcome the resistances which occur at the beginning of motion, in particular, the friction which is specially great at that stage. *When there is material ready prepared for removal by denudation, all those forces which release the downhill motion, or assist in doing so, are here collectively called the motive forces of mass-movement.*

INCREASE OF WEIGHT

This was the motive force for the cinder avalanches of Vesuvius. It is a question of equilibrium: a body resting on an inclined substratum, after its cohesion has been destroyed, can be set in motion only if the pull exerted upon it is greater than the friction, this latter depending upon the load, and upon the cosine of the angle of inclination. Thus the relationship is given by the equation:

$$mg \sin a \geqslant \rho \, mg \cos \alpha$$

where m represents the mass, $g \sin a$ the component of gravity acting parallel to the angle of inclination a, ρ the coefficient of friction, and $mg \cos a$ the pressure exerted on the inclined substratum. From this it follows that for each weight there is a definite minimum gradient on which it just cannot move along; and the smaller the weight which rests on it, the greater is this minimum angle of inclination. Or it may be expressed thus: other things being equal, greater weights are stable only on nearly level slopes, whilst the smaller ones reach a position of rest even when the substratum is steeply inclined. If a mass, which is just unable to start moving on an inclined substratum, has its weight increased, then, under all circumstances, the downward movement is released.

These relations are important for the downward course of mass-movements; for every part of the slope is not only loaded with the reduced material originating on it, the weight of which increases as the attack of the reducing process progresses deeper and deeper, but it is at the same time a passage way for the rock derivatives coming from higher up. Thus everywhere on a denudational slope there is an allochthonous as well as an autochthonous increase in weight; and this must, in all circumstances, lead to spontaneous transport of the material.

Where there is no difference in exposure or in the character of the rock, the profile of reduction grows in thickness uniformly at all parts of a slope, so that the autochthonous increase in weight is everywhere the same. The distribution of weight, however, changes as soon as any appreciable amount of material leaves its place of origin bringing an allochthonous increase of weight to parts lower down the slope. This increase is zero at the upper edge of the slope, and is greatest at the slope foot, the whole slope being a source of supply for this. Hence the position becomes as follows: The mass-movement set going must continue so long as mobility permits. Where accumulation is taking place, the movement cannot be restricted to the highest horizons of the soil, but must affect the whole of the material, provided its substratum is steeper than what corresponds to the angle of friction. This angle of friction, at which movement of the material resting directly upon solid rock comes to an end, is less than it would be if there were no mass-movement, no denudation, and so no consequent accumulation of rock derivatives on the lower-lying parts of the land. It is thus clear that when reduced material spreads out over very gentle surface slopes, there is a correspondingly small gradient of the substratum.

This is illustrated, to take one example, by the complete covering over (cicatrisation) of the disused beds of watercourses. It is specially well seen in many of the flattish trough-like valleys formerly produced by erosion, which are found, e.g. on the scarpland peneplanes, but also in most of the dry valleys that encircle cut-off meander spurs. The disappearance of every trace of brook or river bed, as well as the whole peculiar transformation of such valley-floors, is in both cases brought about by the migration of slope waste. Often this is not particularly fine-grained, but it is generally of course rich in colloids, and it moves along the very gentle foot-slopes on both sides towards the valley trough, where all the material ends up together.

As we learn from experience of the slumping type of landslide, considerable importance attaches to increase of weight from the presence of water. This is absorbed by rocks with a high capacity for holding it: deposits of loose material, scree, etc., have this, but the outstanding examples are rocks rich in colloids, such as chemically reduced material and sedimentary rocks containing clay. These latter become heavier as water is absorbed, and they begin to move, in so far as the nature of the slope permits. At first the sliding mass acts as a single rigid system which has increased its weight as a whole by taking up water; and it slides along as a whole over a uniform substratum. But once the movement has been set going, this unity is lost. The material no longer slips, its components roll over one another, and the mass begins to flow. In witness of the fact that the migrating body of rock began as a single unit, there remains at its place of origin the landslip scar, a niche bounded by the surfaces of minimum cohesion originally existing in the rock. The mass which slipped down, however, has disintegrated, the tiny pieces of rock are no longer in firm contact with one another, they no more move along a uniform substratum, but each one moves by itself. The result is of necessity the stream-like appearance, or the pulpy mass, so often noticed[103].

Normally, when reduced substances migrate, there is no such sequence of these two forms of motion, slipping and flowing. But the following seems to indicate that the ordinary type of migration is replaced under certain conditions by what is more like a downward-slipping movement. In that case, the movement reaches down to the rock-floor in a more homogeneous fashion; and so, in addition to the consequences of allochthonous increase in weight (set out on p. 85), it provides in a certain way the necessary condition for producing a mechanical effect upon the substratum. In artificial sections which go through rather thick masses of transported material, a sharp boundary, irregular in detail (see p. 68) is to be found between substratum and overlying soil, in place of the ill-defined transitional zone found in other cases. This is the rule for the steeper slopes. Such a sharp demarcation between substratum and overlying material must necessarily come about as soon as there is any considerable movement of solid bodies over the former, this making a slip plane of the upper surface of the rock.

In most continental areas, with their seasonal alternation of thorough wetting and drying out, the behaviour of the colloids is very likely to play a part. When they dry up, they weld together the substances mixed with them into a uniform solid body of rock. This, like sedimentary rock over a layer of wet clay, can then move only by sliding over the layer beneath, which retains its moisture for a very long time. This goes on until the soil has completely dried out.

Increase in weight by the absorption of water is undoubtedly a motive force, and its influence on mass-movement and the effects of that cannot easily be overestimated. Except in completely arid regions, it takes place *regularly* on the whole of the land area from the equator to the edge of the continental ice-cap. It increases with the water-holding capacity of the material, and is therefore greater in material which is rich in colloids or is fine grained, than in coarse-grained clastic facies with their far smaller interior surface. It increases with the quantity of accumulated weathered material, i.e. with its thickness. This latter relationship is of special significance since reduced material accumulates just where there is also a greater amount of meteoric water collecting in cavities and furrows.

FLUCTUATIONS IN VOLUME

For overcoming resistance to the migration of rock waste, fluctuations in the volume of the material take second place. If a body resting on an inclined substratum expands, the movement occurs mainly downwards; if it contracts again, the shrinkage occurs mainly downward. The result is, on the whole, a displacement in the direction of the fall of the ground. The change in position produced by a single fluctuation differs in amount according to what has caused it, but it is always very small. There is perceptible change only when the fluctuations in volume are repeated sufficiently often. The term *fine movement* is therefore used.

These movements obviously play a very great part at the earth's surface, since there is everywhere an endless repetition of change in volume of the material lying upon its slopes. Such changes enable the material to move away even on those slopes where the gravity component is insufficient to overcome the frictional resistance. They further, even if they do not actually bring about, that spreading outwards of rock derivatives to form surface slopes with an inclination of less than 5°, which may be observed at appropriate spots in every climatic region.

One factor responsible for fluctuations in volume is variation in temperature[104] of the land surface: soil temperature. These variations are repeated day in, day out; everywhere, however, their range decreases very rapidly with depth. The upper horizons of the soil are therefore in a favoured position; here the micro-movements are greater, and this causes the upper particles of the soil, in every case, to move gradually away over those lying below. Fine movement of this kind naturally achieves its greatest results in those regions where differences of temperature are greatest and occur most frequently, i.e. in the arid and semi-arid provinces. Their effect will be least in moist regions, and here again less in the tropics than in the temperate zones.

Fine movements caused by the swelling and shrinkage of colloids, as these are wetted and dried, naturally have their home in those parts of the world where the weathered material contains colloids. Swelling increases the dry volume by more than a third![105] Thus the impulse to move, experienced in this way by the reduced material, is very considerable in humid and semi-humid regions. The extent to which it moves away along an inclined substratum merely through this kind of fine movement grows with the colloidal content, and so it generally increases in the soil profile from below upwards. It further increases with the frequency of wetting and drying. This alternation occurs in all parts of the climatic regions under consideration; but it differs from place to place, not only in frequency but also in thoroughness. The position is least favourable in the rainy tropics, most favourable in temperate regions where the succession of wet and dry conditions during the course of the year takes place more frequently than elsewhere. To make up for that, however, the drying out is not so thoroughgoing here as in the semi-humid provinces with their pronounced period of drought. Thin soils, and the overlying parts of thick masses, are the first to dry out completely; it is otherwise with the deeper zones of the soil, where the water is lost only after a longer period of drought. In these, therefore, the extent of the micro-movements is less than in the former cases. Again we find that the overlying parts of the material are more favoured than those beneath.

In the polar regions, in their marginal zones, and on high mountains, where the temperature fluctuates round about $0°$ C. during a portion of the year, water takes over the part played elsewhere by colloids, pushing soil particles downslope as it freezes, whilst with thawing there comes about a further movement, again downhill. In addition, the expansion of water as it freezes, like the expansion of colloidal substances, effects a swelling of the surface layer of the soil. In this way, soil particles are lifted up at right angles to the inclined upper surface; as melting occurs, they sink vertically and this, too, shifts them down the slope[106]. As this last-mentioned process is restricted to parts near the exposed surface, it also leads to more favourable conditions in the upper than in the lower soil horizons for the fine movement caused by frost.

Summing up, it can be stated that there are present in every climatic zone of the earth the conditions necessary for fine movements; and that, so far as is known at present, it is only in the wet tropics that these are not of a most favourable nature. But there, conditions are excellent for mass-movement on an extremely small gradient, because of the constant and thorough soaking and because of the far-reaching transformation of the rocks into colloidal end-products[107]. It is not, therefore, surprising to find that in every region where denudation of the land is taking place, even where running water is not active, reduced material is, at suitable spots, spread out along exceedingly gentle slopes, and this implies spontaneous downward movement along descents that are very slightly inclined.

PERIODS OF MOVEMENT

The motive forces of mass-movement, like the movement itself and like rock reduction, by no means go on without a break; but during the course of the year periods of movement are to be distinguished from periods of rest. This is true for every climatic region. The reason lies in the seasonal march of the elements of climate, on which the processes of weathering depend. These affect especially the development of mobility in the material and the setting in of conditions which, as the case may be, release or assist movement. Frost-weathering is practically stopped so long as the soil temperature does not rise above 0° C. during the day. In polar regions it is a summer phenomenon, as the temperate zone is approached it becomes one of autumn and spring, and finally it is restricted to the winter months. Naturally it is only at periods of thaw that soaking wet frost-soils move along. In regions where colloidal weathered material is produced, [the necessary] chemical weathering is bound up with the wet seasons. They are at once the periods of mobility, and of increase in weight through the absorption of water; and therefore they are periods of mass-movement. In times of drought all these processes are suspended. In the semi-humid areas with a pronounced seasonal drought during which the cover of vegetation is dying off, rock reduction by insolation can come into play at this time. But the rock waste is immobile because of the intermixture with colloids which cohere when they are dry. A study of mass-movement in, for example, Central Europe, must therefore be made in early spring (snow melt— spring rains) or in autumn, but not in summer; in the Mediterranean region it must be in winter, in the semi-humid tropics in summer. At other seasons there is no sign of movement in the respective areas, only rest. The transition periods from dry to moist are not only periods of fine movement and changing mobility, but also of fluctuating weight through the taking up and giving off of water. They occur twice in the semi-humid parts of the world, at the beginning and at the end of the dry season; in temperate regions they are more frequent and more irregularly distributed throughout the year; and in the wet tropics there is scarcely a trace of them.

Just as the wet tropics are characterised by having no season when rock reduction, mobility, and transport of rock derivatives are less than at other times, so in deserts there is no noticeable interruption of insolation and the removal of insolation rubble[108]. On the other hand, in semi-arid regions, into which seasonally rainy periods may penetrate, in winter from the poleward, in summer from the equatorial side, greater differences again appear; times when the rock waste is thoroughly wet are those of lively downward movement, e.g. in the Tien Shan, in eastern and southern Tibet, in the Karakoram, and in the eastern part of the Puna de Atacama, as travellers have found to their discomfort ('flowing rock'). In the transitional period when drought is approaching, the material loses its high mobility, reduction by insolation becomes again predominant, and, when it has completely dried out, the mass, once more in a dry condition, moves slowly downwards as in the desert ('moving rock waste').

Thus, over very wide areas, the spontaneous migration of reduced material, in short, sheet denudation, temporarily ceases. It is not a continuous process, but regionally it is a periodic one. The alternation of times of movement and of rest correspond exactly with the times of high and low water in the rivers; and for these, too, it is only at high water that work is done and morphological effects produced. In establishing the periodic character of denudation, no assertion is being made as to its intensity. And it is certainly not permissible to deduce different amounts of denudation in unit time from the differences in the time at which it commences in the individual climatic regions.

Now this is also leading towards an answer to the question of what length of time should be taken as the smallest unit for the present investigation and for morphological and geological processes in general. In theoretical physics we understand by time-differential a space of time —thought of as infinitely small—during which a force produces an infinitely small effect. For prolonged, slow-acting processes, like rock reduction, by which we can measure the very slow processes of denudation, and, indeed, as will be shown, even crustal movements which are just as slow and extraordinarily long drawn out, the infinitely small unit of time is no measure for a very small noticeable effect. Summation of such infinitely small amounts would lead to the result that no effects are produced, and that there exists, therefore, an unchanging state of equilibrium. Obviously this is wrong. The observed phenomena, rock reduction and mass-movement, are the result of very different forces each of which acts for itself at a given place with its own special intensity at any given moment. Corresponding to seasonal changes, this has a yearly period which may on the whole be considered constant for successive years. We do not, however, observe the effect of each individual variable factor, but only the total effect of *all* the forces acting in the course of a year. The yearly period is therefore the smallest unit of time during which all the conditions working towards rock reduction and the subsequent denudation come into action at least once in a specific manner and with specific strength. *Hence the smallest unit of time with which we can reckon is the year.*

3. WAYS IN WHICH MASS-MOVEMENT TAKES PLACE AT THE EARTH'S SURFACE

Since A. Penck's first attempt at systematic treatment, observations on mass-movement have multiplied to an extraordinary extent in all parts of the world[109]. Identical or similar phenomena of migration have been found in the most varied climatic regions; slow, imperceptible movements, and more rapid ones, make their appearance at all spots where there are adequate predisposing conditions. Thus, in classifying observations about mass-movement as should be done when presenting them, the geographical standpoint is not the one to consider. G. Braun chose the rate of migration of the material as starting point for his attempt[110], making the assumption that this depended on the gradient. He arranged the movements in order of decreasing gradient, as a series with decreasing velocities, and believed that he had found in this a parallel to the erosion cycle. However, it is but a small section of the phenomena which can be dealt with in this way. Moreover, the velocity depends not only upon the gradient, but also upon the weight of the moving material.

There are differences in the mechanism of the movement according to whether the loosened rock particles migrate singly or in association as members of a system growing by accumulation—an 'accumulative system'. In the former case there is free fall, or a modification of it; in the latter, the movement is a kind of flow. It is further of importance whether the mass-movement takes place at a freely exposed surface or beneath a cover of vegetation. On steep slopes, this latter prevents the loosened particles from moving quickly down the valley. This is the reason why cumulative migration occurs on considerably steeper slopes in humid regions—especially in the tropics[98]—than in regions of the arid or semi-arid type where vegetation is absent or scanty. Any interruption in the vegetation cover automatically changes the slow sub-cutaneous migration into a quicker down-flowing or into slipping at that place. Accordingly a distinction can be made between *free mass-movement and mass-movement bound down by vegetation*. Free mass-movement may occur whether substances are rich or poor in colloids, and even if they are devoid of them. In the first case they move only in the presence of water; in the latter, they migrate either wet or dry.

(a) MIGRATION AS INDIVIDUAL LOOSE FRAGMENTS

This is the form of denudation that occurs on freely exposed rock faces, where the declivity is too great to afford a resting place for any small piece of rock loosened from its connection. Its departure means the exposure of a fresh rock surface to the attack of reduction. This is the simplest case of denudation. In regions free from vegetation, i.e. in the arid, semi-arid, polar and nival provinces, bare rock always forms the steeper slopes. According to my observations in the Atacama Desert, it begins (without any assistance from rainwash) as soon as the slopes have an inclination of about 25°. When the gradient is above 35°, there are no slopes which are not rocky. The way in which pieces of rock leave these precipices is not free fall, but a rolling tumble. In the high parts of our own [European] mountains, downward movement of loose fragments is familiar to the mountaineer as a rock-fall[111]. It occurs most often in the morning and is associated with the action of frost wedging. Like any other process of weathering, it finds favourable lines of weakness along planes connected with the structure of the rocks, with their joint planes and with their cleavage planes; and so the summit forms of rocky mountains often show in a very marked way their dependence upon the character of the rock[112]. Mention must also be made of the loosening of platy, scale-like portions of rock which, by their direct departure from bare rocky heights, leave dome-shaped mountain forms. They are interpreted as desquamation forms, but they are not confined to regions where the insolation effects are powerful or exclusive of all others, and in general they seem to be dependent upon pre-existing planes of separation in the rock[113].

In areas with a continuous cover of vegetation, the appearance of rocky walls is for one thing associated with places where vigorous downcutting and undercutting is taking place, whether by running water in valleys, at the outflow of springs, or by the action of breakers on the coast. In addition to the spontaneous weathering away of individual rock particles, there is here developed as a form of accelerated—so to say, forced—denudation, the after-fall of rock complexes undercut and so robbed of their support. As regards the mechanism, it may be classified with the processes treated above; yet, in respect of the material removed and the conditions producing the removal, there is already a transition to land-slides (rock-falls). Where springs issue, the phenomenon may under certain circumstances assume extraordinary dimensions, more particularly in areas of horizontally bedded sediments, differing in permeability. This will be discussed later.

The tendency to produce rock walls differs greatly for the individual types of rock, and not only depends upon the cohesion but is also decided by the arrangement of joints and bedding. Steeply inclined cleavage planes and joint planes favour the formation of rock walls, other things being equal. That is why the outcrops of distinctive rock complexes, more resistant to denudation than their surroundings, readily assume on steeply sloping declivities the form of rock walls or stand out as rock masonry, even if there is no undercutting of any kind. Here it is only spontaneous weathering away that takes place, i.e. migration of the individual little pieces loosened by weathering, exactly as in the case of those exposures of rock which under certain conditions are found on the summits of interfluves, or else which represent the remains of them, like e.g. the granite tors of the Harz or Fichtelgebirge. Finally we must remember the rock faces that were formed under conditions differing from the present ones: corrie walls and the walls of glacial troughs that enclosed Pleistocene névé and ice. These, especially in landscapes where the average gradient of the slopes is otherwise moderate—Black Forest, Riesengebirge, Bithynian Olympus, Bighorn Mountains of the United States, etc.—are conspicuous from a distance on account of their excessive steepness.

The individual tiny pieces that have crumbled off collect at the foot of rock walls to form *screes*, wherever space and other conditions permit. The *upper surface* of the talus has a concave profile, since the falling fragments of rock arrive below possessed of a definite impetus which increases with their mass. Thus the large pieces, as a result of their greater inertia, arrive at or near the lower edge of the talus, and build up its trail; the trajectory of the smaller pieces has already come to an end at or near its summit[114]. *The under surface of the talus* is always a slope with a gradient less than that of the rock face above. This is the basal slope.* It is not always covered with fragmentary material, which is usually absent if another rock wall follows below the basal slope. Excellent examples of such basal slopes without any talus are the stepped rock faces of the Danube valley where it breaks through the Alb, between Tuttlingen and Sigmaringen. It is worth stressing the fact that the step effect of the walls has not the slightest connection with the stratification.

Where the basal slope meets the rock wall, forming a concave angle, is the top of the basal slope.† The accumulation of talus does not simply bury the rock wall and thereby remove it from further decay; but, together with the inclined basal slope, it grows upward at the expense of the wall. This latter, therefore, has no continuation buried beneath the talus, as might previously have been imagined, but it is here replaced by a less steep inclination, as can be seen especially easily in, for example, the Alps near the summit of almost every talus of rock waste[115]. In its upper third the inclination of the basal slope is greater than that of the surface of its covering of rubble; in the lower third of a fully developed talus, however, it is smaller. Both the upper and the under surface of such scree slopes are concave. The thickness of any complete scree slope,

* *Haldenhang.*   † *Haldenscheitel.*

as measured at right angles to the surface, is greatest about the middle (nearer the lower third).

The fact that the under surface of the talus is inclined, makes it impossible for the components to remain immobile in their places. Rather, the whole mass of talus slowly migrates, and in this way it continues the transport of the small pieces which were moving individually from the steep walls above—unless there is a local cementing by deposits thrown out of solution, as can occasionally be observed in limestone regions. The migration is, to begin with, slower than the arrival of material from above: the talus grows. Thus its total weight increases and, further, the components of the rubble on it are constantly getting smaller, chiefly by insolation in arid regions, by frost shattering in polar regions, by chemical weathering in the humid provinces, or in the transitional zones by the processes of rock reduction which are effective there. As the mass becomes heavier, it also becomes more mobile. There must, therefore, arise a stationary condition between supply from above and migration of rubble within the talus, so that in unit time it gives off downwards—to a choked watercourse or to other streams of waste material into which it leads—as much as is added to it. The mass of talus then ceases to grow. Its downwards movement is now and then clearly visible from the way in which it flattens out. This, apart from the increase in weight which is equally effective in all climatic regions, is assisted by the motive forces that are specially important in each particular land area, such as saturation (diminution of friction), fine movement from the freezing of water, or fluctuations in volume due to a regular daily heating up. The type of movement is free mass-movement which, e.g. in the Alps with its heavy soakings, may frequently assume the form of violent rushes of very wet mud.

Examination of the pieces of rubble in the talus proves that this does not consist only of material from the steep walls above, though this is dominant, but that amongst it there are also fragments from the basal slope. They show that the cover of rubble does not prevent denudation from taking place underneath it, and demonstrate that the basal slope is not only a transit region for rock waste derived from the freely exposed rock face, subjected to vigorous denudation, but is also itself a region of supply.

There is another set of phenomena essentially similar to migration by individual loose fragments; but, because of the far greater dimensions involved, they have special characteristic consequences. These are rockfalls and related processes.

Landslides (Rock-fall)

Though individual phenomena, in some regions they so frequently occur in groups that A. Heim actually called them a normal part of valley formation and weathering (by which he meant denudation)[116]. A. Penck and E. Brückner have shown that for the Alps this is the case, especially in the mountain ranges which were once glaciated and where the vanishing masses of Pleistocene ice left behind them beds with over-steepened flanks[117]. Material breaks loose from these, giving rise to rock-falls. They can generally be considered as compensatory movements, the object of which is to get rid of the excessive steepness and to produce that normal slope at which a given rock is just stable. The stability is determined on the one hand by the rock's power of cohesion, on the other by the bedding which decides the arrangement of the planes of least cohesion that may be present in the rock (cleavage planes, bedding planes, etc.). If these are inclined in the same direction as the surface gradient, undercutting creates what is needed for rock movement to take place, and this movement starts when cohesion is lessened and destroyed, and when the plane which acts as slip surface exceeds a minimum inclination[118]. The relations are clearest in an area of tilted sediments where the bedding planes play the part of slip surfaces. Undercutting here makes landslide features a regular phenomenon; and whole valleys, which like the Kandertal run parallel to the strike of the strata, owe their appearance to it[119]. In most cases the lessening of cohesion is brought about by water which collects on impermeable intercalations of clay and transforms them into a highly mobile lubricant. If the inclination of the strata is sufficiently great, the overlying beds slide down (rock-slide); in other cases, if the layer of clay is insufficiently tilted but softened to a pulpy mass (A. Heim's 'squeezed mud' flows), the load of rock may squeeze this out. Also quite thin clay partings along bedding planes, as well as along cracks penetrating the rocks, are, when saturated with water, enough to break up the cohesion. The great importance of water in releasing falls of rock—no small part is played by the increase of weight which saturation with water brings to fissured rocks—is most clearly brought out by the fact that they are generally to be observed in wet years and wet seasons—September and spring in the Alps[120].

As it falls, the breaking rock complex is dissipated into fragments, and these move no longer by sliding, but by rolling, tumbling over and over one another. If the amount of rock material going down is large, the fragments unite into a rapidly moving stream of rock waste which even on flat ground rolls farther the greater the mass and the higher the fall. Like ground avalanches, it comes to a stop suddenly, as soon as its impetus is exhausted. Examples are the stream of rock fragments at Elm, and the cascades of white limestone that flowed down when a rocky tower broke off in the Brenta group (south Tyrol); and E. Howe's photographs of 'rock streams' in the San Juan Mountains of Colorado show the stream formation excellently preserved[121]. Elsewhere, such rapid movement of ever accumulating dry material is to be found only in connection with volcanic eruptions; thus it always denotes special occurrences that set in when great quantities of loose fragments are suddenly ready, in place, on an inclined substratum. Increased interest attaches to these quickly flowing streams of rubble, because of the mechanical work they perform. They scoop out the path along which they move and deepen it considerably during their short course. This has been repeatedly observed with avalanches of volcanic ash and rapid rubble-streams of volcanic origin[122]; but streams of fragments derived from falls of rock have also offered good opportunity for observation, as for example that of Elm and the 'debris-slide' at Bilten in Glarus (29 April 1868) when a furrow six to ten metres deep and ten to twenty wide was scooped out. Because it is confined to a linear path of movement, this kind of mechanical action on the substratum is comparable to the erosion of running water, and the mechanism is indeed the same in both.

At its place of origin, the rock-fall leaves behind a niche-like scar, bounded by planes of minimum cohesion. Here, by the removal of material, a new rock surface has been exposed to destruction and rock reduction; the scar region is an *area of denudation*. The *region of deposition* is where the material comes to rest after the fall. In this way, the arrangement of the three, essentially different, areas typical of all mass-movement, and indeed of all processes of denudation and of their interconnections, can be excellently observed in the features associated with a landslide.

The amounts of rubble, which are brought to valleys at any one time by landslides, are far too great to be removed straight away by the streams flowing in them. If such a stream of fragments crosses a river, this is dammed up to form a lake which remains for a longer or shorter time according to the size and strength of the dam. Thus the lake of Carri-Lanquén (Argentina), dammed up by a landslide of probably Pleistocene age, did not disappear till 1914 when the dam burst, two cubic kilometres of water running off in a single night. Such events have occurred more than once in the remote past[123]. The lake in the Golm valley (Himalaya), dammed up a few decades ago, was reduced in size by an analogous bursting. So far it has remained a permanent element in the valley landscape[124]. The Rhine has long since gnawed through the Pleistocene landslip deposits at Flims, which are 400 metres thick[125].

Landslide deposits often retain their irregularly hilly surface for a long time, and the name 'Toma landscape' is given to it in the Alps[126].

(b) MOVEMENT WHERE MATERIAL IS ACCUMULATING
(α) *Free Mass-Movement*

When material migrates within screes and when streams of rocky fragments are associated with rock falls, this is merely the continuation, on gentler slopes, of the removal of the material. In both cases it is free mass-movement, which can take place even in a dry state, without the help of water. It then belongs to a type of mass-movement which is very widely spread in areas where vegetation is scanty, particularly in arid regions, but also in semi-arid ones. In such areas it is the dominant form of denudation found on slopes with an inclination of less than 25°, except when the wash from rills of rain water effects a quicker and more complete removal of the reduced material and prevents it from piling up to form masses of ever accumulating rubble.

Thorough investigation into the development of dry insolation rubble and its slow downward movement was made in the arid Atacama Desert and its semi-arid marginal zones. The fact of movement is evident from, among other things, the often perfect rounding of the rock fragments due to mutual attrition far from their place of origin, and from uniform mixing-up right to the very bottom of the material: rubble—grit—sand —dust near its source of supply, grit—sand—dust at a greater distance from it. This is the case although reduction by insolation acts only on the surface of the rubble, and thus only the upper horizons undergo further comminution of their components. The uniform penetration of this comminution right down to the bottom of what are often great thicknesses of debris, presupposes a mixing through and through, i.e. movement; and this is directed downslope, as may be seen from blocks travelling along and breaking into fragments on their way, as well as from the petrographic composition. On the slopes, this migration takes place over the whole surface; in the furrows, along a line. Here the debris is in the form of huge streams, which are joined asymptotically by individual ousanding strands of movement, and which have their upper surfaces quite unscratched by any runnel. These valley-like forms with no river bed are in sharp contrast to those, far rarer, depressions along which water flows either constantly or now and again. Streams of debris are not developed in these.

The gradient of these furrows with their rubble streams is always less than that of the bordering slopes. Movement in them seems very strongly marked, obviously because the mass of these streams of detritus is far greater than that of the rubble cover which moves down the mountain flanks. They are arteries for collecting debris, strands of movement continuously increasing in weight. Traces of movement are still distinct; and, on gradients of less than 5°, rubble cones, also without any trace of a watercourse, occur in the great hollows into which these streams of debris discharge their load. They spread out to give surfaces inclined at as small an angle as 2° to 3°. This gives the minimum gradient for movement of the highly mobile mixture of sand and grit which is the final result of reduction by insolation. *Hence it follows that accumulated debris must migrate, and denudation occur, so long as the land slopes at an angle greater than 2° to 3°.*

No increase of moisture came to the high interior of the southern Puna de Atacama with the Pleistocene fluctuation of the climate. At most there was intensification in the formation of rubble, a process still vigorous at the present day. Arid conditions likewise prevailed during the whole of the Tertiary period. This state of affairs makes it highly improbable that it was rivulets which produced the furrows that, filled with their streams of rock waste, are even now becoming steeper and more ramified. Rather, everything indicates that the rubble streams have themselves eroded their beds and deepened them into valleys, or at least that they have had a large share in it. Wherever a considerable weight passes over the rocky substratum, there is stronger mechanical action than in the surrounding parts. This is generally true, and explains how it is that mass-streaming of the type described or of a similar kind, slow as is its movement, not only can trench its substratum to form a furrow, but is bound to do so.

By the time the paths of neighbouring rock fragments unite—and there is ample opportunity for this on every slope—a preference for certain lines of movement has already been established. The weight of material moving along these is therefore perpetually greater than that in neighbouring parts; and so, there must be an intensification of the processes acting on the rock bottom below such united paths (to be considered later [pp. 111 ff.]), and the substratum there becomes trenched. The line of movement becomes a furrow, attracting all the rock fragments near it that have become loosened from the rock texture. This means an increase in the weight moving along every tiny furrow, a further favourable condition as compared with its surroundings, thus leading to its further deepening. It is quite clear that this in turn causes an increase in the material migrating along it, and still further deepening. The individual effects are not only added, but they reinforce one another, since the original causes are intensified. Thus a mass-stream necessarily develops wherever a favoured line of movement has once arisen by the union of the paths of movement of neighbouring single little bits of rock. And just as necessarily, this leads to the formation of a valley without any stream bed. It will be shown later that this phenomenon is widespread all over the world and that its causes are everywhere the same.

In the semi-arid marginal zones of the Atacama Desert, showers of rain, which are not so very rare, have a double effect. In the desert itself, the steeper slopes still have immense covers of rubble. But these are absent in the semi-arid parts, and so there is not the slow migration of a continuous mass of material always increasing in amount. Nor are there any streams of dry rubble. Instead, there is rock, loosened in texture to a quite considerable extent and strewn with stones. The influence of rainwash is here unmistakable. The rock waste, that has been removed, collects as a continuous cover of rubble only when it reaches slopes gentler than would be necessary in the neighbouring arid regions. At times of saturation this accumulated waste possesses extraordinary mobility, and flows almost like mush into the depressions of interior drainage where it spreads out into nearly level surfaces, often measuring tens of kilometres in width. Here, too, one must search long for the rare traces of running water. Where torrent beds from the mountainous margin debouch on to such rubble plains, they quite often become lost; and this proves that the spreading out of the rock waste, which is generally perfectly dry, is brought about by its own movement and not through the transporting agency of running water.

Analogous phenomena have often been described[127]; they are peculiar to the semi-arid regions and are most pronounced in those parts that have gentle average slopes. They also occur on steeper slopes if, for any reason, considerable quantities of loose material have accumulated on them. Then they frequently move away in the form of those striking broadly corrugated rock streams which have been observed in the Tien Shan and elsewhere, and are familiar as a consequence of landslides, and more particularly of slumping[128]. But, on the other hand, for desert areas, little attention has yet been paid to the mass-movement described —of dry material—although such processes are of the greatest importance as regards denudation in arid regions. Still, they have been by no means entirely overlooked. Mention may be made here of the tremendous development of rock waste found in the driest parts of Persia extending as far as the Pamirs, as well as in Tibet and Turkestan, about which numbers of scattered reports are available. The typical way in which dry material everywhere accumulates on the lower parts of the slopes, the size of grain decreasing from above downwards, has been frequently mentioned and shown in illustrations[129]. Both these facts imply that a migration by mass-movement takes place also in these vast areas where saturation by water practically never occurs. It is just the same for the extensive gravelly deserts, the serir of the Sahara, of South Africa, of south-east Iran, etc., the surface of which is covered by rounded fragments of rock. R. Gradmann says truly of them that they could hardly have been formed in a 'pluvial period' since they are never found where there is a rainy climate[130]. They vividly call to mind the wide-stretched gravel flats of the Atacama Desert; and this appearance of coarse deposits is reproduced wherever differential wind action has removed its fine components from the surface of transported insolation detritus. On many serir plains the spreading out of the rock waste may be due to movement of the reduced material itself. This seems probable from the undulating form of the country which Sven Hedin found in Baluchistan and Cl. Lebling on the plateau of the Libyan Desert. The flattish swales are not entirely without fragments of waste; and in the valleys, which are just as flat, there are no traces of water ever having flowed there or of its flowing occasionally nowadays[131]. In some places residuals of the parent rock (siliceous limestone and Miocene beds rich in pebbles) still push up through the Libyan serir. If, as Cl. Lebling imagines, this had been produced by deflation and demolition by the wind, the rubbly material of the serir below the surface rock pavement could not—as has been found to be the case—consist of a mixture with *sand* in it, for the fine components would have been already carried away by the wind's work of reduction. Considered from the point of view of the character of the grains, the composition of the Libyan detritus is certainly that of insolation rubble; and in Libya, too, a distinction must be made between reduction by insolation, the spreading out of the mobile rubble on very gentle slopes, and the armoured coating due to wind action which removes the fine particles from the surface, leaving behind the coarse material. In Libya, as in the Atacama Desert, the reservoir of sand is apparently inexhaustible—witness the dunes piled up in the great oasis depressions in the south. For, to begin with, fine particles are constantly created afresh at the surface, by the comminution of rock fragments; and then, on account of the movement of the rock waste, they are always being worked upward again from the more deep-seated parts to the surface.

Finally, J. Walther, in reporting his observations on the deserts of Egypt and Ethiopia, shows quite clearly that what he had in mind was insolation rubble that had been transported[132]. This short selection of observations has already shown that the slow downhill movement of insolation waste is a world-wide, general phenomenon taking place in all the dry regions of the earth.

Slumping Type of Landslide

In moister climates, apart from movement within screes, which is not restricted to any climatic type, free mass-movement is found primarily in slumping and related phenomena[133]. In this case, the movement is of materials containing some colloidal matter or rich in it, almost flowing when in a saturated condition. As with rock-slides, the beginning of the movement is a slip from which in typical slumping, there develops a niche-like scar surrounded by planes of minimum cohesion, arranged in the form of an arc. But the material very easily disintegrates into its component parts; and then, it presents the picture of a pulpy mush, more or less viscous according to the degree of saturation, which moves slower or faster [as the case may be], and may assume the form of a mud-flow—for example, the 'mud rushes' of South Africa, the 'lame' of Italy, etc. There must first be undercutting. In the majority of cases, the movement is released by an increase in weight due to saturation with water (but it may also be by earthquakes[120]). This saturation reaches a high degree in rocks that are rich in colloids, in those that are shattered, full of fissures or porous, and in those loosely bedded. Where such rocks compose comparatively large areas of the land surface, slumping is quite a common event at times of saturation; and the grouping of such slips together with their frequent recurrence, may give a characteristic appearance to the whole landscape. The zones of flysch in the Alps, Carpathians, Dinaric Alps and Apennines, the molasse of the Alpine Foreland, the zones of thick Pleistocene deposits in the Alps and elsewhere, the landscapes of the Keuper, Lower and Middle Jurassic beds and many other regions of a similar nature are tracts of land especially suited to slumping[134]. Here the slumping is everywhere connected with the natural, undercut outcrops of the rocks concerned; landslip scars are found on the slopes, and deposits in the valleys, where running water gradually carries them away.

A continuous cover of vegetation hinders the occurrence of slumping. It, accordingly, develops most freely in semi-humid regions where, over wide areas, the plant cover is enfeebled and the rainy season brings about a very thorough soaking[135]. However, a continuous plant cover is no insuperable obstacle. [But] it affords only a confined space for material migrating beneath it; and so it becomes arched up and stretched at the places towards which great quantities of reduced material are moving and being dammed back (as occurs regularly towards the bottom of a slope). If such material arrives more quickly than the vegetation is growing, or if absorption of water increases the weight of the dammed-up material to any very considerable extent, the cover tears; and the accumulated material then flows out from the wound. This type of slumping frequently occurs in moist temperate regions; but its chief development is in the tropics, wherever the forest cover, besides being continuous, is also on very steep slopes. Here, beneath the plant cover, the slow migration is carried on by sliding down, or better, flowing out—since it is a matter of material which is usually already reduced, and in every case wet and actually flowing. The cover tears spontaneously under the pressure of the rock derivatives arriving from higher up. The slump leaves behind it an open wound in the forest, but this very soon heals over again. W. Behrmann described how these niches, tearing away in close proximity one after another, and always quickly healing again, lick up the steep forested slopes in New Guinea, and sharpen the crests as soon as they have cut away up to these from neighbouring valleys. K. Sapper reports similar happenings in Central America; and it cannot be doubted that, on the steep slopes of tropical mountains, slumping—as has often been stressed—is the main factor of denudation since it acts with extraordinary intensity (rapidity)[136]. Where slopes are less steeply inclined, slumping becomes less and less important, and the migration of material takes the form of a slow creep, this also occurring beneath the cover of tropical vegetation, a phenomenon which must be discussed later[137] [pp. 108 ff.].

Wherever slumping occurs regularly, one can always notice specially active recession of the valley-heads towards the water partings, as well as the above mentioned sharpening of the crests by upward 'licking' and by the intersection of niches. G. Braun has followed the phenomena in some detail in the northern Apennines. On account of continued sliding away, not only do the sharp ridges become lower, but the whole relief conditions of the country are lessened, provided that rivers are not simultaneously cutting down by the same amount as the intervalley divides are being lowered. On gentler slopes, slumping is no longer possible in the same way; in particular, the movement cannot go on so rapidly. It does not, however, entirely cease. On the contrary, when thoroughly wet, material begins moving even on quite gentle slopes. Thus in the shallow valleys of the Thracian peneplane round about Constantinople, the growing accumulation of reduced material—which during the dry season forms a hard immobile mass, more or less full of stones—can in winter be seen flowing down out of the valleys. The sod, with its sparse covering of grass, tears; and pieces of it take part in building up the corrugations, caused by the movement, which run at right angles to the steeply inclined valley bottom; or they simply float on the material which, in the less steeply sloping minor valleys, moves at a correspondingly slower pace[138]. Mutual attrition is unmistakable, rounding off the corners of the rock fragments borne along. Because of this and also because of the absence of any divisional planes, the migrating material is often reminiscent of boulder clay; and this even led T. English to believe in the influence of Pleistocene ice (and coastal ice at that!)[139].

In addition to the dumping movement, this gradual flowing downwards of reduced material, i.e. of rock that has become mobile and lies almost or quite freely exposed at the surface, is the regularly occurring form of mass-movement in forested stretches of semi-humid regions. Like the 'lama' of Italy, it continues the slumping on to very gentle slopes and brings about the further removal of what has been washed down into hollows and collected there. The part it plays in these regions cannot be overestimated, being almost equal to that of rainwash. Even on slopes where the inclination is noticeably less than $5°$, the wet masses are still in motion, as can be seen from the way in which they spread out over plains several kilometres wide, with a gradient of scarcely more than $2°$ to $3°$ (e.g. on the Thracian peneplane where there are usually no stream beds at the heads of the valleys). This state of affairs again forces us to the conclusion that denudation by free mass-movement, of the kind described above, cannot come to an end before the mean slopes of the country have been reduced to an angle of inclination of less than $5°$.

Slumping at the Level of the Water Table

On account of its great importance, this must be specially mentioned. It occurs when an impermeable water-bearing horizon is cut into, e.g. in the course of valley formation. Springs rise here and wash away the fine reduced material; or clayey horizons become highly mobile and slide away, or rush down. Thus conditions are on the whole similar to those for rock-slides; but the movement looks very much like slumping, and the material moved forward is generally confined within narrow limits. The feature is particularly widespread in regions of gently inclined sediments with beds alternating in permeability or in their tendency towards mobility.

The landslide scars are situated in the overlying rocks which have been passively borne forward, and they are steep-sided as is natural for their type of fracture. They unite to give a steep scarp which recedes more or less vigorously by continued sliding over the water-bearing horizon, leaving behind it a landscape to the modelling of which I. C. Russell has given the name of 'landslide topography'[140]. Excellent examples are found in the scarplands of south-west Germany. Thus the Malm platform of the Heuberg is girdled round by scars due to slumping, and the vigorous retreat of the Malm scarp has led to the beheading of many valleys in their higher parts; so that they now run freely westward along the strike, having already lost their dendritic headwaters (e.g. north of Dreifaltigkeitsberg). Other instances are the retreat of Vermilion Cliff along the Marble Canyon (Colorado Canyon area), the development undergone by the Pliocene scarp of Volterra, or the recession of certain stretches of the Channel coast of France[141].

The bottom of the ground-water horizon may be inclined towards the outcrop below the scarp edge. Conditions are then more favourable for the occurrence of slumping in the direction of inclination of the water table than in any other. It is in this direction, therefore, that a sharply incised V, having once arisen by slips at the scarp edge, recedes most vigorously leaving a valley behind it. This process has been followed pretty closely in the fine-grained deposits filling the troughs between mountain ranges in north-west Argentina[142]. It is developed to a great extent in the Neogene districts of south-east Europe and Asia Minor, beginning at the eastern margin of the Alps, where the late Tertiary beds, generally flat, cover an extremely hummocky ancient land surface. Within the Neogene there are varying levels of the water-bearing horizons; the most constant lies at its base and is associated with the upper surface of the buried landscape, especially with its valley tracks. Where this lowest water level has been cut into by a river, what most frequently happens is that the springs work back up these old valley tracks and expose them again, whether by slumping connected with the outcrop of the water table or merely by a continuous collapse above the springs which are gradually but continually washing out the fine components of the rock. Under certain conditions it is possible for the easily denuded Neogene to be carried away from a wide area without there being at the same time any noticeable destruction or change. For those parts of the old land surface which have been laid bare, F. Schaffer has pointed out such relationships in the district of Eggenburg near Vienna[143], and the writer has recorded similar cases in western Asia Minor[144]. J. Sölch suggests for this the name 'basement stripping'*[145]. It is only possible when, first, the resistance of the substructure and that of the superstructure are *very* different; and secondly, when the main rivers, from which basement stripping starts, do not erode downwards so vigorously as to sink rapidly below the surface of the substratum.

Solifluction

In higher latitudes where the forest vegetation becomes less important, and finally vanishes, it is the exceptional soaking of the ground at the time of snow-melt which brings about migration of accumulated masses of waste, even when this consists of loose rock fragments very

* *Grundaufdeckung.*

poor in colloidal constituents, and that on very gentle slopes, too[146]. This process of denudation is probably general in the higher latitudes on those slopes that are not very steep, and have ceased to be rocky. Where slopes are steeper, the movement becomes so vigorous that the grass cover and even the sparse remains of forest are ripped up and pushed together. This is the 'flowing soil' of polar regions, better 'flowing rock waste', or solifluction, as J. G. Andersson terms it[147].

According to B. Högbom and J. Frödin, the reason for this thorough wetting of the debris is that, during the thaw, the lower parts of the soil remain frozen for a long time, or permanently (the tjaele of the Swedes), so that the melt-water cannot sink in, and it is merely the upper layers of soil that receive any benefit from it. These, having reached a high degree of saturation, move down, they flow (just as in semi-arid regions), and it is only when the thaw lasts rather a long time that the movement reaches down to a greater depth. The tjaele never forms a level plain, but is irregularly shaped. Beneath patches of snow and of vegetation its upper surface is lower than where snow is absent; in the former case the moving mass of rock waste is thicker, and the water distributed through a greater space than in the latter. The material flowing off is thus dammed up at the places which are not free from snow or are plant covered. In the latter, it is also because the turf, at least when the season of movement begins, is still rooted in the tjaele[148]. Those places where the movement is more vigorous are unfavourable to the settlement of plants. Green islands of vegetation in the rubble lands of polar regions indicate zones where the soil covering is thinner, or where the movement has been slowed down. They do not prove its absence.

Frost undoubtedly plays an important part in the movements, but its action has not yet been entirely explained[149]. In any case, and especially on gentle slopes, the fluctuations in volume connected with freezing and thawing help to keep the movement going. Solifluction is not at all unusual where slopes are inclined at scarcely more than 3°. The stream-like arrangement of the material in wide streamless valleys of exceedingly small gradient again forces on us the conclusion that, in the polar regions and their marginal zones, denudation brought about by solifluction and related processes cannot come to an end before the mean slopes of the land have been reduced to less than 5° inclination.

It is, from the nature of the case, necessary that the flowing rock waste should collect into streams. And I think it probable that the polar streams of waste have also, to a great extent, themselves created their beds, the waterless valleys which they fill. It is also true for high latitudes that the transported debris becomes arranged in strands of movement that unite asymptotically[150]; here also it accumulates to a great thickness and works like a [carpenter's] heavy plane as it moves along over its substratum.

The transported waste is a mixture of rock fragments of all sizes, with some of its components fine-grained and with a clayey admixture. But the fine elements, the matrix which furthers movement and reduces friction, are often more or less washed away so that the coarser pieces accumulate at the surface. If rocks from the source of supply show a tendency to break up into coarse blocks, then one block comes to lie upon another and the material presents the appearance of a block stream [stone river]. There is thus an outward resemblance between polar block streams and the seas of blocks found in temperate latitudes.

On the Falkland Islands, early Palaeozoic quartzites furnish coarse angular blocks. In the flat bottoms of the valleys where the material lies as well-defined streams, the fine matrix has been removed in parts, though by no means everywhere, and one can hear water trickling deep down below the blocks. This and the growth of vegetation on those surface strips which retain some of the matrix, explain why those streams were considered to be fossil formations of the Pleistocene period, immobile at the present day. The arguments are not convincing.

B. Högbom showed that occasionally individual blocks in the flowing debris migrate more quickly than this itself; they plough it up, as it were, arranging themselves in strips and uniting to form block streams that float passively downwards on a moving substratum. What matters, therefore, is the *substratum*. That also is exposed at one place in the Falkland Islands—on the coast where a 'stone river' rests upon a recently uplifted underlying stratum and shares in the formation of the cliff. This situation was considered a further proof for the fossil character of the 'stone rivers'; but incorrectly. For the profile, as described and illustrated by J. G. Andersson[150] merely shows that, at that place, uplift and wave action have had a greater effect than denudation upon the rocky floor of the 'stone river'. Its lower layer consists of a loam interlarded with stones. It is extremely improbable that this would not, if it were saturated, move along an inclined substratum. But if it moves, so also does the overlying zone of blocks. The general movement is certainly *very* slow and the material tumbles very gradually over the cliff. There it further suffers the same fate as those fragments which the breakers tear off directly or which fall down after undercutting. The 'stone rivers' will always end above the cliff.

Solifluction is taking place in the Falklands even nowadays. It has been observed wherever a quicker flow makes the movement more easily recognisable; e.g. in the tributaries of the wide shallow valleys, though their slopes may scarcely attain 10°. Thus at the present day climatic and other conditions are favourable to mass-movement. In the very much flatter valley bottoms, the movement of the main streams is not noticeable and has certainly been always extraordinarily delayed. Not only does the waste material coalesce in these valleys, but water collects there, too. Thus its action must be far more energetic here than on the slopes of the catchment basin. Washing away of the packing material and accumulation of the blocks is the natural consequence. *This is why* the 'stone rivers' are to be found just in the valley bottoms. This arrangement does not prove that the whole formation is fossil; but it shows that in the valley bottoms the relationship between the quantities of fine-grained components and of water is different from that on the valley flanks. On the flanks, the smaller quantities of water are completely absorbed by the waste, swallowed as it were, and in such a state of saturation it flows as a whole (*mass-movement*). In the valley bottoms there is an excess of water which simply sweeps away the transportable material (*mass-transport*). This naturally applies in the first place to the fine and very fine components of the stream of rock waste, since water, whatever its quantity, cannot transport large blocks along small gradients. It is not easy to envisage why this should be the case only at the present day, and not equally so in the past. The Pleistocene climate, in particular, could not have had this effect. In the Falklands it furnished greater quantities of melt-water; and though this would have led to the 'flowing' of the 'stone rivers' in their valleys, it would also have produced an even greater washing out of the 'packing' than is to be observed there at the present day.

Undoubtedly, the process forming 'mass-streams' in the Falklands, like that producing many similar phenomena in other parts of the world, goes back to the Pleistocene period and probably much further still. But the conclusion that they are not continuing to develop at the present day, over the whole of their extent, and in the same direction as during the Pleistocene period, is not justifiable either on the grounds that the main streams are depleted of their fine-grained packing material, or because of their apparent lack of movement—and maybe even measurements extending over several decades would give no proof one way or the other.

Solifluction, which takes place over a frozen subsoil, is nowadays confined to high latitudes. Without any line of demarcation, it passes into 'flowing rock-waste' which, in regions where the annual temperature is higher, goes on without the aid of frost, or of tjaele; it is more apt to flow and does so more easily, the greater the proportion of colloidal matter; and above all, wherever there is a sufficiently thorough soaking of the exposed detritus. It must have been the application of the term 'solifluction' to all these forms of movement of rock waste which led B. Högbom to consider it as a process spreading far beyond the polar zone and its marginal districts[151].

During the Pleistocene displacement of the climatic zones, the area of polar solifluction was extended equatorwards. The assumption that traces of it had been preserved intact in the temperate region right up to the present day, is based on the occurrence of similar phenomena and forms of movement in our own latitudes. They had been considered peculiar to the polar zone. That this is incorrect has been shown for the 'seas' of blocks found in the German Highlands (p.66); and it is evident from the fact that analogous free mass-movement is encountered in nearly all climatic regions.

All that can be established is that such block seas, as well as the debris covering the slopes of temperate regions, may have originated in part during a not very distant ice age or [even] earlier, and may then have left its place of formation; but we cannot say that the formation or the downward movement has since suffered any interruption.

(β) *Bound-down Mass-Movement*

This is the prevailing form taken by sheet denudation in districts with a continuous cover of vegetation. This latter by no means always possesses the tenacity necessary to bind the migrating material. If, in consequence of comparatively quick movement towards any one place, accumulation occurs there, the strained plant cover tears as soon as the weight of the downward-pushing material attains a certain value. The weaker turf covering gives way to this pressure more easily than where there is continuous forest. On flattish slopes, therefore, it tears sooner than the ground under trees. These relationships are brought out by comparing landslides (slumping) in forested country of the temperate zone with those in open land; or by comparing the slumping not associated with undercutting, which constantly recurs in mountain regions covered by tropical forest, with the mass-movement of semi-humid and sub-polar regions where the feeble or weakened vegetation cover is unable to stop free flow even on a small gradient.

Damming-up material covered by vegetation, especially when this is forest, so that the cover is arched up on the lower parts of the slope (without necessarily tearing), implies an accumulation of material; and this, in its turn, implies movement of rock derivatives to that place. This sum total of features is sufficient to prove that reduced material does migrate even under continuous forest (see p. 80).

G. Götzinger was the first to make detailed investigations on the sub-surface migration of slope waste. Adopting the English mode of expression, he introduced the word 'kreichen'—creep—for the movement, and 'Gekreich' for the material that has moved[152]. The movement is very slow, but can be measured as it influences the growth of trees. The root system of these is anchored in the deeper horizons which move more slowly, or in the living rock itself, whilst the quicker moving superficial layer presses the upper parts of the root system downslope. This rotation couple makes the trees oblique at the base, while the trunks as a whole tend to grow vertically upwards. Thus they show curvature, convex on the downslope side. This is called *stilt effect*. In exceptional cases it is also found on nearly level ground. But this does not prove—as has sometimes been suggested—that the stilt effect was unconnected with soil movements and that it does not indicate these on the steeper slopes where it regularly occurs. It merely proves that material is still moving even when spread out almost flat. Its upper layers move more quickly than the lower ones, which may even not move at all.

There is a further series of facts which (in addition to those mentioned on p. 85), show convincingly that material beneath the vegetation cover moves downward, even on slopes of very small gradient. S. Passarge pointed out that, in the flat alluvial meadows of our latitudes, the soil shifts towards the beds of the watercourses[153]; and K. Sapper established the fact that the turf thus carried forward by the migrating soil is always being undermined and torn off at the edges of the river beds. He called this process 'turf peeling'[154]. For years the author has been systematically observing such features. It has become evident that they are very widespread. On any valley floor, however wide and flat, whether wooded or grassy, the accumulated material pushes towards the line of lowest level. Should a permanent stream be there, the tendency is to close its bed. This may be expressed in the following way: The vegetation cover—grass or woodland—is undercut by the wash of the water; it overhangs, until finally pieces tear off, and fall into the channel of the streamlet. This happens not only on the undercut side of meanders, where naturally it is particularly well developed, without having any direct significance as regards soil movement. It also occurs simultaneously along both banks of fairly straight reaches. The streams undercut their edges, without thereby becoming wider; which means that they are occupied in keeping their beds open. Every possible stage is found depending on the relationship between the varying intensity of mass-transport by running water and the amount of material coming down from the sides. Scarcely any of the valley-heads on, for example, the peneplanes and flattish country of the Central German Rise shows a trace of stream-bed with either permanent or intermittently flowing water. Such depressions, normally wide troughs but often narrow

gutters, are usually marshy even when the gradient is not particularly
gentle. Drainage ditches cut in the reduced rock material, always thickly
accumulated there, have to be renewed from time to time; for the water
itself is unable to keep its channel open whether, as befits the gradient, it
is flowing lazily or in lively fashion. Under certain conditions, rain or
melt-water as it flows off is able to dig natural channels in the accumulated material; but these do not persist. The larger streamlets have no
trouble in keeping their paths open. They cut right through what has
become heaped up on the valley floor, and—depending upon their size
and the gradient—may even attack the substratum. Watercourses seen
to be eroding vigorously are not free from the features under discussion;
but there one cannot distinguish the share taken by spontaneous mass-
movement from that due to undercutting. Only this much is certain: the
latter must be preceded by the former. Undercutting may locally accelerate the migration of detritus; but what it cuts away is fed from rock
derivatives spontaneously moving to that place from further away.

The fact of subsurface migration of material, even on very gentle
slopes, shown by the observations mentioned above, will be brought out
even more clearly when mass-streaming is discussed in a later section. It
will be shown that even when going on beneath a cover of vegetation,
denudation does not come to an end so long as the average slope of the
land exceeds a minimum value, which is always more than 0°, but less
than 5°. The features we have been considering show further that what
migrates from the valley sides and collects at the foot does not stay
there permanently, even if running water does not remove it. The downward movement occurring on the steeper slopes is continued by further
migration on the rather flat and very flat slopes that follow below. The
material, usually in a more intensely reduced form, is finally brought to
the watercourse even if its bed lies at some distance from the bottom of
the valley slopes. The mass-movement observed over the valley floor
takes place in the zone of water accumulation or even where there is
actually a *flow of ground water*. It is therefore not surprising to find that
there the rate of movement increases to noticeable amounts in spite of
the small gradient.

Bound-down movement is no peculiarity of temperate latitudes, but
seems to occur all over the earth wherever a continuous cover of vegetation is spread over the slopes. Indications of its occurrence have already
been mentioned (p. 109). Since Götzinger's researches drew attention to
this phenomenon, a considerable amount of evidence has been collected
both from the tropics and from the semi-humid regions[155].

(γ) Corrasion and Corrasion Valleys

Just as rock fragments are worn down (attrition) where the material is moving freely, so are those in the detritus which is moving underneath vegetation. They become rounded at the edges and sometimes scratched. This, and the absence of [any bedding or other] directional planes, occasionally causes the material to resemble moraines, a feature of convergence which led to their being formerly mistaken for Pleistocene moraines[156]. Besides reduction, which is greater the longer the time of exposure, so that the components of the rock waste become smaller and smaller, attrition also increases with the length of the route travelled. Thus the talus of uniformly inclined slopes usually shows a finer grain at the lower parts of the slope than higher up.

The mechanical action on the underlying rock, caused by material moving over it, is very marked. It is most easily recognised in the *hooked effect*, the downward bending of layers of bedding and cleavage which are inclined more steeply than the slope of the surface. Mere weight cannot bring about this phenomenon, as each upper edge is underpinned and supported by the one below it. The hooked effect is produced by *weights that have been moving*. It thus informs us in a direct way of the movement of the reduced material. The nature of the mechanical action on the rocky substratum can also be traced; from the resistant upper edges, which project over their neighbours, long streamers of pressed-off pieces trail down the slope and only at some distance from their place of origin do they merge into detritus which shows no directional trend in its arrangement. *The action is not a scouring or polishing, such as occurs under rapidly moving material, but a pressing-off and chiselling-off of rock fragments* which have been partly loosened from their union with the solid rock, but have not been sufficiently reduced to be able to migrate spontaneously. In parts, however, they are still firmly connected to their surroundings and, for example, by the way in which they project from them, offer a surface of attack to the downward pressing material as it is moving along.

The mechanical action on a *uniformly inclined substratum* increases with the weight of the material moving over it. Other things being equal, the extent of the mechanical action on the subsoil increases downslope in the direction in which the talus is accumulating. As the thickness of the moving soil cover diminishes, it is noticeable that the phenomena described become less marked. They are especially conspicuous in dry valleys. The rock exposures are here buried beneath a soil cover thicker than in any part of the bordering slopes, towards which its thickness decreases. The bottom is never smooth. Even in absolutely homo-

geneous rock material, it is full of pockets and pot-holes, like those in a
river bed. Lumps of rubble are pressed into the pockets; and, where the
rock fragments are flatter in shape, they are pushed over one another, in
the direction of movement, like tiles on a roof. Such pockets, hollowed
out, and with their walls smoothed, can be observed on the steeper
slopes; and there it is possible to recognise not only foreign matter from
above, but also pieces taken from the pocket itself, often still connected
with the solid rock. The pockets are not just holes where weathering has
gone down deeper than in the surrounding parts; but material must have
been removed from them since foreign matter has entered in its place.

    We are giving the name *corrasion* to this freeing of loosened rock frag-
ments from their place of origin, which they are unable to leave spontaneously when they lie beneath a thick covering (p.54), this pressing-off
and prizing away of pieces of rock that are slightly or not at all loosened,
and their removal by the material moving over them. The force and
violence of its character distinguishes it physically from the spontaneous
downward movement of rock particles which begins on an inclined substratum only when there has been an adequate amount of rock reduction
(pp. 64, 65). In the one case (spontaneous movement), the force which
leads to the removal of the small pieces of rock from their place of origin
is determined by the gravity component (gradient) and the mass of the
solid body concerned. The result is to expose a fresh surface of rock; and
this is the essential feature of denudation. In the other case (corrasion),
besides the downward pull appropriate to each particular little bit of
rock, the pieces are subjected to the very much greater force of the
material moving over them, a force, moreover, which is independent of
their own mass. With corrasion, too, ever fresh rock surfaces are being
laid bare and exposed to the forces operating (reduction and corrasion).
Thus denudation and corrasion both bring about a renewal of exposure;
but, other things being equal, at a different rate. Denudation, for example, can work only as quickly as mobile material can be made ready
by the process of reduction; corrasion, on the other hand, acts more
quickly. *From this it follows that the removal of material beneath corrading
masses is more active, more intense, than under those which are not corrading.* Should the corrading material unite into streams, the effect due
to increase of weight (mentioned above) comes into play. This means
that the substratum is acted upon more powerfully, that is, corrasion is
intensified. Now, increased denudation beneath a corrading 'mass-
stream' must excavate its substratum into an elongated hollow, dig a
furrow. I should like to propose the term *corrasion valleys* for valleys
with such an origin. Two types occur, connected by intermediate forms:
(1) wide, shallow valleys, trough-like in cross section, their floors gradu-

ally passing into gentle side-slopes and having but a slight gradient; (2) narrower trenches with a steeper gradient and the floor more definitely marked off. In every case this contains a recognioable mass-stream. The valley bottoms never show any sign of a stream bed or anything like it. Since these furrows, which are often united as branching systems, have no erosional history, they stand at one end of a long series of features, at the other end of which is the pure erosion valley, the gorge.

Wide, shallow trough-valleys, having as a rule no stream bed, are the characteristic form found on peneplanes and landscapes of gentle average gradient all over the world. It is only in the wet tropics that no observations have yet been made on them—or rather, they have not been noticed. They are best developed and best known in arid and semi-arid regions (p. 97). They appear to be present in the polar zone (p. 105); and I have also found corresponding features in the semi-humid regions, but only where the country is very flat, probably because only there is rainwash unable to cope with the accumulation of rock waste (p. 102). But even there, as for example in the extremely shallow valleys of the Thracian peneplanes around the Bosporus, furrows due to water, trickling in tiny rills, are not entirely lacking[138]. They have occasionally cut through accumulations of soil often several metres thick, and their bottoms show corrasion features of the kind described above. In those regions where rainwash is dominant, conditions are not very favourable to accumulation of the products of rock reduction, and the joining of such material to form 'streams'; for there is a close-meshed dissection of the slopes, and usually thorough removal of reduced material even from the collecting furrows. For every case in which observations have been made on the flattish valleys that are being discussed here, it has been found that they are marked by a consistent form (independent of the climate), by the complete absence of any indication of beds containing running water, and by the extraordinary accumulation of reduced rock waste on their floors. This material very often shows the stream-form considered above, or its flow has been directly established. Whether, however, such furrows are, or are not, the exclusive work of corrasion, is quite another question.

Analogous valley troughs and furrows are met with in temperate regions, chiefly near the heads of valleys formed by erosion, and are of regular occurrence when these lie in flattish country (pp. 109). Referring to conditions on the scarpland peneplanes, H. Schmitthenner relates their origin to the joint work of trickling water and mass-movement. He points to the instability of such furrowings in the valleys which he calls 'dells'.* They are immediately closed up again by material

* 'Dellen'.

H

taking the place of what has gone, and in that way mass-migration is accelerated[157]. However, the deepening of those valleys cannot well be attributed to trickling water, just as the lowering of the enclosing ridges cannot be put down to rainwash; for in our latitudes, in any case, the continuous cover of vegetation reduces the effectiveness of rainwash to a minimum. Thus water channels develop only at specially favoured places, and have particular difficulty in establishing themselves on the floors of the above-mentioned valleys. With us, these are usually meadowland. Agriculture avoids them, since most of the ground is marshy. Swampiness is the direct result of the accumulation of the detrital material. This becomes saturated with water which it retains long after the wet season; for seepage water collects in these valleys from all the tributary slopes, and the smallness of the gradient is particularly favourable to infiltration at the expense of the surface run off. But the same can also be observed in the steeper furrows. Their swampiness, revealed by the vegetation, is made possible only by the high capacity for moisture which the accumulated material possesses. Where there are exposures of rock, and fortunately these are not entirely absent, either here or in the flat trough-like valleys, the thickness of the soil covering is shown. And there is no artificial cut through these accumulations which does not show, excellently, features due to corrasion. Thus, *if* water should run off along trough valleys which are nowadays without stream-beds, and along the branching systems of 'dells' (which by the way are only in part true corrasion valleys, having in most cases a history of water erosion), it digs a furrow, which scratches into the accumulated waste and not into the rock floor. Any possibility of trenching the latter has thus to a great extent been removed. In the forest, conditions are different in many ways. Water channels are more frequently to be found, and indeed under circumstances where these would not be present in the open country. Obviously this is because turf forms a much more continuous armour-plating over which whatever water has not seeped away runs off without being able to do much cutting down; whilst in the forest the upper parts of the ground are not always protected and made firm by low-growing vegetation. Therefore any water that has not seeped away finds here, between the individual trees, more opportunities for mechanical attack[158].

As regards water content, the 'mass-streams' of our latitudes, as well as of any regions where the ground is at least sometimes richly supplied with water, are extraordinarily well-favoured. They receive practically all the water that falls on the slopes leading to their beds, both what sinks in and what flows off over the surface. It is therefore not specially remarkable to find that in streamless valleys several kilometres long, the material spreads out to a hardly noticeable surface gradient, and that its composition occasionally shows that it has travelled a long distance. Where these valleys (as in their uppermost ramifications) do not all the time reach into the ground water, this long continued moistening of the substratum means, in addition, an intensification of weathering: in unit time more rock material is loosened and disintegrated here than in the surrounding parts. In this way denudation and corrasion are encouraged, specially favourable conditions are created for trenching the rock floor and even more for headward extension of the furrow. This especially applies to the steeper narrower furrows, in the bottoms of which material sometimes accumulates to a depth of several metres. In spite of a considerable gradient there is swampiness with no sign of a stream bed. They may be considered pure corrasion valleys. On steeper slopes they look like the beginnings of V-shaped valley-cuts, and here they often occur in groups, as on the slopes of the lower scarps of the [German] Scarpland region, or on the flanks of moderately trenched erosion valleys of the type found in the Saale valley above Hof. The comparatively steep gradient leads one to expect that during the wet season there will be perceptible motion of the material in them. This would be a good field for making measurements.

Should a mass-stream graze a water-bearing horizon, an actual channel will appear. And from this, dry cracks, variable in their position, may now and then be seen reaching up-valley[159].

The existence and action of linear corrasion is placed beyond doubt by the observations here submitted. It is this which has produced the ultimate and most recent streamless ramifications which, especially in the source regions, reach back from the valleys of gently sloping country. But by no means all streamless trough-shaped valleys of our latitudes can be considered the exclusive work of linear corrasion. Rather do the majority of trough-shaped valleys, both individual features and whole systems, give proof of erosion [by water]. This is true even for those streamless ones characterised by a vast accumulation of reduced rock material on their floors, such as stamp their impress upon the summit landscapes of the German Highlands, the Scarpland peneplanes, etc. This will be treated in a later section [VII, 2]. Interruption of [water-] erosion led to obliteration by the migrating material of any direct traces of it, and it is to the action of this material alone that the further development must be ascribed. Besides trenching, yet to be proved, working in the direction of the uppermost ramifications, it is also necessary to take into account the headward lengthening of these, and the formation of new shorter tributary furrows. *It is these which are the corrasion valleys.*

A further member of this series of phenomena is the wide trough-shaped valley, with a stream meandering along its floor, entrenched in the vast mass of accumulated material, but not in its substratum. Up-valley, such troughs pass over into valleys with no stream-beds, and quite gradually into corrasion valleys (e.g. Upper Main region, south-west German Scarplands, especially the Wörnitz valley above Dinkels-bühl, and the Tauber valley with all its ramifications, etc., above Rothenburg). Down-valley, river action has definitely set in, as can be seen from the appearance of water-transported material, and the occur-rence of steeper sections of the slopes. The gradient becomes steeper, and the valley flanks close in, becoming steeper and higher.

Examination of the material on the floor of these upper courses shows an accumulation of unknown thickness, consisting of colloidal end-products, undecomposed residues and tiny pieces of rock, but no pebbles. The same occurs on the valley flanks, still showing considerable thickness, yet thinning upwards; there are more pieces of rock, amongst which pebbles are conspicuous, often well rounded (but not river-transported). Thus not even in the valley bottoms is there any longer direct indication of previous erosion [by water], least of all in the beha-viour of the streams which share in the seasonal fluctuations of the water table, and when this is low, may run dry in the upper reaches. The ad-vance of the vegetation, from both sides, over the channel margins wit-nesses to mass-movement, as does the spreading out of the material to form almost level plains. It is naturally a help to its movement that this material, right at the lowest part of the valley, lies at the level of the ground water which is flowing slowly out of the valley. Since there are no features whatsoever of damming-up, such as are frequent in dry regions, we must assume that the whole mass moves in the same direc-tion, and thus, in a certain sense, forms with the ground water a single gravitational stream. The concourse of mass-streams of material coming together from all the slopes, is balanced by an equivalent removal. This removal, however, does not generally begin till the running water be-comes more independent of fluctuations in the water table, i.e. at some place down-valley.

Because of all this, mass-streaming must be reckoned with, as playing a part in the shaping of valleys; and, within certain limits, even in temperate regions it acquires the significance of being an important factor in valley formation.

G. Götzinger has already published quite a number of observations on corrasion over the whole surface of slopes. Similar features are nearly always to be seen on the side walls (i.e. in the profile) of natural sections in the lower-lying parts of the country, wherever these reach down to solid rock. It is found that the corrasion is associated with rocks which are not very resistant to weathering and on those easily affected by mechanical action.

Such results depend even more upon the inclination of the ground than upon the character of the rock and the weight [of the moving material] (p. 111). Even under a thick cover, corrasion comes to an end on fairly steep slopes, since the pressure exerted by this material decreases with an increasing angle of inclination.

Further, it has been observed that there is no corrasion in the case of the flattish slopes, covered with a thick layer of soil, which are found in the higher parts of the area. Only the upper horizons of the soil profile are sufficiently reduced to migrate from the place, the lower ones following suit when they have acquired the same degree of reduction. This is characteristic of the region of supply. It is only lower down that, where the inclination is suitable, there are signs of corrasion. These parts of the slope are not only a source of rock waste, but also a region over which material from above travels. Weight therefore increases, and capacity for mechanical work, right down to the foot of the slope. Gradient and rock being suitable, the most pronounced corrasion effects are found there.

Recapitulating, it may be said that vegetation is unable to prevent the individual paths of moving particles of rock from uniting into strands of movement, and thus cannot prevent the formation of mass-streams (p. 98).

Further, there cannot be the slightest doubt, that today as at any other time, mass-movement is in progress on every slope. Solid matter is incessantly being conveyed to the water-courses, by its own movement if it has not previously reached them by processes which accelerate this. For the most part, this movement takes place over the whole surface; but it also goes linear-fashion in mass-streams. Such being the state of affairs, it cannot be maintained that the extra-glacial regions of Central Europe are not developing now in the same manner as they did formerly. In these parts, the Pleistocene fluctuation of climate could cause alteration in only two respects:

(a) Migration of material, which may indeed have been poorer in its colloidal content at that time, went on over the whole surface or along special lines at the same places as now. But it was under polar conditions, freely, not bound down by vegetation, whether there was or was not tjaele, just as can be seen in the higher latitudes at the present day.

(b) There was a shift in the ratio between the amount of material brought down and that carried away by running water, as is proved by the occurrence of terraces in the larger valleys (though not in the head-water regions). This shift can be put down to increase in the amount of material arriving, or to lessening of the water content of the streams, or to both. So, for slopes outside the water-net, not even a change in the intensity of denudation during the Pleistocene period can be deduced, with any certainty, from terraces alone.

There is much to refute the view, but not a single observed fact to support it, that the passing of Pleistocene conditions brought to any un-glaciated area of denudation either an interruption in rock reduction and surface denudation or a change in direction of the latter [160].

CHAPTER V

GENERAL CHARACTERISTICS OF DENUDATION

1. RETROSPECT

RELATIONSHIP TO CLIMATE

The foregoing survey of observations on mass-movement confirms the tenet that it occurs in all climatic regions and on all slopes where the gradient exceeds a minimum. In all parts of the world, wherever slopes have more than a certain degree of steepness, individual loosened particles move away from the bare rock. This occurrence is to a large extent controlled by the vigour of the vegetation: other things being equal, such movement takes place in the tropics [only] on steeper slopes than in the temperate zone, and here again on slopes steeper than in regions where vegetation becomes sparse and finally absent. Below that maximum steepness, cumulative migration takes place as either free or bound-down mass-movement, and this continues, as fine movements, on the very slightest gradients: *therefore there is no climatic region, from the equator to the margin of the ice caps, where sheet denudation can possibly come to an end, so long as the mean slopes of the land exceed that minimum gradient.* As a first approximation, a value below 5° and above 0° has been found. The gradient of the slopes is always greater than that of the collecting furrows.

This feature, common to all mass-movement, proves that it is independent of climate, as had followed from our examination of the prerequisites for its occurrence (p. 71). *It also proves that sheet denudation is not dependent upon climate.* As a matter of fact, areas of similar endogenetic development have also, in all climatic zones, the same denudational forms. This state of affairs has often been questioned[161]; but any doubt of it is far from according with the actual conditions as seen in every part of the world. It follows universally and irrefutably from the fact that all processes of denudation are gravitational streams. *The same land forms must necessarily develop in all climatic zones if the prerequisite conditions for determining the gradients are the same.* It has become clear that these prerequisites are ultimately of an endogenetic nature[162]. The part played by the character of the rock is of course only secondary, affecting details. Observation has, however, shown that under corresponding endogenetic conditions similar forms of denudation appear in different climates *at a different rate*. The reason for this will be shown in a later section when treating of the relationships between climate and denudation along lines of permanent or intermittent rivers and rivulets.

With change of climate, the prevailing type of weathering may shift from chemical to mechanical or vice versa; but the fact that the rock is being reduced, the one essential for denudation, remains unchanged. The composition of the migrating material may change, and the outward form of its movement, from bound-down to free, or in the reverse direction; but the fact of its migration is not altered. With the disappearance of vegetation, slopes of critical angle may turn into bare rock precipices from which individual tiny pieces roll off to collect as scree; or, on the other hand, rugged rocks when encroached upon by a plant covering may become the scene of bound-down mass-movement. But this change no more affects the steepness of the slopes than does their continued reduction and denudation. On steep rock faces there is no change at all.

On the other hand, apart of course from glaciation, a change of climatic conditions may lead to alteration in the relationship between mass-movement and mass-transport, between conveyance of material to running water and its being carried away. This change must take place in the opposite sense in different parts of the earth, as indeed happened in the Pleistocene period. Visible transitory phenomena can, however, develop only at those critical places where the streams of reduced material, moving down all the land slopes, change their type of movement, i.e. along the lines of permanent or intermittent rivers and rivulets. These phenomena, to be discussed later, seem as if they were an interruption in the prevailing conditions of denudation, without being so in reality. The fact that they link up with the paths of water flowing over the surface shows what it is that has been altered: neither the continuance nor the direction of sheet denudation, but merely its quantitive ratio to the further transport of the material by water along a persistent linear path in just the same direction. This may affect the result of its work in some other way, but cannot bring about any fundamental change in the forms of denudation.

2. THE PRINCIPLE OF FLATTENING*

All mass-movement has this in common, that it removes material from elevations and carries it to depressions. If these latter are not at the

[* It seems justifiable by common usage to employ this term (as W. Penck does) for diminishing an angle of gradient, although mathematically it should be reserved for removing irregularities—as of course would occur were all gradients reduced to the horizontal.]

same time deepened by an equivalent amount, the process effects a lowering of the elevations. This necessarily means diminution of gradient, flattening of the hill-slopes. In this case, on a given slope there comes into play, in successive time intervals, movement of the same type and velocity as can be observed on neighbouring slopes, similar in their nature but different in steepness. Should deposition raise the level towards which the material is moving, this means an increase in the rate at which the gradient is diminishing and the flattening taking place. If, on the other hand, this level is relatively lowered, the given slope cannot simply become steeper; but (as will be shown later in some detail) new steeper declivities appear which *replace* the former ones. *No part of any surface on the earth, no matter how denudation works upon it, can ever thereby become as a whole steeper. It can only become flatter. The most important law obeyed during the development of denudational forms is this principle of flattening.*

3. THE CONCEPTS DENUDATION, CORRASION, EROSION

The removal of small pieces, loosened from the solid rock, creates new surfaces of attack for the destructive processes and so brings about *renewal of exposure.* This effect is independent of the type of mass-transport, whether it is spontaneous—mass-movement—or brought about by a moving medium. It is common to all processes of denudation, being the most direct result of any denudation at all, and the necessary condition for its continuance. Two essentially different processes are concerned in this: transport of particles loosened by reduction, and forcible mechanical separation of small pieces from the parent rock. In the first case, renewal of exposure takes place at the same rate as the reduction: this is *denudation.* In the second instance, exposure is renewed more rapidly under the influence of moving material (p. 112). The processes working in such a way are designated 'corrasion' and 'erosion'.

There are some difficulties which are met when we try to distinguish these two concepts from one another, especially as they are not used in a consistent manner[163]. Physically different processes work together, each coming more or less prominently into the foreground according to the given circumstances. Thus quickly moving material polishes and scratches the rocky substratum. This is seen not only in the beds of running water and moving ice, but also in the tracks of rapidly moving mass streams whether dry or wet. The process called 'corrasion' by A. Penck[164], is obviously related to the rate of motion. In addition, there is a tearing away, chiselling off, and pressing away of fragments, this being the chief method in the case of slowly moving material. It takes place over the whole surface of slopes as well as along the lines of subaerial mass streams, of running water, and at the bottom of moving ice. Other things being equal, the intensity of this process increases with the weight of the moving material. For both kinds of mechanical action upon the substratum of solid rock, the conditions are best when the material is collected into streams; it concentrates the mechanical forces along specially favoured lines. If this concentration along lines of movement is the characteristic feature of erosion, the furrows deepened by subaerial mass-streams are erosion valleys, while the polishing of whole surfaces by ice not set in valleys, e.g. ice sheets, is corrasion. But such a definition of erosion is not satisfactory, since it does not bring out the significance of the moving media, and it is the way in which these act that really decides how the denudation occurs and its intensity. In particular, water, on account of being much more mobile, has a far greater tendency to adopt a linear course than has spontaneously moving solid material. For the same reason it is able to impart its motion, which is, other things being equal, far more rapid, to detached solid bodies. Not only does it in this way lead to their being removed more readily from their place of origin, but it also, in particular, increases their power of doing work, enhancing the mechanical action upon the rocky substratum. Thus, in contrast to the far slower mass-movement, polishing and scratching are nearly always in evidence.

These differences are the determining factor in the development of denudational forms, the sculpturing of which depends upon the relationship between what is occurring on the surface of slopes and that along water-courses. Bearing this in mind, *erosion*, as generally understood here, is the mechanical action upon a rocky substratum within the paths of moving media and brought about by them; *corrasion* denotes the analogous processes that come into play beneath material migrating spontaneously, unaffected by any moving medium. So we shall speak of erosion by wind, water and ice; and we shall not accept A. Grund's suggestion of extending the term corrasion to include the process of solution and its results, speaking of karst lands as corrasion landscapes[165].

4. CLASSIFICATION OF THE REGIONS
OF DENUDATION

Any particle, whether it be of water, ice or rock, adhering by its own weight to the surface of the earth, and on an inclined substratum, tends to move by the shortest possible route towards a near-by depression. To begin with, the particles are distributed all over the surface—falling rain or snow, and the rock derivatives that have everywhere been loosened by reduction—and at first they move along over its whole area. At certain places on the way, the paths of neighbouring particles unite to form strands of movement, as can be easily followed in the case of running water and as has been shown to occur with cumulative masses of moving material. These form the starting points of streams which naturally become more and more clearly defined downslope, and tend to deepen their beds. *In this way all the processes by which rock waste is removed develop from sheet to linear processes, and then to definitely directed courses.* With this their effectiveness changes.

In the first place, transport of solid rock particles, whether spontaneous or brought about by rainwash, can take place only when these are completely freed from the solid rock, and never faster than the rate of rock reduction. Such *regions of pure denudation* are found always on the upper parts of slopes. Lower down, the weight of moving material increases, as does the volume of water running off, so that in addition to the denuding action there is more and more corrasion, or erosion, as the case may be. As the water collects into definite streams, erosion becomes more and more noticeable until it is unquestionably predominant, although there is not an entire absence of denudation. For rock is no more immune to reduction when in the bed of running or even trickling water or when beneath moving ice, than it is beneath a subaerial stream of moving rock waste. The material loosened, maybe at low water or any other period when there is slackening or a pause in the movement, is soon carried away. But the relationship of rock reduction to the two processes of corrasion and erosion is very different. The intensity of corrasion can never exceed that of reduction to any considerable extent, since it depends essentially upon the preliminary work done by this. Erosion, however, can be so intense that no time whatever is left for rock reduction to take effect. This is particularly true in the case of running water, and explains why it is so extraordinarily powerful as a sculpturing agent[166].

Consequently it is possible to separate places where denudation predominates from those in which corrasion and erosion are more important. Surfaces of slopes belong to the first group, incised furrows to the other. Transitional forms link them, since in both cases rock reduction, transport, and mechanical attack on the rocky substratum are at work. Mechanical attack increases downslope and is dominant in the erosion furrows. The zones of transition between the areas of denudation and those of corrasion-erosion are found on the lower parts of slopes, especially near valley heads. Down-valley there is ever increasing concentration of rock waste and of water along the paths of movement; streams develop, and the contrast becomes sharper between the lines of corrasion, or of erosion (as the case may be), and the tributary surfaces of denudation.

Even when water falls all over a surface, it is only exceptionally and for short stretches that it flows as a sheet. It soon divides up into a number of rills. So complete is this facility for moving along lines that the regions where corrasion prevails do not entirely coincide with those of erosion, which stretch back beyond them into the zone where denudation predominates. The sides of the erosion furrows that are there developing form new surfaces of denudation, on which the run-off water once more finds the requisite conditions for erosive downcutting, etc. This dissection by valleys brings about further and further subdivision of the areas of denudation; and, *other things being equal*, this increases with the passage of time. The result, however, is not to contract the areas undergoing denudation, but to enlarge them; since for a given area the number of *inclined* surfaces becomes greater. At the same time the network formed by the linear erosional tracks increases in size as it becomes more closely meshed; and so the sum total of rock surface affected by erosion is greater. *Thus, provided there is no change in other conditions, it necessarily follows that, for a given district, the total amount of denudation accomplished in unit time increases with its subdivision (i.e. with the increase of surface exposed to denudation).*

The rate at which this subdivision progresses depends upon preparatory work that differs somewhat in various regions. Continuous vegetation impedes rainwash and incision by running water, confining this to places where the plant cover is less vigorous or interrupted. Therefore, in our latitudes, erosion furrows do not as a rule reach back to the uppermost parts of slopes nor to the extreme ramifications of the valleys. The same holds for arid regions, where the precipitation is too slight or occurs too seldom for the erosional activity of running water to have any lasting effect greater than that produced by mass-movement. In both cases there develops between the district where denudation is dominant and that where erosion prevails a zone of strongly marked corrasion, especially in the neighbourhood of valley heads (the zone of corrasion valleys). It is not so well developed if the vegetation is less vigorous or sparser, for then regularly recurring precipitation, even though scanty in amount, can act directly upon the bare soil. Semi-humid and semi-arid lands are the domain of rainwash and erosion by running water; and, if the water from snow melt is included, so is the sub-polar zone. In such regions erosion furrows usually work right back to the valley heads and almost to the tops of slopes, unless infiltration is in excess of run-off, as in landscapes of very low relief.

5. BASE LEVELS OF EROSION AND
OF DENUDATION

Water can degrade only so long as it is flowing. When it ceases to flow, erosion of the land cannot continue. Thus an absolute lower limit is put to the removal of material by running water. This is the *base level of erosion*[167]. In regions sloping down continuously to the sea, this coincides with sea level; and in regions of inland drainage coincides with what are, for the time being, the lowest depressions of the land. Like all the analogous elements which control the downward movement of gravitational streams, the base level of erosion is not an actual surface, nor a point, certainly not a visible form, but it is *a level*.

The absolute base level of erosion, as defined above, is the ultimate but not the only level which regulates the work of running water. For the Neckar country, the behaviour of the absolute base level of erosion, the North Sea, seems to be of no consequence. The effect of its fluctuations reach scarcely as far upstream as the Rhine Rift Valley. What rivers do there is really determined by what is happening in the Rhenish Schiefergebirge. Similarly, this work of rivers in the Neckar country is controlled not by the position of the absolute base level, but primarily by movements of the Odenwald block, and then next by those of the Rift Valley. The Danubian drainage system presents exactly the same picture. The relative rise of absolute base level at the Danube mouth is not the governing factor for the river's work where it breaks through the Banat Mountains; and its influence does not reach as far up as the Hungarian Plain, let alone into the Alps. To take a further example, this time from an arid region, the Abaucan-Troya system in north-west Argentina[168], which ends in the Bolson of Andalgalá. The behaviour of this absolute base level of erosion has no direct influence upon the river's work in the reaches further upstream where it breaks through the mountains, nor in the depressions crossed by its middle and upper course (the Bolsons of Copacabana and Fiambalá respectively). What happens in these depressions is of immediate importance only for rivers working on the surrounding slopes, and is not the only direct influence determining the behaviour of the Troya river which, coming from outside, breaks through these slopes.

The controlling levels that regulate river action in the reaches immediately upstream are associated with places where the streams leave a tectonically uniform block, and enter an adjoining one which has undergone some different movement, also due to endogenetic causes. These are the general or immediate base levels of erosion. It is common for such levels to recur more than once in the course of large rivers of the type quoted above, and all are ultimately able to work back to the headwater region. Thus, considering the northern part of the Eastern Alps, the level of primary importance for water-courses is where the Alps meet their Foreland, which has been moved in a different fashion. The level of next importance is that of the basin above the Danube's first transverse break through the Carpathians, near Pressburg [Bratislava]; then comes that of the break-through itself. However, repercussions of the Danube's break through the Gran [Esztergom]-Budapest zone of uplift are not felt as far upstream as the Alpine Foreland, but the depositional zone of the Schüttinseln [Velký ostrov Žitný] lies between this and the break-through at Pressburg.

The only cases of coincidence between the immediate and the absolute base levels of erosion are where the slopes of tectonically uniform blocks drain directly to the absolute base level—as for instance on the southern sides of the Eastern Alps, the Maritime Alps, the Ligurian Alps and the outer slopes of the Dinaric Alps, etc., or where the slopes surrounding basins of inland drainage do so.

The immediate base levels of erosion are, like the absolute ones, not fixed but fluctuate; they rise and fall in relation to the denudation areas above them. The causes of this and the repercussions on the work of rivers will be discussed in a later section.

The prerequisite for any work by running water is the existence of a gradient; and so the general principle obtains that no part of a water-course can be permanently deepened below the level of the point next to it downstream. Thus each point is a base level of erosion not only for its adjoining point upstream, but for the whole reach of river upstream, and whatever happens to it will influence the whole course of events above. Among the infinite number of points connected in accordance with this law, points which, ranged together, make up the lines of the drainage net, some coincide with distinct levels which are termed *local base levels of erosion*. These are of two types. One kind is situated where smaller water-courses empty into larger ones, and they mark the level down to which—apart from the point of confluence itself—no part of the tributary course can be deepened, far less sink below it. These local base levels change, on the whole, in a vertical direction only: they sink relatively to their surroundings so long as erosion is taking place, and they rise when deposition occurs.

The second group of local base levels of erosion is found within [otherwise] uniform stretches of a river's course and consists of *breaks of gradient*. These levels separate sections with a steeper gradient from those above or below which possess a gentler slope. Associated with them is a fundamental change in the intensity of river action. They are not fixed in position, but migrate upstream; and this, as well as their variety of origin must be considered in detail later.

The base level of erosion is not some morphological element special, as it were, to running water; but *all gravitational streams, streams the material of which adheres to the earth's surface by the force of gravity, have in the downward direction a fixed relationship to analogous levels*[169]. The effectiveness of moving ice is also regulated by a base level of erosion at the place where the glaciers end. This is the lower limit of ablation, or the place where ice flowing into standing water or into the sea is lifted from its substratum. In such a case the base level of erosion for the ice is submarine.

But more important than all, the course and the effects of mass-movement, which next to running water takes the lion's share in shaping the land, are regulated by the existence of levels which correspond in their essential character and behaviour to the base levels of erosion, and may suitably be called *base levels of denudation*. Surprisingly enough this fact has so far been completely overlooked. To clear our minds on the matter, it seemed desirable therefore to begin by considering what is already known about the relationships of base levels of erosion.

The major fundamental fact is that any kind of denudation over a whole surface, by mass-movement or by rainwash, can take place only so long as there is a gradient along which the rock derivatives can be moved away. It thus directly follows that no point of a slope can be deepened, i.e. denuded, below the level of the actual point next below it. Each point of a slope is base level of denudation for the whole extent of the slope lying above it in the direction of the inclination, and its behaviour determines the development of the inclined land surfaces above it. To take an example: Should there outcrop on a slope a zone of rock so resistant that compared to its surroundings of different material it is practically undenuded, this zone forms for all further development the level below which the slope cannot under any circumstances be denuded. It therefore always forms the foot of a slope which is constantly losing material, becoming denuded and consequently flattened. This resistant zone, with regard to which the flattening occurs, is the base level of denudation; and in the end it forms the lower margin of a slope with such a small gradient that further denudation, whether by mass-movement or rainwash, ceases.

The general base levels of denudation lie at the place where mass-movement ends, and with it sheet denudation (including corrasion). This is along the lines of perennial or intermittent streams. As these do not mark out one level, but as infinite a number of levels as there are points composing them, *the general base levels of denudation are systems of curves, identical with the gradient curves of the water courses.* Their relative position changes with the development of the latter. When the absolute base level of erosion is fixed, and the water-courses on a stationary block have adopted their final gradient curve, the general base levels of denudation also assume in each case a fixed, final position. They then form the lowest possible limit below which not only can no point of the tributary slopes be denuded, but which only their lowest edge, the foot of the slope, can reach[170]. From every point on such a drainage net, at its theoretical final position (Powell's base level of erosion), there arise flattened slopes of a minimum gradient; and on these mass-movement— or denudation by rainwash where the climate is suitable—is just no longer possible. If such a set of flattish forms is called an end-peneplane, it is perfectly obvious that it can never be an actual plane, but must be undulating country with flattish valleys and with a general fall in the direction of its own base level of erosion.

The general base levels of denudation and of erosion coincide when the surfaces that are being denuded rise directly from the erosional base levels. At such places, since sheet denudation is directly affected by the latter, their influence on that denudation is quite different from when it is exerted indirectly through the drainage net. These differences become apparent on making a comparison between those slopes of broad anticlines which look directly towards the broad synclines and the slopes leading down to erosional valleys within the same anticlines. They have often been described—in the Basin Ranges, in the Argentine, in Asia Minor, in Central Asia, in the Balkans, etc.—and we shall return later to the interpretation of them.

It is not everywhere, however, that the base levels of denudation coincide with those of erosion and the erosional tracks. Their independence of the latter becomes evident, for instance at those very many places in arid regions where mass-movement, even in its last outlying portions, does not reach as far as the lines of the intermittent streams. This same lack of dependence, which demonstrates *the functional independence of the base levels of denudation*, is especially clearly visible in scarplands. The development of peneplanes on the scarp summits, like that of the broad ledges in the higher parts of the Grand Canyon (Colorado), is related to outcrops of resistant beds of rock at a lower level, and not to the banks of the streams incised deep down below. These are examples of local base levels of denudation, conditioned by structure. All over the world it is by no means uncommon to find that uplifted older and flatter landscapes are separated from their former base levels of erosion by the interpolation of younger steeper relief. They continue to develop, not with reference to the base levels of erosion from the influence of which they have definitely removed, nor yet with reference to the floors of the rejuvenated deeply incised erosion valleys, but with reference to the break of gradient which separates these uplifted land forms from the set of younger ones now dissecting them.

As a general rule, local base levels of denudation are represented by breaks of gradient. These breaks separate different systems of slopes, the denudation of which is related to different levels. Thus, that of the higher, wider part of the Grand Canyon is related to the upper edge of the steep sides of the inner canyon; and these steep slopes to the Colorado River itself. With the break of gradient comes a change in the angle of slope; the break divides steeper from gentler parts of the declivity, and its angle is concave or convex according to whether the steeper systems are arranged above or below it. The local base levels of denudation thus coincide with either convex or concave elements in the land forms; and their behaviour—like that of the analogous base levels of erosion—varies accordingly.

From the moment it arises until it disappears, each break of gradient forms the lower edge of a slope for which it provides the base level of denudation. So long as it lasts, the denudation of the slope, lying above, takes place in relation to it. That is the essence of a base level of denudation. Thus this base level and the correlated slope above it are one system. *We speak of form systems* [*slope units**] and say: breaks of gradient separate different form systems [slope units]. The difference has its visible expression in the relationships of the gradients and depends upon the intensity of the denudation which, other things being equal, increases with the inclination of the slope. The steeper the slope, the shorter the time required to bring about the mobility necessary for transport of the material, and the quicker the renewal of exposure (pp. 62–72, 78, 85), i.e. on the whole, the more material removed in unit time from the whole of the uniformly inclined surface.

[* Term used by Prof. J. Kesseli.]

CHAPTER VI

DEVELOPMENT OF SLOPES
1. GRADIENT AND FORM OF SLOPES

How local base levels of denudation come into being and disappear is really the same question as that of the origin and development of the slopes which, grouped and combined in many different ways, produce the denudational forms found at the earth's surface. What has been observed to take place, away from the actual lines of water-courses, perennial or intermittent, and the way in which it follows definite laws (see Chapter III, sections 4–9) provide all the support needed to make this absolutely clear. Rock material becomes more highly mobile the further the process of reduction has gone (the longer it has been at work); and it has been definitely proved that the more mobile the material on a given slope, the less the gradient of that slope need be before the material can only just move away. On gentle slopes, therefore, the intensity of denudation is less than on steeper ones: a much longer time must elapse before the material is reduced to such a degree as to become unstable. Where *lower horizons of the soil, forming relatively quickly* (on steep slopes), are set in motion, renewal of exposure takes place far more rapidly than where only the upper horizons, which take much longer to develop, are moving (on slopes of a proportionately slighter inclination). What matters is [i.e. this renewal of exposure depends upon] the rate of formation of the uppermost horizon of reduction, the one which is at that time lying freely exposed. Other things being equal, its exposure is everywhere the same. On a given slope it is the first part that can no longer hold in place, but must move off as soon as the requisite mobility is attained. The rate at which it is formed gives the intensity of denudation. As the topmost layer moves away, the profile of reduction below it sinks to the same extent into the previously unattacked rock. On a slope of *uniform gradient* and equal exposure, a profile of reduction is formed which shows everywhere the same development and the same thickness. In the same time that the uppermost horizon of that profile has taken to acquire the mobility necessary for migration, a rock layer of the same thickness throughout has become reduced. At the close of a further equal interval of time, a further layer of rock, again of the same thickness and of equal thickness at every part of the slope, passes over into the reduced form.

Photo. by K. Lampert

1. Steep relief. The northern Pala group from the Mulaz Pass, South Tirol

Photo. by W. Penck

2. Medium relief. Ranges to the south of the Gulf of Izmit, seen from the north. Western Asia Minor

Photo. by W. Penck

3. Flattish relief. Rolling landscape in Uruguay

I. RELIEF TYPES

What has just been recapitulated holds true only on the assumption that the character of the rock is everywhere the same. It is true for each rock just as rock, but each behaves in a special way as regards reduction and becoming mobile, and so, other things being equal, has an intensity of denudation peculiar to itself. Bearing this in mind, our investigations will be made first of all on the assumption that all the rocks have the same character.

Denudational slopes present every degree of inclination, from those scarcely to be distinguished from the horizontal right up to 90°—leaving aside caves and overhanging crags. Because of the limitations of rock stability, normal gradients are less than 45°, anything steeper than this being quite exceptional. However, these gradients are not distributed over the globe in a haphazard fashion, but by individual regions which are often easily recognisable as tectonic units. They have such a marked occurrence of slopes with almost identical maximum gradients that the average or mean of these is one of the characteristic features of that particular natural region. This long-recognised fact, which is quite independent of the position of the climatic belt concerned and so of the type of climate, makes it possible to speak of *uniformity of relief for a district* meaning by this the total effect of the arrangement and combination of all the slopes with approximately the same angle of inclination. Thus the frequently used term 'Alpine relief' is associated with the idea of the steep land forms found in the Alps; and the less steep conditions found in the German Highlands have provided the type for 'Highland forms'. Since no association that can be reduced to a law exists between the average steepness of slopes and their absolute—in addition to their relative—heights, we shall replace these terms by the purely descriptive expressions: 'steep forms—steep relief' for a set of land forms having average slopes round about the maximum gradient for resistant types of rock; 'intermediate forms—medium relief' for those with slopes which, as in the valleys of the German Highlands, reach a steepness approximating to that of basal slopes*; and 'flattish forms—peneplanes'† for landscapes with slight gradients throughout (see Plate I, illustrations 1, 2 and 3)[171]. It must be borne in mind, though, that we have not gained more than a means of making ourselves understood. For although these three form-types are often actually to be seen as characteristic features, and although they can then be recognised without any ambiguity[172], they are yet merely *types of relief* chosen out of an infinite number of members of a transitional series; round them can be grouped similar types which it is impossible to demarcate from one another except by agreeing to take specific limiting angles for the mean gradients.

[* See glossary; and pp. 93, 135.]   [† See glossary.]

Within any one relief type characterised as a unit, variations in the angle of gradient do, then, occur in individual cases; but, as has been repeatedly stressed, these differences are due to differences in the resistance and attitude of the rock[173]. They are details fitted into the general type without effacing it.

One great problem presented by denudational forms is the way in which *slopes of uniform gradient* are associated together in definite limited regions. The second relates to the *form of the slopes* (see Plate II, illustrations 1, 2 and 3). The slope profiles are convex, or concave, occurring as continuous curves or divided up by breaks of gradient, salient or reentrant; or else they may be stretched out into an approximately rectilinear course. These various forms, too, are not distributed haphazard, but are arranged in a regular fashion. Examination of the slope profiles on the upper parts of the German Highlands or the Scarpland peneplanes, shows them to be *concave* throughout. Comparison with the steeper slopes on their sides, i.e. those of the younger valleys dissecting them, shows that these latter generally have *convex* profiles. These are examples of a rule which is world wide in its application and independent of any climatic peculiarities. Wherever a younger, steeper set of land forms separates an older upraised landscape from its former base level of erosion, the slopes of the older forms are always concave in profile, and the younger forms dissecting the highland characteristically have convex or straight profiles, although concave ones may occasionally appear. Throughout, the convex and straight profiles are associated with zones where there has been vigorous erosion. Also, in broad outline, the distribution of the various forms of slope follows an unmistakable arrangement. It appears that the form associations with convex slopes are most typically found in the two mountain belts, and that they occur less frequently on the continental masses. Hundreds of thousands of square kilometres on the Canadian Shield, between the Guianas and La Plata, between the mountains of the Atlas and the Cape regions, retain the stamp of concavity on their slopes, although otherwise these vary in respect of steepness. Typical inselberg landscapes belong to this group. There is nothing like it in the mountain belts. It is true that on the summits of the chains similar relief types, the uplifted hill country and peneplanes already mentioned, do occur extremely frequently; but there are immense spaces from which they are absent. This large-scale distribution is, naturally, not due merely to chance.

However, in the mountain belts and indeed wherever the slope corresponds to the maximum gradient for the rocks concerned, convex slopes are replaced by what are on the whole *straight profiles*. They find their purest expression in the steep relief of mountains which escaped Pleisto-

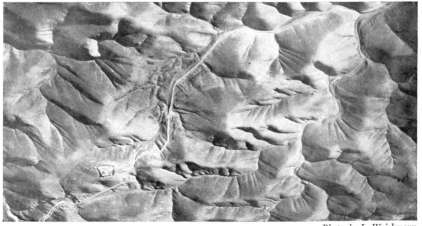

Photo. by L. Weickmann

1. Convex slopes. Road from Jerusalem to Jericho

Photo. by W. Penck

2. Straight slopes. Sierra de Fiambalá, near Anillaco, Western Argentina

Photo. by W. Penck

3. Concave slopes. Cerro Colome, from the south. Puna de Atacama, Western Argentina

II. Forms of Slope

Photo. by A. Penck

1. Convex slopes of Badlands, near Adama, New Mexico

Photo. by W. Penck

2. Straight slopes on a hill near Sanjil, Western Argentina

Photo. by Wichmann

3. Concave slopes. Roca Beds on the Rio Negro, Western Argentina

III. BADLANDS

celle glaciation, whether these are covered with tropical virgin forest or belong to arid regions. They are also very common in the Alps. Nevertheless it must be stressed that straight slope profiles are not a peculiarity of steep relief, but also occur with medium relief. They are the rule for sharp V-shaped valleys of the type found incising the Muschelkalk or the Malm of the Scarplands. They often develop in landscapes where crests-lines are formed by the intersection of slopes; and the steeper the slopes, the sharper the ridge crests, while with gentler slopes they are less sharp. The Badlands are among the areas providing excellent examples of this—as also of convex and concave slopes (see Plate III, illustrations 1, 2, 3).

When two or more surfaces cut one another, lines of intersection or points of intersection are formed. Theoretically, slopes which meet at their upper extremities should, irrespective of their steepness, rise to sharp linear edges or sharply pointed peaks. In nature this is not so. On the contrary, the zones of intersection are always blunted and broadened, the more so the gentler the slopes concerned. This blunting and rounding is a characteristic of intersecting slopes: *these* are flattened near the place where they meet, no matter what the shape of the remainder whether steep or gentle, and irrespective of the type of rock and type of climate. The flattening, however, cannot continue to an indefinite amount. It is never very great, and is obviously dependent upon the gradient, diminishing as the steepness increases. Consequently the degree of sharpening of the zones of intersection most distinctly increases with the gradient of the slopes that are meeting one another.

The upward rounding of convex slopes is evidently part of the convexity itself. With concave or straight slopes, on the other hand, it is obviously an independent problem, since here the rounding-off of the zones of intersection signifies a deviation from the given form of the slope.

G. Götzinger thought that in this flattening from above he could recognise the process by which a ridge of ever-increasing breadth and flatness was produced from a sharp edge[174], and R. Gradmann in his derivation of scarpland peneplanes starts from similar assumptions[175]. This view cannot be correct since—as Gradmann himself recognised— it conflicts with the phenomena of valley deepening. Götzinger has not yet seen this difficulty, but it is shown by direct observation. A rock wall, subjected to denudation, retreats backwards upslope, and a gentler declivity, the basal slope,* is seen to form at its expense and to grow upslope by the same amount as the cliff vanishes[176]. If such cliffs are entirely destroyed, the basal slopes meet in a sharp edge, as may be excel-

* *Haldenhang.*

lently seen at the Paternsattel [Forcella Lavaredo] (Drei Zinnen [Tre Cimi di Lavaredo], Dolomites), and this forthwith experiences that definitely limited amount of rounding which has been mentioned above[177]. The gentler slope, that replaces the steeper one, thus develops at the foot of the latter; and the flattening of the land progresses from below upwards and not in the reverse direction. This fact has not escaped G. Götzinger in so far as the development of cliffs, i.e. steep forms, is concerned. But in his derivation he jumps to a conclusion which cannot be justified by observation or in any other way, taking it for granted that, as further development occurs, the flattening all of a sudden takes place the other way round, viz. from above downwards. If rounded ridges did arise in that way from sharp edges, and flattish forms of convex curvature from such ridges, then it would have to be assumed that denudation was always working more rapidly on the flattish ridge summits than on their steeper flanks. This cannot possibly be expected of Nature, as is obvious, and as was stated years ago[178]. Rounded ridges with convex profiles, such as occur in the Wiener Wald, can never arise from sharp edges. Only the reverse is possible. One of the objects of the following sections will be to show that this is the case.

2. FLATTENING OF SLOPES*

CONCAVE BASE LEVELS OF DENUDATION

A steep slope, say a cliff of homogeneous composition and uniform gradient, rising directly from a non-eroding river, constitutes a form system† [slope unit]; and its base level of denudation lies at the water level of the river (t in the profile, figure 2). The whole surface of the cliff has the same exposure and succumbs equally in every part to the process of reduction. In unit time a superficial layer of rock, of a definite thickness the same everywhere, is loosened and removed. The method of removal is that loosened particles of rock crumble away and fall down. For this to happen the gradient must be too great to allow the little pieces of rock, just loosened by weathering but not further comminuted and reduced, to remain at rest. This gradient is available for each unit of the rock face except the lowest, which is adjacent to the base level of denudation. At the end of time one, therefore, this alone has not been taken away. There is no change in the steepness of the cliff, but it has retreated from its original position t-1 (in the profile) to the position 2′-2. Beneath it there is a ledge left. Such ledges may also appear temporarily in the middle of the rock face as a tiny piece x breaks off. The part of the cliff immediately above is then deprived of its support. It is undercut

[* See note on p. 120]   [† See p. 129 for definition.]

Photo by W. Hahn

1. Concave breaks of gradient. Lilienstein in the Elbe Sandstone Mountains. Cliff above basal slope

Photo. by W. Penck

2. Convex break of gradient. Steep drop of the Sierra de Fiambalá to the Bolson of Fiambalá, Western Argentina

IV. BREAKS OF GRADIENT

and further breaking away is accelerated. The ledge cannot, however, maintain itself, for by the end of the first unit of time the layer *tx* below it has also crumbled away, even before reduction of the more rapidly exposed rock face above *x* (*x* 2) has loosened new material and prepared it for removal.

This same process is repeated in the second unit of time. But only that part of the rock face above the ledge *t* 2′ can be weathered back in the allotted time; and once more the lowest particle (2′–3′) is without that same [necessary] gradient at its disposal, i.e. it has not in the interval acquired the mobility essential for movement on the much smaller gradient. The rock face moves into the position 3′–3, in the third unit of time it retreats to 4′–4, and so on. If sufficiently small units are taken, we come very near to the actual process, and the exceedingly small ledges

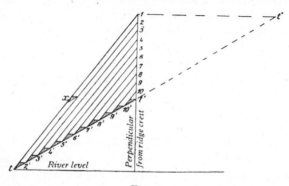

FIG. 2.

t 2′, 2′–3′, 3′–4′, and so on, combine to give a continuous slope of uniform gradient (*t t*′).

This is the *basal slope*,* along which the broken fragments derived from above slacken their pace, to migrate further in free, cumulative mass-movement, provided that conditions are suitable for their accumulation (see Plate IV, illustration 1).

The following statement may therefore be made: *A steep rock face left to itself, moves back upslope, maintaining its original gradient; and a basal slope of lesser gradient develops at its expense.* Should the cliff culminate in a sharp edge, as is assumed for fig. 2, this edge is lowered to the same extent as the rock face recedes; it moves from 1 to 2, then to 3, and so on. After the tenth unit of time, the steep rock face would be gone, and in place of the precipitous ridge there would be a lower one where the gentler basal slopes meet. If, on the other hand, the cliff face is the scarp

* *Haldenhang.*

of a tableland, it would not disappear till after a longer interval of time, in the figure about the twenty-second time unit; and the steep drop would then be replaced by a gentler slope ($t\ t''$) with the gradient of a basal slope.

'After time one, the development of the cliff face is no longer related to the river level t, but to the concave break of gradient which separates it from the basal slope. *This break of gradient is the base level of denudation until the disappearance of the receding cliff face. A new slope unit, the basal slope, is interposed between it and the river level. The upward growth of this is determined by the rate at which the rock of the cliff face is reduced, i.e. by the development of the steeper, higher slope unit, the special development of which was in the first instance related to the position of the river. Whatever may happen to the basal slope, whatever fate may befall its lower end, the development of the cliff face is unaffected by it. This has become independent of the general base level of denudation, and what ensues is related to a newly-formed local base level of denudation. This itself, as time goes on, moves up-slope, and vanishes only in the topmost parts when the higher slope unit has been finally removed and its place taken by the next lower one.*

From its first appearance, the basal slope develops independently, since the rock on it, too, is being reduced. Here, however, the mere loosening of pieces of rock from the general fabric is not enough to produce denudation, as it is on the steep cliff face. A far greater degree of reduction, i.e. far greater mobility, is required for rock derivatives to migrate on the very much smaller gradient, and for this much longer periods of time are needed. The development of the basal slope is therefore very much slower; but it proceeds in the same direction as that of the cliff face above.

It is still being assumed that the rock is all of the same composition and also has the same exposure.* In unit time a layer of definite thickness, everywhere the same, is loosened from the basal slope. But it is only when a multiple of that unit time has elapsed that the loosened material is sufficiently mobile to migrate spontaneously. This occurs as soon as there is a definite degree of reduction, i.e. a definite mobility of the rock derivatives, corresponding to the gradient as it then is (p. 71). In other words: if, after a certain period of time, the rock material derived from the basal slope attains a certain mobility, its downward movement on the existing gradient is inevitable. *That length of time is the unit by which the rate of development of the basal slope is measured.*

At the end of the time unit just defined, a layer of rock, of a definite thickness, the same over the whole of the basal slope, has been changed into a sufficiently mobile form; and during that time the rock particles, one after another, all quit their place of origin[179]. All, then, move down

[* See pp. 36, 52.]

except the lowest, that adjoining the general base level of denudation (*t* in fig. 3), since it is the only one not provided with the requisite gradient for movement. Still maintaining the same inclination, the slope now moves from the position *t a* to 2′–2. The same thing is repeated during a second time interval of equal length[180]. The time available, however, does not allow all the rock particles of the new slope 2–2′ to migrate; for again the lowest (2′–3′) has at its disposal not the same gradient as that for all the particles above but a smaller one, one for which the degree of mobility so far acquired is insufficient to permit of migration along it. The slope moves into position 3′–3, and after a third unit of time it would reach 4′–4, and so on. By making sufficiently small the dimen-

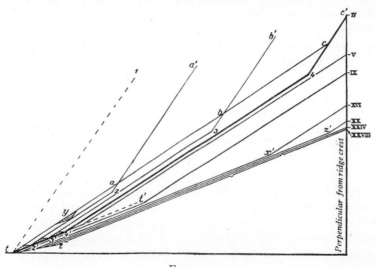

FIG. 3.

sions considered, we come near enough to reality, and find this state of affairs: below the basal slope there is forming a new, flattened-out slope of gradient *t t′*, which grows at the expense of the former, and at the same rate as the basal slope is being denuded. After the first unit of time (as defined above), the basal slope no longer develops with reference to the general base level of denudation, but with reference to the concave break of gradient at 2′, and to that at 3′, 4′ . . . *x′*, etc., which, until it disappears (in the diagram after time twenty), separates it from the slope of diminishing gradient* below. The break of gradient is the local base level of denudation for the basal slope, and it moves upslope from the edge of the river.

* *Abflachungshang.*

There is no need to trace further development in the same detail. Below the slope of inclination $t\,t'$, another still flatter slope unit $t\,t''$ develops. This begins to form immediately the slope above it has appeared, and continues to do so by the same amount as the latter retreats from the edge of the river. Between these two there appears a fresh concave break of gradient, still more obtuse, and the speed with which it moves upslope is determined by the intensity of denudation on slope $t\,t'$. The value of this is but small, on account of the slight gradient. In the diagram (fig. 3) the youngest, flattest slope is not perceptible till after the eighth unit of time—see slope position t IX—and even after the twenty-seventh unit the lowest break of gradient has only reached point t''. By then, all the other local base levels of denudation, which separated higher, steeper slope units, have disappeared.

It is now quite clear that the process obeys a law: *Flattening of slopes always takes place from below upwards*. However, it is not simply a matter of the slopes becoming flatter; but of new and ever flatter slope units perpetually appearing at the general base level of denudation, and growing at the expense of those above. They do this more rapidly, the steeper these are. Finally they replace them; but up to that time they are separated from them by concave breaks of gradient. These, until the disappearance of the slope units belonging to them, act as local base levels of denudation. They always originate at river level all along the drainage net, at the general base level of denudation, and from there they move upslope. The rate at which the flatter declivity extends upwards, at the expense of the steeper slope unit above it, is determined by the rate of denudation of the *latter*. The measure of this, in its turn, is that of the rate of reduction of the rock; and is, indeed, the length of time required for that process to get ready reduced material of the specific degree of mobility needed, in that particular case, to make removal from the given slope just possible—thus making migration inevitable. Since the preparation of the more highly mobile material is proportional to some root of the duration of the reducing process (p. 51), the lower, flatter slope units, which appear later, develop more slowly than the older steeper ones found above them. Development is most rapid when cliff faces are being pushed back and replaced by upward-growing basal slopes; these latter are replaced much more slowly by the slopes of diminishing gradient which are developing from below; and the slowest replacement occurs in that slope unit below which is the slope having the greatest possible flattening and smallest gradient. This undergoes no further denudation; and transport of material from above can take place, at most, to but a limited extent.

To sum up: the process of flattening begins at the general base levels of denudation. *While the position of these remains unaltered, the ever flatter forms that are developing there, one after another, maintain a constant gradient as they recede.* Each successive, flatter slope grows upwards at the expense of the steeper one above it, and brings about its disappearance in the case of the highest parts. Such being the development, it is in these highest parts that the steepest forms are to be found. This is the picture presented by the German Highlands, amongst other places. The last ruin-like remains of rocky steep-forms are found there—in the Harz, in the Fichtelgebirge—as granite tors in the midst of an area composed throughout of the same kind of granite. They are perched upon inter-valley watersheds which *belong to the summit relief*[181]. Similar features may be seen at many places in the Danube valley below Tutlingen, or along the Elbe where it breaks through Saxon Switzerland. The light-coloured walls of Malm limestone are confined to those slopes of the meanders which face upstream[182]. The cliffs do not come down to the river. They are steep-forms originally produced at places where the river undercut its banks. But since then they have moved back from the water, their gradient unchanged, making room for a basal slope below. This behaviour shows that undercutting of its concave banks by the river was not continuously effective, but suffered occasional interruption. Traces of the recommencement of undercutting at the same places will be further considered below.

A result of the independent development of each individual slope unit is that the concave base levels of denudation do not move upwards along straight lines continuing the slopes of which they form the upper edges. The profile in figure 3 shows accurately the correct displacement of successively appearing concave breaks of gradient, this having been worked out from the particular values for angle of slope and intensity of denudation upon which the diagram is based. Other values might have been taken without in any way altering the character of the results obtained. It is only qualitative results with which we are here concerned. The construction has been worked out completely only for the first four slope positions. From it, the break of gradient between cliff face and basal slope can be seen, as well as the first [sic] positions $2'$, $3'$, $4'$ . . . x', of the [next] break of gradient. For later development, only a few slope positions have been drawn. These show the displacement of the lower breaks of gradient of the type $4'$ . . . x', z' and t''. The slope $t\,t''$ is taken as possessing the smallest possible gradient.

After unit time, the cliff face has moved back into the position $a\,a'$, the upward-growing basal slope has reached $2'$–2, and a slope diminishing gradient $t\,2'$ is beginning to appear. The base level for the denudation of the cliff face is actually found not at a but somewhat lower at 2, because of the flattening [at the bottom] of the basal slope [as it weathers back]. The cliff face has been extended a little downwards. After two units of time, the position of the cliff face, the basal slope, and the slope of diminishing gradient are b' b 3, 3–3′ and 3′ t. The base level in question is not at b, but at 3; and it can easily be seen that the amount b 3 by which the cliff face has been increased in length is twice the length of a 2. The development of flatter and flatter slope units thus causes the successive positions of the base levels forming their upper limits to be arranged, not on a straight line, but on an arched curve. If a line is drawn through the points 2, 3, 4, etc., it shows the path taken by the base levels of denudation in successive intervals of time. It is a continuous convex curve. This is generally true for the displacement of concave breaks of gradient. The curvature of the paths along which they move upslope is flatter, the gentler the gradient of the slope units which they separate. For the local base levels marked by the numbers 2′, 3′, 4′, the convex curvature showing the path of the displacement is so slight* that—on the small scale of the diagram—it coincides with the line t 4′ for the first three positions of the slope, and does not become visible before its 9th–16th positions (t IX and t x' XVI). The lowest break of gradient which can develop at all, and which forms the upper edge of the slope with the least possible gradient, is from the outset displaced along a rectilinear path (t t''), for below that slope no further slope unit of still slighter inclination is developed. It already possesses the greatest possible degree of flattening, and widens at the expense of all the slope units above it, extending landwards [back from the river].

It follows that, in general: *If nothing disturbs the process of flattening, the concave breaks of gradient are displaced not only up the cliff, but also further and further back into it. The backward working component—which would be absent were the lower parts of the slope not being flattened—becomes of increasing importance as the distance from the general base level of denudation increases. Thus it is more effective at the upper edge of steep slope units than at that of flattish ones.* This means that the higher, steeper slope units can actually be preserved longer than if those slopes below them were not becoming flatter; and they are removed and replaced by such flatter portions of the slope only at a considerably greater distance from the river than would otherwise be the case.

If left undisturbed, a slope of any gradient whatsoever, provided it is uniform, becomes a slope system concave in profile. In figure 3, if the cliff face was originally of the form t 1, then after three units of time it would have become a slope system t 4′–4 c'. Further development can easily be seen

* [because mobility is attained more slowly the gentler the gradient.]

Photo. by W. Penck

1. Convex break of gradient. Casadero (Eastern Puna), Argentina

Photo. by W. Penck

2. Tors on an intervalley divide. Granitic heights of the Cerros de las Animas, Western Argentina

V. BREAKS OF GRADIENT

from the diagram. It holds so long as the general base level of denudation remains constant. For more on this, see p. 151.

3. UNEQUAL EXPOSURE. ROUNDING OF HEIGHTS

The basal slope and, to a greater extent, the slopes of diminishing gradient appearing below it, are not only regions for the supply of material moving downslope, but also regions of transit for material from above. When the general base level of denudation remains unchanged in position, material is bound to accumulate on the widening flattened parts of the slopes, since here the downward movement slackens. This accumulation is not unlimited, however, as can be seen from inspection. It is not only that an increase in weight (p. 84) is associated with the accumulation, but also that with length of time the material is further reduced and so more mobile. The ratio of gradient to mobility, which is the determining factor in the movement of rock derivatives, has on this account the same value everywhere on a concave slope; the slighter mobility corresponds to the greater gradient and conversely. This constant ratio is inevitable and is the reason why the transport of material coming from above is actually accomplished on the slopes of diminishing gradient right down to that with the least. Obviously, then, on the flattish parts of the slopes thicker profiles are slowed up, and on the steeper parts thinner ones move more rapidly by way of compensation.

But the accumulation of rubble, which increases downward, brings about inequality of exposure (p. 54). Even when the gradient is uniform, rock reduction goes on more quickly at the freely exposed surfaces; the mobility needed for migration is reached more rapidly than on flattish surfaces covered with rubble, to whatever extent. Exposure is therefore renewed more quickly than on the flatter slopes (p. 78). As soon as the migrating material has accumulated to some extent, differences between the various parts of the slope become noticeable: the upper, steeper slope units, where there is nothing to hinder development, are differentiated from the lower, flatter ones on which denudation is impeded. But if, in such a case, the development of newer, ever flatter slope units should be retarded, then the concave base levels of denudation do not recede upwards along the strongly curved convex paths demonstrated in the previous section; instead, their successive positions—in profile—are arranged upon a line which becomes more and more stretched out until it becomes approximately a straight line. This would mean that the upper, steeper slope units would be removed whilst closer to the river, being replaced by the corresponding slopes of diminishing gradient. The great importance of corrasion lies in the fact that it counteracts this process by once more accelerating denudation, which means renewal of exposure and, with this, flattening beneath a thicker covering of soil (p. 112).

It follows that lessening of exposure on the lower parts of a *slope system* does not influence the type of development; but under certain conditions, e.g. when corrasion is absent, influences the rate of development. It does not therefore lead to fundamental changes of form. It is different in the case of slope units which stand up freely, intersecting in the highest parts of the country. If within such a slope *unit*, exposure is greater above than in the parts below, more rock material is there prepared for denudation in unit time, since reduction is penetrating the depths more rapidly. The result is a flattening of the upper, better exposed parts of the slope unit, and this appears *as a rounding of the zones of intersection, rounding of the heights* (see Plate VI, illustration 2, and p. 78).

With the flattening of the higher parts of the slope unit, conditions become less favourable for the migration of reduced material. Greater mobility is required, which necessitates a longer period of reduction. Therefore denudation is decelerated, and with this, flattening from above is brought to an end. This happens as soon as renewal of exposure takes place at the same rate both on the flattened parts of the slope unit and on the unchanged parts below. That means a balance between the slowing up of denudational intensity below, because of soil accumulation, and that above, due to diminished gradient (pp. 64, 65). Then in equal times, similar amounts of rock material leave their places of origin both above and below. But those above, on account of their better exposure, acquire in the same period a higher degree of reduction than those below, where the rate of reduction is retarded (p. 54). This stationary ratio marks the limit of flattening from above, a limit which cannot be overstepped. *The amount of flattening is thus limited, and is directly dependent upon the inclination of the slope, the upper parts of which are undergoing flattening. The less the gradient, the greater the flattening; and vice versa; but its extent remains unchanged, so long as the gradient of the slope unit remains unaltered.* It is thus utterly impossible for broad rounded ridges and from them, ultimately, flattish forms, to be derived from sharp edges or peaks by means of flattening from above (see pp. 133–134).

Rounding of heights attains a strongly marked development when the gradient of the intersecting slopes is equal to or less than that of the basal slopes. For only then is the accumulation of rubble possible. In regions inimical to plant growth, such accumulation does not begin (other things being equal) until the gradient is gentler than that for [climatic] belts where the vegetation cover is continuous. This accounts for the greater sharpness, especially in deserts, of the zones of intersection of slope units which, if of similar steepness in a temperate climate, would clearly show

Photo. by W. Penck

1. Steep forms not rounded from above. Taton Gorge, below Corral de Piedro, Sierra de Fiambalá, Western Argentina

Photo. by W. Penck

2. Steep forms rounded from above. Eastern side of the Cerro Negro Range as it drops to the Bolson of Andagalá, Western Argentina

VI. ROUNDING TAKING PLACE FROM ABOVE

rounding because of dissimilarity in exposure (see Plate VI, illustration 1) Where the reduced material is thoroughly removed by rain wash, as for instance in regions of Badlands, it is most striking to find an almost complete absence of blunting where the slopes (concave or straight) intersect, even when the gradient is slight. Such climatically determined differences of form become especially clear when the comparison is between upstanding areas where intersecting concave slopes are of the same average steepness. In districts of sparse vegetation these, e.g. inselbergs, are characterised by a sharper concave curving of the foot-slopes* and greater sharpness of the zones of intersection as contrasted with otherwise similar upstanding areas in humid regions where the foot-slopes* are less concave and the heights more rounded. This, however, refers only to rocks of the same or similar character. Analogous differences can also be found within one and the same climatic zone between upstanding masses of very resistant rock providing little debris, and those which are otherwise similar but composed of easily destroyed rock. In the former case the covering of rubble is slight, other things being equal, and conditions are favourable for renewal of exposure; in the latter case the reverse holds. For the rubble cover, which causes the difference in the forms considered above, is always the result of a *quantitative ratio* between the amount of rock debris prepared and its removal.

4. STRAIGHT SLOPE PROFILES.
UNIFORM DEVELOPMENT

If the position of the general base level of denudation remains unchanged, as was assumed in the preceding section, it means that the rivers are neither incising nor depositing. A river working merely as transporting agent cannot prevent the upslope recession of a cliff that originally rose up directly from it, nor the formation of a basal slope, nor the development of slopes of diminishing gradient appearing in succession below that. After some time, the whole slope system—with its cliff face above, and its slope of smallest possible gradient below—has retreated so far from the river that this now cuts only the loose material that has rolled down to form the talus heap; after a further period of time it no longer does even this. The whole slope system retreats inwards, ever further from the edge of the river, so that the higher, steeper slope units in the uppermost parts disappear one after another; the steeper ones generally do this whilst they are nearer the river than is the case for the flatter slopes that succeed them below. The slope with minimum gradient is spreading further and further inwards between the rest of the slope

[* See glossary.]

system and the stream. It is the only one of the slope units that is in this way constantly gaining in area.

If the cliff face, or any other slope unit preserving an unaltered gradient, is to remain adjacent to the general base level of denudation, the river must erode it. In every unit of time during which the slope unit recedes by its characteristic amount, the river must remove that lowest particle $t\,a\,x$ (in fig. 4, p. 145) which would become the starting point for a slope of diminishing gradient so long as the position of the general base level of denudation remained unchanged. The river must erode downwards at least from t to a, or sideways from t to a', and must in all the following units of time perform the same, ever-recurring task. In short, *there must be a constant ratio between the intensity of the denudation acting on the slope unit and the intensity of erosion by the stream*, a ratio characterised by the relation:

$$t\,o = t\,a \sin(90 - \alpha), \text{ from which } t\,a = \frac{t\,o}{\cos \alpha} \quad\ldots\ldots\ldots\ldots\ldots\ldots(1)$$

$$\text{or} \quad t\,o = t\,a' \sin \alpha \qquad \text{from which } t\,a' = \frac{t\,o}{\sin \alpha} \quad\ldots\ldots\ldots\ldots\ldots(2)$$

where $t\,a$ = the amount of downward erosion

$t\,a'$ = the amount of lateral erosion

$t\,o$ = the amount of denudation (the amount of the retreat of the slope unit)

and α = the angle of inclination of the slope unit.

in unit time

Figure 4, from which the corresponding values and relationships can be seen for a steep slope (A) and for a flattish slope (B), shows that this formula can be applied to any slope unit immediately adjoining the base level of denudation. *A slope unit can then maintain itself with unaltered gradient only when the intensity of erosion is constant (uniform erosion) and proportional to the intensity of denudation on the adjoining slope unit.* Since this increases with the angle of inclination α, which in its turn depends as regards detail upon the character of the rock, the intensity of erosion has a definite relation to the angle of inclination of the slope unit rising up from the river. The flatter the adjoining slope, the less intensity of erosion is needed to bring about equilibrium; and the limiting case is equilibrium between a river which is not eroding and a slope with the smallest possible gradient (the theoretical condition of the final surface of truncation, the end-peneplane or Davisian peneplain*).

Equilibrium is inevitably established, however, not only when erosion is uniform, but also between any value of the erosional intensity at a given time, and the denudation taking place on the slope unit adjoining

---

* an der Endrumpfläche, dem Endrumpf oder der Peneplain von Davis.

the river *at that time*. Suppose a cliff to rise up directly from a river, and that the river is eroding with less intensity than what is needed to balance the denudation of the cliff face. Let the intensity, however, be greater than that of denudation on the normal basal slope—i.e. the one that would develop if the general base level of erosion remained in a fixed position (see p. 135 ff.). Then obviously the cliff face could not remain at the edge of the river, but would recede from it by characteristic amounts. The slope appearing below it would not, however, correspond to the normal basal slope. Such (*t t′* in the profile of fig. 5) could develop, and maintain its position at the water-course unaltered, only if the stream were downcutting uniformly with an intensity such that its value

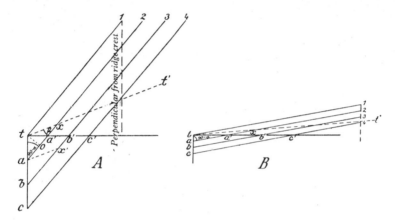

FIG. 4.

corresponded to this equilibrium. But a greater value has been assumed for the river's erosional intensity.

As the cliff *t w* moves back in successive units of time into the positions 1′, 2′, 3′, etc., let us suppose that the general base level of denudation sinks from *t* to a_1 and furthermore, by equal amounts to b_2, c_3, etc. On such an hypothesis, the infinitely small basal slope t_1 which (theoretically, but not in reality) appeared in time one, has been undercut; an infinitely small step $a_1a_1′$ has formed in the cliff. This must migrate upslope at the same rate as the cliff face, since it has the same inclination. If, in time two, this latter has arrived at 2–2′, then that break of slope would be at $a_2a_2′$ and would have left a new basal slope a_1a_2 behind it. However, this has in the meanwhile been once more undercut. The newly appearing step in the cliff, $b_2b_2′$, would have migrated to $b_3b_3′$ by the end of time three, the *a*-step to $a_3a_3′$, the cliff face to 3–3′. The new basal slope b_2b_3 has, however, in the meantime, again been undercut

K   P.M.A.

(c_3c_3'), and so on. If events took place successively in that way, a many-stepped basal slope would develop below the receding cliff, its mean gradient being greater than that of the normal basal slope $t\,t'$. In the diagram the successively appearing steps of undercutting have been marked by the letters a, b, c, d . . . etc., and their positions reached in successive times bear the corresponding indices. After time three, the slope system is represented by points c_3c_3' b_3b_3' a_3a_3' 3–$3'$ (the fine lines in the diagram).

However, in reality, river erosion and sheet denudation, over the

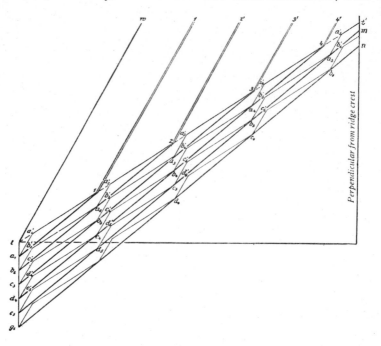

<figure>
Perpendicular from ridge crest
</figure>

Fig. 5.

whole rock wall as well as that over the slope unit appearing below it, happen simultaneously for all the phases; and so, neither the little steps of undercutting, nor the basal slopes $t\,t'$ below them, actually arise. Each infinitely small undercutting on the part of the eroding river creates an infinitely small slope of steep gradient, on which denudation is more vigorous than at any other position on the growing basal slope. Thus, from the moment of its origin, that infinitely small slope reaches up to what is at that instant the base of the cliff face, swallowing up, as it were, the gentler basal slope. In successive times this latter moves along the same path as it would follow were there no erosion, *since its position is determined exclusively by the intensity of denudation on the cliff face itself.* If the cliff face has already nearly reached the position 1-1', there arises at the edge of the river only the last infinitely small slope of undercutting which by the end of unit time disappears from the foot of the wall, which has during this same time moved to point 1. At each moment, river erosion brings about accelerated denudation, and this is transmitted to the upper margin of the slope unit. If we choose to consider very small values, we come very near to the natural course of events and the deduction becomes exact. Then the infinitely small steps of the slope $a_1a_1'1$ pass into the thickly drawn lines of the gradient a_11.

The slope that develops here is from the very outset steeper than the normal basal slope $t\,t'$. Assuming as before that the rock remains of the same character, it is therefore an area of greater denudational intensity; and it is the lowering of the general base level of denudation, by the river's erosion in unit time, which causes the increase in denudation and determines what intensity is possible on the slope unit rising up from the stream. If E denotes the intensity of downward erosion, A the intensity of denudation on the slope unit immediately adjoining the stream, the

general relationship that holds is: $E = \dfrac{A}{\cos \alpha}$, where α represents the angle

of inclination of the slope unit under consideration. In other words: *The intensity of erosion determines the gradient of the slope unit rising up from the river edge*, the details of the inclination then depending upon the nature of the rock.

So long as the intensity of erosion remains constant, there is one slope unit and one only, its form and its inclination remaining always the same, which can grow upwards from the eroding stream. Under these circumstances, no local base levels of denudation, concave in form, can develop. On the contrary, *the slopes have straight profiles*, and these are maintained so long as the intensity of erosion remains unchanged (assuming the character of the rock to be still the same). This is called *uniform development*. Its primary characteristic is a straight profile; thus, the slopes have a specific form, but not a specific gradient. Rather is it true that slopes of any gradient whatsoever—from the least possible to the greatest which can be formed and maintained for the particular type of rock at the place in question—may acquire a straight profile when uniform development sets in, provided only that the erosional intensity keeps its corresponding value unaltered.

In figure 5 we began with a cliff face $t\,w$. This, if produced beyond the diagram, would meet an analogous slope unit in the vertical line dropped from the ridge crest [$t'\,m\,n$ in the figure]. Further development leads to a single concave break of gradient. As this moves upslope and shortens the cliff from below, the rocky arête becomes lowered to the same vertical extent. Between the time periods four and five, the cliff face would have disappeared and been replaced by the slope e_5m; and thus the arête would have been replaced by a less sharp edge, the intersecting slopes being not so steep as previously. Up to that moment, there has been a lessening of the vertical distance between the zone of intersection and the general base level of denudation which is sinking uniformly, i.e. the relative height (pp. 135–136) has been diminishing. From now on, this is changed. The uniform straight slope is being shortened from above, at the zone of intersection, by the same amount as it is being supplemented from below at the edge of the river. In other words: regardless of the gradient of the slopes which are meeting in the particular case, and irrespective of rounding of the summits—which does not interfere with the stationary condition, but causes it (p. 142)—the zones of intersection are lowered in unit time by the same amount as the rivers cut down. This follows directly from the rectilinear nature of the slope profiles and the constancy of their gradient, and can be read off at once from figure 5: the lengths e_5-g_6 (amount of erosion) and m-n (lowering of the ridge), both between the same slope positions, are equal to one another.

If uniform development lasts sufficiently long, straight slope units are produced in every case; the steeper ones, which emerge from rapidly eroding streams, appear after a shorter time than the flatter ones corresponding to less intense erosion. They then hold the field alone. *As soon as this stage has been reached, the relative heights become constant. Nothing changes in this respect so long as the intensity of erosion maintains a uniform absolute value.*

5. CONVEX BREAKS OF GRADIENT

Development of convex breaks of gradient might be deduced directly from the law that the gradient of slopes is determined by the intensity of erosion. However, we prefer once more to follow continuously the natural course of events so as to reach exact results by this somewhat lengthy method. In order to deal with the problem by constructing a diagram, fig. 6, p. 149, is once again based upon taking definite values for the intensity of denudation acting upon the individual slope units: any numbers may be chosen for these values so long as merely qualitative results are desired, and so long as they fit in with the known law that intensity of denudation, which is equal to the rate of development of the slope units, increases with their steepness. Differently chosen values would alter merely the [particular] gradients of those portions of the slopes which are represented in the profile, and not—as we wish once more to stress emphatically—the fundamental results which alone matter here.

A slope with a straight profile, rising up from a stream which is eroding uniformly, recedes in three successive units of time from its position $m\,m'$ to $t\,t'$. m to t denotes the uniformly maintained amount of erosion, m' to t' the lowering of the zone of intersection by similar equal amounts during the same periods of time. If from that time onward the intensity of erosion increases, development can no longer continue in a similar way: the general base level of denudation is lowered more rapidly; but the denudation of the slope unit with its given gradient cannot be accelerated during the same period. The balance has been upset.

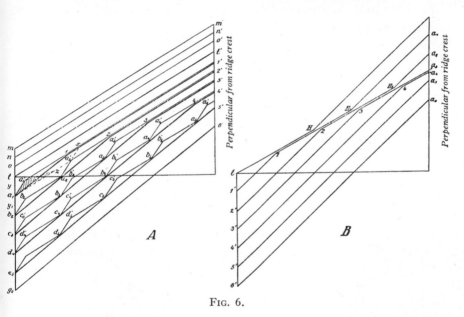

Fig. 6.

Starting from the position $t\,t'$, the slope can, and must, reach position $a_1'1'$, in time one, because of the renewal of exposure taking place on it at a definite velocity. In the meantime, however, the general base level of denudation has been lowered from t not only to y but to a_1, which would be just double the amount occurring in the previous time intervals. Theoretically, therefore, there remains a small undercut declivity a_1a_1' which separates the slope $a_1'1$ from the general base level of denudation. But in fact neither this nor its similar successors, shown in the diagram, ever develop. For at every instant the river, eroding with increased force, brings about a minute undercutting, produces a minute steep slope, which from the moment it appears is a surface of more intense denudation. As such, it recedes vigorously upslope and eats away the lower end of the slope unit which is simultaneously receding, but at a slower rate. If, at the end of time one, this reaches the position $1'1$, then the last of these minute undercuttings (i.e. slopes with an inclination of maximum gradient) has been produced at the river's edge, and has vanished at point 1. This point is as far as the undercutting can recede upslope in unit time on account of the intensity of denudation peculiar to *it*.

Thus, while the one slope unit moves in successive times from $t\,t'$ to $1'-1$, $2'-2$, etc., there is also a new slope unit growing up from the more intensely eroding river. This might be considered to have arisen discontinuously, as has been shown on p. 146 for an analogous case. The newly formed slope would then be dissected by exceedingly small steps which one after another would reach upslope, as is illustrated by the fine kinked line in the position $e_5 5'$. However, to make a sufficiently close approach to the continuous course of nature, the discontinuities must be taken as infinitely small. Then the very minute steps disappear in a uniformly inclined plane (thick line) which at successive times occupies the positions $a_1 1$, $b_2 2$, $c_3 3$, and so on.

This new slope unit has a straight profile, since constant values have been assumed for the increased intensity of erosion. It is steeper than the slope unit above it. Therefore it is the scene of increased denudation and it is obvious that this is now necessarily in equilibrium with the erosion.

Between these two slope units, a convex break of gradient appears. It forms the local base level of denudation for the flatter part of the slope lying higher up. This, until it disappears, is denuded in relation to that break, and is uninfluenced by any further changes in the general base level of denudation. The convex break of gradient recedes upslope, since the steeper slope unit, being a surface with a more rapid rate of development (intensity of denudation), retreats upwards more vigorously and eats away that part of the slope which is above it, undercutting it and thus preventing it from being flattened. This latter slope is displaced only in a direction parallel to its former position; but it is continuously shortened from below until it disappears from the parts at the highest altitudes.

Thus in general: *Convex breaks of gradient owe their origin to an increase in the intensity of erosion*[180]. *They originate at river level all along the drainage net, and from there they recede upwards at a rate that is determined by the intensity of denudation of the steeper slope unit. On account of their presence, the development of the higher, flatter slope unit becomes independent of the behaviour of the erosional channels, i.e. independent of the base levels of erosion* (see Plate IV, illustration 2, Plate V, illustration 1).

ADDITIONAL NOTES ON THE ORIGIN OF CONCAVE
BREAKS OF GRADIENT

In their origin, behaviour and function, convex breaks of gradient agree in every way with concave base levels of denudation. Both start from the general base levels of denudation, *both recede upslope, and in both cases the rate of retreat is determined by the intensity of denudation, which equals the rate of development of what is at that time the* STEEPER *slope unit.* Both are local base levels of denudation and render the development of the respective slope units above them independent of the behaviour of the erosional channels and of the base levels of erosion.

These analogies, and especially the fact that the change in position of the convex as well as of the concave breaks of gradient is determined by the rate of development of what is at that time the steeper slope unit, make it now possible to add to what has been said about concave base levels of denudation in areas which are composed of homogeneous material. It is by no means only when there is a fixed base level of denudation, as was assumed in section 2, that they arise. They do so *in every case where there is any diminution in the intensity of erosion.* If this intensity becomes zero, there is the possibility that flattening may occur down to the smallest possible gradient. Interruption in the lessening of erosion, on the other hand, naturally limits the process of flattening as well. Up to that time, viz. up to the cessation of erosion, the diminution of gradient in each phase of the development of the erosional intensity can only be such as to bring the intensity of denudation peculiar to that slope into equilibrium with what is at that time the value of the intensity of erosion (see pp. 145, 147 and fig. 5 on p. 146). Thus the succession, from above downward, of flatter and flatter slope units, together with their actual inclinations, provides a picture of the kind of decrease in erosion that has taken place and its limit. Other things being equal, a sharply concave curve of the slopes indicates rapid deceleration of the erosional intensity, a concavity of less strong curvature indicates a slower rate of deceleration (cf. with this, pp. 159–161).

6. DEVELOPMENT OF RELATIVE HEIGHT
WAXING DEVELOPMENT AND WANING DEVELOPMENT

Figures 2–6 show the development of the relative altitudes. To simplify matters, the lines along which the zones of intersection move in successive units of time are recorded as vertical lines dropped from the ridge crests. No account has been taken of the rounding of heights. When the general base level of denudation is constant, the zone of intersection is lowered, and with this the relative height is lessened (pp. 136–

137, fig. 3). This decrease, however, is not the same for all phases. If the slope positions t 1, 2 a', 3 b' (in fig. 3, p. 137) are produced to cut the vertical line through the ridge crest, the lowering in successive intervals of time is found to be greatest, and—as can also be seen from fig. 2, p. 135—to be constant in amount, so long as it is the same steep surfaces of intense denudation, the cliff faces, which are intersecting (positions I–IV). Suppose, for the scale chosen, that this lowering is 22 millimetres per unit of time. After time three, the cliff disappears, and from then onwards the basal slopes meet in the highest parts of the country. The lowering of the zone of intersection now takes place more slowly; in the diagram, it will be only 10 millimetres between the positions IV and V, i.e. during one unit of time, and it falls still further to 1.2 millimetres in unit time. This amount remains constant so long as the zone of intersection is formed by the basal slopes—positions V to XX—and is in no way affected by the fact that in the meantime further, flatter slope units are developing at the edge of the river and growing upslope. After time twenty, the basal slope has been completely replaced by the next flatter slope unit, in which the zone of intersection now occurs. The lowering of this is hereby further decreased—0.16 millimetres in unit time—and this decreased amount remains constant until the slope unit in question has been itself removed and replaced by the one next below it with the next degree of flattening.

If the general base level of denudation remains constant, decrease in the relative height takes place more and more slowly. This slowing down comes about because, in the course of development, ever flatter and flatter slopes meet in the zones of intersection; and on these, denudation achieves less and less in successive units of time. *The lowering of the zones of intersection depends solely upon the development of the slope units which meet there, and it is determined by whatever intensity of denudation is characteristic of these latter.*

The general base level of denudation is constant only as a special case. This can occur at the end of a series of developments which are characterised by decreasing erosional intensity, i.e. there is a decrease in the amounts by which the general base level of denudation is sinking [in each unit of time] (p. 151). Considering any phase of the development, e.g. that represented by fig. 5 (p. 146), what occurs is as follows: So long as slopes with the gradient t w intersect, the zone of intersection is lowered by an amount proportional to the sine of the angle of inclination of the slope unit, regardless of the fact that in the meantime the river is eroding less intensely and is allowing a flatter slope unit to develop. This becomes evident if in fig. 5, p. 146, the slope positions t w, 1–1′, 2–2′, 3–3′, 4–4′ are produced to meet the vertical line through the ridge crest. Until the flatter slope unit has pushed its way through and forms the zone of intersection, this latter is lowered in each successive unit of time by an amount greater than that by which the general base level of denudation is sinking. *The result is a decrease in relative height.* The relative height remains constant if the slopes, which intersect in the highest parts of the country, rise in rectilinear fashion from a watercourse that is eroding with an intensity which has been decelerating but which—it is assumed—is once more uniform.

The course of development which is due to decrease in erosional intensity may be called WANING *development. It is characterised by the occurrence of concave breaks of gradient, concave profiles, and decreasing relative height.* In the limiting case, the erosional intensity sinks to zero; the slopes then develop with a constant position for the general base level of denudation, and a lower limit is set to flattening only when slopes with the smallest possible gradient appear. As soon as these intersect on the interfluve summits, there is naturally an end to the lowering of the zones of intersection. With this, the lower limit has been reached for the decrease of relative height. This height is determined (*a*) by the inclination of the slope unit which has become the sole prevailing one, viz. that with the greatest possible degree of flattening; and (*b*) by the horizontal distance between the zone of intersection and the edge of the river, increasing with this distance and vice versa. This process ends with cessation of all denudation of the land, with the establishment of minimum angles of slope and of a relative height which can be no further decreased. It is, however, possible only when the course of waning development proceeds completely undisturbed and for an unlimited time. It is called peneplanation of the country. Every phase, except the theoretically final result, is characterised by a concave slope profile. That final result would be the end-peneplane, Davis' peneplain or '*Fastebene*' (see p. 128).

Waning development may follow from the uniform type; but it is just as likely for the uniform type to follow it, and this is what was assumed in the construction of fig. 5 (p. 146). The characteristics *of uniform development* have already been established (pp. 147–148). They are based upon constancy in the amount of erosion produced in successive units of time. Slopes with straight profiles develop, and as soon as these intersect in the highest parts—but not before—the relative height also becomes constant. Then the lowering of the zones of intersection is not only proportional to the sine of the angle of inclination of the slope units which are meeting, but also it is equal to the amount by which the general base level of denudation has sunk.

Fig. 6, p. 149, illustrates the development of the relative height as the intensity of erosion increases. The construction in diagram A starts with a slope unit of uniform development. As far as position $t\,t'$ of the slope, the amounts by which the zone of intersection is lowered, and those by which the general base level of denudation sinks, keep pace with one another. From that point on, it is otherwise. The river incises more strongly, but the rate of lowering of the summit remains unchanged so long as the zone of intersection is in the same slope unit: *the relative height increases.* This goes on until the new steeper slope unit rising from the river, which (according to the assumption) is again eroding uniformly though with increased intensity, has succeeded in reaching the zone of intersection.

The construction of diagram B can now easily be understood. It is based on a system of slopes which is exhibiting waning development, and which consists of cliff face and basal slope $t\,H\,a$. For the sake of clearness, the relationship $E = \dfrac{A}{\cos \alpha}$ has been assumed between E, the intensity of erosion, and A, the rate of denudation of the cliff face $H\,a$ with angle of slope α. Then from the incising water-course there will again rise a cliff face with the same gradient, assuming the character of the rock to be homogeneous. After time one, a slope has been formed, having the position $1'1\ H_1a_1$: a fresh cliff face $1'1$ has appeared and is separated from the receding basal slope by a convex break of gradient which migrates upslope at the same rate as the concave base level of denudation at the foot of the upper cliff face. The basal slope is shortened from below by as much as it is increasing above. Were the erosional intensity greater, the more actively undercut lower cliff face would increase upslope more strongly and shorten it from below more rapidly than it can grow upwards. It would be removed, the lower cliff face would merge into the upper one as a uniform slope unit, over the whole surface of which intensified denudation would then occur, brought about by accelerated caving in of the river bank due to its undercutting. Before this condition had been reached, however, stepped cliff faces would be visible in such a case also. These, occurring on valley slopes of homogeneous composition, show that erosion has repeatedly begun and ceased at the same places (p. 139). Excellent examples of this are to be seen in the valley of the Danube below Tuttlingen. There it is a matter of the repeated action, alternating with its absence, of predominantly lateral erosion at the undercut slopes of the valley meanders: the cliffs are not invariably stepped, nor is the number of steps nor their altitude consistently repeated at analogous places. No terraces, that could be correlated with these cliff steps, have been observed on the corresponding slip-off slopes.

If the upper cliff face intersects a slope unit of the same type then, according to what has been assumed for diagram B, the zone of intersection is lowered by the same amount as the river cuts down, until the basal slope reaches it—see position $3'3\ a_3$. From that time on, the lowering, which corresponds to the rate of denudation of the slope, goes on very much more slowly. The river is now at the same time cutting down with undiminished vigour, and so the relative height increases. This behaviour is again associated with the presence of a convex break of gradient, and once more the lowering of the ridge crest is independent of what is happening at the river's edge, provided that the slope leading from it to the ridge crest is not a single slope unit (lit. a uniform form system). *The occurrence of convex breaks of gradient and of convex slope profiles is as necessarily bound up with increasing intensity of erosion as is the increase in relative height. We call this* WAXING *development.*

This general statement can be made: Lowering of the zones where slope units intersect at the tops of the slopes does not necessarily mean a decrease of relative height, nor a lowering of the general level of the land. *The development of relative height is the story of the vertical distance between the zone of intersection and the corresponding position of the general base level of denudation at any given moment; the lowering of the zone of intersection is the steady decrease in the vertical distance between it and a definitely chosen fixed level, e.g. any individual position of the general base level of denudation.* Lowering of the zones of intersection is the immediate consequence of the denudation that is taking place on the intersecting slope units; like this, it goes on steadily and comes to an end only when denudation ceases. *The amount of lowering is determined solely by the intensity of the denudation on the intersecting slope units, and so is proportional to the sines of their angles of inclination; the steeper these are, at the zones of intersection, the greater the lowering in unit time; and this is independent of what is happening on the lower parts of the slopes and at the general base level of denudation.*

Variations in the relative height, on the other hand, depend upon differences between the behaviour of the erosion channels *and* that of the zones of intersection. If the intensity of erosion diminishes, the relative height becomes less. But this does not occur till the slope systems of concave profile, i.e. those which are broken up by exclusively concave breaks of gradient, have extended up to the topmost parts, without necessarily affecting the rounding of heights previously considered (waning development). If the intensity of erosion increases, so does the relative height. But here, likewise, it is not till the developing slopes, divided up by convex breaks of gradient, have established themselves (waxing development). And it is only in those special cases where straight slopes, due to a uniformly incising stream, intersect on the summits, that the relative height remains constant. Then it does not alter any more than does the inclination of slope, whatever it may be at that time, so long as the intensity of erosion maintains its value, not even when the denudation and the lowering of the zones of intersection are of unlimited duration (uniform development).

7. RATES OF GROWTH AND AREAS OF SLOPE UNITS*

The regular upward recession of concave and of convex breaks of gradient, in regions composed of homogeneous material, brings about a change in area of the slope units which adjoin one another at any given moment. Those immediately above the receding break of gradient are shortened; those which happen at the time to be below it, spread upslope. *This latter process is the growth of slope units.* The rate of growth varies with the intensity of denudation. Since the latter increases with the gradient, steeper slope units grow more rapidly than flatter ones. During their development, therefore, slope units are constantly changing in area; and which kind of change it is depends upon their arrangement. Only with uniform development is there no such alteration; in that case the slopes consist each of a single slope unit, and are uniform and not composite. There is compensation for shortening at the zones of intersection by the addition of an equal amount at the general base level of denudation; the area of the slope unit is in that case as constant as the gradient.

But with waning development, in which the steeper parts of the slopes are at the top, and the flatter ones below (p. 137, fig. 3), each higher break of gradient recedes upslope more quickly than that next below it (p. 150); and so the area of the slope unit between them increases. That increase is not, however, unlimited, nor is it very considerable even over long periods of time; since except between cliff and basal slope the differences of gradient between neighbouring slope units are never very great and they become smaller, the slighter the inclination of the slope units which join one another by concave breaks of gradient. It is only the slope of greatest possible flattening which is continuously increasing its area at the expense of all the slopes above it, since at its lower margin, the fixed general base level of denudation, there is no flatter slope unit appearing.

The arrangement is reversed in the case of waxing development; here the steeper slope units lie below, the flatter ones above. Convex breaks

[* See glossary.]

of gradient, which recede upward more quickly, form the lower margin of each of the slope units. These, in unit time, are shortened from below by greater amounts than the upward extensions of their top edges. All of them thus decrease in area except the one that rises directly from the general base level of denudation. It is inevitable that in this way slope units vanish before they have reached the zone of intersection in the highest parts. This is illustrated in fig. 7, which has been drawn for 13 successive positions of slopes which result from an assumed increasing intensity of erosion. It would occur with a slope which had been produced by first, an increase in erosional intensity, then followed by uniform incision of the amount 1 to 2 in unit time. Two slope units, a and b, are present. A third steeper one (c) becomes associated with them as soon as the river incises more vigorously (from 2 to 3, then 4, 5, 6, and so on), and a further fourth one (d), which rises up from the river when it erodes yet more powerfully still after having reached slope position 9. That fourth slope possesses the greatest inclination that the character of the given rock permits.

Slope unit b is so vigorously undercut and shortened by the slope below, that between the slope positions 12 and 13 it has been completely eaten away and replaced by slope unit c, which then immediately adjoins the much flatter slope unit a. A more pronounced convex break of gradient separates them from one another. This result would have been achieved more quickly had the river erosion increased to greater amounts in unit time than has been assumed. Conditions which could obtain only after the 9th slope position in the figure would then have come about sooner. The amount of erosion by the river in unit time is the rate or intensity of erosion; the increase of such amounts in unit time is the acceleration or increase of erosional intensity (conversely: the diminution of these amounts is the decrease of intensity or deceleration of the erosion).

The removal of intermediate slope units by steeper ones produced later may occur even before those intermediate slopes have extended up to the highest parts; and it takes place the more quickly and, other things being equal, affects a larger area, the greater the acceleration of the erosion (see p. 160). Such a slope, therefore, no longer shows all the slope units, one above the other, as they were successively formed at the general base level of denudation; but some of them are gone and have been replaced by more sharply convex breaks of gradient. They separate the far older and flatter slope units from the far younger, steeper ones. This phenomenon is widespread: sharp breaks of gradient, the origin of which has been explained above, always form the lower limit of upraised landscapes with gentler slopes, and they mark the upper edge to which the younger, steeper slope units have worked back from the deepened erosional channels. It is quite wrong to deduce from this a duality of uplift[183]. Amongst many other examples of this there are the dissected peneplanes of the Vogtland and the Rhenish Schiefergebirge, and the highland landscapes of the Harz and the Black Forest, etc., with their edges eaten into, as it were. The phenomenon is most sharply marked where acceleration of erosion has produced slope units of maximum gradient. If the watercourse in fig. 7 should finally cut down in unit time not only from 9 to 10, but twice as quickly right down to 11, no steeper slopes would develop, not even with a further acceleration of erosion, since the maximum gradient had already been attained. But the slope unit d would increase

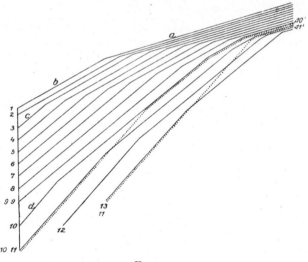

FIG. 7.

to an extraordinary amount. The accelerated undercutting of the higher slope units would lead to their rapid removal (dotted slope positions 10–10', 11–11', fine figures); very soon a specially sharp convex break of gradient would make its appearance, and here the precipitous undercut slopes would directly adjoin a far older and flatter slope unit (fig. 8 and Plate IV, illustration 2).

Such undercut slopes always have a straight profile. It is no longer possible to tell from their shape whether the water-course from which they rise has had uniform, accelerated, or decelerated erosion, whether they belong to the type of uniform, waxing or waning development, so long as the intensity of erosion is more than what just balances the spontaneous denudation on a slope of maximum gradient. If such undercut slopes meet in zones of intersection, the relative height becomes constant. This behaviour, then, no longer indicates uniformity of development, a point which must be kept in mind for later investigation.

Continuity of the Curvature of Slopes

For the accentuation of convex breaks of gradient, which takes place on the removal of intermediate slope units, it is not necessary to presuppose a sudden increase in the intensity of erosion. This has, so far, been assumed in order to facilitate approach to the laws governing slope development. Erosion may be locally accelerated in such a way as to give the impression that the intensity increases suddenly by comparison with the very slow processes of sheet denudation. Such a superficial im-

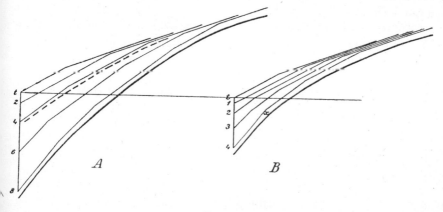

Fig. 8.

pression must not, however, be allowed to tempt us to misinterpret the essential nature of erosion, which changes its intensity only in a steady, not in a discontinuous manner. Erosion is lowering the general base level of denudation at every moment, i.e steadily, by a very small amount. With increasing intensity of erosion, these very small amounts become larger in successive units of time; with lessening intensity, they become smaller. At every moment, therefore, very minute slope units rise up from eroding rivers and, when the amount of erosion increases, they become somewhat steeper in each successive unit of time. *They combine in a continuously curved convex slope*. The kind of curvature can be seen in fig. 8 in which the continuously curved slope profiles are drawn in heavy lines or in broken lines inserted under the corresponding slope positions of the construction. On the left (A) the *acceleration of erosion* has been taken as exactly half that on the right (B); so that in the latter case it is always exactly half the time, as compared with A, which elapses before the erosional intensity has risen to twice, three times or four times the amount of the initial value, the same in both cases. It is only after time eight that A has reached the same erosional intensity as B had already attained after time four. In both cases there appear successively the same number of similarly inclined slope units, but in B twice as quickly as in A. Therefore the area of the individual slope units—of the same inclination—is smaller in B, and the inevitable removal of intermediate slope units by lower and steeper ones takes place sooner than in A. In figure 8 B this has already become visible after time four (at x); in A, nothing can yet be seen of it after time eight. It is apparent that *the curvature of the slopes is more markedly convex, towards the valley incision, the greater the acceleration of erosion, the more rapid the rate of increase in erosional intensity.*

The rounded mountain ridges found, for example, in certain parts of the German Highlands and the Wiener Wald, are instances of upstanding areas surrounded by convex slopes. In the Wiener Wald, G. Götzinger has made them the object of his frequently quoted investigations. They are typical forms of waxing development [184] which of necessity arise with increasing intensity of erosion; and are not, as Götzinger tried to show, forms of waning development.

If in a *continuously curved slope*, slope units of medium gradient have been overtaken by steeper declivities which grew up rapidly from below, there appear, here too, markedly curved parts of the slope, which recede upwards and take on the function of convex breaks of gradient. In particular, they are markedly visible when the acceleration of erosion has led to the formation of slopes of maximum gradient (p. 158).

The break of gradient is a discontinuity in the slope; but it is brought about by a continuous increase in erosional intensity. For the first time we are meeting the case of a steadily acting cause producing a morphological discontinuity. This result is of great importance in the evaluation of the convex breaks of gradient that are being considered here and that play a highly significant part among the world's land forms. It will be referred to again.

Just as increase of erosional intensity goes on steadily, so does decrease. Thus the concave profiles of waning development are also in reality continuously curved. The same naturally applies also to those profiles which develop when the general base level of denudation remains constant, and which suffer flattening to the utmost possible amount. For at each moment there arises here also a fresh, very minute, slope unit of an inclination steadily becoming somewhat slighter. These combine to form an unbroken concave slope. In fact, even the transition from cliff face to basal slope is no sharp nick, as can easily be seen in mountain regions, but a more or less strongly re-entrant curve. The only place where this cannot be clearly seen is where talus reaches up to the foot of the cliff, covers the concave transition between the surfaces of denudation, and in its place allows a sharp nick to appear between the cliff and the detrital accumulation.

8. RISE IN THE GENERAL BASE LEVEL OF DENUDATION

Deposition by rivers brings about a relative rise in the general base level of denudation, whether it occurs in valleys or at the edges of a tectonically independent part of the crust where the general base level of denudation coincides with the immediate base level of erosion (p. 128). Similar results are brought about by a relative rise in level of standing water to which denudation surfaces are directly tributary. Processes of this kind will be termed, for short, elevation or rise of the general base level of denudation. They are changes which do not induce any alteration in the type and shape of the slope units connected with them. It is not till denudation finds a continuously changing, relatively rising, base level that these alter. The resulting features represent a special case of waning development, naturally not that of waxing or of uniform development. In this discussion reference may be made to the previously drawn profiles.

The concave nick, where the surface of the alluvium, or the water level, joins the given slope unit, is the base level of denudation. Whether it remains as such depends on the rate at which this base level rises in comparison with the rate of development of the adjoining slope unit. In the case of a cliff face, the base level of denudation must be raised at the same rate as this recedes, if it is continuously to adjoin a cliff with the same angle of inclination as before; in the time the cliff takes to retreat from t 1 to $a\,a'$ (fig. 3, p. 137), the base level must reach at least the level of point a. If it lags behind, a basal slope develops above it, the lower parts of which become buried; and even when so shortened, this separates the cliff from the general base level of denudation. Flattening of the basal slope cannot take place so long as the base level continues to rise at the same rate. Slower rising would leave proportionately larger parts of the basal slope visible; it would be possible for its normal slope of diminishing gradient to appear [at the bottom of it]; until, in the limiting case, when the general base level of denudation is no longer being raised at all, flattening continues undisturbed. When slope units develop more slowly than the rate at which deposition, or the water level, is rising, they

L

are buried. This obviously takes place more readily and more frequently on slopes of gentle or moderate inclination than on steep or precipitous slopes.

Slope units, that are being drowned, preserve their gradient only when the rate at which the base level of denudation is rising, keeps pace with or surpasses the rate of growth of the respective slope units. This is made clear in figure 9 A. A cliff face adjoins the river t. In successive units of time it moves into the positions $a_1'a_1$, $a_2'a_2$, $t'a_3$, and a normal basal slope $t\ t'$ would develop below it. But the river is aggrading, and the level of deposition rises in the same unit of time to t_1, t_2, t_3. This, according to our premisses, is more than the basal slope can grow upwards, and more than the amount by which the cliff is receding. Under these circumstances, no normal basal slope can develop; if it has already been formed, it soon disappears under the rising floods of sediment or water, still retaining its gradient. However, the lower parts of the cliff cannot be simply buried in the same way, i.e. covered up whilst retaining their form and gradient, since denudation of the cliff face and the rise of base level are at any given moment simultaneous processes.

If, in very minute intervals of time, denudation and deposition followed one another, then, after the first unit of time, the cliff face would be in position $a_1'\ a_1$. There would be a minute basal slope $t\ a_1'$, but it would be buried under the alluvium which has meanwhile risen to $t_1 1$. The upper surface of this is now the base level of denudation. At time two, the cliff would be in position $x\ a_2$, from 1 a new minute basal slope 1 x would have been formed, which again would be buried by the material that had risen to $t_2 2$, etc. Below this material, therefore, there would be a slope with many steps (thick pecked line), removed from any further denudation; its mean gradient would be greater than that of the normal basal slope $t\ t'$, but less than that of the cliff. The slope which is actually formed and which is covered up at each moment of its upward development is, however, not broken when the base level of denudation is steadily rising; but because of the simultaneous working of denudation and deposition it is uniform. It is represented by the straight line t–1–2–3 which comprises all the infinite number of steps, chosen so as to be sufficiently small, of the type $t\ a_1 1$. The result is valid for any slope unit of any given gradient whatsoever: *if the general base level of denudation rises more quickly than the adjoining slope unit develops, the slope unit is preserved at the base level: but below it there arises, and is drowned as it arises, a gentler slope which is more steeply inclined than that normal slope of diminishing gradient which is developed when the base level of denudation remains fixed.*

The uniform rise of the general base level of denudation, as here assumed, occurs only in special cases and for a limited time. In its essence it is a process which is not uniform, which is accelerated at the beginning and then decelerated towards the end. Even when the causes continue to work in the same way, deceleration must take place, since the denudation surfaces of the district as a whole play the part of inclined sides to a receptacle receiving the upward growing alluvium or water. That receptacle is wider at the top—the widening being greater the flatter the average slope of the land concerned— and so, if the level is to rise by the same amount in successive units of time, there must be an un-limited increase in the supply of material filling it in. This is conceivable in parts of the crust which are sinking uniformly, or with accelerated movement, where the surface subjected to denudation becomes in the

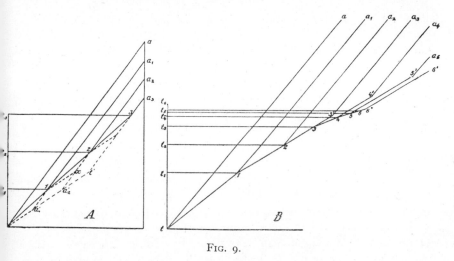

Fig. 9.

end completely covered by transgressing sediments of marine or contin-ental origin; but it is unthinkable in regions that are in any way moving upwards, at rest, or undergoing decelerated subsidence. It may be con-sidered normal, especially in the continental areas, for a rise in the general base level of denudation to take place with deceleration.

Fig. 9 B illustrates how this takes place. Suppose a cliff face to adjoin the general base level of denudation t. While it recedes in successive periods of time (of equal length) to a_1, a_2, a_3, the base level rises at the same time to t_1, t_2, t_3, i.e. by ever smaller amounts, or more slowly. And it has been assumed that, in time one, the base level of denudation rises more quickly than the normal basal slope can grow upwards: the buried fragment of slope t 1 is steeper than the basal slope (as shown in fig. 9 A). From the upper surface of deposition $t_1 1$ there arises as before a cliff

1 a_1. In time two, the rise from t_1 to t_2 just corresponds to the rate of growth of the normal basal slope; this (1–2) is buried. Yet still there rises out of the alluvium, t_2?, a cliff 2 a_2. In time three, however, the rise of the base level of denudation has already slowed down: from the alluvium $t_3 3$ there rises the upper part of the growing basal slope (3–3′), no longer entirely covered up, and above it the cliff (3′ a_3). In time four, because of their different individual intensities of denudation, they have reached 4–4′ and 4′ a_4. At that stage the general base level of denudation is rising more rapidly than the basal slope develops (i.e. than its normal slope of diminishing gradient grows). The part (3–4) of the slope that has been covered up during period four, when the alluvium rose to t_4, is gentler than the basal slope but steeper than its normal slope of diminishing gradient. This latter appears only during period five (4–5), covered by alluvium (t_5–5), above which the basal slope (5–5′) and the cliff (5′a_5) rise up. In time six there appears above the surface of the alluvium $t_4 6$ [sic, ? $t_6 6$] a fragment of the slope of diminishing gradient (6–6′), no longer covered over; and above it the basal slope (6″–6) and so on.

Slopes which are becoming buried by material accumulating with decelerating growth, have a convex profile. Their curve is continuous, provided the deposition is steady; when the general base level of denudation rises discontinuously with pauses, the slopes are divided up by convex breaks of gradient and so broken. Above the parts which are buried and so withdrawn from denudation, there comes a region of progressive denudation and flattening, and concave profiles of waning development appear. Usually such convex slopes, developed under a covering,* also continue downwards, since the deposition is, as a rule, linked to decrease and cessation of erosion, i.e. to waning development. A picture of such a complete system of slopes can be obtained by adding a concave profile at the left hand side of point t in fig. 9 B, as in the fourth position of the slope in fig. 3, p. 137. Such profiles are specially characteristic of the low hilly relief formed in homogeneous Devonian shales and greywacke which are overlain by Pontian and Levantine beds in the neighbourhood of Constantinople [Istambul]. The valley sides, immediately above their buried floors, are concave, passing up into continuously convex curves and then merging into the flattish slopes of the Thracian peneplane, which was formerly partly submerged by the youngest horizons [of the later beds] but only at its edges. On the peneplane, concave profiles again predominate. The buried hilly landscape[185] was thought due to the preservation of youthful forms. That is incorrect. The buried forms which appear to be entrenched in the peneplane surface cannot be those which characterised the denudation landscape before and during aggra-

* *Eindeckungshänge.*

dation; it presumably had steeper mean gradients and greater relative heights, and it was only during the transgression that the buried forms originated from it. This is made plain by the convexity of the upper parts of the valley sides, which might well be regarded as slopes developed under a covering. They might, however, also be interpreted as forms of waxing development, and there would be no difficulty arising from the fact that the convex slopes change downwards into concave ones, the flanks of extremely wide trough valleys. For it will be shown that in certain parts of rising crustal segments, it is the rule for waning development to follow the waxing type. It would be desirable to have fresh investigations made in the regions of the Thracian peneplane. In that connection, attention should be drawn to the extraordinary way in which Devonian sediments in the strata below the transgressing Neogene have been worked up. A zone of soil, several metres thick, has been found, and this (especially towards the upper margin of the buried valleys, and so towards the heights over which the peneplane extends) allows the underlying greywackes to pass quite gradually into the overlying Neogene sands and gravels. This makes it improbable that the sinking of the land and the transgression associated with it occurred very quickly, and that previously produced denudation forms were buried intact. The buried land appears far from being intact [i.e. it shows signs of weathering] and this is increasingly so in its upper parts, which seems to indicate that it is really a matter of slopes developed under a covering. If that be proved, it would mean that there was hilly country before the Thracian peneplane replaced it; and that this latter is therefore to be classed as an end-peneplane or peneplain.

This is a general indication of the extraordinary importance which the marginal zone, between the areas of deposition and denudation, possesses for the evaluation of peneplanes. For here, if anywhere, there is a possibility of finding a part of its previous history preserved in the form of an earlier relief below the correlated* strata. If this preceding stage is another peneplane, i.e. a graded transgressional surface of continental origin, then the peneplane in question can obviously not be an end-peneplane, a peneplain, which developed from what was previously more dissected mountainous country. These most important relations will be considered in detail later.

9. INFLUENCE EXERTED BY ROCKS OF HETEROGENEOUS CHARACTER UPON THE DEVELOPMENT OF SLOPES

So far, in our investigations into the origin and development of slopes, it has been assumed that the rocks are of a homogeneous character.

[* See glossary.]

The results obtained are neither altered nor limited by the influence which has been exerted on the course of denudation by the variety found in the composition of the earth's crust. That influence is based on the different resistance of the various types of rock on which—other things being equal—the intensity of denudation depends. In each type of rock —whether of great or small resistance—the development of slopes follows the same laws. But the speed varies, and the maximum gradient for any slope unit differs according to the prevailing character of the rock. More intense denudation in a region of less resistant rocks means a swifter rate of development and growth of the slope units; and consequently more rapid flattening as compared with analogous processes in more resistant surroundings. When there occur side by side rocks, which on account of their composition, texture, structure or bedding react differently to denudation, multiform changes of slope occur: the same angles of slope occur in slope units of differing stages of development; and slope units, which have had the same duration and degree of development, have different gradients as well as different surface areas.

STRUCTURAL BASE LEVELS OF DENUDATION

The features of an area in which there is variation in the character of the rock are well known. Earth sculpture leaves the strong parts standing out from their less resistant surroundings. In fig. 10 [p. 168] the profile illustrates the course of development and the rules that apply. It begins with a slope unit F 1 which at the given time just touches, at point r, the outcrop of a very much more resistant rock, such as an eruptive dyke B. For what first happens, the way in which the slope unit has developed is of no importance. Should it result from uniform development, the base level of denudation F would coincide with a water-course; in the case of waxing development, a steeper slope $F\beta$ would follow below F; in the case of waning development there would be a gentler slope $F\alpha$ below F.

In the region of rock A, the slope unit recedes in successive periods of time into positions shown by the numbers 2,3 and 2′,3′, etc.; in rock B, however, it would reach only x $a_2′$ on account of the lessened intensity of denudation here—taken as one tenth of that in A. The surface $a_2′$ x a_2 of B is laid bare. It is not preserved, however, since from the moment it has been laid bare, it also is exposed to denudation. The maximum gradient $a_2a_2′$ that can be reached by rock B is realised, since the position of rock $a_2′x$ a_2 is deprived of any support, i.e. is undercut. This undercutting takes place to the same extent in any successive moment of time, so long as a slope of the gradient and of the rate of development of slope unit I adjoins it below in rock A. While this, in time two, reaches $3'$ a_3 and then a_4, in B the undercut slope must keep its maximum gradient and move to $a_3 a_3'$ and $a_4 a_4'$, even if by itself it would recede, not at the same rate, but more slowly through spontaneous denudation. *The rate of development of the lower slope unit determines that of the slope above, which is steeper in the more resistant material.*

As to the slope above the outcrop of B: it recedes with the speed characteristic of rock A, but in no place can it be deepened below the outcrop of rock B which is being denuded more slowly. Below the slope unit that receded to 2 b_2 in time one, there appears a slope of diminishing gradient r b_2, which in its turn is undercut during its formation by the simultaneous shifting of the rock boundary from r to a_2'. It can easily be seen that the little undercut slope a_2' c_2, which actually appears in time one, is bound to have just such a gradient that denudation on it (rock A) works at the same rate as on the steeper slope below (rock B). *Above the exposed rock of greater resistance there arises a concave profile of waning development.* In these early developmental stages, however, the concave slope is convexly curved against the boundary of the rock outcropping below it, and yet still above the [actual] boundary against the more resistant rock which is giving rise to the feature as a whole. This steepening of slopes, with an approximation to steep steps following below one another, due to more resistant types of rock, can often be seen.

The slope, originally homogeneous, has been broken by the exposure of a body of more resistant rock. A number of breaks of gradient have appeared which separate the newly produced slope units and act as local base levels of denudation. In relation to these, the slope units develop independently. In the third position of the slope they are represented by the numbers I–V.

The breaks of gradient are of two types: the one set is associated with rock boundaries. In the diagram, these are labelled a_2, a_3, a_4, and so on (type a), and a_2', a_3', a_4', etc. (type a'). *They do not migrate upslope, and do not vanish in the highest parts; but they follow the shifting of the rock boundaries brought about by denudation, and every moment they are produced afresh at those places. We call them structural base levels of denudation, since they are connected not with the drainage net but with the structure of the crust. They arise wherever rocks of different resistance are being laid bare on a slope, and they are independent of the position and behaviour of the general base level of denudation.* In function they correspond exactly to local base levels of denudation in homogeneous rock. Their arrangement is always such that a convex break of gradient appears at the rock boundary on the uphill side, and a concave break of gradient on the downhill boundary, provided that the outcropping rock is more resistant than its surroundings. If not, it is the other way round.

The second type of break of gradient behaves normally: the breaks are formed at the structural base level of denudation and from there migrate upslope. If the character of the rocks does not change (differences in resistance remain unaltered, and bedding remains the same), slope unit III is produced, so long as a portion of slope of gradient I bounds rock B on the lower side for a sufficiently long time. When all the slope units above III have been removed in the highest parts, then only two breaks of gradient, of types a and a', remain. These separate the three sections I, II and III of the slope, which keep their gradients unchanged. The gradient of the last named is of course steeper than that of the ori-

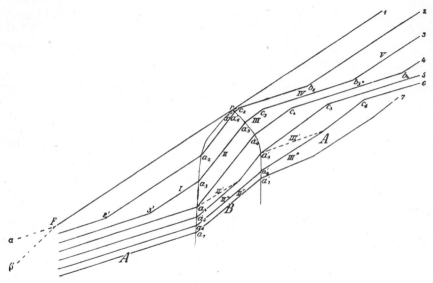

FIG. 10.

ginal unit F 1; steeper, too, than that of unit I which, since its development has been unaffected, has preserved the gradient of F 1.

The base level of denudation for III is, however, constantly being lowered, and on account of this there necessarily follows—as has been previously shown—an intensification of denudation and consequently a steepening of the gradient: the development of III is under the direct influence of the denudation on surface II, and so is influenced indirectly by the rate of development of I. In general this rule holds: *The intensity of denudation of the lower slope units is one of the factors determining the development of those parts of the slope which are situated above them in an area where the rocks are of other types and differ in resistance.*

This explains the fact that in land forms with predominantly gentle slopes, e.g. peneplanes, the denudation forms are obviously and, within certain limits, practically completely independent of the structure of the crust. This becomes evident when we follow up the development in fig. 10, where it has been assumed that, after time three, slope unit I has been replaced by its slope of diminishing gradient, which in its turn just touches the part of the slope a_4a_4' which has the maximum gradient. If that part had its base level of denudation a_4 fixed, it would recede as far as a_5' because of its specific intensity of denudation, and in so doing leave a normal slope of diminishing gradient II' below. This, however, is being undercut during its formation by the simultaneous lowering of the local base level of denudation from a_4 to a_5; so it does not actually appear, but in its place there arises the steeper slope unit II''. After time five, this alone prevails in the region of B.

Also, the convex break of gradient of type a' moves downwards, by amounts that become smaller in successive times. This is of decisive importance for what happens on the slopes above. If the base level of denudation a_5' were fixed, the normal slope of diminishing gradient III' would be found below the slope unit receding to c_6. Its local base level of denudation, however, sinks to a_6' at the same time, and so no surface III' appears, but in its place the steeper slope of diminishing gradient III''. For the same reasons, a gentler slope section is formed below it by the end of time six, and so on. It can be seen that waning development is not fundamentally disturbed when a more resistant type of rock outcrops on a slope. The concave profile appears, but it is interrupted by a convex break of gradient at the boundary between resistant rock below and less resistant above. For waxing development an analogous statement may be added: The convex profile is interrupted by a concave break of gradient between less resistant rock below and more resistant above.

With waning development, flatter and flatter slope units approach the rock mass B from below. Therefore flattening progresses more and more in its neighbourhood, and so the breaks of gradient at its boundaries become ever blunter. A comparison of the slope positions 3 and 7 brings out the diminution of the feature which is interrupting the slope—caused by the exposure of rock B. This interruption can disappear only when the lower part of the slope (in rock A) has reached the smallest possible gradient and therefore has been removed from further denudation. Then the flattening in rock B catches up with it. But even before that, the disturbance in the slope may not be noticeable. This occurs when there is little difference in the resistance of the rock materials.

Here is an important general relation: If slope units occur in rocks of a varied nature, the difference in gradient for a given difference in rock resistance is greater, the steeper the mean gradient of the slopes. Since this mean gradient is an expression of intensity of denudation, the above statement means: the more rapidly denudation is effected, the more markedly apparent become differences in the character of the rock. *Adaptation of denudational form to crustal structure is a function not only of the duration* (p. 49) *but above all of the intensity of denudation.* Therefore the way in which the character of the rock causes subtle adaptations in individual forms as, for example, in the Alps (steep relief) is to be contrasted with the far-reaching independence of crustal structure found in peneplanes (flattish relief). This independence is by no means complete, as the above investigation shows, and as is apparent to the eye; but it causes interruptions of gradient to become imperceptible when they are due to small or moderate differences of resistance in the rocks. On the other hand, the greater differences of resistance are by no means wiped out morphologically from peneplaned landscape, but are preserved as convex prominences standing out where the most resistant types of rock occur. In American literature they are termed monadnocks; German writings use the far better expression coined by Spethmann—*Härtling*[186].

When differences in the rock are less than has been assumed for fig. 10, the structural base levels of denudation form more obtuse angles. To convince oneself of this, suppose that in fig. 10 rock *B* (but not rock *A*) possesses a slighter resistance. Then slope unit II of maximum gradient is less steep than in the figure; and so it joins the units above and below, the steepness of which is unchanged, in more obtuse angles. This is true for all the developmental stages in which flatter and flatter portions of slope approach the rock boundary *A–B*. In a more advanced stage the concave and convex breaks of gradient, which interrupt the slope at the rock boundaries, become still less noticeable than in the diagram. Taking a certain mean gradient, e.g. that in fig. 10, the structural breaks of gradient are more obtuse, the smaller the differences in rock material; and when these become nil, the breaks disappear altogether, i.e. the slope has a uniform gradient, uninterrupted by any angle on its surface, whether re-entrant or salient. *For a given gradient of medium slope, the adaptation of individual forms to crustal structure is more pronounced the greater the difference in rock resistance.*

Among the innumerable and varied combinations of rocks of differing resistance, one group has for long been specially noticed on account of the conspicuous features associated with it: the alternation of layers of different resistance in flat-bedded [i.e. unfolded] strata. They are the prerequisite for the formation of a special type of land form, *scarplands*, and seem to afford the simplest illustration of the most strict adaptation of individual forms to the character of the rock. The example of scarplands which has been the most studied and commented upon is that between the Fichtelgebirge and the Black Forest. Resistant strata of Triassic and Jurassic age, mostly permeable rocks with considerable cohesion and stability, form steep escarpments of varying height and different gradients; and between them lie widely spread, flattish landscapes, peneplanes, extending over strata of less stability, usually impermeable and mobile sediments, rich in clay content. Near the step below them, these reach out on to the firm rock of the step. R. Gradmann has shown[187] that these peneplanes are no peneplains in Davis's sense; and that the steps are not tectonic formations arising from or coinciding with flexures or faults, as has often been stated, though this view is in but slight accord with the facts observed. His conception of the part which denudation plays in fashioning scarplands is an important and far-reaching step forward as compared with other less satisfactory explanations. He thought that peneplanes developed from the lowering and flattening of the ridge crests between deeply incised valleys, during a period when erosion was at a standstill.

It is only over this concept, already considered on p. 142, that we will here linger. A period when erosion is at a standstill implies a fixed position for the general base level of denudation. This has been assumed in the simplified profile of fig. 11. Above its foot t rises a slope $t\,1$ which extends over the almost horizontally bedded strata a and b, differing in their powers of resistance. It has the greatest gradient possible. For simplicity's sake, it has been assumed that all the layers marked a and all those marked b behave in the same way with respect to each other. However, a_w is a water-bearing horizon, which the higher a beds are not.

The construction must once again be based upon definite quantitative assumptions as to the intensity of denudation. There can be free choice of the values, without any effect upon the qualitative result. But it must be borne in mind that, in the more resistant rocks, denudation needs a longer time to produce a slope of diminishing gradient of specific inclination than in the less resistant surroundings. Thus, within a definite period of time, the slope of diminishing gradient produced in the more resistant beds is steeper than that on the others. The greater, therefore, the difference shown in the angles of inclination of the slope units at the same stage of development, the greater are the differences in resistance that have to be assumed to exist between adjacent types of rock. A certain margin is allowable in this, but once the differences are settled, the angles of inclination within the respective zones of rock must be kept unchanged. The type of the resulting form of the slope does not depend upon that choice, but only the actual gradient of the slope units composing it at a definite moment of time. This latter does not concern us here. For the sake of clearness, the profile has been simplified in a manner which in no way affects the result: in each space between two rock boundaries, i.e. within each zone of independent development, when concave profiles appear, an infinite number of slope units has not been drawn, nor even a great many, but only a few; and thus there seems to be a greater difference of gradient between them than there is in reality. Hence the concave breaks of gradient appear relatively sharp; but in nature there is a continuous curve and not a sharp nick at these points.

The profile can now be understood. According to assumption, the original position t I has the maximum gradient in all its parts. This is steeper in rock b than in rock a. Because of its specific intensity of denudation, determined by the gradient and by the characteristics of the rock, each of these parts of the slope would be displaced upslope by a definite

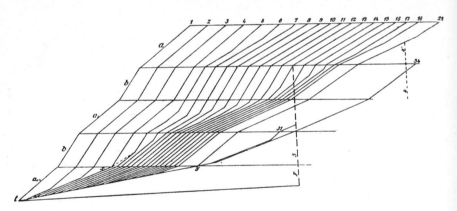

FIG, 11.

amount in unit time, leaving behind a normal slope of diminishing gradient. For the a layers, these amounts may be seen in the first three positions. For the assumed character of the rocks, these amounts are greater than the spontaneous recession of the maximum slope in the zones b. In the lower layer of b, this becomes visible only in positions 4–6; in the upper one, in positions 4–16 [(sic) ? 13–16]. A normal slope of diminishing gradient, however, can arise only in zone a_w, i.e. the water-bearing horizon; since, in the first place, here alone is there no undercutting through the recession of a slope unit occurring below; and, in the second place, the development is not influenced by the layer above. For the water content makes the rock mobile, in so far as it contains colloids, thus allowing it to slide away, and the layer above simply breaks off to a corresponding amount. Landslides (slumping) (p. 103) brought about in this way outstrip the spontaneous denudation occurring in the layers above a_w, and push the whole step back while maintaining its maximum gradient. There is deceleration as soon as the slope of diminishing gradient $t\,x$ has extended up as far as the boundary between a_w and b. Along its slighter inclination the material, assuming a constant water content, slides over a smaller area, moves more slowly and its migration slackens. From that time on, all the slope units of maximum gradient, occurring above, move back into the hill side, each at its own characteristic rate, which for the b layers is less in unit time than before (since there is now no powerful undercutting). The breaks of gradient associated with the rock boundaries are displaced at a slower rate, and so concave partial profiles appear within the individual rock horizons. Abnormal conditions may arise temporarily, if denudation works more quickly in a zone of mobile rock and maximum gradient (such as a_1) than in the more resistant layer (b) above it. If, however, a is deficient in colloidal substances or in water content, etc., it cannot slide away from under b. In a similar way and for the same reasons as in the relationship between rock wall and basal slope (p. 140), there arises an extension of the steep slope downwards, and the sharpest concave curve is no longer found on the rock boundary itself, but below it (zone a_1, positions 5–11). This can be observed in the pediment of cuesta scarps: the less resistant underlying beds with oversteepened surface gradient often share in their construction.

The problem here examined is a special case of waning development. In course of time the whole slope system becomes flatter[188] and acquires a concave cross section. With this, the disturbance of profile caused by petrographic differences becomes less and less. The stepping of the slope disappears, first of all in its lower parts (see position 34). Denudation reaches its goal earliest in the neighbourhood of the general base level of denudation; here the slope unit with the smallest possible gradient ($t\,y$) appears first. Until that has reached up to the lowest rock boundary (between a_w and b) and the undercutting of the upper stratum ceases, there is no possibility of its formation in b. The steepest slopes last longest in the highest parts, even if these consist of but slightly resistant rocks. The gradient is then smaller than if resistant types of rock formed the heights. *Consequently it is impossible for the scarpland peneplanes to have arisen, during a time when erosion was at a standstill, by the flattening of the ridge crests while the steps were preserved.* An extensive undulating landscape of the peneplane type cannot develop out of a high upstanding ridge crest by surface denudation alone. Instead, with waning development a ridge crest never becomes anything but a ridge crest, sharp-edged if steep slopes meet (see position 13; F S is the perpendicular dropped from the ridge), or rounded if gentler slopes intersect. Such would occur in a zone of but slightly resistant rock which had reached a far advanced stage of flattening: e.g. position 22, $s\,s'$ being the perpendicular dropped from the ridge.

This brings us close to the problem offered by the cuesta landscape. The sharpness of its scarps, of the lowest as well as of the uppermost, demands continual renewal of the structural base levels of denudation, to at least the extent of remaining the same, and that *during* the peneplanation of the differences in level between the individual steps. This renewal can be brought about only by a network of eroding water-courses which are working so as at least to preserve the slopes arising from it. The very formation of peneplanes demands the existence of a drainage net on them. This takes over, or took over, the part of general base level of denudation for the denudation and development of the flattish slopes occurring where the rock had but slight resistance. But if such a drainage net exists, or has existed, there must have been from the very first the possibility of its development, even in the region of rocks of slight resistance over which the 'stepped peneplanes' extend. That presupposes an original surface on which the 'soft' strata outcropped between the resistant layers and offered places upon which a stream system could develop. R. Gradmann has derived the scarplands from such an original surface (see his profile, *loc. cit.*, p. 127), correctly, as is shown here. It is no mere construction, nor only a theoretical necessity; but fragments of it are still clearly recognisable at the present day. The previous existence of a surface, which cut across the outcropping members of the whole set of strata at an acute angle and from which the scarpland was carved out, is a fact. That surface, of course, was not a peneplain.

The existence, side by side, of scarps and of widely extending peneplanes between them presupposes the individual parts of the drainage net to possess different values as general base levels of denudation. In this respect there may be distinguished: (*a*) the main branches which could cut through the scarp ridges, i.e. which are incised below the outcrops of the resistant layers in the foundation beneath the peneplane surfaces, and possess a direct connection with the general base level of erosion for the area; (*b*) the ramifications on the peneplanes themselves, which erode more slowly, or not at all, above the outcrops of those horizons by which they were once, or are still, held up. It is in relation to them that the further modelling of the peneplanes, as well as the recession of the final upstanding scarp fragments, takes place.

Thus the character of the rock, which determines not only the surface denudation, but even more particularly the erosion, is responsible for the origin of peneplanes in the scarplands. Other things being equal, the intensity of both denudation and erosion is lessened where resistant types of rock occur, and this lessening may have a far-reaching effect in a less resistant terrain above the outcrop of the strong rock. Flattish forms, peneplanes, are produced not only in scarplands, but also with a different arrangement of rocks provided the strong rock lies below, the less strong on top. When they are directly connected with the outcrops of resistant rock (structural base levels of denudation) they are developed only at the margins [of the less resistant beds]. Elsewhere, however, and this is the usual case, these peneplanes are related to a drainage net (general base level of denudation), the downcutting of which is retarded, or may in the end be practically stopped altogether, above the place where it meets that particular outcrop. Such structurally conditioned peneplanes may originate at any altitude. They depend only on the arrangement of the rocks and their properties, and are independent of the base level of erosion. They are not forms belonging to an earlier state of affairs, that have acquired their present altitude and general position in the surrounding landscape by some definite endogenetic movement; but they are adaptations of form to crustal material, and as such they are of the same age and have the same significance as the steeper forms, developed near by in the lower position. H. Cloos has pointed out these relationships in his description of Erongo, a South-west African inselberg[189]. Extensive flattish landscapes are found above the steep outer flanks of the mountain and the slopes of these face the source region of a stream system which originates in the heights, is impeded in its downcutting by resistant tracts of rock and, below these, leaves the massif in deep, narrow gorges.

The features of adaptation are no less characteristic when the different kinds of rock are arranged beside one another instead of one above the other. In valleys, which cross successively rocks of different resistance, a noticeable change in the valley cross section goes hand in hand with the change in rock material. The less resistant the rock bounding the valley, the less the inclination of its sides, and so the valley width seems greater. This holds even when the intensity of erosion is the same at every place. In what follows no account is taken of the inconstancy of erosional intensity which is found along all water-courses, e.g. as seen in the alternation of undercut and slip-off slopes.

For a given intensity of erosion, the sections of the slopes rising above the stream, in the less resistant rock a, are flatter than those in the adjoining stronger rock b. In both cases the slope units are at the same stage of development. The differences of gradient between them depend solely upon the differences of resistance between a and b. With increasing intensity of erosion (waxing development) slopes of maximum gradient finally appear. These are less steep in a than in b, and therefore appear in a sooner than in b[190]. If a has already reached its maximum gradient, whereas *b* has not yet achieved it, increasing intensity of erosion brings about increasing undercutting, and consequently the *a* slopes recede vigorously uphill. They intersect in the highest parts while, in *b*, slopes which are becoming still steeper develop above the stream. Convex profiles (in *b*) are then visible beside straight ones (in *a*). If finally the *b* slopes meet in ridge crests, these—because of their greater steepness—are relatively higher than the ridges in the region of rock *a*.

The relative height is dependent on the nature of the rock material, as has been long known and as can be observed everywhere in areas of heterogeneous structure, e.g. in the northern Limestone Alps. *When slope units at the same stage of development intersect in the highest parts of the country, then, other things being equal, the relative height in less resistant rocks is not so great as in stronger parts round about.* This is particularly clear in cases when the intersecting slopes are on the whole straight (uniform development and undercut slopes of maximum gradient).

With waning intensity of erosion, concave slopes appear first in rock *b*. They can be seen beside the straight *a* slopes until erosion has been decelerated to such an extent that even in rock *a* slopes of maximum gradient can no longer be preserved.

With the change in rock material, changes come about not only in the gradient of the slopes, but at certain stages of development in their shape also. This is true in areas where the character of the rock varies, both when the intensity of erosion is constant and when it fluctuates. Such conditions obtain when the rock boundaries do not cross the stream (which may follow a line of disturbance), or where the change of resistance to denudation over the whole surface, associated with the rock boundaries, does not also imply a change of resistance to erosion. In many instances this is not the case. Very frequently, especially if there are differences in the strength (cohesion) of rocks, the intensity of erosion is affected in a manner analogous to that of surface denudation. It is this above all which accounts for the often deep-seated difference found in the shape and inclination of the slopes along streams cutting through rocks of different strength. A short reference must suffice here.

A bank of rock, which is particularly strong as compared with its surroundings, may lessen the down-cutting of a stream in the whole reach lying above, and may have a lasting influence. The adjoining area of denudation [upstream] acquires the concave forms of waning development, and in this way differs fundamentally from the tracts lying immediately below. The less the strength of the rocks concerned, the more progress does waning development make in the area where erosion is checked (but not brought to a complete standstill). The concave slope systems then recede far back from the edges of the rivers. This effect, in combination with the increased meandering which takes place in rivers with impeded erosion, may lead to extensive removal of readily mobile rock material. The removal of the Neogene beds from the broad synclines of western Anatolia is due chiefly to these processes. There, the hindrance to erosion starts at those spots where the rivers enter the border zone of the broad synclines, which has been uplifted by tectonic movements, and consists of strong crustal material.

In their origin, the ledge-like denudation terraces, A. Hettner's *Landterrassen*[191], also belong here; they are associated with the courses taken by running water (i.e they are in valleys) and with the boundaries between flat or horizontally bedded strata of different strength which the water has laid bare. The most famous example is that of the platform of the Colorado Canyon[192]. Such terraces occur regularly in scarplands, in close connection with the peneplanes which they continue as ledges along the side of the deeply incised valleys into the region of the next higher scarp. The necessary condition for the formation of denudational terraces is that an eroding stream should, at one and the same place, lay bare, *one after another*, rock types of different strengths. Their further independent development depends upon the way in which this stripping takes place, and on the character of the rocks. Schmitthenner[193] has recently given his attention to this in the northern part of the Black Forest, and R. Gradmann in the scarplands (see p. 171 ff.).

The importance of the adaptation of denudational forms to the character of the rocks cannot easily be overestimated; for the characteristics of the *individual forms*, as well as their arrangement, depend to a large extent, as has been shown in this section, upon the nature and distribution of the rocks exposed at the earth's surface. It will be of great importance, therefore, now and always, to examine those processes which effect the adaptation. It may also contribute to further clarification of the processes of denudation. It must be borne in mind, however, that these are matters of detail, modifications, and not the fundamental laws of denudation and land sculpture. The adaptation is only part of the feature; it obeys the general laws of denudation and presupposes the causes which make denudation possible at the surface of the crust. This fact has often been overlooked.

10. SUMMARY

It is now possible to give a complete survey of the origin and development of slopes. Above streams, to whatever extent they are incising, banks grow upwards and become valley slopes. During their formation they are subject to denudation over the whole surface, and this, in its effort to remove the slopes, works everywhere in the direction of

M

lessening the gradient. The smaller the amount of erosion in unit time, the longer it takes for inclined surfaces to arise from the erosional tracks, and the greater the chance for the simultaneously operating denudation to come nearer to its goal. On the other hand: the quicker the downward erosion of the stream, the greater the speed with which the valley sides grow up above them, but the farther from their goal do the effects of denudation remain. *The intensity of erosion determines the gradient of the slopes rising above the drainage net; the details of their form then depend upon the character of the rocks concerned.*

In particular it has been shown that along the lines of the drainage net —the general base levels of denudation—fresh slopes of uniform gradient are always arising; their denudation is in equilibrium with the intensity of erosion and must always be so. If the latter changes, a new slope necessarily appears with a gradient such that the above-mentioned equilibrium is maintained. With increasing intensity of erosion, steeper and steeper slopes arise; with decreasing intensity, they become flatter and flatter. Between the successively formed sections of the slopes, breaks of gradient appear. They denote the levels to which the denudation of the uniformly inclined surface above each is related; they are the nearest (local) base levels of denudation. The surface of uniform gradient together with its base level of denudation make up one slope unit (i.e. form system)*.

Continuous change of erosional intensity leads to the formation every moment of a very minute slope unit. The breaks of gradient do not become visible as such, but a continuously curved slope takes the place of a slope system composed of many slope units. It is concave with decrease and halt of erosional intensity, and convex with its increase, continuously convex only so long as those breaks of gradient, which subsequently arise, have not yet appeared [see fig. 7, p. 158]. In both cases there are limits to the formation of new slope units: the slopes can become steeper only up to a maximum value which cannot be exceeded, and which is determined by the character of the rocks; the flattening (diminution of gradient) ceases with the appearance of the least possible gradient, on which further denudation can no longer take place.

The intensity of denudation which, for rocks of the given character, depends upon the gradient, is specific to each slope unit and determines its rate of development. All slope units, except those which are based upon the interruption of a slope because of a change in rock material, are produced at the edges of the streams of the drainage net, and it is here that they obtain their specific gradient. Maintaining that gradient, they shift back parallel to themselves. In addition to this, each slope unit

[* See glossary.]

grows upslope, and at the same time it is shortened and finally replaced in the highest part of the slope by the next lower slope unit which is always younger, having originated later. As a result of this behaviour the breaks of gradient which separate them, i.e. the local base levels of denudation, move in the same direction. Any slope unit which can at the present day be observed in the highest parts must—unless it belongs to the above-mentioned exception—have at one time immediately adjoined its respective erosional track in the same manner and with the same gradient.

The succession one above the other of slope units with different gradients provides a sensitive means of following up the erosional intensity at a definite place: a convex slope is proof of an increase in erosional intensity, a concave form proof of decrease. Changes in rock material may produce deviations from the normal form of slope. However, these do not obliterate the concave or convex type either everywhere, or permanently, and do not interfere with the sureness of this diagnosis. But it must be borne in mind that in many cases—always for waning and uniform development —the majority of the older slope units in the highest parts have already disappeared and been replaced by their younger successors. Even for waxing development, preservation of the oldest slope units is by no means the rule. Therefore, for a given area, the form of the slope does not always record the whole of the development up to the present day, but generally only the last phase of the erosional intensity. And so a complete investigation into the facts must take into consideration further characteristics, especially as regards the correlated deposits* and the surfaces on which they rest.

Upon investigating the conditions associated with change in erosional intensity and its causes, it becomes quite clear that the form of the slope is of outstanding importance as a means of diagnosis. It also helps in deciding the often discussed question as to how the drainage net of the German Highlands has created its present visible effect, the valleys. There is no lack of answers. The problem arises partly because of the small amount of erosion which can be proved to be taking place at the present day; partly because the changes along the drainage net since glacial times are noticeably insignificant compared with the total extent of the existing valley development. From this evidence it has, on the one hand, been deduced that erosion is working continuously but at a rate which might be considered infinitesimally slow as far as one can judge; on the other, it has been presumed that there is variability of erosion, especially in view of the way in which normal conditions are interrupted by periods of flood which occur only occasionally but are responsible for

[* See glossary.]

practically the whole of a river's work. Every river, at least in a temperate climate, first of all works rapidly towards a preliminary goal; only to continue its almost completed task by merely stagnating, as at the present day[194]. According to this view, the German Highlands should possess the forms associated with a great acceleration of erosion, i.e. they should be characterised by ridges of a flattened appearance, their flanks having sharp curves down to the valley bottom; and at their abrupt foot they should show the beginning of waning development.

Such profiles do occur. They are characteristic of the small furrows which originated in very recent times, or are now in process of formation, on the flanks of already incised valleys. But an entirely different type may be noticed along those parts of the drainage net which have shared, for a longer or shorter time, in the tectonic history of the mid-German rise. Within each drainage system, zones can be very clearly marked off according to the form of slope, which alone is being considered here. There are those in which the main amount of erosion is a thing of the past; and these are separated from others where the gradually increasing intensity of erosion has a present value that has never yet been exceeded. The multiplicity of the phenomena shows the need for specific investigations instead of incorrect generalisations.

To sum up: Any wearing away of land over its whole surface, if not due to moving air or moving ice, is connected with the action of permanent or intermittent streams. *The problem of the gradient of a slope* turns out to be a question of erosional intensity. When individual regions possess slopes with a specific mean gradient, this characterises them as zones in which the erosional intensity has a definite mean value. The question then arises as to what conditions decide this. *The problem of the form of the slope* has been traced back to the way in which the erosional intensity developed with the passage of time. What must now be investigated is why this should have increased in the one set of land regions, characterised by convex slopes, and have decreased in the other where concave slopes predominate.

On the whole, it appears that the sculpturing of land forms by denudation is fundamentally linked to the problem of intensity of erosion.

CHAPTER VII

LINKING OF SLOPES, FORM ASSOCIATIONS AND SETS OF LAND FORMS

1. OCCURRENCE AND COMBINATION OF CONVEX AND CONCAVE SLOPES

By itself, denudation over a whole surface can produce only concave slopes. Differently shaped profiles appear only when erosion takes part in the formative process. Erosion, as will be shown, is a process which varies from place to place, and from time to time, and is limited in space and time; on the other hand, denudation over a surface operates everywhere and practically continuously. Hence concave profiles are definitely the predominant ones. *They are the normal type of form.* However, they cannot be the original primitive type, for they arise from slopes leading down to a drainage net that is entrenched in the crustal structure. And these slopes are not parts of an original crustal surface, such as might be supposed to cover a rising fragment of the earth's crust; but they are the flanks of sharp erosional incisions. Each concave slope presupposes a phase of development during which erosion set in and advanced to some maximum before coming to an end. In short: waning development implies previous waxing development. Concave slopes should therefore grade *upwards* into convex profiles. This in fact is the usual form of slope, e.g. in the German Highlands along those valley stretches where concave slopes rise from streams eroding at a diminished rate, or that have now ceased to erode at all, provided that these slopes have not already removed those of preceding stages, and so reached up to the intervalley watersheds. This simple arrangement is specially typical of reaches in the upper courses and head waters of the drainage net found in the German Highlands and of the belts of dissected Mesozoic strata between them. The phenomenon is not peculiar to the Central German Rise, but occurs all over the world and presents a definite, general problem: what are the causes leading, at these places, to periods of accelerated erosion followed by periods of decelerated erosion?

The question is the same for the *terraces*, stepped series of shelves which here and there divide up the valley slopes and which have originated from former valley floors. They consist of several alternating concave and convex profiles one above another; and in the first place they signify merely a repeated change from acceleration to deceleration of erosion along the valley stretches concerned. In the region of the Central German Rise, terraces are found chiefly along the main lines of the drainage net. On the slopes of the Highlands they can be traced from the heights down nearly to the deeply entrenched valley mouths. But there they often disappear completely; and the stepped slopes which, as they approach the valley floors, have their steps ever closer and closer together, are then replaced by uniform convex slopes or by steep slopes of maximum inclination. Moreover, this behaviour is a general feature where terraces occur, and shows clearly what a complicated problem is presented. Justice is by no means done to this complexity in the usual interpretation given for uplifted terraces, viz.: uplift—erosion, then conditions of rest, followed by a renewed jerk of uplift—erosion, etc. Such an interpretation results from the faulty premiss: uplift, with denudation setting in only after this has been accomplished.

Concave and convex profiles appear not only above one another but also adjacent to each other in one and the same form association. Wherever the valley floor is not completely occupied by the stream belonging to it, this change is brought about by the inconstancy of the river meanders. They do not always touch and undercut the valley slope at one and the same spot, but they shift the undercut slope downstream. Where undercutting occurs, whether the erosion is solely lateral or is combined with downward incision, slopes of maximum inclination appear, or else convex ones; close by, at those parts of the slope which the stream just fails to touch, concave profiles develop. The occasional convex profile found in valley stretches where erosion has slackened, or even ceased, are of this type. As a concave profile is the determining morphological element in such conditions, the effect of these convex ones is never very marked. Conversely, concave profiles are not impossible in valley stretches where increasing erosion is in full play and convex slopes are predominant. *The individual slope profile has a diagnostic meaning only for the particular place at which it occurs. It reflects the course of erosion there. It does not, however, say anything about the development of erosion within the whole set of land forms to which it belongs, let alone about the development of the whole tectonically uniform block. In its individual parts this may have entirely different types of denudational relief, to one of which this particular profile belongs.*

Thus attention must be focussed on that type of land form which by its constant recurrence gives the characteristic imprint to the form association. Slope profiles are very often combined in such a way that those sloping towards streams of the same type or of equal power are consonant with one another, and fundamentally different from those which accompany the branches of a drainage net belonging to a different order. Plate III, illustration 3, shows very clearly that main slopes are concave—obviously they are growing up from a general base level of denudation which is falling at a diminishing rate or has already become fixed. It further shows that they are dissected by gulleys which are vigorously deepened whenever water runs into them, so that they are bounded by convex curves. Here the eroding lateral tributaries contrast with the main lines of the drainage net where erosion has ceased. This arrangement within the form association is extremely characteristic for certain regions. It is, for example, found regularly along the wide-floored main lines of the valley network in the Central German Rise (see amongst many others, the Wupper and Salza valleys in the Mansfeld district, the valley of the Mulde coming down from the Erzgebirge, the Saale valley above Hof, etc.). Here concave slopes rise up from the valley floors, and these completed slopes are the inclines on which new lateral tributaries develop. As is worked out in a later section, these side branches are intermittent watercourses, or they may even already have become perennial; and their immediate base level of erosion is practically fixed, since it is the floor of the main valley which is not now being any further deepened. They have to catch up with all the erosion already accomplished by the main river. They are outside any endogenetic influence, and unlike the main rivers, they did not receive their impulse to erode from the uplift of the block on which they flow. Instead they behave like streams which do their work on a motionless block, with an intensity determined by the already fixed gradient. Here, this is quite a significant amount relatively. The downcutting of these tributary streamlets, therefore, attains a considerable intensity, and so convex slopes are formed. These clear connections, however, do not really touch the problem, which is concerned with the arrangement shown by the form associations. The convex slopes of the tributary furrows, which have frequently developed into extensive branching systems, may give a characteristic appearance to whole tracts of country. As one gazes around, the most noticeable feature is the constantly repeated rounding of convex profiles appearing above them, and, in comparison with this, the concave slopes of the main valley tracks fade into the background. Increasing density of the valley net, produced by the headward recession and ramification of tributary furrows, is obviously in full course of development here. This is a feature not found in other regions in which there is equally pronounced vertical dissection but where the concave forms of waning development are in full possession and characterise the tributary valleys as completely as the main ones. In such places increase in density of the valley net seems to have come to an end. No subordinate furrows are developed on the completed valleys slopes, or only a very few; and here it is not the convex slopes which predominate, but concave profiles do so absolutely. *The core of the problem lies therefore in the question of the dissection into valleys and their increase in density, i.e. the development of the valley net.* In the one case, the slopes of the main valleys, on which dissection into minor valleys begins and progresses towards the intervalley divides, are not very old. Their floors—the base levels of erosion for the backward working tributary furrows—have not been in their present positions very long, and it is only a relatively short time since waning development began in the main valleys. In the other case, the practically fixed positions of these main valley floors were reached far earlier, and did not undergo any later changes. Thus the dissection of their slopes has practically reached the intervalley divides; and now the tributary furrows, which at one time were vigorously cutting back, are also entirely under the sway of the waning type of development.

In regions like that just considered, there is only one type playing any important part in the form association, in this case the concave slope. We may therefore speak of uniformity in the set of land forms in contrast to the combined or mixed features in that of the previously mentioned type. One of the most noteworthy facts about the earth's surface is that each of these types occurs *in areas that are separated from one another.*

As an instance of a type which fits in here, we may consider the Scarplands, discussed in a different connection on pp. 170–175.

2. CUESTA LANDSCAPE (SCARPLANDS)

This is not the place to go into details. Let us consider the following general features that may be observed in south-west Germany: In the region of the watershed between the uppermost reaches of the Danube and the Wutach, we come across only two units. (*a*) The gentle uniform eastern slope of the Black Forest, which—apart from the valleys sunk in it—shows no division into parts except on close examination, when one discovers a stepped effect (not, however, scarplands) which will be considered later [p. 201]. (*b*) The Malm scarp, the continuation of the Swabian Alb, which, as we shall see later on, is a tectonically independent block. The outcropping Triassic-Jurassic horizons between them are never associated with denudation scarps, although the series of strata possess throughout the special character suitable for producing them. This can easily be seen in the neighbourhood of the Wutach, which is

eroding comparatively vigorously: the deeply sunk valley is bordered by
denudation steps, the beginnings of a scarp landscape, and they are
formed by the same stratigraphical horizons of the Upper Trias (Trochitenkalk and Stubensandstein), the Lower Jurassic (Arieten- and Psilonotenkalk of Lias) and the Middle Jurassic (Blaukalke of the Sauzei
Zone) which immediately to the north have not yet led to scarp formation. There, apparently, the essential preliminary condition is lacking:
the uncovering and constant renewal of the structural base levels of denudation by a drainage net which is eroding, or has at some time eroded,
with the rather considerable intensity typical of the Wutach or the
Neckar. Thus very old denudation forms have been preserved on the
heights between the valleys, which are not incised; and these are fragments of that surface into which, further north, in the drainage basin of
the Neckar, the scarp landscape has been entrenched, and from which it
has been sculptured.

Somewhat eastward of Donaueschengen, between the slope of the
Black Forest and the edge of the Malm receding from it north-eastwards,
there become noticeable—more or less clearly as the Neckar system is
approached—the first indications of scarp steps, still gently inclined
(Arieten- and Psilonotenkalk of the Lias α, to the north, in the region of
Schwenningen, in addition to the Trochitenkalk and Steinmergel bands
of the Gypskeuper and Sauzei beds). This is the entrance into the Scarplands which stretch away in constantly repeated, characteristic forms
from the summits of the northern Black Forest and the Bunter Sandstone of the Odenwald to the distant edge of the Malm scarp bent out
far to the east, and reach beyond that, east of the Franconian Jura, up to
the edge of the Bohemian massif[195]. Everywhere in this region two essentially different parts of the drainage system stand opposed to one
another: (a) the main trunks with their abundant water supply: the Main,
the Neckar, and their larger tributaries, which are entrenched in the
scarpland and so have cut through the scarp-forming horizons; while
above them, close at hand, there occur flattish form associations, often
stretching out as wide peneplanes; and (b) the ramifications, scantily supplied with water, which lie on the high surfaces of such peneplanes near
the sources of the streams and thence work back towards the edge of the
next higher scarp, which they dissect into lobes. These branches end
downstream with a *break of gradient in the longitudinal profile*, connected
with the same stratum as gives rise to the scarp in question, and the
associated denudation surface of the 'tread' above it; in general, this is
more sharply pronounced, the more resistant such a scarp-forming
stratum is to mechanical action. The scarp forming horizon of the Upper
Muschelkalk usually gives rise to the sharpest breaks of gradient of this

kind, as well as to the peneplanes which reach over from this horizon to the Lettenkohle and the Lower Keuper beds, and are the most extensive, as well as the flattest, most level of their kind.

The main lines of the drainage net show the natural features of progressive downcutting, which will be dealt with in a later section. Along certain reaches the downcutting seems to be in full swing; in between there are extensive stretches in which this was the case a short while ago, geologically speaking, and will be so again as soon as the eroding sections have worked back upstream. On the whole the valleys have slopes of considerable mean gradient, which are convex, straight or broken by terraces. Usually, but not everywhere, they are joined below by concave foot-slopes, and above them outcrop the horizons of scarp-forming strata which have been cut through. The longitudinal and transverse profiles of the *lateral branches*, originating from the above valleys, are very characteristic; they gnaw gradually into the body of the intervalley divides and they lead to a progressive lobing and disintegration of the scarp faces overlooking the main valleys and of the peneplanes above these. Near their mouths they have the shape of the main valleys; they are, for instance, canyon-like and accompanied by rocky walls as far as the main valleys are so (like the valley stretches in the Malm, e.g. in the Franconian Jura); up-valley they rapidly become narrower, as rapidly gain in gradient, and are then excellent examples of sharp V-shaped valleys; all at once, they widen out into gently sloping, shallow troughs, this taking place as soon as the scarp-forming stratum, and the longitudinal break of gradient associated with it, have been crossed (fig. 12, p. 187).

In such places there is an extremely sharp border line between essentially different parts of the drainage net. It is far less obvious, but still always clearly recognisable, where the headwater tributary, or indeed the upper course of a main stream, lies on a scarp peneplane: as, for example, the Tauber above Rothenburg. The break of gradient in the longitudinal profile of the watercourses separates two sets of land forms: the mixed ones of the valley entrenched in the scarpland, and the uniform set on the intervalley divides, recognisable by their concave profiles. Here the denudation forms found are the flattish relief of the peneplanes and the medium relief forms belonging to the next higher scarp face. This gradually recedes under the influence of denudation, a considerable part being played by slumping at the water-bearing horizons. The general base levels of denudation for this are the courses of the neighbouring streams belonging to the peneplane; and their local base level of erosion lies at the outcrop of a scarp-forming stratum at the above-mentioned break of gradient. Its level may be considered as practically fixed with reference to all its tributary slopes; and denudation here, the development of the scarpland peneplanes as well as of the scarps rising up from them, is completely removed from endogenetic influence.

Every portion of such a steep scarp is a slope ready prepared for the development of a new watercourse, for example, along the track of a corrasion furrow or, more often, resulting from the issue of a spring, etc. They find a strong gradient, consequently they cut down vigorously, invade the body of the step (as will be elaborated later [p. 188]) and so elongate by means of headward erosion. At short intervals such sharply V-shaped valleys, the upper continuations of the shallow flattish valley troughs of the low relief lying in front, may be seen encroaching upon the upstanding scarps. Most of the streams are intermittent. As a rule,

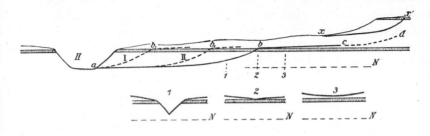

H	Main valley	1,2,3.	Positions for cross profiles of lateral tributary ac (as shown below)
abcd	Longitudinal valley of a tributary working backwards		
I and II	Previous positions of the same tributary		Scarp-forming horizons of the sedimentary strata
b	Break of gradient in longitudinal profile	xx'	Longitudinal profile of one of the most recent gullies, working back from the peneplane into the up-standing scarp (supposed to be lying at some distance behind the section abc)
$b_1 b_2$	Previous positions of this		
N	Level of the floor of the main valley		

FIG. 12.

and this is what one would expect, the eroding stretch is limited to the hindmost section, working up into the steep scarp face. Along the greater part of the length, down to where it runs out on to the peneplane lying in front, there is no longer any erosion. Thus the scarp appears cut up into lobes, eaten into, with narrow dividing spurs between streams which are invading it from the land in front and are responsible for the lobate effect. The development of these intervalley divides, which often jut out like bastions, takes place in the same way as that of the outer slope of the whole step. They in their turn are cut up into lobes by valley furrows of a higher order which start from the streamlets just mentioned. There is recession of all the scarp slopes which face this increasingly close net-work of furrows eating back into them. A flattish declivity is left behind which, in the limiting case, has the least possible gradient. This, together with the ever increasing density of the network of steep-sided valleys cutting into the scarp face, dissecting it into units of smaller and smaller orders, very often leads to the well-known breaking up of the intervalley spurs into isolated hills which remain for a while as residuals in front of the retreating scarp. They have concave profiles and become lower as soon as the last remnants of the flattish form system have been removed from them (see Plate VII, illustration 1). They may be considered classic examples of waning development. After their disappearance they, too, leave an intervalley spur, bounded however by flattish slope units and belonging to the peneplane in front of the scarp.

The structural base levels of denudation, which determine the preservation of the peneplanes adjoining the scarps, are thus renewed from two directions: First, they are affected by those powerful strands of the drainage net, which have cut through the scarp-forming horizons and so appear entrenched in the scarpland. They have been able to effect downward erosion in every part of their course; in many parts they still, at the present day, have power to do this, and nowhere is the possibility permanently lost. Along these branches of the drainage network, erosion and denudation for the last time retain their connection with the general base level of erosion, and so are not withdrawn from endogenetic influences. Dissection, disintegration and destruction of the peneplanes on the divides between these entrenched streams work outward from them. Thus the peneplanes or, as the case may be, the homologous flattish forms, grow at the expense of the receding scarps rising above them. Secondly, here, in the region unaffected by endogenetic conditions, scarps are preserved as the typical form because of the way in which freshly forming and ramifying furrows work back, starting from the foreland and cutting sharply into the scarp faces. Thus, parts of the stream course which have great erosional intensity, are perpetually invading them, at countless places, at the same time; and *these* are responsible for the indispensable renewal of the structural base levels of denudation.

This shows that there is an *erosional history* for the network of valleys on the scarpland peneplanes; and generally this goes back further, the farther the parts of the valley system under consideration are removed from the next higher step. Direct traces of this previous history, however, are as a rule completely wiped out by the mass-movement of rock waste, which is considerable, corresponding to the slight resistance of the material, for the most part rich in colloids, of which the country here is composed. The absence of stream channels from many of the shallow valley troughs, and even from whole branching systems of them, is an *acquired characteristic*. It is due not only to the extent of the migration of rock derivatives, highly mobile when soaked with water, but just as much

1. Zirkelstein in the Elbe Sandstone Mountains

2. Inselbergs in Herero Land, South-west Africa

VII. INSELBERGS

to the nature of present erosional activity at the scarp face. For it is an established fact that streams, which are but feeble or intermittent, erode only at times of flood—as is to be expected. They then incise their sharp Vs in the scarps, and so lay out the plan of the valley furrows. It is amazing what a quantity of rock material is brought out by a single storm from those parts of the valley-course which are farthest back and which are usually very steep. As these eat further and further into the body of the upstanding step, they leave behind them lengthening stretches of lessened gradient, often entrenched far below the scarp-forming bed so that they come to lie in a terrain of but slight resistance, readily becoming reduced to a mobile condition. Such a position for the general base levels of denudation necessarily leads to the phenomenon first noticed by R. Gradmann, viz. the outcrop of an often very thick series of mobile strata on the immediately adjoining concave scarp-faces. This may include the whole succession of beds lying between the level of the scarp-forming stratum and that of the neighbouring general base level of denudation. It appears impossible for the stream beds, thus entrenched in surroundings of mobile rock material, to be preserved for any length of time once they have lost their steep gradient and when, before that, they were used only occasionally or by what were (at times of low water) mere narrow threads. They become closed up by material moving down from the sides; and this often happens even before they issue on to the peneplane in front. For they lack not only the mass of water but also the gradient which together can produce the force necessary to keep them open[196].

No part of the drainage net belonging to the scarpland peneplanes can be deepened below the local base level of erosion. Instead, a gently concave longitudinal profile is produced, which always rises gradually from the break of gradient to the higher parts of the country. The heights of the intervalley divides above the valley floors bear a definite relation to the erosional curves of the drainage system, the general base levels of denudation. They have a similar magnitude; since similarly gentle inclines lead up from the valley bottoms with average slopes that are similar or even the same, and intersect on the intervalley divides. For this reason the scarpland peneplanes have a general inclination in the same direction as their drainage lines. R. Gradmann has already drawn attention to this[197]. The scarpland peneplanes may behave in either of two ways as regards the structure. In the one case they slope down in the same direction as the dip, or at least *the valleys belonging to the peneplane* drain in that direction. An example of this is afforded by the peneplane which slopes down eastwards from the Stubensandstein edge of the Steigerwald towards the foot of the Dogger Malm scarp of the Franconian Jura, and ends above the slopes on the left side of the Regnitz valley, slopes which do not rise very high above the river. Starting from here, far-reaching dissection of that peneplane has already taken place. Following the tracks of the valley troughs that dissect it, wide trough-like valleys invade the main body of the peneplane from the Regnitz westward. They soon become narrower in this direction, and not far from the scarp summit of Steigerwald, the longest and most persistent of them may be seen to reach back in a steep curve to the break of gradient. This separates them from their continuations, shallow trough-shaped valleys in the high-lying and undissected peneplane. Convex slopes characterise these uppermost steep beginnings of the entrenched valleys, just as they do the analogous stretches of all their lateral ramifications which are eating into those parts of the peneplane that are preserved at the height of the intervalley divides. The high plateau above the Malm scarp (Swabian Alb), although inclined similarly with reference to the dip of the strata, is of quite a different type and origin and, as must be mentioned here and specially stressed, in no way illustrates the relationships under discussion.

The other kind of scarpland peneplane has a general slope in the *opposite direction* to that of the bedding, since its valley network drains that way. The residual scarpland plateaus between the Swabian Alb and the Neckar, the main artery of the whole region, are of this type. Starting from the deeply sunk main streams of the drainage net, *dissecting tributaries* from all directions invade the foundation of the peneplane. Some of these side branches flow in the same direction as the dip and therefore *against* the general slope of the peneplanes lying above the Stubensand-stein scarp which they are dissecting (many tributaries of the Jagst, Kocher and Murr). They were interpreted as stretches of consequent drainage[198]. If this implies that the origin of the rivers and valleys was due to a former flow of the water along inclined bedding planes, it must be emphasised that the bedding planes have nothing whatever to do with it. It is rather that the backward extension follows or has followed an inclined water-bearing horizon to the base of the Lias; and obviously this took place by the process of *headward erosion* to be considered later. This seems to be notably true for the 'retrograding' tributaries of the Murr and Jagst, but it can still be definitely proved only for a few places in the basin of the Jagst since the Lias has in the meanwhile been reduced to scattered island-like residuals. By far the greater part of the headward erosion here took place in past times; but it has left behind valleys which, having been eroded backwards, continue to develop, continue to deepen and continue to elongate backwards.

Photo. by L. Waibel

1. In a semi-arid region. Omatako in Herero Land, South-west Africa

Photo. by R. Land

2. In a humid region. Achalm, Swabian Alb

VIII. INSELBERGS

3. INSELBERG LANDSCAPES

Quite a number of the characteristic phenomena, shown in the relationship of the scarpland peneplanes to the scarp faces rising above them are, in their development and in their appearance repeated with slight variations in the inselberg landscapes which first became well-known from the African examples[199]. The fundamental characteristic in their outward appearance is the special relationship existing between the forms of denudation worked down into the crustal structure and the projecting parts left between them. When an uplifted portion of the earth's crust has been divided up vertically by denudational processes into mountains and valleys, the elements givings its special character to that set of land forms are the hollows, the valleys: the course they take and their depth, the shape and gradient of their sides, determine the arrangement and character of the intervalley divides, the projections lying between them. This ceases to be true in the case of an inselberg landscape. Here it is the insular projections which are the striking, determining element. Obviously the remnants of the once continuous country at a higher altitude[200], they rise above peneplanes which have replaced not only individual valley tracks, but whole valley systems. Indeed the mountain flanks occasionally rise with extreme steepness above the gently swelling peneplanes which are crossed by shallow valley troughs and which, here and there, seem in addition to have been graded, levelled, by subsequent alluviation. Perhaps these very conspicuous contrasts have diverted attention from the way in which the foot-slopes of the inselbergs are shaped. At any rate every observation made upon these shows the error of the view, constantly repeated in the literature of the subject, that there is a sharp nick where the sides of the inselberg break off against the surrounding peneplane. Fantastic hypotheses as to the origin of inselberg landscapes, which led to the purely speculative notion of an aeolian origin for peneplanes in general, are partly based upon this error[201]. *The slope profile of all inselbergs is concave.* A continuously concave curve always forms the foot-slope between the steeper slope units of the higher parts of the mountain and the flattish slopes of the surrounding peneplane which likewise have a concave form[202] (see Plate VII, illustration 2 and Plate VIII, illustration 1). *The inselberg landscape is the characteristic landscape of waning development.*

The height of the highest inselbergs above the surrounding country indicates the minimum extent of vertical dissection which the area has undergone by stream-cutting during the period of waxing development which necessarily went before. Fairly often the maximum relative height, which the present inselberg region ever attained, has been preserved almost unaltered to the present day. This is true, for example, wherever the mountain summits still consist of flattish slope units. It is only when these have been removed and steeper slope units have taken their place that there can be more rapid lowering of the inselbergs, leading to their ultimate demolition. In this case it is of no consequence whether the earth's crust is at rest or in motion (see pp. 152–153). Thus it is found that the plateau-like inselbergs of a region, even when they are not the relics of scarplands, are all about the same height, while the pointed hills derived from them have smaller relative heights that are individually quite different from each other. Here the process of lowering can be followed specially well: the lower the elevations, the gentler as a rule are their flanks, other things being equal (see Plate VII, illustration 2). Standing at the end of the series are gentle surface swellings ending in sharp points—in granite country crowned by tors or piles of boulders. When these vanish, they leave behind intervalley spurs bounded by flattish slopes. These then form part of the surrounding peneplane, and are incorporated in it.

What determines the development of inselberg landscapes is the behaviour of the drainage net: *the weakening of its erosional intensity until it comes to a standstill.* The cessation never takes place simultaneously everywhere along the drainage system, but becomes noticeable first of all along the main streams; these react in a direct manner to movements of the general base level of erosion, and so they are also the first to give up their erosive work when the base level has reached a fixed position and remains there for a long time. To begin with, concave slope profiles appear in the lower courses, and here also flatter slope units first begin to work up towards the intervalley divides[203]. Here the rivers are already widening their valleys by the increase in size of their meanders, so that there is growth in valley breadth and the distance apart of the upper edges of the valley, measured at right angles to its trend; the steep slope units are moving back from the alluvial valley bottom and below them the slope of minimum gradient is appearing (pp. 138–140, 143); whilst, in the uppermost reaches, erosion still continues. Downcutting there is associated with the uppermost, steep sections, which are sunk furthest into the crustal structure. This is in accordance with a law which has already made its appearance in connection with the scarpland areas, and which will be treated in detail later. These *eroding portions* work upwards and lengthen the valley incisions, which are bounded by correspondingly steep sides. This process must continue so long as there are any parts of the land at all which stand up above an erosional curve of gradually increasing gradient—to be defined later. Thus the eroding stretches go on ceaselessly working back into the most centrally lying parts, and eventually dissect or disintegrate them also by means of correspondingly steep-sided valleys. The same thing happens to the intervalley spurs belonging to the main valleys, their tributaries and the lateral branches of these. For everywhere here the valley flanks provide steep slopes all ready to form starting points for fresh backward working furrows, from which again sharply V-shaped valleys, still younger and of a minor order, originate. Thus there arise lateral branches of the second, third and x-th degree, all without exception bounded by similarly steep slopes, since generally speaking the eroding portions are all characterised by the same erosional intensity. The last and youngest of this kind are the gashes that furrow the slopes of the inselbergs. The steepness of their sides shows that the erosion is transmitted without loss of intensity right up to the ultimate ramifications of the valley system[204], even when only single branches of this remain, the greater part having already vanished, i.e. having become valley troughs on the peneplane.

As the eroding portions, which multiply upwards, splintering as it were into an increasing number of ramifications, work headward, the intervalley spurs, like the central regions, become disintegrated into progressively smaller units. They become pinnately divided into ridge crests, the 'feathers' of which are again split up, and so on; and where ramifications meet from opposite sides, saddle-like passes develop, dividing the crests into rows and groups of peaks. *These are the nuclei of the inselbergs.* This penetration of the eroding portions into the highest, most central parts of the country—central in relation to the lower courses of the main streams—together with the increasing ramification, means not only that the valley density is increased (this is by no means identical with the river density) but also that the valley courses lengthen. And so the eroding portions leave behind them lengthening valley sections along which erosion is growing weaker, so that waning development begins—and, as before, succeeds in establishing itself along the lower courses of the main drainage lines. Just as the zone of erosion and, with it, the whole zone in which correspondingly steep slopes are produced, spreads from lower reaches of the main rivers towards the most central parts of the country, so does the succeeding zone of valley widening and slopes with concave profiles or, more shortly, the zone of waning development. It arrives there quite independently of what may be happening in the meanwhile to the general base levels of erosion. If these, for example, are affected by some renewal of erosion in the water-courses, then waxing development, with its characteristics, sets in afresh in the lower courses and spreads up-valley along the drainage system; but that does not prevent waning development from meantime reaching into the neighbourhood of the watersheds. However, it is clear that under such circumstances waning development in the regions of the lower courses of the streams has *not been completed and cannot be simultaneously nearing completion in the most central areas.* For the steeper slope units which are rising up from the watercourses now incising themselves intensively, push vigorously upwards in the direction of the intervalley divides; and on reaching the tops of these, they swallow up the flatter concave form associations before these have been reduced to that degree of flattening which it is possible to reach there (a consequence of the difference in the intensity of denudation on steep slope units and those that are less steep; see p. 71, and chapter VI, section 7, p. 155).

The inselberg landscapes of the continental areas, however, are characterised by the fact that they exhibit form associations of waning development which extend over very vast areas of tectonically uniform parts of the earth's crust; and they stretch with equal completeness from the lower courses of the main lines of drainage, where the development is already complete over wide areas, up to the most centrally lying parts where it is nearing its completion. This implies that the general base levels of erosion must have remained in relatively unaltered positions throughout very long periods of time[205]. There is thus a deep-seated, fundamental difference from those zones which show the characteristic land forms of waning development, but are confined within exceptionally narrow limits; they are to be found on the top of very many mountain ranges (broad folds) in mountain belts, especially in the arid and semi-arid provinces, or on the high parts of the German Highlands and Scarplands. Here, the region of waning development, always narrow, is everywhere separated from its present general base level of erosion by a zone of steep slopes, a zone of renewed or increased erosion. It is only exceptionally and where there are favourable circumstances (e.g. the character of the rocks—Scarplands) that the waning development attains its goal, peneplanation, and scarcely more than the upper or headwater districts of the valley-net belong to its domain.

Whenever there are valley stretches along which erosion has ceased, the steep slope units retreat, and slopes with the least possible gradient broaden out at their expense. The projecting intervalley spurs are narrowed, the extremely gentle slopes merge into one another around them and over the previously mentioned saddle-like passes; they meet in softly curving flattish divides between the valley troughs, now become wide and shallow. In this way the peneplane grows at the expense of the intervalley divides, the relics of which remain visible for a while as inselbergs. These usually form a zone lying between the completed peneplane and a central more or less continuous mountainland. It is quite analogous to the zone of residuals which occurs in front of the retreating edge of an escarpment (see Plate VIII, illustration 2). *This zone of inselbergs* naturally appears first in those places to which the waning development penetrated earliest. This is the case for the regions under discussion, in the neighbourhood of the lower courses of the main lines of drainage. As waning development spreads towards the central parts of the area, the zone of inselbergs also advances in the same direction. Meanwhile the inselbergs have already disappeared from the region of the lower courses; and, in the source region, valley dissection of the continuous higher-jutting country is gaining ground. Thus, as has been mentioned, the position of the inselberg zone is between the central mountainland and the continuous peneplane surrounding it; and it ceases to be so only when the central mountainland has itself become disintegrated into inselbergs.

Erosion and denudation work at a slower rate where the rocks are resistant. Such rocks become visible as eminences above the surrounding country when this, on account of its slighter resistance, succumbs more quickly to the wearing-away process. It is therefore to be expected, and has been confirmed by observation, that with waning development the intervalley divides remain longest preserved as upstanding heights when the district is one of strong rocks, and that the inselbergs tend to be associated, as by preference, with such zones of more resistant rock. The designation '*Härtling*' refers to this[206]. It is, however, a mistake to think that inselbergs must always be '*Härtlinge*'—or 'monadnocks' as the Americans call them—and such a view by no means corresponds to the facts[207]. The inselberg type of scenery also develops on perfectly homogeneous crustal material, if only the necessary conditions are present for undisturbed waning development. It is an absolutely normal link in the series of denudational forms through which a portion of the earth's crust passes if its general base levels of erosion (which may be the local ones) remain in a relatively stable position for a long enough time. The inselbergs themselves are relics of the highest parts of the country, where the steepest slope units have been longest preserved. They are relics of intervalley spurs, which after their disappearance leave behind further intervalley divides, but such as then belong to the surrounding peneplane. This is an end-peneplane, a realisation of Davis' peneplain.

The process of waning development is completely independent of climate. The sole factor needed for its occurrence is the weakening of erosion; the sole factor needed for its completion is the elimination of endogenetic influences from the processes of denudation. These influences would be expressed in relative fluctuations of the general base levels of erosion, and would be propagated upwards from them, following the drainage net. They may be absent either because the general base levels of erosion remain for sufficiently long in a relatively fixed position;

or because the areas subjected to waning development are separated from the general base level of erosion by the sufficiently slow working-back of steeper types of land form and of breaks of gradient in the longitudinal profile of the main streams (forming local base levels of erosion). Both cases lead to the formation of inselberg landscapes and peneplanation of wide stretches of country. Thus neither the genetic relations nor the observed facts afford even the slightest support for the view frequently put forward that the origin of inselberg landscapes is connected with a special type of climate or with a change of climate. Typical inselberg landscapes are already known to exist in almost every climatic belt. In South America they stretch from subtropical Uruguay to the completely tropical Guianas, and they are a speciality of the Brazilian shield[208]. J. Walther describes them in North Africa at the junction of the Nubian Desert and the Sudan (Kassala Mountains), and compares them with those of the Coromandel coast which has its time of drought in winter only[209]. Even as far south as South Africa, they have long arrested the attention of travellers in the east, west and south-west of that hot continent[210]. They characterise the Deccan[211] and turn up again in Australia. *They are distinctive not of any one climate, but of the continental masses.* Their origin, as well as their extensive development, is based upon the properties of those rigid crustal areas which have been long withdrawn from the processes of mountain building. They are not found in the mountain belts nor in the adjoining parts of the earth's crust included in their movements. *This* is the problem presented by the inselberg landscapes.

It must, however, be mentioned that in some details of their characteristic features there are differences which may be traced back to climatic influences. There is general agreement in stressing the sparseness of the soil cover, not only on the slopes of the inselbergs, but also on the peneplanes of countries where vegetation is scantily developed or where conditions are actually hostile to it. As F. Behrend, E. Obst, G. L. Collies[212] and more particularly H. Cloos have pointed out, this is a consequence of the spreading out of rainwash over the whole surface, so effecting a comparatively thorough and rapid removal of the reduced material from even very slight slopes. It thus lays bare extensive denudation surfaces and keeps them continuously exposed. This, as was shown on p. 143, reacts on the shaping of the foot-slopes of the inselbergs. In areas where precipitation is rare, but not too rare to find a surface of attack—especially in the semi-humid and semi-arid regions—these actually show a sharper concave curvature than in the case of inselbergs of the same type but overgrown with a continuous cover of vegetation.

4. PIEDMONT FLATS AND PIEDMONT BENCHLANDS
(PIEDMONT STAIRWAYS)

Though this has so far remained quite unnoticed, the forms characteristic of inselberg landscapes are strikingly connected with other form
associations found upon tectonically uniform portions of the earth's
crust, when these belong to a definite type including, amongst other
examples, the German Highlands. A distinction must be made between
the form associations occurring on the heights between the valleys that
are sunk in the highland, and those of the valleys themselves. The former
only will be considered here. In some places, dissection by somewhat
recent valley furrows has already advanced so far that the old form associations, characterised throughout by their very much more gently inclined slopes, have already been entirely removed from the intervalley
divides, and replaced by the steeper slope units that are working their
way up from the valley incisions. This is especially the case on the
sloping sides of the German Highlands. Yet not throughout. The completely dissected western slope of the Black Forest, disintegrated into
rugged mountain country with forms of intermediate steepness, stands
out in contrast to the eastern slope which is almost intact, especially in its
southern sections. And in spite of the way in which valleys have pene-,
trated into that side of the mountain block overlooking the Rhine, such
considerable remnants of its older form associations are still preserved on
the intervalley divides that it is possible to diagnose them and to fit them
into their place with certainty. It is the same with the western descent of
the Fichtelgebirge. What can there be seen as more or less extensive
remnants, on the heights between the deeply sunk valleys, is still visible
in continuous form on the wide-stretched northern slope, where it is
only just notched by occasional valleys and their still short, backward
working, side branches.

(a) THE HARZ

But little has been preserved of the former northern and southern
slopes of the Harz mountains; more, proportionately, of its summit. The
flattish forms of this join with a sharp break of gradient the steep slope
units originating from the valley courses (of the Oder valley and Bode
valley type) that invade far up into the body of the mountain mass. The
breaks of gradient here are just as sharp as those which have arisen from
the numerous and often short, sharply V-shaped valleys at the actual
edge of the mountain mass. Convex slope profiles are characteristic of
the entrenched valleys which, at the mountain edge, are so close together
that their steep slopes have already met on the intervalley spurs. Thus,

the ancient land forms of the summit are narrowed down—having been already removed from the edges of the highland mass; hence the impression of mountains which they give; and it is only between the larger valleys, standing well spaced from each other, that the summit landscape extends as far as the edge of the massif.

The land forms of the summit are characterised by the concave slope profiles of waning development, except for occasional sharp V-shaped valleys (*of very recent origin*) which reach up the sides of the inselbergs. This holds throughout, being true also for all the side branchings of the valley network. The general form is an undulating peneplane, traversed by very wide shallow valley-troughs. Above it there rises a still continuous group of mountains, relatively steep-sided—the Brocken, with its associated summits—as well as several lower, not very steep elevations, which may be adjudged to be of the nature of *Härtlinge* (Auerberg, near Stolberg, is typical: a volcanic stump of Permian quartz porphyry)[213]. Some of these latter show an unmistakable connection with definite types of rock (Achtermannshöhe is of metamorphic rocks of the granite contact halo; Schalke, south of Goslar, and the high ridge of Acker as far as Bruchberg, are of Kahleberg quartzite of Lower Devonian age). However, this adaptation to rock material decides merely the delimitation of such heights, not their relative altitude; for similar rocks and zones of resistant material likewise take part in the composition of the surrounding peneplane. Furthermore, this peneplane extends over parts of the massif of Brocken granite, which also forms the core of the central highland—here there is absolutely no connection between upstanding parts and the character of the rock—and it extends right over the Bode granite stock. Yet granite is by no means a specially resistant rock!

The central mountainland of the Harz does not owe its existence to any particularly resistant type of rock; it is *not* a group of monadnocks of resistant rock, but higher standing country dissected by valleys. Its intervalley spurs *are associated with zones of strong rock, where these outcrop at or slightly above the existing mean level of the intervalley divides*[214]. The same is true for the peneplane, the resistant monadnocks of which lie at another level, and naturally have a smaller relative height and flatter modelling than those of the central mountainland. In general: *the character of the rock, and the way in which forms are adapted to it, does not determine their mean relative height, but does decide the arrangement of the intervalley divides. And monadnocks of resistant rock, i.e. isolated elevations, project above them only when the outcrop of the more resistant type of rock occurs at or just above the existing general level of the intervalley divides, a level which has been determined by other circumstances.*

On the north side of the central mountainland the peneplane is only narrow; but it is extremely clearly developed (in this case on the Brocken granite, on its metamorphic aureole, and on the Kahleberg quartzite). Southwards it occupies a wider space. Towards the east, it stretches out evenly over the mountain mass from its southern to its northern edge. Thus the land-form character is the same as that found in the inselberg landscapes of continental regions, and the arrangement similar. However, not only is there the absence of a sense of spaciousness but, above all, of the characteristic signs which, in inselberg landscapes, force upon one the conclusion that the general base level of erosion has remained fixed for a long period of time: viz. the completion of waning development in the regions of the lower courses and at the same time its carrying through into the headwater regions. Only the latter can be observed in the German Highlands and in the Harz, it is only the headwaters of the drainage system that belong to the highland landscapes. The lower courses, on the contrary, leave the mountain areas in deeply incised valleys, thus indicating that at the mountain edge the general base levels of erosion do not remain in a relatively fixed position.

The history of the valleys shows that this evidently has always been so. By following up any of the deep valleys that are working further and further into the mountain mass, a zone is reached, at a varying distance from its edge, where the gradient rapidly increases and the steep convex slopes approach close together. Above this, a break of gradient in the longitudinal profile must be crossed. This denotes the spot up to which the latest and relatively youngest eroding section has worked back. The valley continues upstream with a gentle gradient, a greater width and a slighter depth—now bordered by concave foot-slopes into which the convex curves of the upper valley slopes pass downwards—until a fresh zone of increased gradient, increased narrowness, and again convex converging slopes lead to a higher-lying break of gradient. Then one finds oneself in a still wider, shallower trough-valley, the concave slopes of which, however, change as before into convex curves towards the upper parts. In this way, by steps becoming ever lower and gentler, steps which are expressed as an alternation from steeper to lesser gradients, the wide shallow valley-troughs of the peneplane are reached. Their flattish slopes are concave and widely opened-out. The concavity, here too, does not reach up to the divides between the valley-troughs, but gives place in that direction to a convex curvature which, for all the flatness of the slope units, cannot be overlooked[215].

The type of valley just described, which is constantly repeated, but which, however, comes out distinctly only in the valleys of older origin, is characterised by having several breaks in its gradient. These separate from one another stretches of river-bed, which are concave in form, but which join together to give a curve that is, on the whole, convex. The vertical intervals between any two breaks of gradient generally become smaller from below upwards. In this direction the sections of steeper gradient become *shorter and less steep* so that it is the peculiarity of concave portions of the profile to have smaller mean gradients the higher the valley to which they belong (shown diagrammatically in fig. 13). The uppermost member of the system is a valley-trough, frequently without any stream, on the peneplane itself.

Thus eroding sections of various ages, which can have originated only one after another at the general base level of erosion, move upstream, behind one another, along one and the same valley furrow. The point, up to which each of those portions has cut back, up to which each has carried into the body of the mountain mass a deepening and steepening of valley and slopes respectively, is visible in the form of a break of

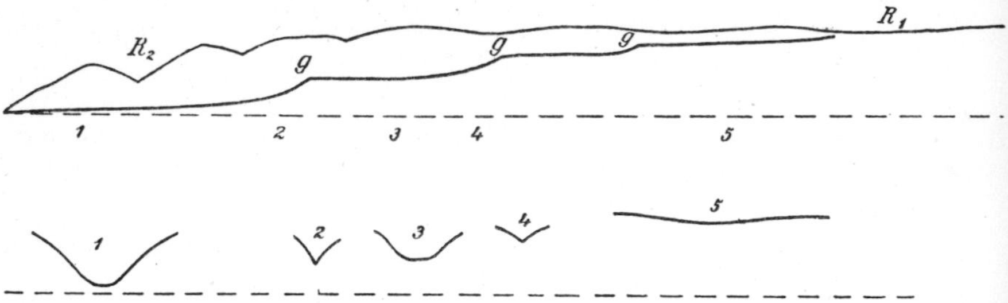

g Breaks of gradient in the longitudinal profile *1–5 Transverse profiles* R_1 *Peneplane* R_2 *Medium relief*

FIG. 13.

gradient[216]. There is no difficulty in recognising that the eroding sections, which follow one another downstream from the upper reaches, represent not only a simple series as regards age, but a series of increasing erosion, increasing valley deepening and increasing steepness of the valley slopes. This development begins with the formation of valley-troughs on the peneplane, a conclusion permitted by actual observation. The slope profiles of these prove beyond doubt that the flattish forms of the peneplane have not been derived from the flattening of once higher, steeper elevations, but conversely, that their forerunners had even gentler slope units which are still preserved on the watersheds between the valley-troughs. These latter are therefore very ancient stages of the valley history which has been trending towards dissection. Consequently the peneplane, in spite of the agreement of its form-characteristics in many of their features with an end-peneplane like that of the widely spreading inselberg landscapes found in continental regions, cannot

however be one. It does not, like these landscapes, replace higher projecting parts of the country, now vanished. And, in addition, in spite of a
formal similarity, the central mountainland of the Harz is not analogous
to such relics of a higher surface as are found in inselberg landscapes. For
it never had the wide extent which is today an intrinsic property of the
peneplane. However, this does indeed widen at the expense of the
mountainland, which it penetrates in the form of valley floors, as soon as
waning development sets in there. This has come about not because the
general base level of erosion remained in a state of relative rest, but
because the central mountainland *has been separated* from that base level
of erosion by the insertion of more steeply inclined eroding portions
along the courses of its main arteries of drainage. Since the first, oldest
system of breaks of gradient arose in the longitudinal profile of the
streams, the further denudation and development of peneplane and
mountainland, and dissection of this latter, have taken place in relation
to those breaks of gradient, uninfluenced by the behaviour of the general
base level of erosion. These are local base levels of erosion for all tributary streams and slopes and, as will be shown later, they do not experience any relative lowering. Their first appearance, therefore, signifies
the change-over to waning development, which has, since then, been the
predominant type in the sculpturing of summit landscapes, and will continue to be so until their destruction by backward working dissection.

*For that type of peneplane which, like the high country of the Harz, sur-
rounds a central mountainland, we will use the term piedmont flats.*

A preliminary survey of the Black Forest and the Fichtelgebirge shows
that here, too, there is a central mountainland disintegrated into individual domeshaped hills and surrounded by a peneplane. Since both elements are composed of the same rocks, there is no question of *Härtlinge*,
and so it seems as if the conclusion might be drawn that those highland
landscapes, above their dissecting valleys, consist of a central mountainland and a piedmont flat. Indeed the history of the valleys and the
development of the slopes prove quite clearly that the peneplanes are of
the same type as in the Harz and are not end-peneplanes. However,
closer investigation reveals the new and surprising fact that it is not a
single peneplane which covers the summits and slopes of the highlands
in question, but that here *there are several peneplanes of the same type
recurring step-like one above another. Such an arrangement may be called a
piedmont stairway* [or *piedmont benchlands*].

(b) PIEDMONT BENCHLANDS

This type can be studied particularly well in the *Fichtelgebirge* and on its northern slope. Only the main features will be given here, details being omitted[217].

The central mountainland consists of a widely extending group of individual elevations, only loosely connected with one another, which are grouped around the headwaters of the Eger and Röslau. It is advanced far towards the western edge of the Bohemian massif, and towards this edge relatively short, deeply dissected slopes lead down, to end abruptly above the marginal fault. Reference will be made in another connection to this marginal zone, in which the relatively unmoved Mesozoic foreland is lying right up against the underlying pre-Mesozoic structure that has been powerfully uplifted and is rising even more vigorously at the present day. To the north, east, and south, on the contrary, the land falls away only very slowly, after the manner of the gentle slopes of a flattish dome, the axis of which culminates in the Fichtelgebirge and is continued north-eastward in the Erzgebirge.

Two different types of land forms occur amongst the elevations of the central mountainland: (1) Those with sharpened crests which, when they are composed of the Fichtelgebirge granite, frequently end in tors surmounting flanks of concave curvature (the type of Kosseine, Rudolfstein, Grosser Waldstein, Hoher Matzen; and (2) *dome-shaped mountains*, the most striking characteristic of which is the convex rounding that appears above the concave slopes and leads over to wide-stretching, almost level surfaces crossed, in the summit region, by extraordinarily shallow troughs. These dome-shaped mountains belong to two independent levels; the lower one (at about 870 to 900 metres above sea-level: the ridges between Grosser and Kleiner Waldstein, Hochhaide, Platte, the western extension of the Ochsenkopf) is separated from the upper (Ochsenkopf, Schneeberg over 950 metres) by a zone of rather steep, convex slopes and remarkably steep valley furrows. The flat surfaces at both levels possess each its own system of valley troughs showing a very slight gradient. These are the uppermost parts of valleys which, on the slopes, are V-shaped, steep-sided and becoming deeper, in general terms the highest ramifications of all of the whole valley system. Thus there can be no doubt whatever that the surfaces are not isolated flattish land forms, but fragments of a flattish form association. Those at the 900 metre level occur all round the land which projects above that height. The accordance of altitudes, *but in especial the limitation both upwards and downwards by the same zones of convex systems of slopes, which separate them from corresponding levels of flattish form associations above and below,* make it certain that the fragments of flattish relief occurring at the same height are parts of one and the same peneplane (P_2 in fig. 14).

But it is not, after all, the highest and oldest peneplane of the mountain mass. The highest domes, Ochsenkopf and Schneeberg, have in their turn considerable relics of a higher one from which isolated tors—insignificant but clearly recognisable remnants of a mountainland once rising above it—project above the flattish intervalley spurs that belong to it. The *record* of the history of these mountains begins, therefore, with the features of almost completed waning development which are to be found at the summit of the highest and oldest elevations. What is preserved of the peneplane has the characteristics of an end-peneplane (P_1 in fig. 14), which has spread at the expense of some sort of mountainland. Of this latter only a few rather steep slope units remain. Nothing has been preserved to show the waxing development which must have preceded the waning development that is continuing to the present day in this oldest part of the mountain mass.

Similar conditions are found at the lower level. The peneplane P_2 at one time uninterruptedly surrounded a 'central mountainland', of which only the highest elevations still bear relatively restricted remains of the oldest flattish relief (P_1). The lower peripheral elevations no longer show anything of this. Here the steep concave slopes rising up from the P_1 surface already intersect in sharpened crests (e.g. Kösseine); or else—in the closer vicinity of the highest projections—what remains of it are merely isolated rather steep slope units on the top of the flattish intervalley spurs of the P_2 surface: the granite tors[218]. This means that the waning development, which started from the P_2 surface, has been almost completed in the peripheral region of what was once the central mountainland, but in the innermost part of it is still a considerable distance from its goal.

The progress of the waning development is associated with shallow, but fairly steep-sided erosion furrows, which reach back up the slopes of the dome-shaped mountains and debouch on to the P_2 surface, this being their nearest level of reference. In addition to them, there is a considerable number of larger, deeper, and more steep-sided valleys, V-shaped in cross-section, which start from different yet always lower levels of reference (local base levels of erosion); and it is quite clear that they cut back more vigorously the lower the altitude of their reference level. Valley courses, which have dissected the P_2 surface also into separate fragments, act as such levels; and naturally they could become the starting point of these V-shaped valleys only after they themselves had worked right back to the most central part of the mountain mass[219]. In the region of the upper courses of the Eger and Röslau, two such levels

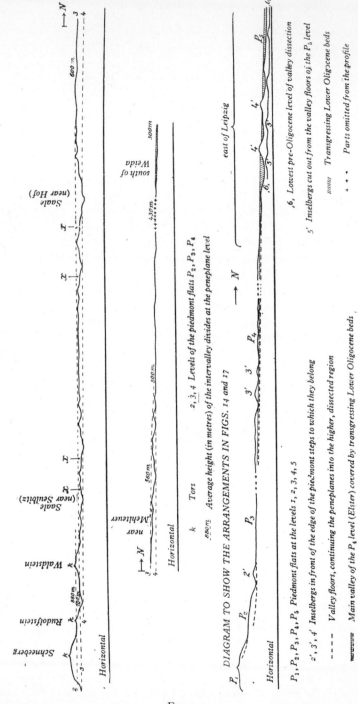

DIAGRAM TO SHOW THE ARRANGEMENTS IN FIGS. 14 and 17

2, 3, 4 Levels of the piedmont flats P_2, P_3, P_4

$\overline{880m}$ Average height (in metres) of the intervalley divides at the peneplane level

k Tors

P_1, P_2, P_3, P_4, P_5 Piedmont flats at the levels 1, 2, 3, 4, 5

2', 3', 4' Inselbergs in front of the edge of the piedmont steps to which they belong

- - - - Valley floors, continuing the peneplanes into the higher, dissected region

═══ Main valley of the P_4 level (Elster) covered by transgressing Lower Oligocene beds

6, Lowest pre-Oligocene level of valley dissection

5' Inselbergs cut out from the valley floors of the P_5 level

ⅢⅢⅢ Transgressing Lower Oligocene beds

• + • Parts omitted from the profile

FIG. 14.

can, in the main, be observed. These are [1], the very broad, undulating heights with an exceptionally level appearance, found between the sunk valleys of the Eger, Röslau and their tributaries, and [2] these valleys themselves. The tops of the intervalley divides have their own system of exceedingly shallow, often swampy and peaty valley troughs, and keep at an even height throughout (on the average 670 metres). They are broad fragments of a uniform peneplane which extends over granite, gneiss and quartz phyllite indifferently. In the Kessel von Wunsiedel, framed round by the central mountainland, it has a gentle general slope from the foot of Schneeberg (slightly over 700 metres) eastward to about 650 metres; and low *Härtlinge* (felsite porphyry of Thierstein) and relatively recent outpourings of basalt project here and there above it. The wide trough-valleys of the Eger-Röslau system are sunk into *this P₃ surface* (fig. 14); their most recent lateral branches, bordered by convex slopes, are working back to the intervalley spurs and effecting their progressive disintegration.

In the form of *wide valleys* the P₃ surface leads between upstanding parts of the central mountainland in the Markt Redwitz district southwards into the region of the Naab, westward over Weissenstadt-Gefrees to that of the Main, and northwards between Kornberg and Waldstein to the Saale area; and it is thus in uninterrupted connection with the extensive north and south slopes of the mountain mass. This connection is not destroyed nor rendered unrecognisable by the fact that very much narrower, younger valley furrows are sunk in the above-mentioned gaps.

North of the central mountainland the peneplane P₃ is the dominating form element. Characterised throughout by a uniform flattish surface, made slightly undulating by valley troughs, it goes on from the edge of the central mountainland, where its intervalley divides reach approximately 700 metres, over the Münchberger massif of gneiss and the surrounding Palaeozoic outcrops of the Frankenwald and Vogtland northwards as far as the Schönberg-Mehltheuer-Syrau district to the north of Hof, where its intervalley divides lie at a mean altitude of only 560 metres. It has a general slope northwards, and ends in the district named as a multilobate edge (a zone of steeper convex slopes); while, lying in front of this, groups of hills and inselbergs, cut out from the peneplane, witness to its once far greater extension northwards. We shall refer later to this and to its present state of dissection into valleys.

The P₃ peneplane not only borders the high parts of the central mountainland which carry the flattish relief P₂, but trenches upon this in the form of valleys. It thus denotes a level from which there originated the first definitely established dissection of the higher parts of the land by valleys. The dissection of the P₂ surface into separate fragments goes

back to these far distant times and has been in continuous progress right
from the beginning up to the present day. It has been brought about by
waning development. Concave slopes lead up from the P_3 surface, where
it borders on higher rising country. They already intersect in sharpened
crests, crowned by crags, in places where the side valleys debouching on
to the P_2 surface are sufficiently close together (Hoher Matzen, Epprecht-
stein); here and there, the higher parts of the country have already been
completely removed, except for crags. Mention must be made of the low
block-like summits, crags and boulder heaps set upon the intervalley
divides of the P_3 surface as found, for instance, on the heights between the
entrenched valleys of the Eger-Röslau system[220]. Here, too, the P_3 surface directly adjoins the main mass of the highest elevations, on the
flanks of which (east side of Schneeberg) particularly steep concave
slopes (with a sharp convex break of gradient) lead up to a highland
which corresponds to the *upper* level of crags (about 880 metres) [P_2 in
fig. 14].

We can now recognise the following general relationships: each peneplane of piedmont benchlands continues in the form of valley-floors into
the regions rising up above it. Each lower peneplane is thus the level at
which dissection starts for the zones where the upper surface is a higher
peneplane. Every lower peneplane must therefore in its origin be younger
than the next higher one, and the highest parts of the country are also
the oldest areas of denudation. Dissection by valleys is a consequence of
erosive incision. At the present day—and apparently always—this is
associated with the steeper slopes which connect two peneplane levels. It
is there that convex valley-side profiles and convex longitudinal profiles
occur in the headward cutting tributary valleys. In short, the peneplane
levels are separated from one another by zones of convexity. The eroding portions that are working backwards find their *nearest* reference level
on the next lower peneplane, on to which they debouch (leaving out of
consideration the younger valley courses that are already dissecting that
surface). The eroding sections leave behind them zones of decelerating
or of completed erosion. The waning development starts, therefore, on
each lower peneplane, and spreads upslope from it. *Piedmont benchlands
are thus characterised by zonal alternations of the features of waxing development (convexity) and of waning development (concavity), as they have
been followed through in what has been said above.* With such an arrangement, therefore, each peneplane is in fact related to the one next above it
in the same way as a piedmont flat to its central mountainland. Just as in
such a system of waning development, the central mountainland disappears along its edges, and the piedmont flat spreads at its expense, so
does each peneplane of a piedmont stairway spread at the expense of the

next higher peneplane step. This latter is progressively disintegrated into a mountainland by the invading valleys, and the watersheds between these valleys become increasingly notched and dissected, till finally nothing is left of them but inselbergs. These, therefore, are always to be found in a zone in front of the lobate edge of each peneplane step, and their height accords well with that of the step or is lower. This may be particularly well seen in the northern sections of the Fichtelgebirge (and Erzgebirge) slopes. As soon as the conditions for waning development occur on a peneplane (viz. separation from its own general base level of erosion), each one of the whole piedmont series spreads in consequence towards the higher and older regions; at the same time, it is narrowed down by the next lower step, is disintegrated into a mountainland of accordant height, and finally removed. Thus each piedmont flat has a part lying towards the higher country (a proximal part), which has the characteristics of an end-peneplane. *This is the part* which grows so long as anything remains of it and of the land rising up above it.

It can readily be understood that the downright 'eating up' of the peneplane, by the step next below it, must have reached the maximum amount at the places where denudation, in the form of waning development, has been acting longest (counting right up to the present day). This is the case for the highest and oldest parts of the area: of the P_1 surface in general, only such fragments still remain as correspond to the proximal part, which has the nature of an end-peneplane. Of the P_2 surface, there are substantially larger remnants and the greater part of them lies *outside* the zone of crags (Waldstein ridges—Kornberg, and western foreland of Ochsenkopf and Schneeberg). It is at least unlikely that they are of the nature of end-peneplanes. By far the greatest part of the P_3 surface is of just the same type as the Harz peneplane, in view of its analogous features. This is undoubtedly the case in the region of the Münchberger gneiss[221].

The lobed northern edge of the P_3 flat (north-west of Plauen, Vogtland) rises less sharply than the upper steps. Extremely wide troughshaped valleys invade its domain there[222], and dissect it into no less wide intervalley spurs. However, in the region considered, these no longer exhibit an undamaged peneplane; but they are in their turn dissected by the shallow trough-shaped tributary and headwater ramifications of those valleys into a disturbed hummocky landscape, the summits of which at first reach almost to the height of the P_3 surface (about 560 metres), becoming, however, noticeably lower to the north. In this direction there is a complete breaking down into inselbergs, which look as if they stood on the intervalley divides of a *lower* peneplane (P_4 in fig. 14). North of the narrow inselberg zone, this extends unbroken and absolutely flat[223], disappearing under the Tertiary and then under the Pleistocene materials of the lowland embayment of Leipzig.

The arrangement is again characteristic: the P_4 surface continues, in the form of valley floors, into the step on the top of which the higher peneplane extends, and in front of which there is a relatively narrow strip set with inselbergs. The two peneplanes are separated from each other by a zone of steeper convex slopes which are nevertheless not so high and are noticeably less steep than the analogous zones between the higher peneplane levels (P_3–P_2, P_2–P_1).

Peneplane P_4, also, has a general slope down towards the north. Near the edge of the step next above it, there are the intervalley divides belonging to that surface at a height of about 500 metres, at 450 metres or less in the neighbourhood of Zeulenroda-Naitschau[223], sinking down northwards to 400 metres (south of Triptis and Weida) and further to 350 metres (north of Triptis) and 300 metres (around Weida). Here, where the Elster, Weida and Auma unite, the peneplane is preserved only in narrowed fragments on the heights between the shallow valley system entrenched in it. But it can be clearly recognised, and that not only on account of the system of valley-troughs which is peculiar to *it*, but particularly by the aid of the Tertiary beds, which transgress from the north as far as that [224]. The peneplane in this belt passes from the folded Palaeozoics (Cambrian to Kulm) over the Zechstein on to the Lower and Middle Bunter sandstone.

The Tertiary beds which transgress farthest southwards over the P_4 surface belong to the upper stage of the continental Lower Oligocene. The lower division of this (which may, however, already be of Eocene age) did not stretch out so far. It, therefore, does not appear on the mountain slope till a slightly more northerly latitude has been reached; and in the area where it is best developed, the lowland embayment of Leipzig, consists of clays, fine sands (or quartzite) and intercalated seams of brown coal. By contrast, the further-reaching upper division is characterised by the coarser facies associated with proximity to the mountain mass; it consists of fluviatile sands and gravels, the composition of which points to *long continued* transport (not necessarily from a great distance). Its lower surface is anything but a plain. Apart from the slight inequalities which result from the mantling of the system of valley troughs belonging to peneplane P_4, one can notice a gentle sinking of the surface of transgression at both sides (not, however, tectonically conditioned) towards the valley of the Elster near Weida and south of it: an old, very wide and shallow valley course, into which the Elster and its meanders have been sunk, has been filled in by Oligocene material. Within this valley track and a few of its side branches (e.g. near Netzschkau) the

Tertiary penetrates far southwards to Ölsnitz, south of Plauen; and there, on a very pronounced ledge on the valley side, high above the Elster, it reaches to more than 400 metres above sea level[225]. It is this valley track, the most important, the largest and therefore also the deepest, still followed at the present day by the Elster, which belongs to peneplane P_4 and from it has invaded the higher region to the south[226].

This situation is significant for deciding the age of the peneplanes. If, where the exposures preserved in this area seem to justify it, one dates the peneplane P_4 as of Lower Oligocene age, then it is quite clear that such an age can apply *only* to the P_4 surface and to some former stages of the *valley dissection* of the higher parts; the higher peneplanes which occur there must, on the other hand, be in every case older—and in parts substantially older—*so far as their origin is concerned*[227]. This latter must be stressed, since we have recognised that every peneplane belonging to a piedmont stairway, any peneplane at all above which higher land rises, is continuing to grow, up to the present day, and must go on growing until the higher upstanding parts vanish, however far back its first appearance may reach. Therefore even extremely ancient peneplanes of this kind always possess parts which have a geologically recent origin. Though their existence can be established, they cannot, however, be distinguished from the older parts.

Before looking for further evidence as to the date of formation of the peneplanes, let us cast a glance at the present dissection by valleys, the history of which adds substantially to the picture so far gained of the piedmont stairway. All its steps are sharply incised by valleys, younger in origin than those cutting through the peneplane levels bounding them at either side [i.e. top and bottom]. The arrangement and characteristics of the peneplanes are preserved intact and uneffaced only in those parts of the watershed regions between the main valleys which are far from the streams themselves (in this case the Saale and the Elster). Side branches from these push upwards towards the main intervalley divides, and disintegrate the peneplane steps on them in the same manner as can be observed at the frontal edges of the peneplanes. This is happening not only today, but has been happening all the time from the moment when one of the main watercourses began to cut through the individual peneplane levels. Thus along the main valleys the features, including the forms, of valley dissection are analogous to those at the corresponding level on the frontal edges of the piedmont flats. Here and there it is possible to identify them, since dissection by valleys follows certain rules, in the same way as has been already shown for the Harz. *Identical stages of valley dissection have not only concordance of form, in longitudinal and transverse profile. They are also separated from stages, both above and below, which have forms concordant with one another, by similar convex fragments of slope or zones of slope (in the valley cross-section), and by similar convex breaks of gradient (in the longitudinal profile).* The most reliable starting point for the investigation is the uniform level established for a particular peneplane.

Following the main valleys upstream, one quite usually comes to zones of decreasing valley depth, increasing valley width and diminished gradient of the valley slopes. The same arrangement is found in all the side valleys, so that their headwater branches have absolutely the same character as the headwater reaches of the main rivers. They show the oldest, earliest stages of valley dissection; at their lower ends appear later stages with greater depths and especially with steeper side slopes. These have not worked so far upstream, and they are separated from the first group and from one another by breaks of gradient, steeper reaches of backworking erosion. Along the main valleys, and along those tributaries very plentifully supplied with water, these breaks of gradient hardly ever occur, and have never been established with certainty. The reasons for this will later be found to lie in the mass of water and in the length of the stretches of valley along which the gradients and the *differences* of gradient are distributed. Entry on older stages of stream dissection is here revealed primarily by the lessening of the gradient and of the height of the valley flanks, even when these rise directly from the down-cutting stream. On the other hand, in the shorter side branches, the breaks of gradient are developed very clearly; the floors of the older stages of valley dissection—now cut into by headward erosion—can often be traced as terraces close to the headwater region, i.e. in the area of the very early phases of the valley history. For the whole valley system the rule applies that eroding portions are steeper and have a greater difference in altitude between any two breaks of gradient, the lower the level to which they belong, i.e. the later they have arisen at the base level of erosion. The system is based upon the valley troughs of the peneplane in the same characteristic way as in the Harz. *Thus it is quite certain that the parts of the piedmont flats which lie outside the zones of crags or inselbergs, as the case may be, are not end-peneplanes.*

This applies especially to the extensive surfaces of the P_3 and P_4 levels. The flattish and often streamless valley troughs of the P_3 surface have exceptionally flat and broad valley troughs, of somewhat greater depth, sunk in them. And it is only at this level, which may be called for short the T_x stage, that the narrower, yet still always very wide, trough-shaped valleys work back into the slope towards the main valleys and towards the northern edge of the step. These valleys debouch on to the P_4 surface and so represent its continuation into the region of higher land ('T$_4$ valleys'). The T$_x$ valleys are an intermediate stage of development which intervenes between the formation of the P$_3$ surface and the slightly lower P$_4$ surface. And indeed, if the convex and concave fragments of slope are attentively followed along the course of the valley in question, it is seen that this is really only the most important of *several intermediate stages*, for which an exit on to the corresponding piedmont flat (which must lie above P$_4$) has not been observed (fig. 15). On both sides of the Saale valley above Hof, right up to the foot of the central mountainland, there are T$_x$ valleys, which have caused far-reaching dissection of the peneplane(P$_3$), converting it into a hummocky landscape, and near the main valley almost into an inselberg landscape (see the profile of fig. 14 on p. 204). And the same stage is reached in the region of the headwaters of the Eger and Röslau at the edge of the highest innermost parts of the country. The final ramifications of the whole of the valley system entrenched in the P$_3$ surface belong to this intermediate stage. Below it the narrower trough-shaped valleys follow as the next

a,b *Stages of valley dissection, starting from the present position of the Saale near Hof*

T$_4$ *Stage of valley dissection corresponding to the P$_4$ surface*

T$_x$ *Intermediate stage*   k *Zones of convex slopes*

FIG. 15.

stage in valley dissection, everywhere well developed and well defined. On account of this arrangement, it is with the similarly-shaped T$_4$ valleys that they can alone be identified[228]. From the Saale, which near Hof has already cut down below this level, steeper stretches of valley are working back; and in their lower courses these approach close to one another. The landscape around Hof owes its characteristics to these convex slopes in the younger V-shaped valleys[229]. In the Saale valley itself, the bottom of which is entrenched below the T$_4$ level, there is nothing to indicate that its present condition could have been brought about in any way other than the backward working of a uniform portion of the stream with increased erosional intensity: from the moist alluvial valley-bottom, convex slopes rise up above the concave foot-slopes. Yet if the corresponding side branches are followed upstream, a whole series of intermediate stages, arranged one behind another, is to be found there. All are sunk in the bottoms of T$_4$ valleys; upwards they pass into these, downwards they are characterised by increasing depth, increasing steepness of the slopes, and decreasing width, and they also merge into one another. *The* '*intermediate stages*', *as these observations clearly show, are not separated phases in the process of dissection, but members of a continuous developmental series; and this points to the steady nature of the course of the natural events.* This is also shown by the 'intermediate stages' lying between the P_3 and P_4 surfaces. They result from the steady action of erosion, which began at the level of the P_4 surface. In the longitudinal profile of the backward-working valley branches, the intermediate stages are to be found arranged *one behind the other*. In cross-section they are revealed even more clearly and may be more easily recognised in the slope units of decreasing gradient which follow *one above the other* in the *continuously convex curve of the slopes*. These begin from the above-mentioned steepest slope unit produced by the act of erosion and pass upwards gradually into the flattish forms of the dissected peneplane. It is not only along all the valleys sunk in the P_3 region that this convexity is found; but it occurs also along the whole multilobate and incised edge of the P_3 surface (its end in the direction sloping away from the mountain mass), and in particular at the inselbergs which lie in front of that edge. These are characterised throughout by foot-slopes of concave curvature, above which follows a section of the slope with the maximum possible gradient having the same inclination everywhere. Above this lie convex slopes decreasing in gradient up to the flattish, often almost level, summit (see figs. 14 and 15). The magnitude of the difference in gradient between the flanks and the summit surface, which is sometimes of considerable extent, makes it impossible for *this* convexity to have originated from the rounding of a sharp edge. Indeed there is as yet no sharp edge at all, i.e. the concave slopes of the flanks do not yet actually intersect at the tops of the inselbergs considered; but the top is formed by a remnant of the flattish forms which, under the circumstances, can belong only to the dissected piedmont flat. Below this there follow in order the slope units of the 'intermediate stages', which are characterised by increasing steepness —phases of increasing erosion; below that again, as far as the P_4 surface, by decreasing gradient—phases of weakening erosion.

Now it has already been emphasised that the inselbergs rapidly diminish in height with their distance from the P_3 step. In the light of the features established, it follows that this cannot be a matter of lowering by denudation, since that cannot begin until the concave slopes have intersected at the top of the hill. *But obviously the P_3 level approaches the level of the P_4 surface in the direction of the general slope of the mountain mass. Both converge in the zone of the inselbergs and originally passed over into one another* (see fig. 16, p. 214). This relationship of piedmont flats to one another can be traced between all the *lower* steps of piedmont benchlands; it is found on the northern slope of the Erzgebirge, especially clearly in the Black Forest, to the piedmont benchlands of which we shall return in another connection, and elsewhere[229a]. On the other hand, it cannot be traced between the *higher* steps—not because the same relationship did not exist there, e.g. between P_3 and P_2, between P_2 and P_1 of the Fichtelgebirge, but because denudation has already destroyed the connection to a far greater extent: the central regions of piedmont benchlands are always zones in which denudation, in the direction of waning development, has already been going on very much longer than in the peripheral parts. Thus, in these central parts the peneplanes have already extended considerably at the expense of the step above, and they have even been much shortened themselves by the level next below. The *original* boundary zones between the piedmont flats, the only places where decisive observations are possible, have thus completely disappeared. It cannot even be established with certainty whether, between the still existing levels, there once lay intermediate levels of piedmont flats, which since then have been removed by the energetic upward working of the valleys and steep slopes cutting back from the lower peneplanes. At all events, the fact that the scarps between the oldest and highest peneplanes are steeper, higher and sharper than in the peripheral younger parts of the mountain slopes, points in this direction[230].

Thus it becomes evident that the scarps between the peneplanes are not an original feature, nor are they in any way connected with previously formed scarps; but they are the result of a definite process of denudation, viz. of dissection into valleys, commencing at a lower level of the peneplane, which is not an end-peneplane. In this way eroding portions work back at many places into the region undergoing dissection by valleys, and carry right into it slope units of increasing steepness. The steepest of them, which corresponds to the maximum erosional intensity reached in the given case, is also that which develops the most rapidly. It is the most vigorous in working upslope, extends at the expense of its flatter predecessors, and so becomes the decisive factor for the mean gradient of slope found on the flanks of all the valleys, side branches and ramifications. These are therefore uniform in character, are bounded by slopes having the same average gradient, and preserve this fundamental trait even after waning development has set in. For, on the one hand, the slope units retreat from the lines of the drainage net, preserving their gradient meanwhile; and, on the other, fresh V-shaped erosional valleys arise on the flanks of the already developed and widening valleys. In these new valleys, the same erosional maximum is reached as is characteristic of the process of dissection, so long as there are still steeper slopes leading to land which stands up higher. If side branches meet, they

detach some 'complex' or other from the region which is undergoing disintegration. Both valley branches and detached fragments are bounded
by valley slopes of a definite average steepness. The complex that has
been separated off forms inselbergs, and the equally steep slope of the
opposite side becomes a part of the scarp face which separates the dissected peneplane from the lower piedmont flat. *The scarps between the
various peneplane levels of a piedmont stairway are valley slopes or have
originated from such slopes. This explains the character they bear throughout: the division into lobes, with everywhere the same average steepness, and
especially the way in which their nature and trend are completely independent of the character of the rocks. This last most conspicuous characteristic
must be particularly stressed.*

Since the dissection and the waning development achieve their end
soonest at the edge of the higher region which is suffering disintegration,

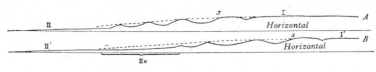

CONDITIONS AT A FURTHER ADVANCED STAGE OF DEVELOPMENT

A *on a younger, lower (peripheral) step*

B *on an older, higher (more central) step*

- - - - - *Distal part, now eaten away, of surface I, no longer following the same direction
as its youngest continuation (surface II), but tilted*

IIe *End-peneplane*   s *Edge of step*   *Piedmont flats: I, I' higher, II, II' lower*

FIG. 16.

the *original* border zone between the higher and lower piedmont flats is
also the first to be destroyed and removed. Its place is taken by the zone
of inselbergs, and the part of the lower peneplane that is spreading upwards, and possesses the character of an end-peneplane (fig. 16). If at a
later stage of development, this spreading part of the lower surface has—
so to say—consumed the upper peneplane to such an extent that there
remains only the proximal part of the latter with its end-peneplane
character (like P_2 and P_1 in the Fichtelgebirge), then they are end-peneplanes that can be observed rising step-like above one another. It is the
only case of this kind which can possibly occur anywhere on the earth.
It can be produced only from a piedmont stairway. And so we are
brought nearer to the problem which this presents.

The origin of a peneplane is like the origin of the *flattish slopes* which
stretch from the floors of valleys to their intervalley divides. Flattish
slopes are associated with those reaches of streams where the erosion is
sufficiently slow, or, in the limiting case, absent. They meet so as to give

flattish relief, i.e. form a peneplane, where the whole drainage net of a denudation area is characterised by an intensity of erosion with values which lie between zero and a definite upper limit, and remain at this value. This occurs, and can occur only, when this condition applies also to the main watercourses, viz. when the streams directly tributary to the general base level at the edge of a tectonically uniform segment of the earth's crust—e.g. one which has been moved uniformly—have been sufficiently long without the occurrence of any cause leading to a rise in their erosional intensity above the afore-mentioned limit. In the history of any part of the earth's crust, which is exposed to denudation and is still actually undergoing it, erosional intensities between zero and a (small) upper limiting value appear twice in those reaches of streams which are directly tributary to the general base level of erosion—and it is they alone which matter: (1) at the beginning of each period of erosion, and (2) at its close. Or, to summarise it more exactly: at the onset of the causes which compel running water to erode, and at their cessation. The end-peneplane is composed of the combination of flattish slopes which occurs as erosion comes to an end. The course of its formation is characterised by progressive flattening, and is expressed by the appearance of characteristic features. It has, on the contrary, been established for piedmont flats, that they are not end-peneplanes, but that their development is in the opposite direction, that of progressive steepening of slopes. This indicates, not that erosion has gradually died down to an intensity of zero; but that, on the other hand, there has been an increase from zero to the limiting value, beyond which one can no longer speak of a peneplane as such, but only of its dissection. Peneplanes of this kind have been called *primary peneplanes*[231]. Their origin can be defined in a general way as being due to the first onset of the causes of the erosion, causes acting in such a way that their intensity increases sufficiently slowly from zero in the direction of that upper limiting value which has been so repeatedly mentioned.

The problem of piedmont benchlands can therefore be referred back to the *causes* of the erosion, the variations of their onset in space and time, and the differing degree of their effects. These causes always come into play for the first time in one zone after another, each zone in turn having been pushed ever further down the mountain slope; and erosion, as it began, obviously found only slowly the opportunity for increasing its intensity. On the other hand, upwards from this peripheral zone, there are simultaneously to be found the causes of the increased erosion, and these follow after one another into several zones lying each one above and behind the other. For each individual one of them it can be established that erosional intensity increases to a definite maximum. The valley's history shows that these successive maxima become greater. In our example this is valid right up to the present day for the sharp V-shaped valleys which cut through the Oligocene beds and the relief covered in by them.

The transgression of the Lower Oligocene on to the peneplane of the P_4 level does not, however, prove it to be of Lower Oligocene age. That becomes evident from the outcrops east of Leipzig, where there has been a slightly stronger raising of the general slope of the mountain mass, so that its northern edge appears pushed farther out towards the North German Plain than in the Elster region. Lower portions of the piedmont stairway have been disclosed in the region of the Mulde. On the divides between the present valleys, which are not sunk particularly deep, there appear wide stretches of flattish landscape, portions of a uniform peneplane, dissected merely by those valleys in which the P_4 level can be recognized with certainty. But the old peneplane is preserved intact only beneath the still existing remains of the transgressing Oligocene. Where this has been removed, there has not been a simple re-exposure of the P_4 surface, but some alteration of its form—the change, however, being kept within narrow limits. The system of valley troughs, going back to the Oligocene, continues in a similar manner in the stripped substructure. In other words: the flattish post-Oligocene valleys transmit themselves, as it were, to the substructure which bore the P_4 surface with *its* own valley net, sometimes taking a different course. We must therefore start from the form associations buried beneath the Tertiary.

From the Elster region, the P_4 level can be followed into that of the Mulde as a uniform peneplane. It extends from the Variscan folds of the old Palaeozoics, south of Gera, over the remains of the transgressing Zechstein and Bunter Sandstone which are preserved there, on to the Rotliegende of the Erzgebirge basin, and goes over the Granulitgebirge and its metamorphic aureole which consists for the most part of Cambrian schists. Associated with these is a series of *Härtlinge* forming broad humps. Northwards it enters the extensive area of quartz porphyry in north-west Saxony. Here, too, it has a general slope downwards to the north; for the intervalley divides at the edge of the Granulitgebirge have on the average an altitude of 270 metres (individual *Härtlinge*, such as the Rochlitzer Berg of quartz porphyry tuff, rise above that to 350 metres); whilst northwards in the region of Rochlitz and Mutzschen, they are only round about 220–230 metres[232].

In the middle of the quartz porphyry district, in an irregular zone running on the whole in a north-easterly direction, the evenness of the rolling P_4 surface is lost; it disintegrates into a hummocky landscape with domes of accordant height, and finally into an excellently developed

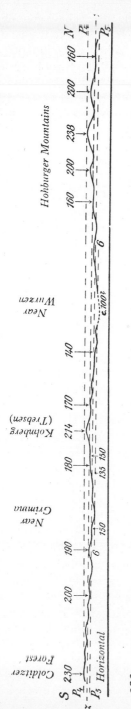

FIG. 17.

zone of inselbergs. When the lower surface of the Oligocene is mapped, the following features appear[233] (fig. 17): the Lower Oligocene has been removed, except for scanty remnants, from the broad shallow valley troughs that belong to the P_4 surface[234]. Trough-shaped valleys, slightly narrower and with somewhat steeper sides, are sunk in these troughs; and these often still contain a rather thick series of Oligocene beds with remnants of brown coal. These break up the peneplane into hill country with low rounded heights. In front of it, these shallow trough-shaped valleys unite into a sort of piedmont intermediate level invading the P_4 region, which is but slightly higher, in the form of extremely wide valley courses; while in front of the P_4 region it forms a broad continuous platform, and further to the north surrounds the inselbergs belonging to the P_4 level (of the type of Kolmberg near Trebsen, Hohburger Mountains, Oschatzer-Kolmberg, etc.). In the same direction as the slope of the mountain mass, that is, in a *general* northward direction, the intermediate level sinks from about 200 metres in the south to about 180 metres north of the town of Grimma and 150 metres north of Wurzen.

Sunk in the slight valley troughs of the intermediate level are trough-shaped valleys of considerable size and great width filled in some places with thick Oligocene deposits. They are already visible in the neighbourhood of the piedmont flat P_4 (the height of the valley floor being about

170–180 metres), where they unite in themselves the little valleys coming down from the intermediate level, and may be traced as continuous features westwards and northwards. In the last named direction they visibly dissect the intermediate level into smaller complexes and break up this too into inselbergs. North of Wurzen, in the Hohburger Mountains, nothing but these are to be found. They are characterised by wide summit flats, relics of the flattish forms of the intermediate level. They rise about 30–40 metres above the bottoms of Oligocene-filled valleys, which, there, are still only about 120–130 metres above sea level, and group themselves around the last of the inselbergs originating from the P_4 surface. In this way they indicate that the latter had for a very long time been surrounded by a piedmont-like fragment of the intermediate level; which also, however, had been undergoing dissection up to the time of the Lower Oligocene transgression and had become completely broken down[235].

The valleys in question belong to a lower main level, which we may distinguish as P_5; and it can be inferred that it extends as a continuous piedmont flat, slightly northwards and westwards of the region considered, into the basement beds of the North German Plain. This is indicated by the extraordinary width of the surfaces belonging to it which are still visible, overlain by Oligocene beds, and penetrate from north and west in between the inselbergs; it is only further up that they narrow to the size of individual valley courses of slight depth but noticeable width. It is further indicated by the coronet of scattered inselbergs which stand up above the plain, or have been found by boring, and accompany the northward-dropping edge of the mountain slope. Before this finally sinks below the Pleistocene deposits of the plain, one becomes aware of the outliers of a yet lower level, valley courses which are sunk in the valleys of the P_5 level. In the Mulde region this lowest pre-Oligocene valley-level is clearly to be seen as far as the junction of the two branches of the Mulde near Grossbothen. There it lies at an altitude of about 150 metres. Downstream it is best exhibited north-east of Grimma (near Bahren), where the floor of the valley belonging to the P_5 level has been broken up by various side branches into a miniature inselberg landscape (the height above sea level being about 135 metres). Further northwards the same valley course leads down into an extraordinarily wide valley, which seems to reach into the mountain slope from the west. It is filled to a considerable depth with Oligocene deposits, overlain by Pleistocene material, and near Wurzen the altitude of a valley floor may scarcely reach more than 100 metres. All other connected features are mantled by deposits.

We have here a quite characteristic zone of disintegration between two peneplane levels of a piedmont stairway: inselberg zone, dissected region, scarp, lie one behind the other in the direction of the mountain ascent. The lower upward-spreading peneplane invades the higher region in the form of valleys. This relationship holds not only between the main levels P_5 and P_4 but also between these and the intermediate levels—of which only one has been described in detail, though there seem to be a number of them[236]—and between the individual ones of the intermediate levels. Old levels are separated from one another by zones of convex slopes and can thus be distinguished. At present all levels are inclined downwards to the north, all are characterised throughout by the concave forms of waning development, and the Lower Oligocene transgresses over them all. This shows that the transgression of the Lower Oligocene is not only later than the time of origin of the P_4 surface, but later than the beginning of the phase of dissection by valleys, and so later than the time when the valleys of the lower P_5 level came into existence. It is also later than the long-continued periods when this level was spreading at the expense of the next higher one (P_4). For the Lower Oligocene overlies those parts of the P_5 surface which possess the characteristics of an end-peneplane and which surround the inselbergs of the P_4 level as a wide flat. The transgression of the Lower Oligocene, the lower horizons of which, containing brown coal, presumably pass down into the Upper Eocene, did not begin until the early stages of the *dissection* of the P_5 level *into valleys* had reached back into the proximal part of the surface. Thus the origin of the lowest piedmont flat that can be recognised (P_5) is pushed back into the *Eocene*, and quite obviously into its older divisions. The P_4 surface is older still. A *lower* age limit is provided for it from the fact that it extends back over the Cenomanian, as may be seen a little to the north and west of Freiberg in Saxony[237]. As far as this, the Saxon Upper Cretaceous encroaches from the north-east with the lowest horizons so far known (basal conglomerate, and above that the Credneria stage and the Lower Quader); it appears to follow a shallow downfolding of the basement, subsequent further warping down of which does not seem impossible. In that region only scanty remains of the Cenomanian transgression are present, on the tops of the existing intervalley divides; the flattish relief, which is extraordinarily widely developed and preserved, here stretches out indifferently over it as well as over the crystalline basement and the Palaeozoic cover of the neighbouring Granulitgebirge. The identity of this peneplane with the P_4 level rests not only on its continuous and unbroken connection with this same surface in the area of the Granulitgebirge—undergoing alteration of form in the same way as well as to the same extent (see p. 216)—but it becomes especially evident from the fact that on the one as on the other remains of the Lower Oligocene transgression are still found. In particular they occur even on some of the residuals of the Cenomanian itself[238].

The undersurface of the Cenomanian transgression is on the whole undulating, and in detail, too, it is not perfectly even, but has trifling flattish unevennesses; consequently there are frequent local fluctuations in the thickness and facies of the lowest Cenomanian horizon, and the outcrop of the transgressing surface with its almost horizontal arrangement of the beds is only approximately like that of the outcrop of a horizontal bedding plane.

The arrangement of the facies, however, uniformly shows this fundamental feature: towards the south-west the clayey-sandy facies of material deposited at a distance from the highland changes into one of a sandy conglomerate. In the Freiberg district, the basal conglomerate increases westwards and south-west by approximately the same amount as the overlying Quader is diminished[239]. Obviously the outermost edge of the Cenomanian transgression is near there; and not far to the west and south-west was the area of contemporaneous denudation rising above it. At the present day there is found in that direction, beyond a wide stretch of the higher part of the P_4 surface that is free from Cenomanian deposits, a scarp leading up to the higher peneplane level; and in front of this there is no dearth of inselbergs belonging to it[240].

It is highly probable that the higher peneplane, which from its whole position can be identified with the P_3 level, continues under the Cenomanian transgression. The gently undulating lower surface of this shows red weathering extending deep into the crystalline rocks[241]. It is a surface of subaerial denudation, not of marine abrasion; and its relatively graded condition places the matter beyond doubt that it is a pre-Cenomanian or Lower Cenomanian peneplane. From its position with regard to the higher land in the south-west, from the relationship in which it stands to the P_4 surface, and from the facies of the transgressing beds, it seems by no means impossible, but rather very probable, that it represents in fact the peripheral parts of the P_3 surface. After a lowering of the marginal zone of the highland slope had brought it below sea-level, the crustal strip with its load of sediment became, on re-emergence, the place for the development of the P_4 surface, just as did the analogous sections of the highland slope, at the same altitude, which lay further to the west. These have been found to be connected in the same manner with the rest of the highland, but not to have experienced the Cenomanian interlude of flooding by the sea. The diagrammatic profile of fig. 18 shows the relationships which are considered to be possible, and even probable, here.

In any case, it is only a period of time corresponding to that of the uppermost Cretaceous deposits, or at most to that of the oldest beds of the Eocene, which can be considered for the *origin of the P_4 surface*, the dissection of which has been recognised as commencing at latest in the Eocene period. The *origin of the P_3 surface* falls, with a high degree of probability, into the Cenomanian period. It is clear, then, that the uppermost and oldest treads of the piedmont stairway, P_2 and P_1, as far as their *origin* is concerned, date far back into the Mesozoic era. There is nothing more to go upon, yet it is definitely not too risky to assert *that in the Fichtelgebirge there are form associations which originated in the same way (not at the same place—see pp. 208-209) during the Jurassic period, and which since then have developed further, preserving their character the whole time.*

The Upper Cretaceous and Lower Oligocene transgressions are not events that are peculiar to the course of development of the *mountain mass*, belonging to it organically as normal phases of development; but they are episodes which interrupted the normal development of the peri-

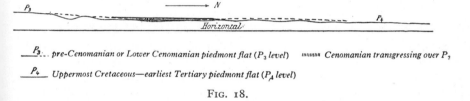

P_3 $\longrightarrow N$

Horizontal

P_4

_P_3_ pre-Cenomanian or Lower Cenomanian piedmont flat (P_3 level)   ⬛⬛⬛ Cenomanian transgressing over P_3

_P_4_ Uppermost Cretaceous—earliest Tertiary piedmont flat (P_4 level)

FIG. 18.

pheral parts of the mountain block and have their origin in a course of development which is peculiar to the *part of the earth's crust which bounds it on the north*, the area of sedimentation. The following facts show that this area is on the whole characterised by a constant tendency to sink, which it has retained all through the Mesozoic-Tertiary periods, during which the Central German Rise may be said to have appeared, right up to the present day: the completeness of the predominantly marine succession from the Trias to the Neogene, the thickness of the Pleistocene deposits, the low levels to which they descend, and the existence of areas now covered by the seas which are to be found between the Central German Rise and the North European zones of uplift (in part very old). This is not the place for going into the history, very varied in its detail, of what has befallen the different parts of this great area of sedimentation, which has nevertheless preserved the fundamental characteristics mentioned above. It is reflected in the extent of marine sediments and their continental equivalents, which fluctuated within wide limits in the facies of the beds and in the position, varying in detail, of the boundary zone between sedimentation and the area of denudation.

This boundary zone migrated to and fro, according as the area of subsidence increased and again diminished in size at the expense of the
adjoining region of elevation to the south, the Central German Rise; i.e.
according to whether the condition of subsidence spread out beyond its
own proper sphere or again became more closely restricted to it. Thus
the transgression of the Cenomanian over the peripheral parts of the
mountain slope (treated above) was not the result of a subsidence of the
whole body of the highland; but it was due to gradual inclusion of a part
of the marginal zone of the uplift-denudation area within the region of
subsidence-sedimentation, which was temporarily growing in width.
This process is recorded in the way the Cretaceous horizons transgress
over each other from the Lower Cretaceous to a maximum in the Cenomanian[242], and in the retrogression of the sea and presumably also of
sedimentation to the north and north-west in Danian times.

The Lower Oligocene transgression represents a similar sort of behaviour. The marine Eocene, including the Bartonian, seems to have been
still entirely confined to the northern or rather north-western edge of the
North German Plain. Subsidence and flooding by the sea advanced in
the Lower Oligocene period as far as the region of Magdeburg, in mid-
Oligocene times as far as Leipzig; by the Upper Oligocene period the sea
had moved back again to the north and in Miocene times was restricted
to the north-western part of the Plain. This is, however, established only
for the advance and recession of the sea and not for the sedimentation
as a whole, since this still continued in the form of a continental facies
far south of what was at that time the coast. Within a transgressing area
of deposition, the coastline merely denotes the boundary on one side of
which the intensity of subsidence has exceeded (or just balanced) the
intensity of sedimentation, whilst on the other side conditions are
reversed. If, in order to make out the course and total extent of the spreading crustal subsidence, the bounding edge between transgressing formation and area of denudation is followed, there is found a similar ebb and
flow from Eocene to Miocene, but no strict parallelism with the shifting
of the sea-shore. This, in Bartonian times, lay across the northern parts
of the present Plain; and the lacustrine equivalents stretched as far as the
neighbourhood of Magdeburg. In the Lower Oligocene, the coast passed
over these and moved up to this same district, and continental equivalents covered the peripheral parts of the highland slope up to the level
of the P_4 surface, indicating how far the crustal subsidence reached at its
maximum. In mid-Oligocene times, however, the maximum extent of
the sea went to just the same parts of the highland slope; and movement
in the direction associated with emergence of the highland had again
established itself, denudation—interrupted by the afore-mentioned

transgression—having already begun again. This is made clear not only by the absence of the continental equivalent of the marine mid-Oligocene beds south of the region of its occurrence—later denudation might also account for this absence—but especially by the unconformity which can here and there be traced between the continental Lower Oligocene (or perhaps Eocene) and the marine Middle Oligocene[243]. This latter rests upon a denudation surface at the margin of the highland slope.

It becomes very clear that the transgressions are ramifications of processes which have their origin in the subsiding area of continuous sedimentation, and so of conformable bedding, and belong genetically *to it*. This area is separated from the neighbouring crustal segment of continuous denudation (and so of elevation) by a zone of transgressions and unconformable bedding, i.e. of crustal variations. This arrangement is repeatedly found; indeed it is the normal thing all over the surface of the earth.

The warping down of the peripheral parts of the highland slope[244] in the Cenomanian, and especially in the Lower Oligocene, occurred in such a way that the transgressing beds left the existing land forms intact, and simply buried them. It is not possible to detect any development of slopes beneath a cover. Obviously this is to be explained by the extraordinarily flat nature of the land in Cretaceous and early Tertiary times; so that with even small amounts of subsidence in unit time, the transgression and its deposits could spread, and indeed were forced to spread, not only over great areas but also with relative rapidity. The material of the transgressing beds is to be correlated with denudational processes in the regions that stand up higher. It cannot be said that the Cenomanian and the overlying Cretaceous horizons together with the Lower Oligocene are strata which can be correlated with the formation or origin of a definite set of land forms; but *they are correlated with the epochs concerned in the further development of the given form associations* which, as the investigation into the piedmont benchlands has shown, continues to the present day and has remained unaltered in its direction: progressive dissection by valleys and breaking down of the scarps between the piedmont flats, with the growth and extension of these flats at the expense of those next above them. There is no need to follow here the further development of the highland slope as upwarping recurred at the peripheral parts, which had been covered by the Oligocene sediments, as the overlapping deposits were gradually removed, as their under surface became transformed, and as the sharply V-shaped valleys—which even at the present day are found at the lowest parts of the slope—began to appear.

There has not yet been enough investigation to provide a world picture of the distribution of piedmont flats and piedmont benchlands. It is in the nature of the case, and may be deduced with certainty from the present observations, that this is by no means a phenomenon confined to the German Highlands. The characteristic arrangement of piedmont benchlands may be recognised, amongst other [places], in the *Atlantic slope of the Appalachians*. Only the general outlines are known[245]. We will pass over the interpretations of the features so far given since throughout they are based on the fundamental assumption that the cycle of erosion is applicable, and will consider only the features themselves. The highest and oldest of the known levels[246] is formed by mountainous country which adjoins the main body of the southern Appalachians, and is in a far advanced state of breaking down into inselbergs and groups of similar residual hills. Its relationship to the surrounding peneplane— which once stretched continuously over the Appalachians and is still preserved in North Carolina as fragments of considerable extent—is that of a central mountainland to its piedmont flat. From the accordance shown by the summit heights of its upstanding parts, Willis concluded that these represent the remains of a higher, completely dissected, peneplane level. This conclusion is fully justified by the flattish form associations still to some extent preserved on the convex curves of the mountain tops[247].

The younger school of morphologists believes that monadnocks of resistant rock can be recognised here all over the area.

The surrounding peneplane is generally ascribed to the Cretaceous age. In any case it originated in pre-Neocomian times. It extended uniformly over the Appalachians; and their crests are at this level where fragments of the actual peneplane are not still preserved. The Cumberland plateau and the high-level platform of New England are considered to belong to it[248]. A second central mountainland, analogous to that of North Carolina, projects above it in New Hampshire. Its continuation is found in the under surface of the transgressing Lower Cretaceous beds of continental facies (Potomac, Upper Jurassic to Neocomian), the outcrop of which surrounds the Appalachians as an arc on the east and south in the Atlantic coast region. This under surface is not even, but has the undulating relief characteristic of a peneplane. Between its appearance at the surface and the continuation on the mountain tops, there is a gap which is occupied by the 'piedmont plateau', a third, yet lower, peneplane level. It is the orginal type of piedmont flat. Reaching away over the upper edges of the Cretaceous transgression (Neocomian to Senonian), it goes inland over the crystalline mass of the eastern Appalachian foreland and the blocks of continental Trias let down into it; it approaches the mountains, which rise above it in a pronounced scarp, and continues into them in the form of wide valley floors. The scarp between the two peneplanes is developed in a particularly impressive manner in the southern Appalachians. Well preserved, extensive relics of the Cretaceous (more accurately pre-Neocomanian) peneplane—the Blue Mountain plateau—end in a sharply convex break of gradient above the high scarp with its concave curvature, from which long intervalley spurs, crowned by inselbergs, gradually sink down towards the lower 'piedmont plateau'[249]. Rarely are the characters of a piedmont benchland scarp more clearly noticeable than here!

Up till now, the peneplanes at these various levels, and throughout their whole extent, have been considered as end-peneplanes, as [Davisian] peneplains; but only very vague notions prevail as to their origin, since attention was never directed to the core of the problem, the development of slopes. Nor has investigation of the Appalachian peneplanes ever gone beyond the statement of hypotheses about the mode of origin of peneplanes in general: uplift of an area, and subsequent denudation which achieves its ultimate aim, peneplanation, on a block which is *considered to be at rest*. Under such circumstances, the step-like repetition of peneplanes presented insuperable difficulties of interpretation, and it remained a complete enigma. In his explanation Cl. Lebling (*loc. cit.*) assumed that the scarp between piedmont plateau and 'Cretaceous' peneplane was a receding fault scarp; thus he maintains that both levels are one and the same peneplane which have come to be at different altitudes on account of the throw of the fault. Not only can this working hypothesis be dispensed with, but it in no way accords with the geological facts.

To begin with, the fault in question has not been established. No throw cuts across the Cretaceous-Tertiary strata which loop round the southern end of the mountains transversely to the Appalachian strike. The strike faults in the piedmont plateau appear throughout to be of pre-Neocomian age. Hence Lebling assumes further that the fault peters out southwards. However, the lobed scarp does not end in the direction mentioned, but borders the Appalachians along the whole of the eastern and southern slopes. Its highest part is at the latitude of the central mountainland of North Carolina, and becomes lower to the north and to the south. Hence no other conclusion can be drawn but that the conditions, which led to the creation of a particularly high central mountainland, continued to operate in the same area and permitted the development of a specially great difference in level between the two lower peneplanes. Apparently this has been continuing right into the most recent period, since in this same area the Appalachian rivers were again able to incise particularly deep V-shaped valleys in the piedmont plateau. At the latitude of the central mountainland the differences in altitude between *all* the denudation levels appears to be greater than farther to the north or to the south.

Finally W. M. Davis, dealing with New Jersey, published his conclusive research on the relationship of the piedmont plateau to the 'Cretaceous' peneplane. There the gently undulating lower surface of the Cretaceous passes over the crystalline material, with the Triassic blocks downfaulted into it and the beds of diabase trap intercalated in the Trias. Inland, these same diabase layers rise up as lines of heights above the piedmont flat, which is capped by the uppermost beds of the Cretaceous, gain in height north and north-westwards, and reach the level of those parts of the 'Cretaceous' peneplane which are still preserved there[250]. Thus they play the part of inselbergs which lie in front of the margin of the higher peneplane level, stand up above the lower and (as has been shown) younger piedmont level, and make it possible to establish here and there that the higher surface plunges beneath the Cretaceous transgression.

The geological age of the piedmont plateau is given as Tertiary. It was probably formed in the early Tertiary, during the phase of retrogression between the marine transgressions of the Senonian and the Miocene[251]. Here is repeated the phenomenon which has been treated in more detail for the slope of the Erzgebirge: the area of continuous denudation (the Appalachians) is separated from one of continuous deposition, in the Atlantic Ocean, by a zone of oscillation—of transgressions and retrogressions; for in the Cretaceous-Tertiary series, which was laid over the edge of the present continent, not only did the facies change from continental to marine, and back again, but there are gaps, unconformities due to erosion, which, as one goes inland, comprise ever longer intervals of time. Conditions of bedding make it clear that here, too, the processes concerned are fundamentally connected, not with the region of uplift, but with the properties of the adjoining area of subsidence. The strata dip seawards and the gradient is greater, the older they are. By way of contrast, there is the upwarping of the 'Cretaceous' peneplane[252]. *The direction of movement does not alter, either in the area of uplift and denudation, or in that of subsidence and deposition; but the latter area increases and diminishes in size during the periods of time considered.* This holds true right up to the present time, during which the peripheral parts of the piedmont plateau, till then undergoing dissection, have subsided together with the sharply V-shaped erosional furrows (e.g. Hudson submarine channel), far below sea level.

Observations on *Scandinavia* are also available; and these indicate that, just as in the Appalachians, the present actively progressing dissection has affected a system of peneplanes, arranged in steps one above another, grouped round a central mountainland in the south of Norway. According to Reusch, the ancient upper surface at the summit of the Scandinavian Shield is called palaeic, and is to be considered a relic of the Caledonian Mountains[253]. Ahlmann was able to distinguish on this surface a central mountainland and a peripheral peneplane. It cannot have been till late Tertiary times that this palaeic area was pushed up, and exposed to dissection by valleys which started from a lower peneplane level, the 'strandflat'. This surface, considered by H. Reusch, J. H. L. Vogt, E. Richter, F. Nansen and others to be a formation due to marine abrasion, by A. G. Högbom to be a [Davisian] peneplain merely modified and further levelled by this, bears inselbergs which become increasingly important northwards and sometimes have abruptly rising flanks (Lofoten). It is thus, in fact, extraordinarily like a piedmont flat, and in its turn has been sharply cut into by erosion furrows dating from pre-glacial times[254]. There is much here which still needs to be elucidated. The absence of correlated* strata means that not only is the dating of individual form associations at present absolutely uncertain, but is also a hindrance to any sure judgment on their type and connections. However, Ahlmann's investigations lead one to expect that the pre-glacial land forms of Scandinavia will turn out to be a piedmont stairway of asymetrical shape and of widely extending dimensions.

As far as one can judge from the observations available, and as far as the literature on the subject gives any information, piedmont benchlands *of the kind described* have been found so far only outside the mountain belts. However, knowledge of the actual land forms of the earth is still too slight for us to see any more in this than the expression of our present state of knowledge; yet it may be more than a mere impression that these piedmont stairways are typical of the regions of uplift outside the zones of instability. Support is lent to this view by comparing the features known to occur in the denudational areas of the mountain belts. But here again knowledge is at present restricted to the main outlines, since it is only in a few scattered spots that studies have been made in any considerable detail.

5. BROAD FOLDS

Peneplanes have been found in the mountain belts in great numbers and in various combinations with other form associations[255]. They have here excited particular attention; all the same, until recently they stubbornly resisted any attempt to provide a satisfactory explanation. The reason for this is easily seen: so long as the theoretically deduced mode of origin for end-peneplanes, or [Davisian] peneplains, was ascribed to all

[* i.e. correlated with the denudation by containing its debris.]

peneplanes without distinction, the occurrence of such flattish form associations in the zones of instability had to remain a complete enigma. For, as far as our knowledge of them goes, these belts have not the fundamental prerequisite for the development of end-peneplanes: 'tectonic rest', i.e. long persisting absence of movement in the earth's crust. Thus, explanations about them are very diverse and have to make extensive use of various working hypotheses, which are sometimes found to be in striking contrast to morphological facts and even more to geological ones. We must come back to this. At present the primary consideration is a description of the actual features. In view of the great gaps in our knowledge of the configuration of important parts of the mountain belts, any attempt at this might appear hopeless. But numerous isolated observations, spread over most diversified zones of the mountain belts, focussed at several places into more detailed investigation, already make it possible to recognise with perfect clearness that not only are definite types of form associations constantly recurring, but that their combination in a definite manner is obviously typical of vast areas. We will limit ourselves to characterising those types of relief.

(a) The Alps

This is difficult in mountain ranges like the Alps, where the set of land forms has been transformed by Pleistocene glaciation; for, though the extent of the remodelling is not known accurately, it must in any case have been considerable. Moreover, it has masked the connection between the pre-glacial form associations and their correlated deposits. Furthermore, although it is possible to observe these beds in the foreland and even as far as the outer parts of the mountains themselves, yet even for such a relatively recent part of the history of the development of land forms in the Alps, the relations have been interrupted by the continuance of folding into the early Tertiary, the strata of the foreland being also involved. This advance outward of the crustal movement has added new peripheral zones to the mountain area. According to Alb. Heim[256], these zones are characterised in Switzerland by a certain correspondence between the surface form and the structure (anticlinal crests, synclinal valleys) in contrast to the inner parts of the mountainous region. Similar features are to be observed in the southern limestone belt of the Eastern Alps. The south Alpine rivers, east of the Adige, traverse the more recently added portions in deeply scored antecedent valleys and gorges. From these there rise steep slopes which are convex upwards and pass into intermediate or even flattish relief forms on the summits of those chains which have not been much broken up into individual peaks. Such well-marked forms of waxing development are not unknown in the interior of the Alps, in spite of these parts being far more completely broken down into peaks and ridge crests. They are here arranged longitudinally, following the trend of the mountain chains, and the absolute altitude of the intervalley divides remains considerably less than that of the sharp ridges and peaks belonging to the belts of higher mountains at each side. In contrast to these latter, which may be called ridge zones, the former appear as depressions. They are followed by the great longitudinal valleys of the Alps, such as the Rosanna, Inn, Salzach, Enns, Puster, Save, Rhone, etc. valleys[257]. Newly discovered relationships of the glacial deposits lying within these longitudinal valley tracks in the Eastern Alps make it probable that, in relation to the high zones bordering them, they are strips of crustal subsidence (left behind [in the general movement]). For some of them, this character has been traced back[258] as far as the Lower Pliocene (Gail-Drau valley), Middle Miocene (Mur-Mürz) and Oligocene (Save, Enns [?]*), and in the majority of cases probably reaches far back into the Tertiary.

Here the characters of the pre-glacial land forms glimmer through a veil of glacial remodelling, so that there is no longer full scope for views as to their nature. What has already been established above shows that, before the Pleistocene glaciation, the Alps were not characterised merely by steep relief or by intermediate forms over their whole extent[259]; but that, as today, there were zones arranged parallel to the strike of the mountains where steep slopes, leading up from flat valley bottoms to high ridges (steep relief) alternated with others in which convex slopes, arched strongly upwards, met in intervalley divides with a lower average height. This latter type is met with at the outskirts of the mountains and, within them, along the longitudinal valley furrows.

However, the profiles of the steep slopes in the above-mentioned ridge zones are not everywhere of the straight-line type, and this can be specially well seen on the projecting spurs. This is true even above the uppermost limit of glacial rounding, a limit which can be recognised with *certainty* from specific features (striations, erratics, etc.). There, too, convexity of profile is very often quite characteristic. Into those convex profiles the forms of the glacial period have been notched as concave sections of the profile. They are subordinate to the former, creating discontinuities or breaks in them, but not obliterating them, and thus prove that they are developments imprinted later upon the landscape. In the region of the cirques, it is these which make the discontinuities; along the valley tracks, it is the sharp V-shaped valleys above the shoulders of the glacial troughs. The case is similar in the main valleys; but the breaks are far less distinct, and relics of the pre-glacial valley

* W. Penck's [?].

floors have been recognised in them here and there. On the other hand, sometimes it is merely a matter of fragments of slope and convex breaks of gradient which form component parts of the general convexity of profile. Projections and re-entrants which are structurally conditioned are not being considered here. That location [on the general convexity] and the fact that, even after allowing for the deepening due to glacial action, they are often at a really great height above the bottom of the valley, permits one to recognise, in these interruptions and breaks of gradient, features that are not only pre-Pleistocene creations, but undoubtedly *of very ancient origin*[260]. Perhaps there is an inner [? genetic] relationship with the '*Ecken*' [steps on the intervalley spurs] which J. Sölch has studied in the Eastern Alps[261].

The pre-glacial land forms of the Alps bear the imprint of waxing development, which has been 'overprinted', but not completely obliterated, by glacial remodelling. The forerunners of the steep slopes—the association of which is the essential factor determining the nature of Alpine relief (steep relief)—were slopes of slighter inclination. They have been preserved towards the tops of the intervalley divides in the zones of the longitudinal valleys as well as in the zones of the higher ridges, although to a very different extent in the two. Observation of the form of the slope confirms the conclusion which, as I have already stressed above, follows from the facies of the Tertiary strata of the foreland, from the Stampian to the Sarmatian stage: the grain increases in coarseness from below upwards; and the conglomerate facies, which indicates proximity to the mountain border, generally extends further north-westwards into the foreland in the higher horizons than it does in the lower divisions (furthest in the Vindobonian). This proves that on the whole there was a general increase of the gradients in the Alpine region during the Oligocene and Miocene, and therefore an increase in their altitudinal modelling[262]. The mountains have been increasing in height from the earlier Tertiary periods to the time of the Pleistocene glaciation, and the inclinations of the longitudinal profiles and flanks of their valleys have been becoming steeper. This last condition accounts for the narrowing of the valley cross-sections downstream, the lessening of the distance between the upper edges of the valleys, which we were also able to establish in the same way for the valleys of the German Highlands. In the Alps this is seen most clearly wherever glacial remodelling has not completely removed the convex profiles[263].

It must be stressed that the difference in the form of the slopes and in the altitude of the intervalley ridges, as found in the zones of the longitudinal valleys and the ridge zones, has not the slightest connection with the character of the rock. The same Hauptdolomit and Wettersteinkalk

Photo. by C. W. Kockel

1. Sharp Alpine ridges composed of different rocks. Wetterstein from Taneller

Photo. by W. Penck

2. Gipfelflur at the western edge of the Cerro Negro Range, Western Argentina

IX. GIPFELFLUR

which compose the high, sharp-edged ridges and pyramidal peaks of the Lechtal Alps and east of it, form rounded bosses ('*Rundlinge*') along the furrow of the Inn valley. These bosses are preserved in many places, and are characterised by a lower altitude, similar, however, amongst themselves. The various crystalline rocks of the Silvretta and Ötztal nappes outcrop south of that longitudinal valley zone to form the steep flanks of soaring knife-edged crests; but within it they give rise to rounded ridges with flattish summits keeping to about the same level as the previously mentioned ridges of Triassic limestone and dolomite, etc. This arrangement is the more conspicuous because elsewhere in the Alps the adaptation of *individual forms* to rock material is extremely close, as is to be expected in regions of great denudational intensity (steep relief). That adaptation is most clearly expressed in the arrangement of the final branchings of the valleys and of the furrows working up the slopes. These follow zones of less resistant rocks and make them apparent by the course of each section of the valley, by the gradient of the individual slopes, and by the relative height of the individual intervalley spurs, but *not by the shape of the slopes*. Within a zone of ridges the rather gentler slopes, which meet in lower ridges, are associated with mobile types of rock (e.g. the Liassic Fleckenmergel) as contrasted with the adjacent more resistant limestone or dolomite (see Plate IX, illustration 1). But they are sharp-edged, and not rounded ridges with convex profiles. It is not, therefore, difference in rock resistance which leads to the development of the two different types of form that are to be met with in the ridge zones and longitudinal valley zones of the Alps.

A further feature that is independent of glacial remodelling is the uniformity of the summit levels. This proves to be independent not only of the folded structure but also, within wide limits, of the nature of the rock. A. Penck has termed this the *gipfelflur* and has shown that, so far as it is a matter of Alpine conditions, it cannot well be the heritage of an hypothetical peneplane which once stretched over the Alps and out of which the present relief might be supposed to have been sculptured later[257]. On the contrary, the gipfelflur shows a notable connection with the distribution of slope form. If one thinks of it as a surface which is tangential to the peaks and to the summits of the intervalley divides, that surface does not form a simple arch, including the whole mountain system from north to south; but it has in cross-section the form of an arch with undulating curves or one compounded of undulations. In the region of each ridge zone, it swings up as a wave crest, and it sinks like a wave trough along each zone of longitudinal valleys. *The downwarping of the gipfelflur coincides with those strips of the mountain system in which very flat slope units are still to some extent preserved on the tops of the intervalley divides, these being the very ancient forerunners of the steep valley flanks; the upward swings of the gipfelflur coincide with equally elongated and narrow portions where nothing can now be seen of such former flattish precursors of the steep slopes.* But that these were here also, though at a much greater height above sea level than within the zone of longitudinal valleys, is proved beyond question by the convexity which can still be established for the profiles of the slopes.

The Alpine gipfelflur shows gentle curvature up and down, not only in its cross-section but in its longitudinal section as well. This is directly visible to an observer turning his gaze to the distant mountains from somewhere in the Black Forest or on the southern slope of the Swabian Alb. There the gradual upswingings of the gipfelflur appear clearly above the glaciated massifs and groups of peaks bounded by lines of longitudinal and transverse valleys. Very often the names given stress the fact that these groups are units (Bernese Alps, Titlis-Dammastock, Tödi group, Silvretta group, Bernina group, Ortler group, Ötztal Alps, etc.). In between, the gipfelflur sinks down, and most of the great transverse valleys, and the low gaps forming passes, are sunk in these areas of depression. Another very conspicuous feature is clearly connected with the arrangement of the gipfelflur: strict as may seem the adaptation of individual forms to rock materials, *the course of the main Alpine valleys is on the whole independent of the structure of the folds and nappes,* and it is from these valleys that the complete disintegration of the whole mountain system into the well-known sea of peaks has taken its start. Alb. Heim sees in this an inheritance (epigenesis) derived from the 'oldest, first tectonic lines on the upper surface of the rising mountain mass'. He assumes that the course of the principal valleys was, in the main, determined by the earliest processes of folding and nappe formation; and that this course was maintained right through the Insubrian phase of the folding, in a mountain system which might be considered as completed by that time. A subordinate part in directing the waterways is also assigned to later dislocations, again considering only those phenomena associated with the folding of strata and the formation of nappes[264]. This interpretation is based on the assumption—which has yet to be proved—that folding of strata and nappe formation produce a surface gradient which allows water to flow and erode and thus directs its work. So far all that has been established is that the lines of the principal Alpine valleys are independent of the internal structure. On the other hand, a consequence of the recent establishment of this fact has been to draw attention to other relationships: *the longitudinal valleys are incised in the depressions along the strike of the gipfelflur, the transverse valleys usually where its sinkings run transversely to the mountain system.* In addition, there are transverse valleys which are antecedent in their nature, especially in the marginal zones of the mountain region (see p. 228); and those for which it is impossible to decide whether antecedence or backward working erosion has determined their course. The problems which crop up here involve questions of erosion and of the associated development of slopes. This is obvious as regards the origin of the gipfelflur, which is nothing but the result of complete dissection by valleys, and the arrangement of their main lines. It applies also to the up and down undulation of the gipfelflur, which cannot well be the result of later warping, since its risings and fallings—following some definite law and independent of the nature of the rock material—are associated with the occurrence and preservation of different form types. These latter indicate that the causes of erosion were and are different in the zones of depression from those where the gipfelflur rises.

In the north, in the foreland, a peneplane adjoins the Alpine system of pre-glacial form-associations. Of post-Sarmatian origin, it also cuts across the Neogene strata of the foreland, and forms the slightly uneven surface, with only gentle slopes, which underlies the early Pleistocene outwash gravels (first Ice Age). The relation of the peneplane to the mountains is similar to that of a piedmont flat to its associated mountain-land. However, without further information, it is not possible to draw a parallel between the pre-glacial peneplane of the Alpine Foreland and a piedmont flat such as has been considered in earlier sections. An essential characteristic of the latter was its close connection with the land rising up above it: both are superficial portions of one and the same zone of uplift, both belong to a crustal segment which is an endogenetic unit. This is not true for the pre-Pleistocene peneplane of the Alpine Foreland. It extends over a part of the crust which has always been moved in a different way from the neighbouring Alps. Until the Upper Miocene period, it was sinking relatively, and was an area of deposition for the material removed from the mountains which were simultaneously rising. Even at the present day, it still behaves in a fundamentally different manner from the Alps, as is shown here and there by the different character of the erosional incisions. The Alps and their foreland are, as regards their endogenetic type, two different portions of the earth's crust, and so the peneplane in question is not of the usual piedmont type.

Piedmont flats are, nevertheless, by no means altogether absent from the Alpine region itself. Their existence has been established in the eastern part which, in contrast to the west, is characterised throughout by more extensive preservation—on the watersheds between the deeply sunk valleys—of older form associations. In part, this is obviously due to a different course of endogenetic development; the decreasing influence of glaciation towards the eastern edge of the mountains certainly also plays a part; but the occurrence of massive and extensive Mesozoic limestone deposits seems to be of outstanding significance. These, like permeable limestone in general, tend to preserve the forms of denudation— other things being equal—and are less easily dissected into valleys. Thus, on the limestone plateaus of the northern and the southern Calcareous Alps, ancient form associations of the intermediate form type still occur, to some extent, over wide areas. They are not peneplanes, but mountainous country, which possesses throughout the concave slope profile of waning development and has its limits fixed by sharp breaks of slope at the steep declivities of the deep valleys that reach up into it[265].

In the north, the series of limestone plateaus extends from the Inn to where the mountains descend to the Vienna Basin. The ancient land forms on their summits are everywhere of the same type. The general gradient, directed northwards towards the foreland, is unmistakable; and in this direction the differences in altitude lessen so that medium relief approximates to flattish relief, to a peneplane. Furthermore, along the valley ways of most of the limestone plateaus, there are found pebbles of central Alpine origin, which show that watercourses flowing towards the foreland crossed the zone of the nappes of the Calcareous Alps and helped to form the valleys within the plateau areas[266]. Because of these uniform features the view is held that form associations on the heights of the various limestone plateaus are parts of a single uniform region of similar origin everywhere, both as regards type and age, and were formerly at one and the same original level. Their present very varied altitude is to be traced in part to later additional dislocation[267]. That is, however, true only for individual cases. G. Götzinger, who has made the most detailed study of the plateau surfaces in the northern Calcareous Alps, stresses the remarkable independence of their set of land forms not only with respect to fold and nappe structure but also to later faulting[268].

In addition, it has only rarely been possible to find, between adjoining plateau surfaces at different levels, faults or flexures in the stratification to which the variations in altitude could be traced. On the other hand, F. F. Hahn established for the Saalach region (Salzburg Calcareous Alps) two different levels, independent of one another, at which the limestone plateau lands were to be found. These plateaus exhibit a considerable degree of mountain relief, the wide valley floors of which have been partly preserved as planated surfaces. In a southerly group of limestone plateaus (Kaisergebirge as far as Tennengebirge and Übergossene Alm), these show a general rise southwards from 1500–1750 metres or more (on the Untersberg near Salzburg) to about 2600–2800 metres (on the Übergossene Alm). The summits of the peaks (of moderate height) behave in a similar way. In the northern group, however, the planated surfaces are about 1500 metres, the heights of the summits fairly regularly round about 1700 metres. That is the lower level. In two places it reaches as an embayment far southwards into the zone of the higher limestone plateaus (Lattengebirge, Kirchberg-Kalkstein) and so is interlocked with the higher level, just like two peneplanes of a piedmont stairway and not as if depressed by fault or flexure. Apart from these two embayments, the two levels are spacially quite distant from one another and are separated by a low-lying belt in which nowadays the Saalach is incised. It is of just the same type as the previously mentioned 'longitudinal valley zones'; but it has a north-eastward trend and has a pronounced gradient which is to be recognised by the remnants of planated surfaces preserved on the intervalley divides (from 1500 metres in the south-west to about 1000 metres in the north-east)[269].

The depression is not a fault dislocation nor a down-faulted trough, by which fragments of older form associations might have subsided with respect to the plateau zone rising up above it on both sides; but its origin is as ancient as these themselves. It was already in existence before the close of early Tertiary times, as follows from the down-faulting of the brow of the Berchtesgaden nappe which occurred at that time and which coincides with the line of the Saalach. It also proves to be a strip which was being left behind (sinking relatively), with respect to which the northward bounding plateau zone (the lower of the two plateau levels) moved upwards. This process had been recorded in the position of beds of the Carnian horizon. From its position, its arrangement and its characteristics, the Saalach depression can be compared only with a downwarped strip of the gipfelflur. The plateau zones on either side, however, fall into the class of ridge zones of the high arched gipfelflur previously discussed. It thus seems all the more probable that on the high limestone plateaus there formerly existed, and have been preserved to a considerable extent, the less inclined slope units which must once have been also present elsewhere in the zones of ridges, but have by now been replaced by their steeper successors.

Should confirmation be found elsewhere for the relationships here indicated, then the plateau regions must be given a status of greater independence than hitherto. They are not to be considered as relics of a relief which extended uniformly over the slopes of the mountain system, as a single unit from the northern margin of the Alps right up to their crest. Rather, they appear to be fragments of a set of land forms peculiar to the individual wave-like or range-like upswingings of the mountain system, which are arranged, on the whole, parallel to its strike.

This would not necessarily imply a different age for the plateau lands.

There are, however, some indications of difference in age, notably between the plateau flats of the Fore Alps and those of the High Alps. An
early Miocene or pre-Miocene age has been ascribed to both, since in
the Vienna Basin shore lines of the Pontic Sea have been cut into the
steep faces of such limestone plateaus, implying that at that time the
plateau lands were already dissected by deep valleys incisions, and were
separated by steeper slope units from what was then their base level of
erosion. A further proof of age is that the sea level of the second Mediter-
rannean and of the Sarmatian Seas apparently lay at a lower level than
that of the Pontian Sea. From this it is concluded that in Middle and
Upper Miocene times the plateau surfaces at first lay quite high above
the base level of erosion and cannot have been first formed at that period.
They had already undergone dissection, a process which must have begun
in the Lower Miocene at latest[270]. Thus a first approximation would
give a pre-Miocene, presumably Oligocene, age for the *origin* of the
plateau country in the High Calcareous Alps[271]. However, some of the
plateau regions of the Fore Alps, similar except for lying at a lower level,
may be younger. Thus N. Krebs draws attention to thick gravels which
in the Hausruck (north of the Calcareous Alps in Upper Austria) overlie
the upper freshwater Molasse beds, and to the fact that the level at
which they were deposited rises rapidly southwards, and seems to continue into the plateau surfaces of the zone of the Fore Alps[272]. This
would make those surfaces of approximately Pontic age, so that they
might be considered as fragments belonging to a more recent addition
to the main mountain mass. Something similar may possibly be true
for the Saalach district, where the lower, peripherally lying plateau level
is without doubt more recent than the higher one of the High Calcareous
Alps. The present state of knowledge does not allow us to carry our con-
jectures further.

In the southern Calcareous Alps similar limestone plateaus appear
with relics of ancient landscapes preserved on their summits. The plateaus of the Dolomites (Heilig Kreuz, Tofana, Sella, Pala, etc.) and of
their eastern continuation as far as the Julian Alps, are more or less comparable to the zones of the High Alps in the north, and they occupy a
higher position. On the marginal chains south of the Val Sugana-
Bellunese lines, the plateaus are lower and correspond to a zone of Fore
Alps. There is no connection between the two groups. Indeed they are
separated from one another by the trough region of the Val Sugana and
the Bellunese basin, synclinal areas, complex in their detailed structure,
and the western one, at least, already evident in the Lower Miocene
(marine Lower Miocene, from Barco to Pieve Tesino). Both have remained as longitudinal valley zones of relative subsidence (left behind in

the raising); and they separate, as more youthful additions, the marginal chains (Folgaria—Sette Communi—Venetian Alps, approximately as far as the Cellina) from the main trunk. Thus the hilly landscape of their summit regions appears to be an independent development belonging to the tops of individual mountain chains, analogous to the ancient landscapes which we shall meet with on the summits of many broad folds, and not merely lower levels which dovetail into the higher one of the Dolomite plateau. Those associations of slope units, flattish or of medium gradient, found on the summits of the marginal chains, are the forerunners of the steep slopes which work upwards into their flanks and from the antecedent transverse valleys. The *origin* is of early Miocene date, if not older (first appearance of marginal chains). The further development into a lively-looking hummocky hill-country, its present character, may fall within the Miocene period; the separation from its base level of erosion, by the upward growth of steep slopes, within the Pliocene[273].

The plateau surfaces of the Dolomites have not yet been investigated. Like the northern High Alpine zone they are mountainous country with wide valleys, framed by concavely rising flanks which, towards the upper part, often curve again into convex bosses and higher plateau fragments. This similarity of character points to a similarity in the development of the plateau country of the northern and southern Calcareous Alps, but *in no way to simultaneity in their development*. So far no evidence whatever is known for the geological age of the developmental intervals seen in the forms of the plateau surfaces, i.e. the period of waxing development and the subsequent one of waning development, on to the separation of summit regions from their base levels of erosion (so far as the commencements of the two last-named processes do not coincide).

(b) Eastern Slope of the Alps and its
Boundary against the Karst

More is known of the connecting link between the Julian Alps and the Karst, along which the Pannonian-Adriatic watershed has lain since Eocene times. The high Julian Alps, south of the zone of the longitudinal valley of the Save, end eastwards in the impressive mountain fragment which surrounds the Wochein [Bohinj] in an arcuate form on the west and south. From Triglav to Krn it has the character of a plateau and bears considerable relics of ancient mountainous country (Triglav-Krn). These have a quite recognisable general slope towards the south and south-east, from over 2500 metres (with peaks rising over 2800 metres: Triglav) to slightly over 1800 metres; and they break off precipitously on all sides towards deeply sunk valleys. Between the headward-working tributaries of the Wocheiner Save [Bohinjska Sava], Bača, Selzachtal [Selška Dol] and Pöllandtal [Poljanki Dol], the plateau surfaces have already been removed, and are only just indicated by mountain ranges of corresponding height (the mountain chains of Hradica-Schwarzenberg [Rodica-Pasja Rav] and Porzen-Blegas) [Poljane-Blegaš][274].

This is the highest level so far discriminated. It rises above a second lower level which has the character of a peneplane. This is continued as a piedmont flat into the valley floors of the higher level, and shows a general slope eastward, on the average from 1500 to 1300 metres. This lower, slightly hummocky surface belongs entirely to the Save region. It extends over the heights around the Wocheiner See [Bohinjsko Jesaro], so filling up the concave part of the previously mentioned festoon of the High Julian Alps, and continues as the Pokljuka and Jelovka plateaus[275]. A third level is formed by broad areas of planation widening out to plateau surfaces, which are sunk like valleys into the second level and end above the line of the Save at an altitude of about 1000 metres. They are followed by the present deeply incised valleys of the Rotwein [Radorna Sava] and Wocheiner Save [Bohinjska Sava].

Sufficient observations have not yet been made for the dating of these three elements geologically. The following points have been established: the Wochein [Bohinj] is a synclinal region in which, as in the Save embayment (longitudinal valley zone), marine Middle Oligocene has been deposited on a sinking substratum, with lacustrine Upper Oligocene over it. The facies of these beds[276] show continuous subsidence in contrast to the surrounding parts of the area. These bear the plateau landscapes of the first level. Hence its origin cannot be later than pre-Middle Oligocene and perhaps goes back to Eocene. Its development, i.e. the wearing away by valleys (producing a hummocky landscape) may perhaps be correlated with the Wocheiner Oligocene. The second level (Jelovka surface) is younger, since it apparently goes over Oligocene of the Wochein which, in the meantime, had been again disturbed; and it may be considered that the strata to be correlated with the formation of that piedmont flat are to be sought in the Mediterranean beds (especially the Lower Miocene) of the Save embayment. For the third level it might be possible to arrive at an approximate determination of the age if there were confirmation of what is so far only probable, though probable in a high degree: that it is the continuation, as valley forms, into higher rising ground of the peneplane which, as an exceptionally flat formation, extends over a great part of the mountain area between Trieste and the Save. This surface directly adjoins the same *outliers* of the Julian High Alps (Blegaš range) just as the surface of the second level

(Jelovka plateau) does on their northern side. It is, however, rather severely dissected in the region of the Pölland valley. Both stand in the relation of piedmont flats to one and the same narrow fragment of the main watershed, but lie at very different heights at the edge of the two mountainlands to which they belong: the peneplane to the south of the Blegaš range has an altitude of about 1000 metres, which is exactly that to be expected for the piedmont flat at the exits of the wide valley features of the third level mentioned above. It is worth noticing that this piedmont flat is by no means peculiar to the Adriatic mountain slopes, but extends over all the tectonic elements and rock types into the Save region and even farther. It is the main peneplane of the transitional region between Alps and Karst, and, after the termination of the Julian High Alps in the Blegaš range, itself carries the main Adriatic-Pannonian watershed running south-eastwards. Thus it is most highly probable that the valleys of the third level, which F. Kossmat observed in the Save region, do not in fact debouch on to it. We therefore consider the main peneplane to be the third level.

On the Adriatic side it has been dislocated by unlevelled fractures, parallel to the Dinaric strike, and broken up into narrow strips which are in general inclined north-westwards towards the Italian lowland. Hence the individual portions along the meridian of Trieste have very different latitudes. From the fact that, as the throw of the faults disappears south-eastwards, so do the steps between the peneplane fragments, F. Kossmat has been able to prove that it is not a matter of various peneplane levels, but of dislocated parts of one and the same surface.

The main fragment is the Ternovaner Wald [Selva di Tarnova]. Here the surface rises from an average of 700 metres in the west to 900 metres in the east, and over 1000 metres in the north-east. It is warped into the shape of a saddle, as is seen from the course of the transverse valley of Čepovan which has now become functionless[277]; and the downfaulted blocks of the Veitsberg plateau, in the north, and in the south the coastal Karst near Trieste—further broken up by strike faults—correspond to the troughs on the two sides. The peneplane with its regular height (800–900 metres) and graded condition encroaches on to the Birnbaumer Wald [Selva di Piro] with its totally different structure, there extending over, amongst other features, the famous window of Grafenbrunn (Cretaceous material over Eocene flysch, south of Adelsberg [Postumia]); and it can be followed, absolutely homogeneous, at a constant altitude over the wide area surrounding the Laibacher Moos [Ljubljana Moor]. In the trough region of the Save district, characterised by the appearance of Oligocene-Miocene beds, F. Kossmat sees its continuation in the extensive hill country at the same moderate height, east of Ljubljana as far as the Sann [Sana] (wide elevations of 900–1000 metres). This country is penetrated by synclines striking east-west, of Upper Oligocene and Mediterranean, above which lie Sarmatian beds, the 'Save folds' sunk as narrow bands between wide anticlinal zones that are almost devoid of Tertiary material. Here a tumbled-looking denudation relief, obviously of complicated structure, extends over Palaeozoics and folded Trias. Taking that as a peneplane and equating it to our third level, Kossmat reaches a definite conclusion as to the age of that level: on the one hand the peneplane goes over the steeply infolded Sarmatian strata, on the other hand these are overlain at various places by transgressing *Congeria* beds of Pontian age. From these facts he deduces a Pontian age for the peneplane[278].

However, the relations seem to be by no means so simple. From F. Teller's survey[279], it follows that even by Middle Oligocene times the marine beds extended not only over a folded basement, but over a relief which, in the longitudinal valley zone (Save region), may have been graded almost to a peneplane, though in the region rising north of this to the Steiner Alps [Kaminški Alpi] it was highly uneven, in fact mountainous[280]. This was still true in even greater measure for the lacustrine Upper Oligocene transgression. Any future morphological analytical investigation of the region must certainly take into account the possibility that relics of the Oligocene land surface[281] may be preserved on the anticlines of the Save folds and that they may have merely suffered undulatory deformation, but not been destroyed, in the process of folding. The same is true for the Miocene transgression and the form associations covered in by it. The Miocene, commencing with a coarse transgressional facies, extends over the older substratum and over the denuded remnants of the Upper Oligocene Sotzka strata. On the map (Cilli-Ratschach [Celje-Radeče] sheet) these latter are confined to narrow synclinal zones into which later the whole conformable Miocene sequence was also downfolded (locally marine Aquitanian, usually marine Lower Miocene to Sarmatian overstepping it). Two conclusions follow from this: (*a*) The undulatory deformation was already in progress before and during the uppermost Oligocene and the Lower Miocene. Along the line of troughs, the latter overlaps the Upper Oligocene, which is preserved there only, and it extends over the anticlines from which the Upper Oligocene had already been stripped. (*b*) The denudation surface at the base of the Miocene does not coincide with the upper surface of the pre-Upper Oligocene times. On the anticlines it must somehow or other have been sunk into the latter, been lowered into it (or replaced it); in the troughs it goes between (Aquitanian beds), Miocene beds and Sotzka beds, and so here it lies *above* the Oligocene surface. Hence remnants of Miocene land-form elements are to be expected on the broad anticlines also.

For the time being, no more accurate information can be given as to their nature. The following features may be pointed out. Away from the entrenched valleys, the anticlinal zones of the Save folds show nothing in the way of peneplane. Instead there is a knobbly-looking upland of broad flattish domes, the altitudes of which, with all their individual differences, show a systematic drop in the direction of the synclines on each side and where the folds die out. They thus in a way reflect the anticlinal structure. It is probable that these flattish slope units on the tops of the small convex domes will turn out to be fragments belonging to a single flattish (almost completely dissected) surface, which is bent down towards the synclinal tracts. While the tops of the domes on the summits of the anticlinal zones now lie between 900 and 1000 metres, and even reach 1200 metres, the lower surface of the marine Miocene beds in the same region, even where relatively little disturbed, e.g. north-west of Ratschach, still does not reach to 750 metres (the maximum altitude so far observed). It seems to follow from the whole arrangement that in the *anticlinal regions* the Miocene there found a relief already considerably dissected, and filled up the valleys before it flooded over the heights. One might almost perceive, in the above-mentioned *hummocky surface*, relics of Oligocene origin (in the form, for instance, of a peneplane warped anticlinally); and, in the buried valleys, remnants of the Lower Miocene relief to which the flatter form associations of the anticlinal flanks and the *courses of the synclines* (i.e. the peneplane-like lower surface of the Miocene) correspond.

At any rate this much is now clear: in the region of the Save folds no uniform peneplane is present, which could be considered as the direct continuation of surfaces at a similar altitude, whether those in the north (Steiner Alps [Kaminški Alpi]) or in the south (High Karst). These last are more likely to be rising or uplifted parts of the mountain system, which are equivalent, not to the individual Save folds, but to the whole synclinal region (zone of longitudinal valleys) within which the Save folds occur as a special deformation.

In particular, the explanation here cannot be that of a peneplane which bevels the Neogene synclines. A lower denudation level is developed, on the Neogene of the Save folds, at a height of about 500 metres; sinking eastward and westward it yet remains at a considerable height above the present valley level. It is characterised by lines of entrenched valleys, which are by no means confined to the Neogene but extend on to various tectonic and petrographic zones (Palaeozoics, Trias) as an independent level. This valley level is of Pontian age, as is proved by the penetration into it of unfolded *Congeria* beds near Lichtenwald.

Thus, in the area under consideration, there is nothing to go upon for dating the main peneplane of the coastal High Karst. For the time being the commonly accepted generalised date—Miocene[282]—cannot be verified and more sharply defined. The origin of the third level is certainly later than the main Oligocene folding.

Thus we are still very far from any exact knowledge of the geological interval which lies between the times of formation of the denudation levels treated here, from their inception until they were separated from their base levels of erosion by the intercalation of steeper and younger slope units, i.e. until they began to be dissected. But this one thing is certain: in the boundary zone between the Alps and the Karst, there occur *at several levels, one above another*, ancient form associations, of subdued modelling, sometimes of a most symmetrical character, which are connected with one another after the manner of piedmont flats. The approximate time of their formation is between the Eocene and the Upper Miocene, a short interval of time compared with the rate at which denudation can work, a time during which continuous and vigorous crustal movements were occurring. In view of this, it is surprising that no doubt has been cast on the correctness of the assumption that all these peneplanes, and peneplanated fragments, developed as typical end-peneplanes, [Davisian] peneplains, during pauses in tectonic activity. The desire to find these has often had the effect of prejudging the issue as regards establishing them. This is especially true of the adjoining areas to the south-east, the Dinaric Karst, where are to be found the most nearly graded peneplanes known anywhere. In parts they have been shown to belong to different levels: like true piedmont flats the lower ones continue as valley forms into the higher ones[283]. But as regards the level fragments on the summits of the various chains, separated by strike depressions containing series of polyes together with lacustrine deposits of various ages, the identification is quite uncertain. The tectonic constructions invented to fit it seem to have absolutely no foundation[284]. The intervals of tectonic repose which the 'peneplanation' of the whole mountain area demanded, and which were accordingly found, could not possibly have been anything but so short that whole mountainous regions must have melted away, like butter in the sun, for them to have reached the condition of an end-peneplane in that time. Neither at the boundary between Alps and Karst, nor in the Dinaric Mountains, is it a matter of true end-peneplanes, but of a primary peneplane. The piedmont flats, widespread in both cases, fall into the same category. The trend of their development, from the moment of their inception onwards, is the same as has been found to be characteristic of piedmont flats. The manner in which their development in the Karst was carried out was, of course, somewhat different, being determined by the special processes of denudation associated with a terrain of soluble limestone. Yet even in the Karst, piedmont flats grow at the expense of land rising above them, and in their turn become shortened from below by the growth of lower flats. This is the way in which the steps have been formed between the peneplane levels (or planation levels) in the Dinaric Mountains, steps which have long attracted special attention on account of the grandeur of their scale[285]. Their slopes rise up concavely from the lower flats and pass over as convex curves or, with a sharp convex break of gradient, into the higher fragmentary levels. The flight of steps begins at, and progresses from, the valley-ways which cut into these surfaces and divide them into lobes. The valleys debouch on to the piedmont flats where they find their nearest base levels of erosion[286]. As A. Penck had recognized and A. Grund, O. Maull[287] and others later worked out in more detail, the enlarging surfaces thus not only have an inclination which corresponds to the direction of the drainage, but are directly connected with individual main watercourses. The intervalley divides between the backward cutting tributaries become narrower, and disintegrate into inselbergs which rise above the peneplaned surfaces ('mosors' of A. Penck*). They are excellently developed, like all the other characteristic features due to the extension of piedmont flats in the boundary region between the Alps and the Karst; and they have been studied here by N. Krebs and F. Kossmat. In groups and singly, they rise to an average of 400 to 500 metres above the chief graded peneplane (third level) and by the same amount on its faulted fragments. They usually still show flattish tops, and south-eastwards they gradually merge into a higher plateau surface (Mrzovec, Goljak, Nanos, Javornik, etc.). They are the relics of an older peneplane level, which has been preserved in such extensive fragments in the direction of the Schneeberg [M. Nevoso] of Carniola [Slovenia] that the flat character of its relief can be readily perceived. The south-eastern Tschitschenboden [Monti dei Vena] also belongs here. The altitude of this highly disintegrated surface corresponds perfectly with that of the second level on the eastern slope of the Julian Alps. The two may be identified with one another, since both lie on the same strip of mountainland between the same downfaulted areas (Save zone and Adria). The Schneeberg [M. Nevoso] of Carniola [Slovenia] rises like an inselberg above the second level of the coastal High Karst. It is the north-western outlier of a group of emin-

[* A. Penck, *Geomorphologische Studien aus Bosnien und der Herzegowina* (Zeitschr. deutsch. und öst. Alpenv. XXXI, 1900).]

ences which seems to have a yet greater significance in the neighbouring Croatian Karst, and by its age and position appears to belong to the first level of the Julian Alps. This inselberg zone extends on one and the same crustal strip from the extremity of the Julian Alps south-eastwards along the strike of the mountains; F. Kossmat is correct in assuming it to be the fragments, already reduced to a minimum, of the earlier Adriatic-Pannonian watershed.

On glancing back, we find the Alps to consist of an arch which is diversified along its strike by upswingings like wave crests and depressions like wave troughs. This form is reflected in the course taken by the *absolute heights* at which the gipfelflur is maintained. This is a character which, as will be shown, is of outstanding importance for diagnosis. The whole wave system, as the Alpine arching may be termed in a purely descriptive sense, is furrowed by valleys and extensively disintegrated into ridge crests and individual peaks, the wave crests being equivalent to the ridge zones just as the wave troughs form the zones of the longitudinal valleys. This disintegration becomes noticeably less towards the eastern end of the mountain system, as expressed in the older, gentler form associations on the intervalley divides of the High Calcareous Alps (which correspond to the zone of ridges). Three further sets of features must be pointed out, which become more and more marked in the eastern part of each mountain group and at the eastern end of the Alps themselves:

(*a*) As the absolute height of the gipfelflur (discounting the above-mentioned wave-like manner in which it is divided) diminishes towards the northern and southern edges of a cross section through the ridge crests, so also it lessens in an eastward direction along the trend of the mountains. Together with this, even on the summits of the centrally-lying ridge zones, flattish and intermediate form associations appear ever better preserved and extended more widely, forerunners of the steep slopes belonging to the present sharply V-shaped valleys. As yet these have been little studied, though they have often been noticed[288] (e.g. Bachergebirge, Saualpe, the northern end of the embayment of Graz, etc.); and their analogy with the plateaus of the Calcareous Alpine zones has been rightly stressed. They are their equivalent in developmental history, but whether this is also the case as regards time is still unknown[289]. In its main features, this whole configuration is independent of the fold and nappe structure as well as of the character of the rock[290].

(*b*) Not only does the mountain arching, taken as a whole, sink eastwards, but also in this direction its undulations become ever sharper, and this can be recognised as a tectonic characteristic. The origin of the zones of longitudinal valleys has here proved to be, in parts, very ancient. By mid-Tertiary, and locally early Tertiary, they were in being, as may be seen from the intercalation in them of strata of corresponding age. These can be correlated with the progressive denudation of the accompanying ranges. The beds are not parts of a uniform nappe which was once more brought down into the troughs of the longitudinal valley zones, depressed or faulted into them and so preserved there; but they invade zones which were sinking, relatively, and were thus becoming areas of sedimentation. Moreover, they do not lie on the floor of an hypothetical syncline, but mantle a denudational relief which the zones of the longitudinal valleys had preserved, a relief which therefore had, as it were, been carved in the floor of an hypothetical syncline. Crustal movement, continuing right up to the present day, has distorted the invading Tertiary beds, and has caused their further relative subsidence (partly through faulting). Aside from this, what can be observed near the end of the mountain system is a repeated alternation of sedimentation and denudation, shown especially clearly in the area of the Save longitudinal valley zone. Here, according to investigations made by F. Teller and F. Kossmat, the following stratigraphical development is to be found (see p. 240):

Above a surface of denudation (*unconformity*), marine Mid-Oligocene (corresponding to the Castel Gomberto strata) here follows the folded Palaeozoics and Trias. It is a littoral facies.

Unconformity—surface of denudation.

Lacustrine Upper Oligocene with *Cyrena semistriata*, *Cerithium margaritaceum*, *Anthracotherium magnum* (Sotzka beds corresponding more or less to the lower freshwater Molasse of the Alpine Foreland).

Unconformity.

Marine Aquitanian (limestone with *Lepidocyclina*); locally restricted, i.e. lying in the hollows of the relief; above it there follows conformably and stretching far out[291]:

Burdigalian ⎫ which extend westward a considerably shorter distance
Helvetian ⎬ in the synclinal region of the Save than do the Sotzka
Sarmatian ⎭ beds (e.g. not so far as the Wochein [Bohinj] trough).

Unconformity.

Pontian. Pebbles and *Congeria* beds. The transgression extends only as far as the outer edge of the Save folds.

Denudation surface.

Levantine. The transgression no longer extends to the edge of the mountains.

There is on the whole a retrogression, a moving outwards of the spheres of sedimentation, a swelling out of the area of denudation. The process has not, however, been continuous, but has run a periodic course, interrupted by transgressions of a secondary order.

(c) The backward and forward oscillation of the area of Tertiary sedimentation is no peculiarity of the Save embayment, but is characteristic of the whole zone within which the Alps plunge eastwards into the Pannonian Plain. Although, according to what is at present known, the exposures nowhere indicate so great an age in the Tertiary sequence as in southern Styria and northern Carniola; yet from the detailed investigations of W. Petraschek, J. Sölch, A. Winkler, V. Hilber, A. Aigner and others[292], the following may be considered an assured general result: *in the eastern marginal region of the Alpine arching, a zone of unconformities separates the mountainous district in the west from the area of continuous sedimentation in the east.* This applies above all to the sections of the Tertiary with which we are here concerned, those up to and including the Levantine. Thus exactly the same phenomenon is repeated as that which was also observed at the edge of zones of uplift in the region of the continental massifs (pp. 223, 226).

(c) ANATOLIA

In spite of the considerable disturbance by folding which has affected beds as late as the Upper Miocene Sarmatian in the east part of the Eastern Alps, it is evident that their great wave-like undulations along the strike are comparable with the tectonic type of broad folds. The earliest account of the form and development of broad fold structure comes from Anatolia[293].

Considering origin and arrangement, two regions are to be distinguished there: (a) the western part of the peninsula within the Tauro-Dinaric festoon, and (b) the festoon itself.

(a) The western and north-western broad folds are characterised by the way in which their course (E–W) is entirely independent of the structure of the folded strata. In these latter, it has so far been possible to distinguish fold features, possibly of pre-Cambrian, certainly of Palaeozoic age (apparently *two* late Palaeozoic phases), pre-Cretaceous to Lower Cretaceous, Lower Eocene and (posthumous) Oligocene.

(b) In the festoon, the strike of the broad folds coincides with that of the folded strata, which are of Eocene age in an inner zone and of approximately Mid-Oligocene in an outer zone (referring here only to the Western and Lycian Taurus). There are indications that even at that time folds, which had just arisen or were arising, and rock slices, collected into fasces, emerged as individual ranges, i.e. as anticlines of a major order, which shed their debris into adjoining troughs of a similar order. For the main part, however, in both areas the formation of broad folds, of their present extent and appearance, falls into the subsequent period, lasting from the Upper Oligocene to the present day, and there is nothing to show that the movement is yet at an end.

The strata to be correlated* with the broad folding, are found to be mainly, but not exclusively, in the synclinal areas, the broad troughs. As far as is known at present, they do not correspond everywhere to an equally long interval of time within the Tertiary period. In individual regions the oldest beds so far recognized are equivalent to the Aquitanian; the Mediterranean stages (Burdigalian, Helvetian) have been traced locally; Sarmatian equivalents seem to be more generally distributed. Pontian strata denote a climax in the regional distribution of the Anatolian Neogene, which seems only locally to pass up into the Levantine[294].

The author was the first to make continuous investigation into the petrographic facies and the bedding, over a major part of the area of the peninsula. These show that Neogene deposits were laid down in areas of relative subsidence[295]. These, however, did not everywhere, nor during all the divisions of the Tertiary that are concerned, coincide with the present synclinal zones. In Miocene, even as far as into Pontian times, they occupied a greater area. In course of time the number of mountain ranges with an east-west strike has increased by the arising of new anticlines out of the broad troughs. Thus the regions of deposition not only become divided up, but their area more and more diminished. The ranges, therefore, are of different types. Those of earlier origin were never covered by Neogene. Instead, this lies against their flanks with a mountain-foot facies of coarse clastic material. This facies passes into fine-grained calcareous marl as the interior of the trough is approached (e.g. the marine Lower and Middle Miocene of the Lycian ranges; the Neogene, presumably going back to the Lower Miocene, on either side of the Bithynian Olympus, etc.). Distortion of these and later deposits indicates continuation of the arching. The younger chains, on the other hand, formerly lying right underneath these same Tertiary strata, arched them up into anticlines as they rose, and for the most part they became rid of them through contemporaneous denudation. In the troughs on either side, the correlated strata were deposited as younger Neogene beds. The mountain-foot facies is turned towards [lies at the edge of] ranges of earlier as well as of more recent origin; and everywhere, or at any rate along the margins of the latter, it transgresses unconformably over the older, disturbed Neogene.

[* See glossary.]

The unconformities within the Neogene sequence are not at the same stratigraphical level either regionally or along the edges of the individual chains. They cannot, therefore, without further evidence, be used in determining the age of the group of strata lying above or below. Rather, they denote the appearing of new ranges at different periods for each case (unconformities of the first order); or else they occur in conjunction with continued movements executed by one and the same range (oscillations of the axis type, to be treated later). Occasionally these unconformities of the second order are repeated in several storeys one above another, and they indicate a continuance of the movement on account of which the strata just deposited were continually being disturbed, dragged (even folded), exposed to denudation at the edges, and immediately covered up again by younger beds of the series. These are local marginal phenomena. Investigations by Oppenheim, however, lead one to suppose that the above-mentioned unconformities of the first order occur most frequently between the Middle Miocene and the Pontian beds. This would mean that the Upper Miocene was already a period of intensified broad folding, as indeed the author has proved to be the case for the succeeding periods of the Levantine up to the present day.

Thus Neogene facies and bedding not only give detailed information as to the development of the whole system of chains, but make clear the anticlinal character of the ranges and the synclinal nature of the longitudinal, strike, depressions. The complications in the stratification do not mask this fact. They are due to the fact that the Tertiary strata, especially the younger divisions (Pontian–Levantine) at the edges of the chains, flooded over a diversified hummocky mountain relief, and here— particularly in the old buried valleys—have frequently suffered peculiar disturbances by a process of dragging, which is suggestive of a large-scale settling down accompanied by much faulting. Further, it must be mentioned that the broad folding reacted on the strata filling the troughs not only in the sense of dragging them along, but at certain places it has even folded them. The conditions under which the folding occurred have not yet been elucidated. All that is certain is that the older Neogene horizons appear *in general* to be more strongly pushed together than the younger ones. Yet they are by no means folded everywhere, just as the Pontian and Levantine equivalents are not entirely without folding. From this it can be deduced with certainty that tangential forces came into play, which however could not have been situated outside the system of broad folding, but only within it[296]. Finally the fact must be pointed out that longitudinal faults occur along the strike of the broad fold system towards the west, i.e. in the direction in which there is generally an increase in the amplitude of the broad folds (viz. in the difference of altitude between the crest line of the ranges and the Neo-gene-covered floor of the troughs). The connection between the development of faults and the increase in the amplitudes is unmistakable, and impresses the observer who follows up the fault systems from the west towards the high land of the interior: the faults, for the greater part, peter out in that direction; the ranges, comparable to horsts in the west, become fault-free anticlines; the depressions which, according to A. Philippson, frequently have the form of downfaulted troughs there, become synclines. Ranges and depressions do not disappear, but the majority of the longitudinal faults do so[297].

The differences in origin of the ranges are naturally paralleled by diversity in their outward shape. The *Bithynian or Mysian Olympus*, the Keshish Dagh [Ulu dağ] of the Turks, may be briefly considered as being typical of a range trending almost east-west and of a somewhat early origin[298]. Several levels stand out sharply from one another. The highest and oldest (I), on the summit of the range, is hill country of subdued relief, its slopes consistently concave in profile, with wide trough-like valleys, the floors of which are at about 2200 metres above sea level, while the peaks rise to 2500 metres. It extends but a slight distance east to west, along the strike, and is then replaced by a blunt ridge where younger, steeper slopes meet. These are identical with those[299] leading down by convex curves (convex above) to the next lower level; and on the north side of the range, they end below in the so-called 'upper terrace'. This surface II fringes the highest central mountainland as an undulating piedmont flat, stretches of it being dissected, in no trifling manner, with some of its shallow valleys still ending upon the terrace itself[300]. It is bounded on the lower side by further steep slopes, giving a sharply convex break of gradient, and its edge has obviously been already worked back considerably. In some places these slopes belong to the steep relief which has developed upwards from the present day, sharply incised valleys on the mountain flanks (north-east section of the mountains); but in others they end below in undulating surfaces distinguished by a shallow valley-system of their own. These surfaces penetrate into the upper region as valleys and are preserved in broad fragments (III) on the intervalley divides of the north-western section of the mountains. The so-called 'lower terrace' belongs here. It is actually a lower piedmont flat. Like the higher one (II), it shows the following peculiarities:

1. Along the meridian of the central mountainland (I) it is not yet in existence, or has already been replaced by a more recent steep relief; westwards its width increases in proportion as the central mountainland becomes lower and disappears. Where this has come to an end as a

narrow crest along the strike of the range, surface II now extends over the correspondingly lower summit (about 2000 metres). There it is dissected, especially by valleys which open out on to surface III; but on the ridges between them, as well as on the broad domes on the tops of the ranges, fragments of it are well preserved.

2. Both piedmont flats are strongly warped, in a direction transverse to the strike of the mountains. This follows, for one thing, from the great inclination of the remnants still preserved intact, which far exceeds the original gradients; and also, more especially, from the fact that new, steep-walled, sharply V-shaped valleys are incised into the area of deformed relief and *are confined to it*. At their lower ends these finish above that convex break of gradient up to which the most recent steep relief has reached, working up from the mountain foot. It is perfectly clear that those sharply V-shaped valleys are not caused by the general upward movement of the whole range, to which in the last resort the above-mentioned steep relief owes its existence. They have arisen because of a steepening of the old form associations, due to warping which has been continuing for a long time. For surface III, this warping is two-sided, i.e. anticlinal. The whole forms a group of features often met in regions of broad folding.

At the margin of the range, surface III reaches away on to the steeply tilted Neogene beds; with a lessening of its general gradient it enters the broad syncline of Brusa-Abuliond [Bursa-Apulyont] ('Little Phrygia') lying in front of it and, there, stretches over the slightly disturbed Neogene filling as an exceptionally extensive peneplane. Valleys are incised in it; and along the major water-courses they occasionally widen out into broadly excavated lowlands. The bordering steep slopes, which are relatively low, are morphological equivalents of the high rugged steep relief found in the region of the ranges. In that region, steep relief nowadays characterises the deeply-scored lower courses of all rivers coming from the interior, as well as the stretches of antecedent transverse gorges, and consistently forms the lower parts of the flank of the chain where this shows the highest uplifts. The present-day valleys, which give rise to the steep relief, form a fourth—the most recent—main level (IV) which is broken by terraces into a succession of several stages (intermediate levels). These are of no special interest at the moment.

There are thus piedmont benchlands present. The number and arrangement of the constituent parts bear a relation to the height of the chain. They are warped transversely to its strike. On comparing the Keshish Dagh (i.e. the high eastern part of the extensive anticline in the south of Little Phrygia) with its lower westward continuation, the following features are apparent. The number of steps between independent denudation levels is greater in the Keshish Dagh than in the west. The 'treads' are generally narrower the lower they lie. Along the strike of the range they widen with its reduction in height. At the same time the number of levels decreases, the highest being the first to disappear; and *there* [*Keshish Dagh*] the uppermost piedmont flat passes westward into a summit plane. *There* steep relief has already developed upwards from the most recent erosion furrows into a uniform flight of steep slopes which constitute the mountain side (Bursa district [of the Keshish Dagh]); to the west [of Bursa and of the Keshish Dagh] no such flight of steep slopes has yet appeared. The steep relief is just as steep, but extends only up to a much lower altitude, and seems on the whole confined to the valleys themselves. It becomes evident that the causes of increased erosion are present to a different extent in the two sections. That is only part of the problem. The direction in which the piedmont flats stretch out [? and increase in number] indicates that in which the first onset of erosion appeared (see p. 215). In other words, they denote the direction in which the zone of denudation is growing, i.e. increasing in area. The existing arrangement shows that in process of time the range must have grown in width and in length, to a very varied extent, however. The increase in width is restricted, and evidently soon reached its limits: surface III is narrower than surface II—its extension over the neighbouring depression cannot be considered, since this is connected with the character of the syncline and not with that of the broad anticline—and none of the terrace levels belonging to the steep relief unites at the margin of the range with a lower, what we might call, piedmont-like levelled surface; they are limited to the zone of steep relief (and indeed converge towards the mountain foot)[301]. On the whole, the chain has grown in length, a fact which is illustrated in a specially impressive way by the antecedent transverse gorges of the streams coming from the interior. Formerly they flowed round the highest (in its time the sole) mountain region, the Keshish Dagh; but later, they were forced to become antecedent by elongation of the broad anticline (Ülfer Chai). Transverse to its strike, the conditions leading to erosion *appeared* in the course of time, *to an increased extent* everywhere: the angle of slope systematically steepens from the summit to the foot of the range. Its *growth in height* is connected with this. The distance has become greater between level I and what was, in successive periods, the level of the adjacent area of accumulation. The required comparative levels are represented by [1] the upper edge of the Neogene transgression, now at the high level to which it has been lifted by deformation; [2] the gravels, which are at any rate pre-Pleistocene. These lie considerably lower, transgress over surface III, and are occasionally found at the edge of the broad syncline; [3] the present day surface of deposition. The character of the forms and their arrangement also teach the same lesson. If, of the three dimensions of an anticline, its extension along the strike is designated as length, its height as amplitude, and its breadth as phase, the state of affairs may be formulated thus: *with continued growth in length and in amplitude, the range in question has* NOT *continued to increase in phase in the same way.*

At the present time it is not yet possible to date these elements geologically with any certainty; for neither the divisions of the correlated strata nor their ages are known exactly. P. Oppenheim, who worked on A. Philippson's collection, making use of his stratigraphical observations[302], takes the calcareous Neogene beds of Little Phrygia to be the equivalent of the Miocene, possibly even of early Miocene; and considers the gravels transgressing over them to be possibly Pontian. Fuccini, however, ascribes this age to the calcareous beds of Sultanshehr, which occur in a southerly embayment of the Little Phrygian Neogene belt[303]. Late Tertiary strata approach Olympus mainly as a mountain-foot facies of sandy conglomerate; the calcareous formations above it have not so far yielded any fossils. They may be of Miocene age, in the widest sense of the word, up to as far as the Pontian stage. I take the transgressing gravels to be younger, probably Levantine. In that case, surface III might be of Levantine origin, the piedmont surface II would then belong to some Miocene stage, and the heights (I) might even be considered an early Tertiary, perhaps Oligocene, relic[304]. The western continuation of the Keshish Dagh belongs to the type of more recent broad anticline, such as is shown in its simplest form by the coastal range between Little Phrygia and the Sea of Marmora[305]. As a rule only three main levels of successive origin can be distinguished in these. An uppermost one extends along the tops of the convexly rounded summits. Flattish slope systems are frequently still preserved over great areas of these, belonging to old form associations which have been subsequently dissected. These latter show that the gipfelflur, which has been developed in the meantime, possesses an inherited and not a newly acquired character[306]. In the coastal range, this element [of form] appears only on isolated upswingings of the mountain mass, arranged as brachyanticlines along the strike of the chain, like a string of pearls, and separated from one another by extremely wide depressions in the crest of the range. A large part of these latter still consists entirely of Neogene beds, composed of sandy marl, conglomeratic in the lower horizons. There is well developed anticlinal bedding[307]. The trend of the mountains coincides with the strike of the strata. As is indicated by residual remains, the higher upswingings of the mountain mass, now almost entirely free from late Tertiary strata, were also originally completely covered by them.

They are archings up of the substratum of the Neogene, and the course of the gipfelflur exactly reflects the brachyanticlinal bedding in the strata[308].

The next lower level is given by the floors of the valleys which invade the upraised parts of the mountains and debouch at the edge of the broad undulating peneplane. This piedmont flat passes over from the sub-structure on to distorted Neogene beds. In a manner analogous to surface III, it extends on the one hand over the later Tertiary of the adjacent broad syncline, and on the other over the wide depressions between the brachyanticlines. Here it can be seen clearly how the upswingings of the mountains, by elongation along their strike, grew together into a single range of uniform appearance. The lowest level occurs on the floors of the valleys dissecting the peneplane. These are wide and shallow in the region of the broad synclines (where there is excavation and fresh aggradation, conversion into swamps); narrow, deeper, and with steeper walls in the zones between the brachyanticlines, more precipitous and deeper still in these themselves.

Apart from dissection of the systems by the latest formed of the steep V-shaped valleys, the broad anticlines of recent origin present a picture of central mountainland and surrounding piedmont flat. Both are stretched out in the direction of the strike of the mountains, and the forms of medium relief belonging to the central mountainland have their slopes characterised by convex profiles. Thus a contrast is evoked between the general concavity of the older form associations out of which the mountainland has been carved, and the forms of the still higher levels which are to be seen on the ranges, or portions of ranges, of earlier origin. Compared with these earlier chains, the broad anticlines of simple morphological structure, which appeared later within the broad fold system, seem to be more numerous. The same is perhaps also true for Macedonia, that part of the Dinarids in which F. Kossmat is inclined to think that it is mainly the younger type which he can recognise[309]. Further detailed investigation will undoubtedly reveal ranges older in origin—and of more than one age—and as the correlated Tertiary beds are extensively preserved, it will be possible, by means of their stratigraphical sequence, to determine the various [denudational] elements geologically. Isolated observations made by J. Cvijić seem to me to point in this direction. They are, however, too meagre and disconnected to allow of a definite judgment[310]. O. Maull's research in the Peloponnese and central Greece provides additional facts[311]. On the whole, sufficient observations are available on the facies, arrangement and stratification of the Tertiary beds, spread out over the basins and longitudinal depressions, to remove any doubt as to the broad fold character of the

Balko-Greek Dinarids. And I consider it probable that the morphological differences noticed between the inner and the marginal parts of the mountains in the north-westward continuation towards the Alps, are differences between older broad folding—of varied ages—and that of more recent origin[312].

(d) THE ANDINE SYSTEM OF MOUNTAIN RANGES

We turn to observations that have been made in the *Andine system of mountain ranges*. The chief characteristic is the alternation of more or less closely ranged chains and depressions, known in North American literature as 'basin range structure', from its prorotype in the west of the United States of America. Since the classic researches of Gilbert[313], whose interpretation was accepted and carried further by J. C. Diller, Powell, Dutton, etc., strike faulting has been taken to be the essential tectonic element concerned. These faults are considered to have divided the mountain mass into long narrow strips, which have been displaced relative to one another in such a way that the upraised horst-like strips, or the raised edges of blocks that are merely tilted, became mountain ranges. The depressions are considered to be either the hollows left between tilted blocks or to be fault troughs. The altitudinal configuration of the chains is thus attributed to vertical displacement. Hence a direct relationship is assumed between the height of a range and the throw of the fault; the drop on one side of a range or on both, as the case may be, appears as an unlevelled fault scarp. It is considered comparable to the Quaternary faults which cross various mountain basins longitudinally as unlevelled fault faces, though of smaller displacement, and may have been produced by earthquakes[314].

Like other systems of mountain chains, the Cordillera [of the American continents] has many places where strike faults, sometimes with an extraordinarily great throw, have in fact been discovered; as in the Basin Ranges, the Pampean sierras of the Argentine, and elsewhere. Thus their significance in mountain building cannot be doubted. But it has not by any means been geologically proved to be the rule for the ranges to be bounded by faults—even in those parts where a geological survey has actually been made. This state of affairs, and more particularly the existence of ranges where it is known for certain that the structure is unfaulted, show that faults do not play that part in mountain building which has been ascribed to them. This has, indeed, been deemed such a firmly established fact, that often enough their existence has been taken for granted without any attempt to prove it, or even without troubling further about it when the evidence was negative. Instead, morphological criteria have long been used as evidence that faults probably exist, in areas difficult of access for geological examination. And W. M. Davis attempted to develop further this theory about faults, on the basis of the cycle theory[315]. Since then, steep drops in the mountain flanks on the side towards the supposed fault, facet-like surfaces which there truncate the mountain spurs at the foot of the range and are interpreted as practically unaltered portions of the actual fault plane, together with erosion valleys, sharply V-shaped in cross section, which persist till they debouch at the mountain edge, are taken to be irrefutable proof, without any possibility of misinterpretation, of the faulted nature of the margin of the range[316]. Nevertheless, such a possibility must be admitted in the case of the features just described. Flexure of parts of an upper surface, without any faulting, leads to morphological modifications which are similar to dislocation by faulting. It is just in regions of broad folds that this can quite well be seen; and it constitutes a problem, the general solution of which can be found only if it is treated as a case of slope development.

On the other hand, little attention has been paid to the fact that strike faults of great throw, actually established as present in regions of mountain ranges or near their base, do not as a rule appear as unlevelled fault scarps and do not form boundaries between various types of relief, as might be expected if they separated crustal strips each having a fundamentally different sort of movement and so a different endogenetic origin. In this case, no dislocation is visible in the development of the relief features in the way that there is along the western marginal fault of the Fichtelgebirge. But, apart from differences due to rock materials, the steep, medium, or flattish relief—as the case may be—usually passes in the same manner and unbroken over the line of disturbance[317]. The faults are not indeed the prime conditioning element in the formation of the ranges, but under certain conditions they appear to accompany this, being incidental to the occurrence of a main movement consisting of an undulatory bending of the crust, viz. warping into broad folds. C. King recognised this fifty years ago for the Basin Ranges[318] and recently C. L. Baker has emphasised it[319]. There are features which prove these connections, such as the anticlinal attitude of the correlated* strata at the edges of the chains, where typical unconformities appear between stages of differing age, and a similar attitude for the covering beds which still occasionally arch over the summits of the ranges[320]. These have not escaped the notice of either older or more recent observers in the North American Cordillera. But it appears that the theory of tilted blocks has diverted attention from any other evaluation of what has been observed. In addition, exposures of that kind [i.e. showing the attitude of the beds]

[* See glossary.]

do not appear to be at all frequent in the Basin Ranges and their continuation; and connected sets of correlated strata are rarely developed
to any great extent.

Some parts of the *Argentine Andes* afford further insight into this
matter. Correlated strata from the Upper Cretaceous to the present day
have been preserved, particularly in the north-western and northern
Pampean Sierras. In part, these lie in front of the block of the Puna de
Atacama on its east side; in part, southwards, they are separated from it,
and then form a belt in which they rise like islands from the central
Argentine plains as north-south ranges in front of the High Cordillera[321].
With the help of these, it has here been possible to reveal the broad fold
nature of the 'basin range structure'[322]. The morphological investigation
is still in its first stages. Special attention may be called to the following
points:

The easternmost member of the Pampean sierras is the complex of the
Sierra de Cordoba, emerging isolated and meridian-wise from the Pampa, divided up in the same direction by several depressions. The earliest
observers described the individual parts of the mountains as high
plateaus, and called special attention to the asymmetrical nature of the
ranges[323]: steep drops westwards as contrasted with gentler eastern
slopes. These eastern slopes are formed, as is now known, by fairly level
peneplanes, which lead down, with a slight eastward tilt, from the two
main ranges, the Sierra Comechingones—Sierra Grande and the parallel
one, reaching further northwards, of the Sierra Chica. These are being
scored by precipitously incised valleys. Over a good part of the west sides
of the ranges, on the other hand, peneplanes are absent; instead, the
noticeably steeper western slopes appear to be disintegrated into a deeply
dissected steep relief. This gives the impression of steep breakings
away[324]. Closer examination, however, reveals the following facts: the
greatest descent of the Sierra de Cordoba, from the general crest line to
the plain lying at its foot on the west, amounts to a maximum of 2000
metres (latitude of the Pampa de Achala); further south (Sierra de
Comechingones) to about 1400 metres; generally averaging about 1000
metres. But these differences in altitude correspond to an average horizontal distance of 10 to 15 kilometres from the summit of the chain to its
foot. This means a slope with a mean gradient of 5° (maximum about
11°). That is not what could be called a steep drop to a marginal fault, as
has been assumed just at that place and shown in a profile with exaggerated vertical scale[325]. Nor can faults along the mountain base be deduced from the steep relief into which the slopes in question are broken
up; nor from the scarps, dissected by valleys and lobate in form which,
as Schmieder was able to show, exist between the various peneplane and

denudation levels. The first feature, the steep relief, merely indicates the full effect of vigorous downward erosion on the shorter and therefore steeper western slope, in contrast to the eastern side of the mountain which, because its slope is longer and gentler, is correspondingly further from equally complete dissection. But to judge from the precipitous nature of the valleys sunk in it, downcutting must be working with approximately the same intensity in it as well. Vast fragments of peneplane still extend over the divides between those valleys. The second feature [that of the scarps] is obviously equivalent to the peneplane steps which we have already learnt to recognise in the most diverse parts of the world. On the west side of the Sierra Chica I saw an extraordinarily well developed piedmont flat encroaching valley-like into the higher part of the range; and the same may be assumed for the other similar scarps which Schmieder discovered, though there are no observations available upon this point which is of decisive importance.

Thus there does not lurk within the above-mentioned morphological features that indication of faulting desired and ascribed to them, faulting that was held responsible for the delimitation of the mountain mass and its meridian-wise division after the manner of tilted blocks. There is no proof of its existence. Nevertheless, faults play an important part in the interpretation offered for the results so far observed. The peneplanes appearing at different levels are interpreted as fragments of a single surface dislocated by faulting; and here, as well as on the other ranges of the Pampean sierras, they are considered to be the re-exposed Palaeozoic peneplane on which the continental Gondwana series (the 'Paganzo' beds, principally of Permian and Triassic age) have transgressed over the old folded substratum[326]. This looks like simple transference of the doctrine, long held in Germany, according to which the peneplanes occurring on the summits of the German Highlands were bared portions of the Permian land surface. There, however, it was long ago demonstrated that conditions did not exist for such surface stripping; that further, the peneplanes to be observed today do not coincide with portions of late Palaeozoic or early Triassic surfaces, but cut across them; and finally that the Permian land surface had a mountainous character and was not a peneplane. Peneplaned surfaces occur only in the very limited zone of early Triassic denudation. We shall come back to this point later. In Argentina, no close investigation has ever been made of the nature of the lower surface of the Gondwana series. It has, however, become known in the meantime that there are quite considerable variations in thickness within the Gondwana beds; on account of which—as G. Bodenbender's excellent investigations in La Rioja have shown—rocks belonging to quite different systems (Permian, Triassic and even Rhaetic) transgress directly on to the old folded basement. It therefore follows that the lower surface of the Paganzo strata is no plain, no peneplane, but mountainous in relief, with differences in elevation of several hundred metres[327]. Further, at several places, also in the Sierra de Cordoba[328], it is possible to follow directly the passage of the present peneplane from the crystalline basement on to the denuded remnants of the Gondwana-Paganzo beds. Thus there can be no doubt that the above-mentioned interpretation is erroneous. The present land surface cuts across the Permo-Triassic one; where it is on crystalline rocks, it lies below it by an unknown amount; where on the Gondwana beds, it lies above it. *Like those of the German Highlands, the peneplanes of the Pampean sierras are fresh creations, which are causally connected with the history of the formation of the Andine ranges.*

According to the observations so far available, the highest and oldest levels are confined to the Sierra Grande[329], and are found in that part called the Sierra de Achala (fig. 19). According to Schmieder, this part

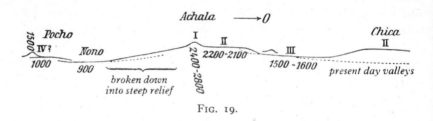

FIG. 19.

of the mountains bears a peneplane lying between the altitudes of 2200 metres (in the west) and 2100 metres (in the east), and has inselbergs rising above it. These latter are the remnants of a central mountainland which has by now been completely disintegrated. Judging from the marginal position of the inselbergs, it formed the watershed, which seems to have been pushed far towards the west even in early times. Concave profiles of waning development characterise the mountain sides, and the cross sections of the valley troughs in the surrounding peneplane. This latter is a typical piedmont flat; the fragments of it today visible may perhaps already correspond entirely to the proximal zone, and have the character of an end-peneplane. It forms a strip approximately 60 kilometres long, extending along the strike of the mountains, and only 4 to 8 kilometres broad (II in the figure); and to the north, south and east it is separated by a zone of convex slopes, about 500 metres high, from the next level below it, the most extensive, main peneplane level of the mountain mass. The scarp is not, on the whole, very steep[330]. It is dissected into valleys, and so has a somewhat lobate outline; and there seems to be no lack of inselbergs lying in front of it and rising to its height, especially on the north side. The valleys, which cut sharply into it, run out on to the peneplane lying in front, which can thus also be recognised as a piedmont flat (III in figure). It, too, is extensively developed along the strike and on the eastern slope of the range, but not on the west. On that side the slope, broken down into steep relief, sinks to the narrow depression of Nono, with a north-south trend and its floor at about 900 metres altitude. It separates the Sierra Grande from a secondary adjoining range (Sierra de Pocho) lying in front of it to the west. According to Schmieder, this latter also bears a peneplane which lies at an altitude of about 1000 metres, is said to have an upcurved western edge, and to sink northward beneath the Pampa. The relationships are still uncertain, and for want of correlated strata the connections with the levels of the main range to the east cannot be identified.

The Sierra Chica is no different. This range, which has an eastward sloping peneplane on its summit, is, on the west, inclined more steeply towards the depression separating it from the Sierra Grande. Following this depression northwards one comes, near Capilla del Monte, to the district where the excellently developed piedmont flat already mentioned lies in front of the west flank of the Sierra Chica. This surface sinks north-westwards beneath the Pampa, and as it does so the valleys eroded into it visibly decrease in depth; and so it seems that the same surface which extends over the northern end of the Sierra Grande, sinking in that latitude, is arched up here. At all events, this place offers the possibility of finding out how the various peneplane levels in the individual parts of the mountains are related as regards position, and the periods of their respective development. By this means, further morphological research will be able to start from the fact that the depressions between the ranges, in so far as they come within the region of denudation, bear peneplanes more or less dissected by valleys, just like the broad troughs in Anatolia. Evidently these function as piedmont flats to *both of the ranges bordering them and to both at the same time.*

Nothing is known as to the geological age of these elements. At the western foot of the Sierra Chica, in the neighbourhood of the piedmont flat, which he called 'foreland', E. Richmann found sands, laminated clay, and marl, which he considered to be the equivalents of G. Bodenbender's Upper Cretaceous Los-Llanos beds, a formation occurring at the edge of the Pampean sierras in Central Argentine[331]. Conglomerates were found above these, and they were considered as possibly belonging to the Tertiary 'Calchaqui beds'. These strata, like the Gondwana series resting on them, are supposed to have once completely covered the present Sierra Chica[332]. Quartz-porphry, a rock which occurs only in the northernmost range of the system, the Sierra del Norte[333], plays a part in their composition; and this seems to stamp the strata in question as correlated with that range and as being deposited at a time when there was as yet no Sierra Chica. Further investigation is still needed. What has been discovered about the facies, bedding and correlation of the Cretaceous-Tertiary sediments, derived from the neighbouring sierras to the north-west, justifies the assumption that surface forms of early Tertiary origin, if not even of Upper Cretaceous, may be found in the Sierra de Cordoba also.

The mountains form a system of several north-south ranges, which sometimes replace one another, sometimes are separated from one another by depressions. Morphologically, as far as present knowledge goes, the chains represent a type which is in many ways similar to the German Highlands or the Appalachians, and deviates from what we have so far learnt in broad folds and from what will be shown later. The deviation consists in this, that piedmont flats occur which, just as in the German Highlands, extend not only along the strike of the mountains but also at right angles to it. Bearing in mind the symptomatic significance of piedmont flats in the interpretation of the development of zones of uplift, this means that the ranges of the Sierra de Cordoba have grown mainly in length but also considerably in breadth. It is certain, however, that this growth has not occurred to the same extent in both directions. The considerable extension, to the north, south and east, of the second as well as of the third level in the Sierra Grande shows that this range has evidently been growing from early times in these directions, but not everywhere westward: no recognisable piedmont flats lie at the foot of the Sierra de Comechingones and the Sierra de Pocho on the west side. This might in fact indicate the presence of a fault which had originated at these places during some stage or other in the development of the ranges. Thereafter it separated the rising block from the neighbouring area which did not move but remained at the lower level; and thus it limited, towards the west, the growth of the range, i.e. the further extension of the region of uplift and denudation. Of course this has not proved the existence of longitudinal faults! (see p. 270).

From the geologico-tectonic point of view it must be stressed that the Sierra de Cordoba lacks not only that degree of uplift which is shown structurally by the deformation in the sedimentary cover and morphologically by the amplitude, but is also without any trace of folding in the covering strata; in addition there is an absence of great overthrusts associated with dislocations along the strike, such as characteristically appear in the west and north-west of the high ranges welded on to the main mountain mass of the Andes. It has been shown that there, at an earlier

Photo. by W. Penck

1. Sierra del Cajon from Alto Muñeco, Western Argentina

Photo. by W. Penck

2. Sierra de Fiambalá from San Salvador. Famatina Range in the background. Western Argentina

X. Broad Folds

stage of the broad folding, those structural elements were still lacking and the ranges had less amplitude[334]. The Sierra de Cordoba today represents this stage. That is by no means the same as saying that it must have risen later; but up to the present it has not arrived at that further advanced stage of broad folding which today characterises the ranges at the southern margin of the Puna. There now follows the conclusion reached above, which showed the Sierra de Cordoba as the type which with growing amplitude *increases* in length and *in phase*.

In the *parts of the mountain mass which adjoin the High Cordillera and the Puna de Atacama and are attached to them,* dislocations along the strike outcrop as the characteristic *structural* elements over wide stretches of the younger sections of the Andine mountain formations. They are often in the nature of overthrusts, and in that case they hade towards the west in the western parts of the system of ranges, towards the east in the eastern parts. At the boundary of the two zones there occurs a broad syncline, overthrust from both sides, the Bolson of S. Maria or the Calchaqui Valley (Province of Catamarca)[335]. West of this, all the mountain ranges are directed towards the high region of the Puna and penetrate from the south into the high country, imparting to it the same north-south seriation which is characteristic of the Pampean sierras to the south of it. With that entry, the overthrustings and faults come to an end, without any exceptions so far as can be seen at present. The mountain ranges cross the rise of the Puna as unfaulted anticlines. The termination of the faults, however, is not accompanied by any alteration in the orographical behaviour of the ranges, nor in that of other structural features or in their morphological character; this applies even to details, so that here it is evident in the most impressive way how insignificant a part strike faulting plays in determining the altitudinal configuration and the set of land forms. On the other hand, the most abrupt morphological changes take place where the mountain ranges encounter the edge of the highland. This usually takes place without any essential change in the absolute altitude. But the relative heights in the Puna are about 1500 to 2000 metres less than to the east and south of it, since its longitudinal depressions, the broad synclines, do not lie as low as the bolsons between the Pampean sierras, but at a greater absolute altitude. This means that there is today a considerable difference in altitude between the general base levels of erosion on the two sides of the Puna edge. And by following the morphological development of the ranges, it can be seen that there has been no fundamental difference in this respect at earlier stages in the formation of the Andine mountains. Thus, in the areas considered, the *type* of configuration of the mountain chains differs according as to whether they belong to the Puna or to the

Pampean sierras. For both regions there is remarkable uniformity within themselves.

The broad folds to the south and east of the Puna form high ranges. Their summit levels average between 4000 and 5000 metres and occasionally exceed 6000 metres. The aggraded floors of the neighbouring bolsons lie at about 1000 metres or less in the southern sections, at 2000 metres towards the edge of the Puna. In spite of these majestic altitudes and differences in altitude, there is very little to be noted in the way of disintegration into a sea of Alpine peaks such as may be observed on the high chains which are situated in a moister climate and, in addition, have experienced considerable Pleistocene glaciation (the High Cordillera further south, the Eastern Cordillera of Bolivia and Peru, etc.). The broad folds of north-west Argentina meet the beholder like a wall, with an even crest-line apparently unnotched. This impression is produced by the preservation of very ancient form associations with but shallow dissection—forms of medium relief or peneplanes—on the summits of the *ranges that are earlier in origin*. As a rule these ranges also rise to a dominating height and have a great width (see Plate X, illustration 1). On the other hand, on the flanks, nothing more could be desired in the way of jaggedness, i.e. of having been broken up into a rocky steep relief; and this feature continues down to the base of the ranges, and the parts where, towards their ends, they gradually become lower until they plunge beneath the alluvium of the lowlands. The steep slopes of the flanks already meet in sharp edges and pointed peaks, and these are arranged so as to give a distinct gipfelflur, such as usually characterises, over a wide area, the plunging ends of the ranges (see Plate X, illustration 2). This reproduces or simulates their anticlinal form: i.e. a surface tangential to the sharp edges would have the form of a pitching anticline. Ranges which have proved to be of *later origin* show the same breaking up into a steep relief, but show it over their whole extent. Of the less rugged precursors of the steep forms, either nothing at all has been seen here, or merely scanty relics which have the character of forms of medium relief, never of peneplanes. Instead, the convexity of the steep slopes is often developed in a quite classical manner (see Plate VI, illustration 2, and fig. 20). The form associations of the latter type are in sharp contrast to the steep relief which is found on the straight slopes of maximum gradient. These two form-types appear in separated areas; either the zone of steep relief for the time being belongs wholly to one or the other, or else both forms occur next to each other within one and the same zone of steep relief; but even then each is characteristic of a high-lying zone well marked-off from that of the other. Thus, the lower parts of the eastern slope of the north-south range Cerro Negro—San Salvador,

A TYPES OF RANGES OF YOUNGER ORIGIN

Cross sections.   Vertical and horizontal scale the same

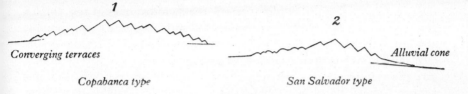

B TYPES OF RANGES OF OLDER ORIGIN

Simplified cross profiles.   Vertical and horizontal scales the same, c.1:160,000

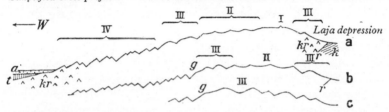

     a Bolson sediments of Quaternary age   *k* Upper Cretaceous—Lower

     t Bölson sediments of Tertiary age   Tertiary deposits laid against the

     kr Substructure (crystalline,   side of the range immediately to

            pre-Cambrium etc.)   the east (C. Fraile)

                     r Merginal overthrust

C *Longitudinal Profile.   Vertical scale twice horizontal scale (c. 1:800,000)*

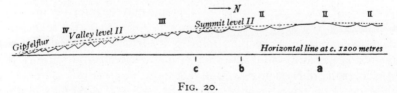

FIG. 20.

which separates the basins of Tinogasta and Andagalá (Province of Cata-marca) from one another, is characterised by steep convex declivities; on the other hand, in the higher parts—the summit region of the range—straight-line slopes, of maximum inclination throughout, are equally typical (see Plate VI, illustration 2). Further, the intervalley divides of the two zones belong to different levels; the rounded ones of the 'convex zone', to use a more concise expression, fall short by quite a considerable amount of the level reached by the sharp edges in the crest region. A sur-face tangential to those rounded intervalley divides would not indeed give the appearance of a peneplane, but would be uneven, with humps; yet everywhere it is closely adjoining the foot of the straight steep slopes which lead from it right up to the sharp edges of the crest region. This arrangement is peculiar to a definite type of the ranges of more recent origin (fig. 20, A 2), in contrast to the other type in which the dominant steep slopes are exclusively of maximum gradient (fig. 20, A 1)[336]. Since the other conditions (climate, rock materials) are similar, the difference between the two surface forms here developed can, in general, be due only to this: that in the one case the causes tending to produce slopes of maximum gradient have not been in operation for so long as in the second case; so that there the convex forerunners have not yet been re-placed by the slopes of maximum gradient which ultimately appeared. Or, in other words: the causes leading to an increase in the intensity of erosion, up to the value for which slopes of maximum gradient are bound to appear, have existed for different lengths of time in the one place and in the other, i.e. have made themselves felt for periods of different lengths as reckoned from the present time.

One can only fitly speak of a gipfelflur when the mountain masses have been broken up into peaks and sharp edges by incision of steep relief forms, and when slopes of maximum gradient meet in such edges. They have straight profiles (see Plate IX, illustration 2). However, in this case, uniformity of development cannot be deduced from this fact. For slopes of maximum inclination develop when the intensity of erosion has increased to a definite limiting value[337]. They retain the same gradi-ent and shape even when the intensity of erosion increases further to beyond that limiting value; and they remain unchanged in form so long as the intensity of erosion is beyond that limit, whether it is increasing at that place, or decreasing again (see p. 158). Slopes of maximum gradient may therefore be a normal part of waxing development as well as of waning development. Their straight-line profile only simulates uniform-ity of development. In reality, however, the only conclusion that it is permissible to draw as to the course of erosional intensity is that it has at least reached the limiting value concerned and so must at all events be very great. The slope development is, so to say, *pseudo-uniform* when it imprints its mark upon the steep relief of the ranges and helps to determine the position and shape of the gipfelflur. This latter has no direct dependence upon the conditions associated with the preceding relief, which has been replaced by steep relief forms. On the older ranges, which still bear on their summits fragments of such older and gentler land forms, it may be observed that the gipfelflur does not lie at the level of the earlier relief which has since been removed; nor does it continue unbroken the line of its remaining parts in the direction of the slope or of the strike of the mountains; but on the contrary it is offset from this by a somewhat noticeable jump in altitude. The surface tangential to the peaks and sharp edges does *not* therefore in this case appear to be a relic of an otherwise completely vanished former relief. Still less, as has often been rashly concluded for similar cases in other parts of the world, does an unlevelled fault line separate it from remnants of this other relief, lying at a higher altitude and still preserved. But its position is directly dependent only upon the character of the sharp V-shaped valleys and of the rock. Its relative height is greater, the greater the inclination of the steep slopes, with maximum gradient, which intersect at that height, and —as A. Penck has explained—the greater the average distance betwen adjacent erosional furrows. Its absolute altitude, on the other hand, is subject to the general laws concerning absolute heights, which will not be treated till a later section[338].

The *Sierra de Fiambalá* (Province of Catamarca) is a range which has all the characteristic features of *the older type of broad fold*. It enters the Puna about latitude 27° S., and its greatest altitude, exceeding 5000 metres (the 'Tolar' or 'El Volcan'), is here. The granitic heights show surface forms with exceedingly gentle slopes which shelve down with convex curvature to the wide high-lying valleys which surround them. Tors are superposed upon the flattish relief. It is a case of the diminishing remains of a peneplane which has replaced a more elevated landscape of unknown form and extent (I in fig. 20 B), like what has been noticed on the dome-shaped mountains of the Fichtelgebirge [p. 214]. From the further developmental history it must be concluded that this relic of an end-peneplane has developed from a piedmont flat. As for the rest, it has been already completely replaced by an intermediate type of relief, the broad trough valleys of which are incised in it to a depth of about 500 metres. The land forms (II in fig. 20 B; cf. Plate II, illustration 3) bear throughout the features of waning development. It has but a slight extension at right angles to the strike of the mountains (and that mainly westward, not eastward); along the strike it forms an elongated zone which (next to I) occupies the highest parts of the range. The zone is

surrounded on all sides by a strip of country more deeply divided-up into
rounded eminences; their steeper talus-graded slopes have convex forms,
and lead down to high-lying valleys which are comparatively deeper and
narrower. Near the higher parts of the country they are often still quite
narrow; towards the periphery they have widened out showing alluvial
floors and concave foot-slopes[339]. It can be seen how waning development is beginning to penetrate from the outer part. This periphery is
everywhere sharply delineated; there is a break of gradient the line of
which, like the contour lines, forms a re-entrant angle along the valleys—
the longitudinal profile of which experiences a sudden interruption—
and a projecting angle along the ridge crest where it separates the system
of gentler slopes above from the rugged rock slopes below (see Plate IV,
illustration 2). The rocky steep relief of the mountain sides and at the
ends of the ranges reaches up to the break of gradient. This occurs at an
altitude of about 3500 metres.

The characteristics of the relief above the break are, as has been mentioned, those of waxing development. However, as the mantle of rock
waste indicates, its slopes are still far removed from the maximum
gradient. This waxing development has been interrupted by the appearance of the break of gradient, i.e. by the increase of erosional·intensity to
the value at which slopes of maximum inclination arose, first at the
general base level of erosion, then spreading briskly upwards. The relief
type of convex slopes (III in fig. 20 B) forms a narrow strip on both sides
of II along the downward slopes of the range; also for considerable
distances it covers the summit when, on account of the gradual diminution in height towards the end of the range, II has disappeared in this
direction (southwards). Below the peaks of the mountainland III, wide
flattish ridges and rounded summits spread out. Their heights are
similar; and as a rule they do not occur above the level at which the
valley bottoms (not the peaks) of relief type II would be found by re-
constructing earlier conditions. The first mentioned of these features
indicates that there can never have been higher, more steeply inclined
country in place of the flattish dome-like heights—flattish forerunners of
the steeper slopes below; the second makes it fairly certain that these
heights are the last remnants of a piedmont flat, of which the valley-like
protrusions into the older region appear in the wide valley bottoms of
relief type II[340].

On other ranges of similar age these relationships are still preserved
intact, as for example on the broad anticline which lies in front of the
Puna to the east, forming in those latitudes the eastern marginal range
of the whole mountain system (Aconquija Range—Cerros de los Animas). Starting from its western foot in the Calchaqui Valley (see p. 261),

the break of gradient, its line running irregularly in and out, is to be found above the zone of steep relief (corresponding in form to IV in the Sierra de Fiambalá, fig. 20 B) within which the eastward hading marginal overthrust outcrops[341]. Above that is a deeply dissected medium relief which has convex slopes mantled with waste and concave foot-slopes (corresponding to our relief type III). A break of gradient, scarcely less sharply developed, separates this form association from the relief of mountain heights above (alto muñeco) corresponding in form to our type II. This extends alike over craggy granite (see Plate V, illustration 2) and granitic gneiss, and over andesitic lavas and breccias which show no crags; while near the western edge of the broad mountain summit it extends across a strike dislocation which in places brings the old granite on to the top of the young andesite. On the broad main watershed, and between the rather wide and deep valleys of relief type II, there are now preserved extensive fragments of a peneplane (corresponding to I) set with low tors. It continues far southwards, along the strike of the range, as far as the northern edge of a series of high peaks superimposed on it, extending over a length of many kilometres. These are elevated more than 500 metres above the peneplane, and end southwards in the Nevado Aconquija (over 5300 metres). Corries are sunk in the line of slopes by which the series of peaks sinks towards peneplane I lying in front of them on the north. Here it is evident that this is a piedmont flat. On the east it is bounded almost at once by steep slopes rising precipitously from the depression.

This type of configuration recurs in all the ranges of earlier origin, even though the arrangement and division of the relief stages may vary in detail from one instance to another. It must be especially emphasised that the form associations which have been classified above into four well-marked main stages, appear, on more detailed investigation, to be susceptible throughout of further division and subdivision. However, leaving aside that and other details, the broad folds of earlier origin have a fundamental morphological pattern which is quite usually given by the following arrangement of form associations from above downwards: (a) a peneplane which is preserved as more or less extensive remnants, and in locally circumscribed places surrounds a central mountainland, occasionally reduced to small relics (tors); (b) medium relief on all the slopes leading down from it; (c) steep relief on the flanks and the plunging ends right down to the bottom of the ranges. These three main stages are all elongated in the direction of the trend of the mountain ranges; at right angles to it, so far as they are present, they are limited to narrow strips.

It must specially be noted: a central mountainland, in the relationship described above, occurs only on the oldest ranges, and marks those parts of the broad folds which were the first to appear. Hence it is met with on by no means all the ranges; and its original extent, as well as that now found, is always far less than the present extension of the ranges. As a rule there is far-reaching dissection of this central mountainland, which is characterised throughout by forms of waning development, and has often broken down into inselbergs. At many places, however, its individual summits (which are then rounded in a broadly convex fashion) bear more or less extensive remnants of an older higher peneplane. Examples are found on the Nevado Famatina, over 6000 metres high, as well as on the Cerro Palca (5300 metres), an analogous elevation in the northern section of the Famatina Range; and apparently also on the Nevado Aconquija. As far as is at present known, these are the oldest form associations which occur on the broad folds of the region.

The peneplane (relief type I) has the character of a piedmont flat, or [else] is the summit peneplane of ranges, or parts of ranges, of correspondingly later origin. Its nature has been shown to be that of a primary peneplane. [Cf. p. 210 and pp. 213–215.] It is very significant that in every case so far investigated the medium relief (type II–III), occupying the slopes on both sides of the ranges, has suffered powerful and easily recognisable *warping*. A characteristic of it, which can have only one meaning, is what has been called the 'upper gorge zone': sharply incised, steep, erosional ravines, which are alien forms traversing the medium relief of the mountain flank which is otherwise smoothed and rounded; they are not outlines of the young steep relief (IV) but end high above that. Indeed they peter out on surfaces which mark a level of accumulation and belong both by age and mode of origin to the medium relief. These surfaces are thus, so to say, old bolson floors which are now raised high up, dragged up at the edges of the ranges, tilted, and often already worn down to terraces by the encroachment from below of steep relief (IV)[342].

That the upwarping, or more accurately doming, of the broad anticlines above the neighbouring depressions persisted, throughout the stage during which the steep relief was developing, is shown by the convergence towards the mountain foot of even the youngest of the terraces of uplift.

The succession of form associations, arranged from above downwards, in the manner just mentioned, obviously corresponds to a *time sequence*: the highest, uppermost, of them were also those to originate the earliest; the lower ones appeared later, one after another in the same sequence in which they are nowadays to be met, adjoining each other, from above downwards. The form associations were therefore termed stages of relief;

they are successive stages in the development of the older ranges. The characteristic feature of the general trend of development is *increase in the angle of slope* (*flattish* relief—*medium* relief—*steep* relief). With the appearance of ever steeper slope units and slope systems, convex breaks of gradient developed; and this meant that the form associations which at any given moment lay above them, were separated from the general base level of erosion, and were pushed into a course of waning development. Since then *this* type of development has dominated the course of denudation within these form associations, up to the present day. Naturally it has now gone furthest within that form association which has been longest subject to its action, that is within the oldest and highest stage of relief: little more is preserved of the flattish relief which once covered the central mountainland. The surrounding piedmont surface (I) has continuously widened at its expense, and has broken up the district rising above it into inselbergs and tors, either at its margin or all over it. Relief II is already almost everywhere marked by concave slopes and wide valley troughs; these, however, still form a uniform set of connected valley courses. In relief type III the commencement of waning development is just noticeable, while it is entirely absent from the steep relief type IV.

If one compares the earlier stages of development with the later ones, a further very characteristic circumstance comes to light. The central mountainland has been surrounded on all sides by the piedmont flat (I), especially extensive along the trends of the ranges. This state of affairs betokens that the ranges of earlier origin originally increased their length *and* their phase as they grew in height. This is the stage which is still represented today in the Sierra de Cordoba, which is as it were in a primitive state compared with the high ranges of the Puna edge. Further, it can scarcely be doubted that relief type III, in so far as it forms the summit of the ranges lengthwise along their trend, has resulted from a more youthful lower piedmont flat. So far, however, the same cannot be said with certainty of the very narrow strips of the same form association on both flanks of the ranges. The initial forms of steep relief IV, which have been preserved in many places, are of the medium relief type with convex slopes (like III) and not remnants of a peneplane. Thus, if relief III on the flanks of the ranges has arisen from a piedmont flat, this already covered approximately the same zones as the steep relief IV occupies; and this steep relief was sculptured out of it by way of relief III. And finally: in front of the deeply dissected steep relief IV, along the mountain foot, there are alluvial cones but no young piedmont flats, except for such as belong, not to the growing broad anticline, but to the adjacent broad syncline moving into the region of denudation (Anatolian type). Thus younger and lower piedmont flats cannot be detected on the flanks of the earlier ranges; and this is not only because the structure has been thoroughly dissected by erosion, but because here, in the last phases of development, they did not form at all. *It must be particularly stressed that this fact has nothing whatever to do with the existence of longitudinal faults.* The western edge of the Sierra de Fiambalá has *no* faults, and there is just as little indication of young piedmont flats there as on the edges of other ranges of similar age. This is so, whether, like the east side of the Famatina Range in its northern section, they lack that kind of longitudinal disturbance, or whether they have such faults, which then outcrop within the zone of steep relief (western margin of the Aconquija Range, eastern margin of the Famatina Range in its southern section, etc.), or continue—or are presumed to do so—along the foot of the mountain range beneath the alluvial deposits of the neighbouring depression. Instead, the form associations present on the mountain flanks show the above-mentioned warping. *This makes it perfectly certain that, during the later stages of their development, the earlier ranges increased as before in length and amplitude* BUT NO LONGER INCREASED IN PHASE. *Instead, there occurs warping of the existing zones of denudation and of the form zones.* This statement does not hold in its entirety for the more recent and most recent ranges. The arrangement of the zone of steep convex slopes and of the straight slopes of maximum inclination, on the ranges of the type of San Salvador, has been mentioned (p. 263, fig. 20, A 2). It indicates the former existence of a piedmont flat (or of some other form association equivalent in function) from which the zone of steep convex slopes must have arisen. The youngest piedmont flats are in fact often to be observed at the edges of such ranges, as is excellently seen, for example, on the west side of the Salvador Range. The surface concerned is narrow, it lies in front of the mountain foot proper, and here it is sharply incised by streams; thus it has already been uplifted and tilted. Hence the remaining fragments are in the form of terraces which plunge down beneath the alluvial deposits of the adjoining depression, and converge towards other lower members of the terraces due to uplift. It is not a matter of dissected alluvial fans, but of *rock surfaces*. Also they are not connected with the mouths of individual valleys, but follow along the edge of ranges concerned for some considerable distance. If they are cut into by streams which flow along these ranges, they then turn a steeply broken-off face to the adjoining lowland. Amongst other places this may be seen along the margin of the rugged rocky range of Carrizal, which together with several other secondary ranges, of a similarly low order of magnitude, forms a mountain bridge from the Sierra el Ambato (Catamarca) to the Sierra Velasco (La Rioja), and so oloooo in tho Boloon of Andagalá on the south. There occurs here not only *one* such longitudinal terrace, but several, one above the other, similar to what has also been noticed by O. Schmieder on the slope of the Sierra de Cordoba that goes down towards the depression of Nono[343]. Certainly the formation of these marginal or longitudinal terraces, as they may be called, is closely connected with river activity; but in origin they are fundamentally different from valley terraces. The stream flowing along the range lengthwise produces the terrace scarps, the marginal brows of the rocky surfaces, but not the terrace surfaces themselves. These are, rather, results of the denudation effected by the waters flowing from the range and so are tributary to their respective paths [not to the main longitudinal streams]. They testify that the area of denudation has moved out from the former foot of the range towards the neighbouring region of deposition, that the range has increased in phase. They are piedmont flats, or, as the case may be, piedmont benchlands on a small scale.

Comparing the two types of younger ranges leads to the recognition of an advanced stage of development in that which possesses piedmont flats as contrasted with the youngest ranges which have no such surfaces and so have *not yet* begun to increase in phase. The drawing of attention to the 'not yet' is justified by the arrangement of form associations which is quite different in the younger chains from that in those which originated earlier and are *no longer* increasing in phase. These older ranges show the form association of convex slopes *above* the zone of steep relief at the mountain foot; the younger ones show it below the steep relief, at the mountain foot itself. These are deep-seated distinctions, which denote a quite different course of development in the two cases[344]. They touch the core of the problem, which has now been illustrated from different aspects: the way in which the ranges have grown, and the causes which have led to their growth.

The similarity in the formation and arrangement of the form associations on the various ranges proves similarity in development, but by no means indicates simultaneity in the stages of development which possess the corresponding shapes. This is usually assumed for the peneplanes on the tops of the chains. They have been observed in all sorts of places in the mountain girdles; they are very widely distributed in Central Asia, on the ranges of the mountain systems which form a broad belt round the Tarim Basin, in the Pamirs, and so on, in the most varied regions of the North and South American Cordilleras, and also in the western and south-western half of the circum-Pacific systems of mountain chains. They were always considered to be uplifted ('upfaulted') fragments of a uniform end-peneplane, once connected over a wide extent, e.g. the whole of Central Asia, which had its relatively depressed parts beneath the accumulations in the hollows, longitudinal depressions, and basins. This erroneous interpretation was obviously due to the firmly fixed notion which, too, is the basal assumption of the erosion cycle as it is applied (uplift, *then* denudation), and which prevented *the recognition on the peneplanes of form associations peculiar to the mountain ranges on which they occur.* Whenever correlated strata have collected in the broad synclines, and been preserved there—and it is only in arid regions that this is so: witness the Eastern Alps and Anatolia—the conditions at the edges and within these synclines allow it to be established by direct observation that the peneplanes on the summits of the ranges are not continued at the base of the deposits in the hollows, and have no connection or relationship at all with similar peneplanes on neighbouring chains. It can be seen at once that the features in the hollows are very varied, since these themselves differ in age, and naturally their contents have a fuller stratigraphical history the longer they have existed. Only typical arrangements are shown in fig. 21. In the region treated here, the correlated strata are continental formations throughout; in the adjoining Puna they are predominantly volcanic materials (lavas, agglomerates, tuffs and tufaceous sediments)[345]. The sediments extend from Upper Cretaceous to the present day, but not all divisions are to be found in every depression. Their extraordinary thickness, up to more than 10 kilometres, shows that they have been deposited on a relatively sinking basement. The facies development reveals the same feature; each series is divided into a coarse clastic mountain-foot facies and a sandy one deposited at some distance from the mountain. The first is a typical alluvial cone formation; amongst present alluvial deposits, the other finds its counterpart in the fine sandy beds which compose the interior of the bolsons. These extensive alluvial bottoms ('Barreal' of the natives) are often as level as a parquet floor.

The present distribution of the two facies, in conjunction with the attitude of the bedding, shows that in course of time the areas of sedimentation became narrowed and were divided up. This was because fresh ranges rose up one after the other, or else the already existing ranges grew longer in the direction of the strike and, as it were, grew into the zones of what had been, till then, undisturbed sedimentation. The attitude and facies of the correlated layers form a sure means of distinguishing whether the ranges, or parts of ranges, are older or younger in origin. The profiles are the same as in Anatolia, but on a far grander scale and affording a clearer view of the whole arrangement[346]. The unconformities within the sequence of strata are sharply marked; they extend in a regular manner along the margin of the range and pass into a concordant condition, i.e. the bedding planes do so, towards the interior of the bolsons. The unconformities are directly connected with the peneplanes found on the ranges; they form an immediate continuation of them and themselves have a graded appearance. *Thus, the peneplanes of the range summits pass over into unconformities, with a peneplanated character, when they reach the edges of the adjoining broad synclines; and pass into stratification planes as they approach the actual basins.* This state of affairs proves quite definitely first, that the peneplanes concerned are of the nature of primary peneplanes, and secondly, their geological age. For the unconformities are no other than the covered in, and so preserved, forms of the forerunners of the peneplanes [now found] on the summits of the ranges. But it is possible that as far back as the stage when there was still no denudation at all and sedimentation was still undisturbed (concordant bedding), these forerunners never had any other denudational form than just a peneplane. In that case those peneplanes must in fact be the first primitive type of denudational forms which came into being on the ranges, just as they were beginning to appear. That is the essential character of a primary peneplane.

The peneplanes on the ranges have been more or less uplifted, the process continuing to the present day; and because of this they have been a prey to destruction. The unconformities belonging to them have been arched up with them and tilted, the more steeply the older they are; in their whole course they reflect in profile the anticlinal form of the ranges. These unconformities lie at a lower stratigraphical level, the older the peneplanes which correspond to them. The peneplanes continue as unconformities between the corresponding divisions of the correlated strata. And it is this fact, *and this only*, which shows the similarity in age of such peneplanes on the various ranges of the mountain system.

Fig. 21 A illustrates this in more detail. It reproduces the conditions to be observed west of the Sierra de Fiambalá, omitting disturbing details, such as local folding and overfolding of the correlated strata, overthrusts developed here and there along the eastern edge of the range, etc. At this latitude the profile cuts through four ranges, or portions of ranges, which have originated at different periods. The oldest member is the Sierra de Fiambalá, for its rock types had already appeared in the Lower Tertiary Calchaqui strata[347]. These latter surrounded the growing mountains with a conglomeratic facies (*c k*). Westward they pass into formations of fine sands which have their greatest development in the Sierra Narvaez, which at that time had not yet arisen, and there they lie conformably above the Upper Cretaceous sandstones[348]. The lower surface of the Calchaqui beds, wherever it is accessible, is an almost level surface of denudation[349]. It cannot, however, now be decided with

S

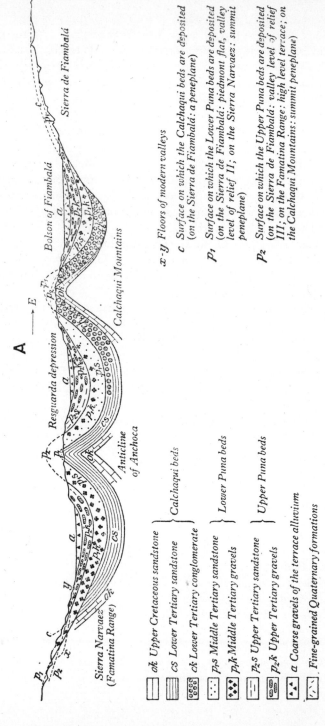

FIG. 21A.

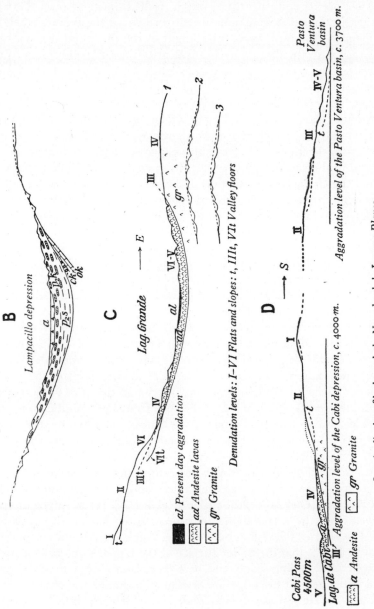

B

Lampacillo depression

a

p_2^s

ck;
ok

C

Lag Grande → E

II

IIIt VI
VIt

IV

III

IV

VI-V

ad al

gr

al

1

2

3

al Present day aggradation

ad Andesite lavas

gr Granite

Demudation levels : I–VI Flats and slopes : t, IIIt, VIt Valley floors

D → S

I

II

II

III

IV-V

Pasto
Ventura
basin

t

Cabi Pass
4500m
V

Lag. de Cabi
III

II

IV

t

gr

a Andesite

gr Granite

Aggradation level of the Cabi depression, c. 4000 m.

Aggradation level of the Pasto Ventura basin, c. 3700 m.

a Andesite

Longitudinal profile through the Nevados de la Laguna Blanco

FIG. 21B, C, D.

certainty, whether any elements of the present mountain surface, and if so which, are its equivalent, i.e. which result from the Lower Tertiary form associations that were undoubtedly present on the mountain heights and maintain the form type. The origin of the piedmont flat (I), contemporary with the dissection (equivalent to the commencement of the removal) of the central mountainland, can be correlated with the Lower Tertiary Calchaqui beds with a high degree of probability. Not only does the facies (dissection into valleys—conglomerate) support this, but in particular the fact that the Upper Cretaceous sandstones of both east and west sides taper off here towards the Sierra de Fiambalá; so that even before the Lower Tertiary, this range separated two areas of deposition, in the east and in the west, from one another. The fineness of grain of the Cretaceous sandstones indicates that the relief was slight in the neighbouring area of denudation. One is therefore led to suppose that the central mountainland, which today has vanished except for tors, was covered by the Upper Cretaceous peneplane as its oldest, first form association (primary peneplane); that in the Lower Tertiary period this oldest zone of denudation was surrounded by a piedmont flat and became itself a central mountainland subjected to dissection by valleys; and that it was here that more actively working erosion prepared material for the Calchaqui conglomerates.

The under surface of the Lower Puna beds provides better information. It is a bedding plane [extending] from the Bolson of Fiambalá to the area near the flanks of the Famatina Range. Puna *gravels*, derivatives of the newly appearing Sierra Narvaez, lie conformably on the Lower Tertiary Calchaqui sandstone; in the interior of the once wide depression: Puna *sandstone*, formed at a distance from the mountains, is conformable to the Lower Tertiary Calchaqui conglomerate appearing below it. On both sides of this zone of conformity, the strata transgress over the disturbed basement with a sharply marked and well-levelled unconformity. This unconformity passes into the summit peneplane of the Sierra Narvaez; and on the Sierra de Fiambalá passes into the hummocky level of relief III (= the valley level of relief II), as can be directly followed from the considerable remains of strata left on the mountain flank. It is only in the region between the Calchaqui Mountains and the Famatina Range that the under surface of the Upper Puna beds can still be traced as a bedding plane; and here there later arose one of the most recent anticlines. At the edge of the Famatina Range the coarse Upper Puna gravels are already encroaching upon [definite] relief; and their under surface cannot be distinguished there from the valley floors of the so-called High Terrace, which belong to the type of relief III. The same surface has been completely graded on both flanks of the newly risen

Calchaqui Mountains, and would have been a summit peneplane if that younger range had still borne one.

Thus the age relationships, to the first approximation, are as follows:

Range of earliest origin *Sierra de Fiambalá*	Range of later origin *Sierra Narvaez*	Range of younger origin *Calchaqui Mountains*	Range of youngest origin	
Primary peneplane (?); not preserved	—	—	—	Upper Cretaceous
				to
Dissection of central mountainland by valleys Piedmont flat I	—	—	—	Lower Tertiary
				to
Relief II Piedmont flat =summit level of Relief III	Summit peneplane Relief type ⏐ II	—	—	Middle Tertiary
				to
Relief III	Relief type ⏐ III High Terrace	Summit peneplane (certain in parts)	—	Upper Tertiary
				to
Steep Relief IV	Steep Relief	Steep Relief (Badlands)	Steep Relief (Badlands)	Present Day

This table simply shows the age differences of similar form associations on the ranges which differ in age. It does *not* mean that the relief types tabulated are separated from each other by sharp boundaries as regards either time or form.

An important feature of more general significance is the repeated alternation of facies, from coarse to fine and back again, in one and the same vertical section, e.g. in the Reoguarda depression or at the eastern edge of the Calchaqui Mountains (fig. 21 A). A superficial judgment might see in this the signs of a repeated alternation of uplift—powerful denudation (hence the conglomerates), and standstill—lowering of the land, peneplanation (fine-grained deposits). However, that is by no means the explanation. As is shown by the composition of the strata, the overlapping facies have different source regions, belonging to different ranges in differing states of development. As each range first appears, predominantly fine-grained derivatives are thrown into the adjacent areas of deposition; and then, as time goes on, the coarse components increase. It can generally be seen that the coarse mountain-foot facies in the higher horizons of such a complex of strata reaches out further and further into the region of sedimentation. The Calchaqui beds behave in this way, starting from the associated range of the Sierra de Fiambalá; the same holds for the Lower Puna beds, beginning from the ranges of similar age enclosing them on both sides (Sierra de Fiambalá, Sierra Narvaez); and the same is also true for the Upper Puna beds if their development is followed out from the two associated ranges (Calchaqui Mountains in the east, Sierra Narvaez in the west). And it may further be observed that once a range has started to provide coarse ingredients, it continues doing this, right up to the present moment. Thus the sections through the 'Calchaqui Mountains' of today show, from the Lower Tertiary to the Upper Puna beds inclusive, nothing but coarse material derived from the Sierra de Fiambalá, there being no doubt petrographically as to its source; and this facies continues to the present time as huge alluvial cones at the base of the Sierra. In the same way, from Lower Puna strata to the present day, only coarse formations have been coming down from the Sierra Narvaez, and their development shows an increase in the coarse-grained components and in their extension into just those areas where previously there were only fine clastic beds of Lower Tertiary age ($c\,s$). By comparison with their spread, the facies region of fine-grained Lower Puna beds (p_1s) has not only been narrowed down considerably but has been *shifted*, i.e. pushed eastwards closer to the Sierra de Fiambalá, and so has come into the area which previously, in the Lower Tertiary, still belonged completely to the region of the mountain-foot facies of the Calchaqui beds ($c\,k$) (Calchaqui Mountains, fig. 21 A: Lower Puna *sandstone* p_1s above Calchaqui conglomerate $c\,k$). Corresponding features are to be found in the upper division of the Puna beds. Their region of fine-grained facies (p_2s) has been contracted to a narrow strip within the depressions between the Calchaqui Mountains and the Sierra Narvaez; and it has, in its turn, been shifted with respect to the more widely extended p_1s region, this time westward, to the position to which the inner part of the trough has been displaced by the newly risen Calchaqui Mountains. Thus it is there that the sandy Upper Puna beds (p_2s) occur over the conglomeratic lower division (p_1k). The same is true of the Quaternary formations. They are fine grained only on a narrow belt in the interior of the Bolson of Fiambalá, the lowest part of the trough which still persists after the process of range formation. This fine-grained material, bordered on each side by coarsely clastic talus cones, differing in width, occurs where only coarse Upper Puna gravels had been previously laid down.

Thus in successive periods there has been a horizontal displacement of the facies regions. The facies laid down at a distance from the mountains is restricted to that part of the trough which is lowest at the time; and as fresh chains arise this is not only narrowed down but also shifted to varying meridians. Conditions along the present watercourses show quite clearly how the sedimentation and its facies adapt themselves to this[350]. If a fresh range emerges from the area of sedimentation, it means that the streams flowing to the new lowest parts of the trough not only have the lengths of their courses altered, by elongation or shortening, but that in every case there is a lessening of gradient in the region of the developing synclines. This forces the rivers to deposit their load, no matter whether they are breaking through the younger rising chains as antecedents or not. The same thing happens as broad anticlines, already present, come up more strongly and with increasing rapidity. The sedimentation thus forcibly accomplished is essentially a *damming up*. It is particularly great where the streams have suffered shortening, which will always happen if the lowest part of the trough is pushed nearer to an already existing range. The waters then rid themselves of the coarse material and naturally do this nearer the mountain foot than previously; and again it is only the fine constituents which as a rule reach the lowest part of the neighbouring syncline. The region of the coarsely clastic facies becomes narrower and to make up for that it rapidly swells to a great thickness.

The development and arrangement of the facies in the correlated strata [i.e. correlated with the denudation] include nothing which could in any way be connected with a change in the altitudinal form of the ranges, with an alternation of uplift and standstill; and, as far as can be seen at present, other regions of broad folding do not seem to show conformity to any different laws [i.e. there has been continuous uplift]. Rather, as climatic changes since Lower Tertiary times are out of the question in this case, there is only one conclusion to be drawn: each individual range, from the moment of first appearing until now, has been constantly increasing its relief, steepening its gradients, and thus becoming a place of constantly increasing erosional intensity. In consequence it has provided detrital material of which the size of grain has always been increasing and never decreasing. This is true for each broad anticline and is true for the totality of the ranges making up the system.

The first [continuous increase in relief] follows from the way in which the facies development corresponds in a law-abiding manner to the stratification divisions correlated with the [rise of] individual ranges; the latter [increasing coarseness of facies] follows from the general diminution in size, equally conformable to law, of the region where the facies indicates distance from the mountains, and the proportionately growing extension and thickening of the mountain-foot facies.

Somewhat different conditions are offered by the ranges which, joining the Sierra de Fiambalá on the east, extend into the Puna (type of fig. 21 B). On their summits extensive remains of a peneplane may still be recognised in places, and its downwarped portions are also occasionally still visible as broad surfaces on the mountain flanks (west side of the Sierra del Cajon). As a rule, however, it has already been replaced here by a medium relief with convex slopes (type III); adjoining this, on the lower side, there is often, but not always, a zone of steep relief. The peneplane passes over small scattered remnants of Upper Cretaceous sandstone and over Calchaqui conglomerates, which are locally very thick, and so it is obviously later in origin than the Lower Tertiary. On the other hand, judging from observations which I was able to make in the longitudinal depressions of San Fernando, Lampacillo, and in the Cajon[351], it seems to continue to the base of the Puna beds, only the upper division of which has been found in the above-mentioned troughs. From a tectonic point of view, the bordering ranges belong to a system of later affiliation which, as far as observation goes, appeared about the beginning of the Upper Tertiary between the very much older Sierras of Fiambalá and Aconquija - Cerros de los Animas. So far this is true only of those parts of the ranges which extend southwards from the Puna into the lowlands of the Pampean Sierras; and at present it cannot be said also of the northern sections of the ranges which continue far out into the Puna.

The type of configuration is fundamentally the same as that of the older ranges. The summit peneplane is of the same kind, though obviously of more recent origin (corresponding in time to the under surface of p_2 in the Calchaqui Mountains). And furthermore it seems, as has been remarked, to belong to a surface formerly continuous over a larger area, which has been arched up on the ranges and bent down in the depressions. Whether this actually happened cannot, however, be affirmed with certainty whilst more exact observations are still lacking. In any case, in the continuation of the ranges that are already within the southern Puna (district of Laguna Blanca—Laguna Grande), it can be seen that the summit peneplane is *not* identical with the basal surface of the deposits in the troughs, which there consist of volcanic material, but

Photo. by W. Penck

1. Range of the Laguna Pastos Venturas, North-western Argentina

Photo. by W. Penck

2. Mountains at the eastern edge of the Laguna Helada, North-western Argentina

XI. RANGES OF YOUNGER ORIGIN

that it passes across them (fig. 21 C)[352]. This fact shows that, though the summit peneplane has originated from the upwarped or rising fragment of a surface, once more extensive, and graded on a grandiose scale, yet it essentially represents a younger creation characteristic of the rising range.

With this we come to *the southern Puna de Atacama*. It is divided up by north-south ranges and depressions—here separate basins of internal drainage—just in the same way as the adjoining region of the Pampean sierras. So far as is known, the ranges have been built up without faulting. The pronounced dislocations and overthrusts which accompany the eastern edge of the afore-mentioned affiliated systems have also vanished with entrance into the high land. The ranges are simple anticlines, the depressions synclines, and the superimposed volcanic material reproduces this type of folding on a large scale, with exceptional clarity. Here, too, the ranges have originated at very different periods. Their fundamental morphological feature is the almost exclusive dominance of flattish and medium relief forms. The following points may be briefly emphasised:

The ranges (mentioned above) in the region of the Laguna Grande are *of more youthful origin*, and the summit peneplane is preserved. On the slope down to the neighbouring depressions this is replaced by a medium relief with markedly convex slopes, which towards the mountain foot makes way for a form association just as deeply divided, with concave slopes rising to a similar degree of steepness[353]. Thus from the surfaces of accumulation in the basins up to this level, waning development makes itself much more noticeable, and in many cases has already determined the character of the ranges from foot to summit[354]. That is not, however, the lowest and youngest form association. This appears as steep slopes, convex or of maximum inclination, along those watercourses—few in number, it is true—which are equal to dealing with the enormous amount of rock waste. These slopes begin at the edge of what has accumulated in the basins; with increasing altitude they penetrate the sharply V-shaped valleys; and they often bound the rubbly or rocky flat floors of the trough valleys with sharply convex breaks of gradient[355]. They indicate *that the prevalence of waning development on the lower parts of the flanks of the ranges, especially along the multilobate margin of the accumulation in the basins, is not due to any lack of altitudinal differences capable of causing erosion and increasing its intensity. But—here, in mid-desert—it is caused by long continued lack of water which flows only occasionally and which is necessary for the work of erosion*. Actually it is only at the higher positions on the ranges, or on their steeper slopes, that a factor of transport tends to counterbalance the intensive formation of detritus and the development of huge streams of rock waste along the valley furrows. There, this factor does seem, at least to some extent, to be equal to the task; and this occurs not only as an exception, the case with the rare streams of constantly flowing water at the edges of the basins.

The characteristic mark of the ranges of more youthful origin (see Plate XI) is that the summit peneplane extends away over a lower disturbed stage of the volcanic accumulation, which must on the whole be equivalent to the Lower Puna beds or a part of them. The flat, however, is by no means always preserved, and perhaps in some cases never existed. The latter case seems to be true for, amongst others, the low ranges in the vicinity of the Salt Lake of Pairique. These extend from the northern edge of the Bolson of Fiambalá towards the soaring mountain mass of the Nevados de la Laguna Blanca, over 6000 metres in height, and one of the older Puna ranges (see below). They are of very recent origin and are completely broken up into a *steep* mountainland (not of maximum gradient, however) with concave forms almost throughout (see fig. 21 C3 and the fig. 3 quoted in note 354). In other cases, on the younger ranges which are already without the summit peneplane, its former existence is shown by at least scattered humps of convex rounding which stand conspicuously above the otherwise concave mountain landscape as uniformly accordant heights (see Plate XI, illustration 2; and part 24, plate 3, illustration 2 of *Geologische Charakterbilder*); or else the ranges throughout their whole extent show the convex forms of flattish domes on the summits, forms absolutely similar to relief type III of the Pampean sierras (fig. 21 C2)[356]. On the whole, steepness of slope and valley depth increase from above downwards, with these features again becoming gentler and shallower at the mountain foot itself. Should waning development be already established there, then as one goes upwards from the lower hills, one passes through zones which, at or near the intervalley divides, are characterised by quite considerable steepness, the slopes being steeper than any present in the summit region of those ranges which are cut through by valleys. Thus in major features as well as in details there is the same trend of development as in the Pampean sierras: increase of gradient as time goes on, taking place from above downwards. In the Puna, what corresponds in developmental stage to the steep relief here, is the form association (generally, it is true, far less steep), that is found on the lower parts of the flanks of the ranges. Even though this is not at its maximum gradient and is modified in various ways by the waning development, it very often leaves an *impression* of steep relief. This is always the case on the *ranges of greater elevation*, whether they are more recent or older in origin. Other things (rock material) being equal, the declivities here are actually greater, and

Photo. by W. Penck

1. Nevado de la Laguna Blanca, Puna de Atacama, Western Argentina

Photo. by W. Penck

2. Facetted spurs on the eastern slopes of the Nevado de la Laguna Blanca, Western Argentina

XII. Ranges of Older Origin

more like those of a steep relief. Paralleling this, there is more vigorous growth in an upslope direction; and so this form association now and again directly adjoins, with a sharp break of gradient, the summit peneplane or the medium relief arising from it on the mountain height[357].

In the southern Puna, just as in the Pampean sierras, the *older ranges* are characterised by greater height and breadth, by a greater number of denudation levels, i.e. of form associations arising one after another and preserved side by side, as well as by an analogous arrangement of these along the strike and on the flanks of the ranges, but not by other types of land form as in the case of the later developed broad folds. The *Nevados de la Laguna Blanca*, an elongated mountainous upswinging with the same trend as the Sierra de Fiambalá[358] (see plate XII, illustration 1), belong to that older type. Even from a great way off the range is striking on account of the broad dome-like shapes which form its summit region and appear there as if built up one above another (fig. 21 D, p. 275). They are extensive peneplane levels, not blurred by any specially advanced dissection into valleys, and separated from each other by extraordinarily distinct zones of convex slopes. These cause the domes of the high parts of the mountains.

A central mountainland, shifted eastward and northward, can be distinguished, bearing broad patches of a flattish relief (very probably a primary peneplane): I in fig. 21 C and D, p. 275. It is surrounded on all sides by an excellently preserved piedmont flat (II) particularly extensive along the trend of the mountains. Valleys with convex slopes cut into it, and in them are to be found the last extensions of that andesitic formation which, away from the old range, lay over the wide-spreading peneplane that was warped by broad folding in the neighbourhood of the Laguna Grande (III in fig. 21 C and D, and see p. 281). The relationship between the lower surface of the andesitic formation and the range is excellently exposed at its eastern side and near its plunging north end. At both places it can be plainly seen that III is a lower piedmont flat which continues in valley-like form into the higher region and, together with its valley-like continuations, was overwhelmed by the andesitic flows. This surface, which is presumably of Middle Tertiary, possibly of Miocene, age (i.e. the period of its origin up to the time when it was covered by andesite, see p. 281), was flexed together with the overlying beds, as already noted, into ranges and troughs of more recent origin (see Plate XI, illustration 1). Naturally, it is so on the flanks of the older ranges as well; and here surface II is also flexed, *anticlinally arched*. It had, furthermore, a very considerable relief, preserved at its margin in the valleys which at one time were cutting back to this position from surface III; and of course the floors of these valleys themselves (III *t*) are included in the bending. They are relatively very steep, unbroken in their course and deeply dissected by the modern sharply V-shaped valleys which run out over the andesite country at the edge of the range, where they intersect the III *t* valleys.

Great interest is attached to the transformation undergone by the brow, *the outer edge of the zone of convex slopes*, between II and III, in consequence of the bending. First of all, along the strike of the range, i.e. towards its sinking ends, the flexing, in so far as it can be called such at all, is very insignificant. Thus the scarp between II and III has here retained its continuously convex curvature and relatively slight inclination, in spite of its subsequent recession, the amount of which can probably be determined (fig. 21 D). The flanks of the ranges show quite a different effect. Here the bending (i.e. arching up) always reaches its greatest value, and leads to those unmistakable features which are dependent upon increase in steepness of all the gradients, and the consequent speeding up of all denudational processes within the zone of warping. On the eastern flank of the Nevados de la Laguna Blanca, the convex slopes in question have vanished and have been replaced by *steeper* slopes which upwards join surface II with a sharp break of gradient, and on the lower side pass down with a concave slope towards the piedmont flat IV or, as the case may be, into the valleys incised in it; for this surface can only just be detected and has already been dissected into a low hummocky landscape. The steep slopes (VI in fig. 21 C 1) occur in a long row facing the Laguna Blanca basin, right along the direction of strike of the warped zone, a direction which coincides with that of the trend of the mountain itself. This, the smoothness of the slopes and the sharp line of demarcation both towards surface II and towards the slopes of the old III *t* valleys leading into the mountain mass, have produced magnificent facetted spurs (see Plate XII, illustration 2), which are quite as fine as those which in North America have been taken as the type for this feature and objectively portrayed [as such]. But there is no fault or fault scarp anywhere here, as can easily be seen from the andesitic formation which is excellently exposed in the valleys penetrating into the massif.

A piedmont flat (IV) has already been mentioned as the next lower level; it occupies the same position as the summit peneplane on the younger ranges, i.e. like this, it extends over the (older) andesitic formation and its substratum. Below these, as on the younger ranges, there follow convex or concave slope systems, belonging to the lower valley levels as far down as the most recent ones. They still await further breaking down.

Thus the ranges of older origin in the southern Puna also show us a picture which does not differ fundamentally from that of the broad folds of the Pampean sierras of the same or similar age, except that they are much less faulted, that their relative height is less, and that the angle of slope is always slighter. But, apart from that, the form associations of different age are found here also, to be arranged next to one another in their age sequence from above downwards. As before, they form narrow strips on the flanks; but, on the summits, they are considerably elongated in the direction in which the mountains stretch out. More particularly, their growth and the direction in which they develop, are the same. Up to the present, no piedmont flats of very recent origin have been observed in the Puna. There is, however, often a sort of petering out of the relief towards the lowest part of the basins containing alluvial deposits. These deposits seem to be intercalated between the relief features framing the basin, and at times encroach far into them, drowning the valleys and overwhelming the crests of the projecting spurs. This relief itself, belonging to the youngest stage of development, diminishes gradually towards the edge of the basin. Not only in its relative height, but also in the inclination of its slopes, it lessens to practically nothing and so very readily allows itself to be covered over by the deposits which are collecting at the bottom of the subsiding basin.

(e) GENERAL SURVEY

At first glance the ranges examined in the foregoing sections appear so diverse as to be hardly comparable; but on closer examination they have revealed agreement in fundamental features. It has turned out that all belonged to uniform systems of mountain chains which were characterised by corresponding divisions into ranges and longitudinal depressions and, taken as a whole, represented elongated domings of the earth's crust. In them all, their altitudinal modelling showed development in the same direction: on all, the form systems (slope units) and form associations were so arranged that the flattest were found above, the steepest below; and each form association showed a great extension along the strike of the mountains, whilst at right angles it was less, the minimum extent occurring there. Finally, all the ranges of the same system were found to be separated from one another by depressions parallel to the strike; and these were, or are, to a greater or less extent, regions of deposition for correlated strata.* It is true that there are great quantitative differences in these, not only between various systems of ranges, but also between individual parts of one and the same system. This last point shows that there is no fundamental distinctive difference in the process of deposition of the correlated beds as between broad folds belonging to different

[* See Glossary].

zones. Further, great differences exist in the degree of faulting and in the degree of dissection by valleys. These differences also are differences in amount and not in type.

The degree of tectonic dislocation is registered by the presence or absence of faults and overthrusts, especially at the edge of the ranges, and in the type of disturbance found in the correlated strata: simple synclinal bedding, or folding in the depressions. In respect of folding, the Eastern Alps, for example, take a prominent place; and it may be presumed that there is a very intimate connection between the causes that produced the folded structure of the Alps and the broad folding which brought about the present altitudinal modelling of the mountains, and was responsible for the way in which the troughs were invaded by the correlated strata and their compression there. I have frequently stressed the fact that in former geosynclinal regions and similar zones of sedimentation, from which the fold-lines of the Mesozoic-Tertiary orogeny were able to take their rise, there must have been a genetic connection between folding of the strata and broad folding; as indeed follows from the partial coincidence in time of the two processes. How it happened is still quite obscure. Perhaps a way to the solution of the problem has been prepared by observation of the fact that several nappes of the central Western Alps and apparently also the north-western parts of the Eastern Alps, have resulted from simple arching, 'ge-anticlines'. Similarly, the Aconcagua nappe in the Andes seems to have been originally a broad anticline; and it is certain that at the edge of the southern Puna the more recent ranges have acquired a type of bedding which can only be termed imbricate structure. Here one is already far outside the late Mesozoic-Tertiary fold-lines of the High Cordilleras; nor is later folding of the strata absent. Sometimes it has happened to the Permo-Triassic Gondwana series, sometimes to the Upper Cretaceous-Tertiary correlated beds [i.e. correlated with the denudation], *but in both cases it apparently took place only where the complex of strata had a considerable thickness.* In the 'Calchaqui Mountains' the Tertiary beds, up to and including the Lower Puna strata, are folded, and are overfolded towards the east. The primary peneplane surface passes over the pile of folds and indicates that the formation of the ranges began with the folding of the strata[359]. The same had been established for the east and south-west sides of the Sierra Narvaez; but [there] the folding of the strata, which includes the Gondwana beds and the Calchaqui beds superposed on them in a *pseudoconcordant* fashion, is older; and across the folds there passes the summit peneplane (= the basal surface of the older Puna strata) which, too, is older [than in the Calchaqui Mountains].

Thus here also the folding of the strata and the broad folding are closely connected. *Where there is a suitable substructure, the broad folding begins with compression of this, and outlasts the compression.* Consequently it is by no means possible to consider the folding of correlated strata within one and the same system of ranges as a process which set in simultaneously throughout the whole region and, as a special phase of mountain building, entirely preceded the broad folding. Rather, it became noticeable at different times in different places, like the first rising of the broad anticlines. Further, the case has been established—both in north-west Argentina and in Anatolia—of ranges which, after they had existed for a very long time, underwent further development, characterised by increased upward movement. It has been shown that then the correlated strata at their edges, though up to that time unfolded, have nevertheless become caught up in the folding. Increase of crustal movement has played the chief part in this; though very likely it may have been helped by the complex of strata achieving a suitable *position in relation* to the rising range, such as might be brought about, for example, by the development of overthrust faults. For it is a fact well worthy of note that the folding of the correlated strata did not become important either everywhere at the same time or generally in every part of the system of ranges. Nor is it doing so nowadays. In any case the features mentioned make one thing quite clear: *broad folds are the work of tangentially directed forces, and this relates the process to true folding.* This further essential point must now be added *in distinct contrast to the areas of continental uplift, say, of the type of the German Highlands: broad folds in all stages of their development grow predominantly in length and height; and, in their advanced stages, practically cease altogether to grow in width.* Unlike the continental domings, the piedmont flats are not here widened in all directions, both along the strike and at right angles to it; but it holds as a general rule that the later the origin of the piedmont flats and the lower their position, the narrower (down to vanishing point) are their appearances on the flanks of the ranges and the more exclusively do they spread out lengthwise in the summit regions.

Dissection into valleys makes it in many cases difficult and often impossible to find evidence for peneplanes and piedmont flats. From our present state of knowledge it may be assumed that such flattish form associations were always present on ranges of early origin. Recently formed ranges, on the other hand, seem quite often never to have had them on their summits. Wherever a relatively late origin could be proved for them, these ranges showed complete dissection and breaking up as compared with older members of the same system. Steep forms and intermediate forms are regionally characteristic of them. And it is only under certain conditions and in certain zones—for instance those where, in consequence of interior drainage (Puna) or rapid relative subsidence ('ovas' in Anatolia), drainage and deposits are *dammed up* in the broad troughs—that the characteristics of waxing development are partially effaced in the region of the youngest and lowest sections of those stages of relief development. In the Basin Ranges and in the Mexican chains, there are perfect parallels to each of the various forms that are to be met with in the ranges of more recent origin. These latter are different only in their state of development at the moment, not (as has been shown) in the *manner* of their development nor in its *direction*. Davis considered them, in so far as they are characterised by intermediate forms, to be the remnants of ranges (that is, tilted blocks), which are approaching peneplanation, after the extinction of the crustal movement[360]. However, they possess throughout, or at any rate on the intervalley divides, the forms of waxing development. We can hardly go wrong if we consider them to be broad folds of rather recent origin.

Quite surprising agreement is shown when the younger ranges in the southern Puna are compared with the lower ranges of Tibet (relatively lower). These are likewise dissected into rounded forms of medium relief, and shrouded in rubble as described and photographed by Sven v. Hedin and A. Tafel[361]. In just the same way the older ranges of the southern Puna are connected, by similarity in modelling, with the high ranges of Tibet. Flattish form associations characterise the smooth broad heights of these also; Sven v. Hedin designates, for example, the top of the Karakoram as a plateau. Peneplanes obviously still extend over a wide area of the mountain summits, or else are replaced by intermediate form associations. These latter show the same change from convex intervalley divides to concave foot-slopes, and the same arrangement of the two types of form on the central summit portions of the chains and in the peripherally lying zone respectively, just as in the high ranges of the Pampean sierras or the southern Puna. Besides this, central mountainlands rise from several ranges, and quite put in the shade anything that the southern Puna has to show in this respect; as they do also in that of extent, of relative and absolute height, and especially in the sculpturing. In many cases they are still glacier-clad, and were so to a greater extent in the early Quaternary: steep slopes border the boldly aspiring knife-edges and pyramidal peaks of these central mountainlands[362]. This, however, cannot hide the fact that in both cases it is a matter of features which are fundamentally similar.

At the eastern edge of the Tibetan highland abysmally deep valleys open up unexpectedly, dissecting the system of ranges that swings round to the south-east. The convex forms of waxing development stand out particularly sharply, and on ranges which are becoming more and more ravined, especially in the region of the longitudinal depressions where inaccessible steeply V-shaped valleys are sunk into their floors. Here broad flattish ridges lie high above the gorges and on both sides there rise up the flanks of ranges which, eastwards, are being increasingly dissected into intermediate and steep forms. Thus zones of sharp edges and of longitudinal valleys, which exhibit the same land forms as occur in the Eastern Alps, develop from the ranges and depressions. But for one thing the dimensions here are enormously greater; and then the form associations have not been blurred by glacial overprinting, but are preserved with their connections intact[363].

According to these observations, for which we have to thank A. Tafel, the south-eastern margin of Tibet is not directly comparable with the southern margin of the Puna. For in Tibet it is not, as at the edge of the Puna, the floors of the depressions which lie at a lower absolute altitude than in the interior of the Highland, but the floors of the incised valleys. The fact of this dissection is certainly, in part though not entirely, due to climatic conditions, since the whole of eastern Tibet is drained to the ocean by the Salwen, Mekong and Yangtse. But at all events the influence of climate in stamping its mark upon the outward form of broad fold systems must, in any case, be rated very highly. It is to be seen on ranges of similar age and in an otherwise similar state of development: in a moist climate they are naturally more completely dissected than in an arid region. It is to be expected that, other things being equal, the last stage of relief should under moist conditions have been more completely established at the expense of its predecessors than where there is aridity. This partly accounts for the transformation of East Alpine ranges into zones of sharp ridges and for the absence of this breaking up in, for example, the equally closely ranged northern Pampean sierras. But only partly so. For it must be pointed out that where the Eastern Alps are becoming lower—and especially towards the eastern edge of the mountains—older, flatter, precursor form associations are preserved, to an increasing degree, on the heights. But the younger steep relief of the lower lying parts, which by no means owes its *origin* to the work of glacial modification, is equally developed in the east and in the west. Here is a problem the roots of which do not lie in any climatic conditions.

The same problem, in an altered form, is found on comparing the longitudinal depressions. It is undoubtedly because of the climate, which has long been arid, that the high-lying basins of the southern Puna have been regions of interior drainage, and so of deposition, since Tertiary times (presumably Lower Tertiary). The similarly high-lying depressions on the eastern margin of Tibet are analogous to the longitudinal valley zones of the Eastern Alps in being deeply dissected, and so do not function as areas of deposition. Yet whether accumulation does or does not take place in the longitudinal depressions does not depend only upon climatic conditions, nor only upon whether the drainage is interior or to the sea. Reference may again be made to the Eastern Alps, within the longitudinal depressions of which correlated strata put in an appearance eastwards in the same direction as the general fall in height of the mountains. These strata do not rest upon an ideal trough bottom, but they are embedded in a [definite] relief, in valleys which have been sunk in the hypothetical bottom of a trough (a sort of hypothetical 'tectonic upper surface'). In the broad synclines of Anatolia, lying at a low absolute altitude, the later and youngest correlated strata mantle a [definite] relief. And the influence of climate does seem to show itself in this case: processes of denudation become effective in *low-lying* basins if the streams draining them are given cause for erosion; on the other hand, they are not effective in the equally low-lying broad synclines of an arid region where there is no outflow. In the latter case, therefore, the correlated strata rest upon the relatively subsiding floor of the trough, and in each individual section this is formed by the upper surface of the next older bed in the complex of strata (conformable bedding, no relief features). Thus it is evident that the varying degree of dissection possessed by systems of ranges, anticlines and synclines, cannot depend upon climatic differences alone; *essentially it is to be traced to this additional circumstance that the causes leading to erosion both were and are present to a different extent in the various systems of ranges and in their individual parts.*

This brings into a clearer light some of the features that have been noticed within the Andine system. Some of the bolsons in north-west Argentina, like that of Fiambalá, the Calchaqui Valley, etc., are not areas of interior drainage and undoubtedly never have been such: the streams draining them are very old, as is indicated by the antecedent manner in which they break through to the lower-lying plain. Notwithstanding, the strata are built up in the way that would be expected in basins of interior drainage, that is, there are—as has been described above—no gaps [in the succession]. This shows that in the part of the basin lowest at the time, there was never any cause for erosive incision, but always only such conditions as led to accumulation. In this there are to be seen rather fundamental differences as compared with the development of the Anatolian type of broad syncline, which has been found to be characterised by repeated alternation of scouring out and filling in. Going northwards, the depressions of the Puna are today found at high altitudes. They have interior drainage. But where the Bolivian Highland enters the moister region to the north, there the basins lying at no lower altitude, are deeply dissected by the tributaries of the Amazon ('Inter-Andine Highland' of Peru and Ecuador), and the conditions prevailing are like those at the south-eastern margin of Tibet. The valley incisions expose immense thicknesses of fluviatile and lacustrine deposits, mixed with volcanic derivatives of Tertiary age. From what has been said, it is absolutely clear that it is not any climatic change, in the sense of increased volume of water, which has been able to effect the dissection of the Highland, but causes for erosive incision have set in at places where formerly the streams had found conditions suitable only for accumulation. The depressions and systems of depressions of the present inter-Andine highland must in earlier times have lain at a lesser height above sea level than now. Finally, in the Columbian-Venezuelan region, with its virgation of ranges, there again takes place—in the humid tropical province—a change to conditions which are analogous to those in the district of the semi-arid Pampean sierras: the mountains, taken as a whole, are lower; the depressions again lie at a smaller height above sea level; and today, as in Tertiary times, they are still, over a wide extent, areas of accumulation[364]. The tectonic differentiation into higher and lower-lying parts is again great, and longitudinal faults have been established. The highland with its deeply-dissected trough regions has vanished.

Not only is broad folding at work in the system of mountain chains, dividing up the crustal surface into ranges and depressions, and causing growth of the former as contrasted with the latter, but obviously there are yet other processes which interfere with it.

Similar phenomena recur at various places within the world's mountain belts. Some features of agreement have already been pointed out. In particular, it has been shown that there are very close parallels with the ranges of earlier origin as they have been found in Anatolia and in the Andes. Their configuration has attracted a great deal of attention since, as they bear peneplanes or gentle intermediate forms on their heights, they possess graded crest lines that often appear almost level. This not only forms a contrast to the steeper forms on the slopes, but departs completely from the customary picture of the Alpine sea of peaks. Only a few features can be briefly cited; and only the mode of formation, the type and the arrangement of the form associations observed, can be considered. For in general far too little is known about the relationships with the correlated deposits; and their treatment, like that of the whole question of geological dating, is obviously influenced by the conception that the peneplanes detected must be end-peneplanes. This idea, as already noted, has also become a decisive factor in the interpretation of the tectonics ('Fault Block Mountains'). No further reference will be made to it.

Peneplanes, or intermediate forms derived from them, extend over the summits of the dominating ranges of the North American mountain system. The slopes facing the neighbouring depressions are steeply furrowed. Asymmetrical arrangement and development of the steep relief, similar to that of the Sierra de Cordoba and the other Pampean sierras, is prominent in the Wasatch Mountains and also in the Sierra Nevada[365]. In this latter case, individual elevations, obviously remnants of a central mountainland, rise above a piedmont surface that is still preserved as fragments ('subsummit plateau' of A. Knopf), dissected by broad valley troughs. This is a medium relief undergoing waning development, and it joins the steep relief of the mountain flank in a sharp break of gradient. F. Machatschek has emphasised the complete morphological correspondence between these mountains and the ranges of Central Asia (Tien Shan)[366]. Similar configuration, and the same arrangement of form associations characterise also the broader arch of the Cascade Mountains, where powerful Pleistocene glaciation has not obliterated the levels established in pre-glacial times—remnants of a central mountainland, an extensive piedmont flat, intermediate forms showing waning development, steep forms in the most recent valley incisions. B. Willis has portrayed them on maps which clearly reflect the far-reaching breaking up of the preceding stages[367]. The number of analogous examples might easily be increased[368]. They all show that the North American ranges have had exactly the same trend of development as the broad folds of the Andes. The same applies to the Central Asiatic systems of ranges, where German and North American investigations have provided fairly detailed information about the configuration of the Pamirs, the Tien Shan, and adjoining regions[369]. Extensive peneplanes, which have been found at the most varied levels both on the tops of ranges—where they often interlocked in the manner characteristic of piedmont steps—and at the foot of the mountains, were, in short, considered as fragments of a single gigantic end-peneplane, which was supposed to have extended over the whole of Central Asia, to have been dislocated by faults in very recent times, and thus to have come to lie at various levels[370]. And it is only over the geological age of the surface and of its dislocation that there are divergent opinions; the Americans consider the hypothetical surface to be late Tertiary, the Germans Mesozoic. What is actually established, however, is the occurrence of peneplanes on many ranges, but not that they are of the same age; the step-like repetition of such surfaces on several of the higher ranges, but not the throw of the faulting which was considered to have produced the steps (since there was apparently no other way of explaining their presence); further, the presence of high ranges which especially in the central mountainous parts are, as it were, superimposed upon the level of the surrounding peneplanes, but are not of the horst nature occasionally suggested for what are obviously central mountainlands; and finally, the development of a comparatively very young piedmont flat, the lowest level, at the edge of several of the mountain systems—but by no means, as is claimed, the identity of this with the peneplanes on the summits of the chains. Undoubtedly there are here structures of the most varied origin and quite different periods of formation, entirely different denudation levels which have been put together on account of the homogeneity of their form elements. Such a result indeed follows from the unconformities within the correlated Gobi strata (Tertiary in the main) which Keidel and Gröber investigated, and from the way in which the lower conglomerates of the same series encroach in the western Tien Shan upon a relief dissected into valleys (F. Machatschek).

The Gobi sediments, which seem to go back as far as the uppermost Cretaceous period, are in their turn lying unconformably upon folded Mesozoic continental formations (Angara beds). But not everywhere. Keidel found them occurring conformably between the southern margin of the Tien Shan and the northern edge of the Kashgar Mountains. Gröber thought he could confirm this observation, but was, however, doubtful about it. Nevertheless, to all appearance this is in fact the transition from the unconformity to a bedding plane, similar to that observed within the correlated strata at the southern edge of the Puna. The peneplanes on the Tien Shan ranges are considered to be equivalent to that late Mesozoic unconformity. Thus the character of a primary peneplane may be considered as established for surfaces where this condition obtains. But it is not certain whether these are the oldest form associations originating in the Tien Shan. For it is not certain whether the Angara beds, which are nowadays absent from extensive sections of the mountains, formerly covered the area completely, or whether, as Keidel presumed, they never existed there. Thus it is possible that they also were correlated, even at that time, with processes of denudation which, over the area of the present mountains, must have created form associations of a relatively early origin. Such an assumption need not be entirely rejected in the case of the very old form associations—already, it appears completely removed—belonging to the flatter configuration out of which the central mountainlands of the highest parts of the massif must have been carved. In the central Tien Shan these form high mountain ranges, strongly glaciated, which are as it were superimposed upon the system of ranges (first level). Relics of the fringing piedmont flat are preserved. They lie approximately at the height of the summit peneplane of the neighbouring ranges, which have been described as a high plateau

devoid of peaks. If confirmation is found that the relationships conjec-
tured do actually occur here, then the central range might be claimed as
the oldest element, to which the neighbouring ranges were added later.
The piedmont flat of the central range would be the summit peneplane
[of the later ranges]; and it might well be that its origin was determined
by the unconformity at the base of the Gobi sediments (second level).

The same arrangement seems to be repeated yet once more but at a
lower level: below the highest of these summit peneplanes there appear
planations which extend as wide strips along the longitudinal depressions
and encroach valleywise into the parts of the ranges rising above them.
Whilst the ranges become still more altered into elongated central
mountainlands, like those of the central range, but far lower, the strips
widen into piedmont flats; and it appears that in the outer parts of the
mountains they form summit peneplanes, which may perhaps pass over
into one of the planes of unconformity *within* the Gobi strata (third
level). We are merely, with every reservation, hinting at such relations
as possible. It may be taken as certain that, in the Tien Shan, peneplanes
are present at various levels and with the interlocking effect characteristic of piedmont flats. Further, there is agreement upon this, that in all
the ranges where there are flat summits, the peneplanes are broken up,
beginning from their edges, into intermediate forms; and, on the flanks,
steep forms pass down to the longitudinal depressions.

These latter are, for the most part, dissected by valleys (zones of
longitudinal valleys). But also, in the interior of the mountains, basin
deposits appear in the wide, deep depressions (Ferghana, Naryn, Ili,
Tekes, and so on). It follows from the distribution of the mountain-foot
facies, and of what is associated with deposition far away from the
mountains, that the deposits were laid down on a sinking substratum, in
synclines. The beds are probably of various ages. They are generally
considered to be Tertiary (belonging to the Gobi sediments). As at the
mountain edge (Tarim Basin), so also in the intermont basins (Ferghana,
Ili, Naryn), they are disturbed, e.g. they are steeply dragged and folded
at the edges of the chains; in the Naryn Basin they are cut across by a
low-lying peneplane—into which the valley system has been sunk—
obviously in the same manner as in the broad synclines of Anatolia.

The type of disturbance found in the correlated Tertiary deposits is
not only deformation at the edge of the mountain arch, or of the adjoining ranges as the case may be, but *folding*, which like the deformation
becomes fainter with distance from the mountains. The localisation of
this folding is dependent upon the distribution of material capable of
folding: *folding of strata could occur in connection with range formation*
only where such sediments were present over some considerable extent

and *in suitable position with relation* to the rising chains (in the interior of the western Tien Shan, the Tertiary is said not to be folded). It indicates what is an essential feature of the processes of movement, namely the participation of tangential forces. The strike faults become *overthrusts*[371], especially at the edges of the system of ranges (Tarim, Ferghana) but also apparently in several of its longitudinal depressions, and this points in the same direction. The correspondence with the ranges at the southern edge of the Puna seems to be far-reaching from the tectonic aspect also. In fact, P. Gröber has recognised and stressed the broad fold nature of the system of ranges; he was able to show observational proof for the stand he had taken in opposition to the erroneous view, held up till then, of the importance of longitudinal faults in the structure of the mountains[372].

Reference has yet to be made to observations which throw light upon the growth of the whole mountain system (as apart from individual ranges). The *general growth in height* is indicated not by the increase in amplitude of the individual chains, but—just as in the Andine system— by the dissection of the longitudinal depressions which have become elevated to a great height; by the general increase in coarseness of grain in the Gobi series from below upwards, Keidel having followed this out along the southern border of the mountains; and by the great absolute altitude to which Lower Eocene marine strata have been uplifted in the western Tien Shan (up to 4000 metres). The zones of folded correlated strata now fit on to this at the western and southern marginal regions of the mountains, and in parts form independent ranges. Leuchs noticed the same thing in the wide zone of sedimentation which *in earlier times* divided the Tien Shan proper from the Dzungarian Ala Tau of the present day. *The mountain system links fresh ranges to itself and pushes its periphery outwards.* The same thing has been observed along the eastern margin of the Andes of north-west Argentina, and seems to be true for the eastern border of the system of ranges far into Bolivia. Their further growth in a direction transverse to their strike, and so a growth in breadth, is shown by the appearance on their outer sides of wide piedmont flats of very recent origin, often still but slightly dissected. Pumpelly found such surfaces at the edge of the Tarim Basin where incising streams had laid bare more strongly disturbed correlated beds beneath formations of Quaternary alluvial cones. Granö[373] describes a magnificent example of this kind at the edge of the Russian Altai. The evenly-cut surface, rising gently towards the mountains, is extremely well graded; it tops folded Palaeozoic sediments and schistose [? or slaty] rocks and rests against the flanks of the system of ranges as well as its end, where it dies away to the west-north-west.

Thus the phenomenon of growth in width is not isolated. It turns up again on the outer side of mountains of Alpine structure, in an apparently altered form as the addition of fresh folded elements and imbricated slices. Fundamentally, however, it is the same thing, and probably the differences are mainly those of rock materials. Where there is no considerable thickness of stratified deposits, this addition brings into the field of vision both the old substructure itself and the manner of its disturbance. From the areas of sedimentation, on the other hand, the strata of the immense superstructure emerge first; and it is the disturbed conditions there which become visible, not those of the basement. It cannot without further investigation, and certainly not invariably, be taken for granted that the substructure remains down below unmoved, that its stratified cover alone rises and is brought up only by folding, since in the central belts of the fold mountains that old basement is uplifted with it. Here, too, the recent additions have the configuration of ranges and depressions which, as at the eastern margin of the Andes of North Argentina or in Lower Albania[374], coincide with anticlines and synclines; or else, as in the Dalmatian coastal zone or on the outer side of the western Taurus, are whole fasces of folds and imbrications collected together into ranges.

Growth in width is paralleled by growth in height. And it seems as if a general feature in the development of systems of ranges is here revealed: *taken as a whole, even in the most advanced phases of development, they increase not only in amplitude but also in phase. Obviously, therefore, the systems of ranges as a whole behave differently from the individual ranges of which they are made up.*

The Altai system of ranges, mentioned above, is in a state of far advanced dissection and breaking up, which in its turn raises the problem of the growth in altitude of the whole system. Many features are reminiscent of the conditions in the east of the Tibetan Highland, but they are far better known in the Altai, thanks to Granö's work there. Various levels of denudation stand out with great clarity, and in some cases it can be proved that they have developed from peneplanes. Under the influence of the concept that those surfaces are of the nature of end-peneplanes, and of their mode of origin according to the cycle theory, Granö considers them to be the faulted fragments of the Central Asiatic Peneplain which have been displaced with relation to one another along fault lines that have had a course of extraordinary complexity, and are merely presumed to be faults. Let us consider the features so excellently observed by the Finnish investigator.

Above the aforesaid piedmont flat at the mountain edge, there rises as the next level a medium relief. This shows convex shapes with their summits at a uniform height, increasing on the whole from the periphery towards the interior of the mountains. On various summits there are more or less extensive relics of flattish form associations. They indicate a former peneplane which, according to Granö's map, bordered the mountains and their north-western extremity in just the same way as the peripheral piedmont flat of very recent origin still does, but it extended between the ranges into the longitudinal depressions. Here it seems to have been of the same type as the wide peneplanes in the Anatolian broad synclines. It is, however, deeply dissected and disintegrated into 'Highlands' (zones of longitudinal valleys). A third level, which is obviously characteristic of the ranges but not of the longitudinal depressions, has even at the present day still preserved—to a large extent—its flattish form associations. Leading up from the main valleys to these peneplane remnants are form associations that are steep below, and of intermediate type above. Their summit altitudes rise rapidly, their slopes become flatter, the depth of their valleys becomes correspondingly less. Throughout, the typical signs of waxing development dominate[375]. On various ranges, in the direction of their strike, extensive mountainlands rise above the peneplanes. These have forms of medium relief, into which steep glacial forms have afterwards been cut ('montagne alpine'); and often they have already broken up into separate mountains or mountain groups. The convex rounding of the summits is worth noting; over wide areas they maintain an accordant height averaging 3000 metres. Actually wider fragments of flattish form associations are repeatedly to be found here. They point to the existence of a fourth peneplane level, above which there rise on some of the ranges, that obviously originated very long ago, individual mountains of over 4000 metres. These are remnants of central mountainlands of early origin, which are still extensively developed in the central mountainous parts of the region fringing Mongolia (Tabunbogdo, Kotuntau), and there are bordered by peneplanes of the fourth level forming piedmont flats. Further to the south, according to Granö, this surface seems to function as a summit peneplane.

This whole arrangement is very characteristic, not however of a uniform surface fragmented by faults, but of a uniformly growing system of mountain chains. The central range, with the highest level broken up into a central mountainland, appears as the oldest fragment. The piedmont surface here is the summit peneplane on that part of the range which is becoming lower towards the termination (prolongation) of the mountains, as well as on neighbouring ranges added later to the system. It undergoes progressive breaking up in the direction of the *general* slopes of the mountains down towards the west and north, and changes into a *lower* central mountainland (finally into inselbergs), which is in its turn bordered by a lower piedmont flat. And this again appears as a summit peneplane on the still lower dropping prolongation of the more recently added ranges. The configuration of the *individual ranges* is entirely of the kind found on the older ranges that have so far been investigated. The distinction lies in conditions found in the depressions, which are deeply dissected just as in the zone of longitudinal valleys in the Alps. But looking at *the mountain system as a whole*—without regard to the fact that the peneplanes belong genetically to the individual ranges—and so considering the position of the form associations in relation to the whole mountain mass, there stands out with extreme sharpness the resemblance to the piedmont benchlands of the continental zones of uplift: what has been found there as close interdigitation of step-like levels arising one above another and one after the other, is repeated here as additions following on one after the other.

The sum total of these observations leaves no doubt as to the broad fold nature of the Altai chains. It may here be mentioned that Granö brings forward yet further facts when he describes the marginal warping of the fragments of the peneplanes that have been preserved and when he gives closer attention to the zones of longitudinal valleys. In some of them extensive accumulation is at present taking place. The rivers leave the wide alluvial floors—along the edges of which, at any rate in parts, fault lines may possibly occur—in very much narrower erosion-valleys. Further, narrow V-shaped valleys are tributary to them. Thus there exists a contrast between the wide zone of excavation within which the streams collect waste and are sometimes dammed up to form swamps, and the incision of the same streams outside the zones of longitudinal valleys. Features of the same kind, but showing perhaps even stronger contrasts, are found in the 'ovas' of Anatolia, and they indicate subsidence of the zones of longitudinal valleys (or broad synclines, as the case may be) with reference to the ranges surrounding them, and consequently a damming back in these zones.

There are but few important points of comparison to be found in the western half of the Pacific framework. Molengraaf assumes 'basin range structure' for the ranges of the Sunda Islands[376]. The anticlinal nature of the ranges was deduced from the development and arrangement of the reefs surrounding the coral-fringed series of islands, in the same way as O. Wanner had previously demonstrated the synclinal nature of the Timor depressions. But morphological investigations are still lacking. From some reports about raised peneplanes, it may be presumed that on the whole the same sort of forms are to be found in east and south-east Asia also[377]. In the mountains of New Guinea, which have quite recently been recognised as a system of ranges, Major H. Detzner (famous for his daring expeditions) met with extensive plateau land-scapes above the precipitously slashed flanks of ranges which for the most part already meet in sharp knife-edges. His clear description easily permits the recognition of intermediate forms of waning development.

It has not been possible here to give more than a hint as to some of the features present within the mountain belts of the world, so far as they are at present known. The far-reaching agreement in configuration of the ranges stands out clearly. Geological proofs that the systems of ranges are all systems of broad folds is indeed still wanting, though there does not appear to be very much room left for doubt about it. The similarity of the configuration, which has been definitely shown, proves at least this one thing: the complete similarity in development of the ranges, and systems of ranges, for all cases that have been closely examined; whether these are systems of broad folds that have been recognised as such, or systems of ranges where the tectonic character still needs elucidation. What really matters, and what has been repeatedly brought out in this work, is the uniformity of the setting of the problem.

NOTES AND BIBLIOGRAPHIC REFERENCES

The following contractions are used below:

A.J.S.   American Journal of Science.

A.S.A.W.(m.-p)   Abhandlungen der Kgl. Sächsischen Gesellschaft (Akademie) der Wissenschaften, Math.-Phys. Klasse. (Leipzig).

B.G.S.A.   Bulletin of the Geological Society of America.

G.J.   Geographical Journal (London).

G.M.   Geological Magazine (London).

G.R.   Geologische Rundschau (Leipzig).

G.Z.   Geographische Zeitschrift (Leipzig).

J.G.   Journal of Geology (Chicago).

P.M.   Petermanns Mitteilungen aus J. Perthes Geographische Anstalt (Gotha).

Q.J.G.S.   Quarterly Journal of the Geological Society of London.

Z.D.G.G.   Zeitschrift der Deutschen Geologischen Gesellschaft (Berlin).

Z.G.E.   Zeitschrift der Gesellschaft für Erdkunde zu Berlin.

Z.M.G.P.   Zentralblatt für Mineralogie, Geologie und Paläontologie (Stuttgart).

W. Penck, Op. 10
W. Penck, Op. 13
W. Penck, Op. 16   works 10, 13, 16 and 17 listed on pp. 352–353.
W. Penck, Op. 17

(1) A. PENCK, *Morphologie der Erdoberfläche*, Bd. I, p. 2. *Bibliothek geogr. Handbücher*. Stuttgart, 1894.

(2) The evidence for this fact is given in WALTHER PENCK, Op. 17.

(3) It may be assumed that they [i.e. fluctuations in sea level] interfere with the crustal movements, but this has not, so far, been definitely proved. R. A. DALY now believes it possible to draw definite conclusions as to the Pleistocene and modern eustatic fluctuations of sea-level from tropical coral islands and atolls, as well as from recent and sub-recent raised beaches. Even if these fluctuations are confirmed, it is clear that, compared with crustal movements, they are small in amount and so of slight morphological importance, at least as regards the main characters found on the face of the planet, though not necessarily for the development of individual features. (R. A. DALY, The glacial-control theory of coral reefs. *Proc. Amer. Acad. Arts Sci.*, 1915, LI, No. 4, p. 157. Also *A.J.S.*, 1919, XLVIII, p. 136; *B.G.S.A.*, 1920, XXXI, p. 303 and elsewhere. A general sinking of sea-level in recent time, *Proc. nation. Acad. Sci.*, 1920, VI, No. 5, p. 246 and *G.M.*, 1920, LVII, No. 672, p. 246).

(4) W. M. Davis, The geographical cycle. *G.J.*, 1899, XIV, p. 481; also *C. R.* 7 *Cong. int. Géog.*, Berlin 1899, II, p. 221. D. W. Johnson has edited a selection of the writings of this American scholar under the title of *Geographical Essays* (Ginn & Co., 1909). The collection does not contain that article of Davis which is of special methodological importance: The systematic description of land forms. *G.J.*, 1909, XXXIV, 2, p. 300. A full German presentation of his theory is contained in *Die erklärende Beschreibung der Landformen* (B. G. Teubner, Leipzig 1912), and a shorter one in G. Braun's edition of Davis' *Physical Geography* (1898) (*Grundzüge der Physiogeographie II, Morphologie*, 2. Aufl., Leipzig 1915), etc.

(5) See particularly *G.J.*, 1909, XXXIV, 2, p. 300.

(6) *Proc. Amer. Assoc. Adv. Sci.*, 1884 and *C. R. Cong. int. Géog.*, 1904, pp. 153, 154.

(7) See amongst other writings of W. M. Davis: The Triassic formation of Connecticut, *U.S. geol. Surv. ann. Rep.*, 18.

(8) See also W. Penck, Op. 17.

(9) See the writings of S. Passarge (Physiologische Morphologie. *Mitteil. geogr. Gesellsch. Hamburg*, 1912, XXVI, p. 133 and *Grundlagen der Landschaftskunde* III, Hamburg 1920) and A. Hettner (*Die Oberflächenformen des Festlandes*, B. G. Teubner, Leipzig 1921, the repetition in a comprehensive manner, with additions, of articles which had appeared earlier in the *G.Z.*). Passarge makes the most far-reaching use of deductions without always basing himself upon adequate observations (see review by H. Wagner in *P.M.*, 1913, p. 176). A. Hettner, on the other hand, is an outspoken opponent of the method of deduction.

(10) The first critical investigation of the 'endogenetic' assumption which is made in the erosion cycle theory, as usually understood, was published by A. Penck (Die Gipfelflur der Alpen, *Sitzungsber. Preuss. Akad. Wissensch., math.-phys. Kl.*, XVII, p. 256, Berlin 1919). Observations reaching back to an earlier date were made by the author in the Argentinian Andes; and these supplied information which showed that assumption to be untenable (W. Penck, Op. 16).

(11) *Die Oberflächenformen des Festlandes*, loc. cit. [note 9], p. 215.

(12) See Walther Penck, Morphologische Analyse. *Verhandl. XX. deutscher Geographentag*, Leipzig 1921, p. 122.

(13) See Walther Penck, Op. 16, p. 389.

(14) The very frequently occurring cases of faults which are later on made visible by denudation are not to be classed as unlevelled fault scarps, for the processes of denudation have encountered rocks which differed in resistance on the two sides. This is not being discussed here.

(15) *C. R. Cong. int. Géog. Washington*, 1904, pp. 153–154; *G.J.*, 1899, p. 7 of the off-print; *Erklärende Beschreibung der Landformen*, loc. cit. [note 4], pp. 146–147, 173, etc.

(16) See amongst other writings that of H. Schmitthenner in his dissertation on *Die Oberflächengestaltung des nördlichen Schwarzwaldes*, p. 59 (Karlsruhe 1913).

(17) 'It is well known that scientific physics has existed only since the invention of the differential calculus. It is only since man has learned how to follow the course of natural occurrences continuously that there has been any success in the attempts made to express in abstract terms the connection between [various] phenomena.' Preface to RIEMANN's lectures on *Die partiellen Differentialgleichungen der mathematischen Physik* (5. Aufl., Braunschweig 1910).

(18) Priority belongs to W. M. DAVIS who, in connection with studies on the Great Plains of Montana, east of the Rocky Mountains, expounded the principle of peneplanation in 1886 (*Tenth Census of U.S.*, vol. XV, Statistics of coal mining). A. PENCK, Über Denudation der Erdoberfläche. *Schriften zur Verbreitung naturwissenschaftlicher Kenntnisse*, XXVII, Wien 1886-87.

(19) For the earliest investigations in this direction see A. PENCK, Die Gipfelflur der Alpen, loc. cit. [note 10], and WALTHER PENCK, Op. 16.

(20) A short presentation of the connection between these is to be found in WALTHER PENCK, Op. 17.

(21) The term 'structure', defined and used in a perfectly clear and unambiguous sense geologically, as identical with 'internal build', has not been used so unequivocally in morphological literature. W. M. DAVIS understands by it not only the condition of the bedding, but also the original altitude and the original surface, purely formal constructions created in order to deduce the cycle of erosion and to serve as its starting point (*Die erklärende Beschreibung der Landformen*, p. 143, Leipzig 1912). But otherwise DAVIS separates the static element (structure) from the dynamic ones (crustal movement, uplift) quite in the manner of the physico-geological meaning, thus departing far less than A. HETTNER from the conception as found in modern geology. HETTNER tried to combine causes and effects, both the dynamic and the static phenomena, in his idea of 'internal build', and even extended it to vulcanism (*Die Oberflächenformen des Festlandes*, p. 137, 197-198, Leipzig 1921).

(22) The fact of this development, and its nature, as well as their extraordinary complexity, prove an insurmountable obstacle in the way of accepting A. WEGENER's simple solution of the whole series of problems in his idea of Continental Drift (A. WEGENER, Die Entstehung der Kontinente und Ozeane. *Die Wissenschaft*, Vol. LXVI, 2. Aufl., Braunschweig 1920). See the discussion on Wegener's theory in the *Z.G.E.*, no. 3-4, 1921, and WALTHER PENCK, Zur Hypothese der Kontinentalverschiebung, *ibid.*, p. 130).

(23) The stable regions which, on account of their lack of Mesozoic-Tertiary folding, differ fundamentally from the mountain belts, show no very intense continuous crustal movement, except in special individual zones of disturbance, e.g. that of the Rift Valley of East and Central Africa. This may be learnt from the comparative rarity of earthquakes, which *indicate* that crustal displacement is taking place. By far the greater number of these occurs within or very close to the mountain belts. It is similar for volcanic phenomena: a very large majority of the active and extinct volcanoes are to be found in the mountain belts. It is only there that gigantic batholiths and hundreds of smaller intrusions of recent age have been discovered. There are many times

that number of intrusive bodies not yet found, but indicated by volcanoes situated above them. The dominant magma is intermediate in nature, andesitic. It is of the Pacific type, rich in calcium, although inclusions of Atlantic magma, rich in alkalis, are not entirely absent. These are generally more recent than the Pacific extrusions, and appear as late sporadic intruders. The continental masses and the oceans show predominantly monotonous, but slightly differentiated basaltic extrusions, some having an extraordinary extent (northern Eurasia, Deccan, Patagonia, etc.). And in between them, Atlantic rocks, rich in alkalis, play a considerable part. The geological arrangement on a grand scale is: mountain belt—predominantly Pacific magmas; stable regions —in the main *not* Pacific magmas, but a predominance of typical Atlantic rocks; and this is as little affected by the increasing number of mixed regions like Sardinia and of transitional cases, as by the increasing number of those who want to assume that there is a closer connection between Atlantic and Pacific magmas than was previously admitted, or who believe it possible to derive the one magma from the other, or both from a common stock (see F. v. WOLFF, *Der Vulkanismus*, Stuttgart 1903.—M. STARK, Petrographische Provinzen, *Fortschr. Min.*, IV, p. 251, Jena 1914.—H. S. WASHINGTON, *J.G.*, 1914, XXII, p. 742. *A.J.S.*, 1913, XXXVI, p. 577; 1915, XXXIX, p. 513.— P. NIGGLI, Die leichtflüchtigen Bestandteile im Magma. *Preisschr. jablonowsk. Gesellschaft*, XLVII, Leipzig 1920. *Z.M.G.P.*, 1920, no. 11, 12, p. 161.— R. A. DALY, *Igneous rocks and their origin*, New York, 1914. *J.G.*, 1918, XXVI, no. 2, p. 97.—WALTHER PENCK, Die Entstehung der Gebirge der Erde. *Deutsche Revue*, September-Oktober 1921).

(24) See A. PENCK's detailed description of the earth's altitudinal form in *Morphologie der Erdoberfläche*, Bd. I, chaps. III and IV, Stuttgart 1894. Also M. GROLL's Tiefenkarten der Ozeane (*Veröffentl. Inst. Meeresk.*, N.F., Reihe A, Heft 2, Berlin 1912; *Z.G.E.*, no. 2, Berlin 1912) and H. HEYDE's Ergänzung (*Z.G.E.*, 1920, Heft 9–10, p. 261).

(25) P. GRÖBER, Estratigrafia del Dogger, Bd. XVIII, ser. B. *Direccion general de minas*, etc., Buenos Aires 1918. BLACKWELDER calls that Jurassic period of folding in the Pacific belt the 'Nevadian' (*J.G.*, 1914, XXII, pp. 633 ff.).—H. STILLE, Die mitteldeutsche Rahmenfaltung, *Niedersächs. geol. Verein*, 1910, III, p. 226. Zur Kenntnis der Dislokationen, Schichtenabtragungen und Transgressionen im jüngsten Jura und in der Kreide Westfalens. *Jahrb. preuss. geol. Landesanst.*, 1905, XXVI, p. 103.—R. BÄRTLING, *Z.D.G.G.*, 1920. Abh. LXXII, Heft 3–4, p. 161, especially pp. 165 ff.—W. HAACK, *Z.D.G.G.*, 1921, LXXIII, Monatsber. no. 4–5, p. 50.—O. BURRE, *Jahr. preuss. geol. Landesanst.*, 1911, XXXII, p. 306. See also the 'Führer zu den Exkursionen der Deutschen Geologischen Gesellschaft, August 1914'. *Niedersächs. geol. Verein*, Hanover 1914, pp. 89 ff., especially p. 123.—O. v. LINSTOW, *Jahrb. preuss. geol. Landesanst.*, XXXIX, Teil II, Heft 1, Berlin 1918. See also the Prussian Geological *Spezialkarten* 1 : 25,000, e.g. Sheet Kleinenberg (Gradabt. 54, sheet 28).

(26) WALTHER PENCK, Op. 10.

(27) Amongst others who do this are A. v. SCHULTZ on the Pamir (*Abhandl.*

hamburg. Kolonialinst., 1916, XXXIII, Reihe C)—the morphological findings, however, leave scarcely any doubt as to there being typical broad folding in the Pamir—and A. PHILIPPSON in Asia Minor (Reisen und Forschungen im westlichen Kleinasien. *P.M.* Erg.-H. 167, 172, 177, 180, 183. 1910–1915). In this latter case, the gap in the observations has in the meantime been partly filled in by the author, and quite a number of assumptions about faults, which till then remained unsubstantiated, have thus been corrected (WALTHER PENCK, Op. 10). Similarly J. G. GRANÖ found himself led to state that the faults constructed by V. A. OBRUTSCHEW and others for the Altai—another broad fold system—were to a great extent non-existent (Les formes du relief dans l'Altai russe et leur genèse. *Fennia* XL, no. 2, Helsingfors 1917). There are many such examples; and the fact that the part played by faults in mountain-building is only now beginning to be cleared up, shows how important it is to discover them and to verify their existence by actual observation.

(28) WALTHER PENCK, Op. 10 and Op. 16. The expression 'broad folding' was first used for individual archings and subsidences, which had tectonically and morphologically, however, only very slight resemblances to folds. These (like the Black Forest and the Vosges, which have been termed 'broad folds') do not occur as folds associated with a system similar in structure, nor are they characterised, as are folds, by the narrowing of their phase with increasing amplitude (see O. WILCKENS, *Grundzüge der tektonischen Geologie*, Jena 1912). E. C. ABENDANON took over the expression, and since there was no precise definition clear of ambiguity to prevent him from doing so, transferred it to arching of any kind and of any order of magnitude (*Die Grossfalten der Erdrinde*, Leiden 1914). Further scientific use of the term has therefore needed primarily a definition, so that it may be used always in the same way and without ambiguity. This definition has been given by the author (see p. 28), and it should be kept to in future.

(29) In any case broad folding indicates a change in the spatial condition of blocks that have been moved. Either their boundaries come closer together because of compression, so that the block undergoes folding, or the boundaries remain the same and the volume of the block is increased by magmatic intrusion, so that again it must develop broad folding. If, on the other hand, a block is divided up into narrow strips, which are displaced with respect to one another, but in a vertical direction only, by the faults separating them, there is no spatial change produced. Thus it implies a fundamental misunderstanding of the tectonic problem if it is considered irrelevant whether or not the movement of the ranges, recognised as broad anticlines, has, with respect to the depressions between them, taken place merely at the fault lines. (A. PHILIPPSON, *P.M.*, 1920, Juli–Aug., p. 175.

(30) See F. KOSSMAT, Die mediterranen Kettengebirge in ihrer Beziehung zum Gleichgewichtszustande der Erdrinde. *A.S.A.W.(m.-p.)*, XXXVIII, no. 2, Leipzig 1921.

(31) A. PENCK, Die Gipfelflur der Alpen. *Sitzungsber. preuss. Akad. Wissensch., math.-physikal. Klasse*, 1919, XVII, p. 256, Berlin 1919.—A. TORNQUIST, Das Erdbeben von Rann an der Save vom 29. Jänner 1917 *Akad.*

Wissensch. Wien, math. nat. Klasse. Mitteil Erdbebenkommission, N.F., no. 52, 1918. The important stratigraphic-tectonic observations made by O. AMPFERER point in the same direction. Über die Bohrung von Rum bei Hall in Tirol. *Jahrb. geol. Staatsanst.* Wien LXXI, Heft 1, 2, p. 71, 1921.

(32) Relevant observations and bibliography have been compiled in WALTHER PENCK, Op. 16.

(33) See the two structural maps on pp. 62 and 94 in WALTHER PENCK, Op. 10.

(34) The same thing occurs in the Variscan mountains. The distribution of the Rotliegende in Germany shows that here the line of folds which developed during the Lower to the Upper Carboniferous period was, until as late as Permian times, divided up into mountain arches, and depressions parallel to the strike. These latter, as relatively sinking areas, received the Rotliegende, and even today can be recognised, by the arrangement and facies of the continental strata, as places of sedimentation of the same type as the bolsons of Argentina, i.e. broad synclines.

(35) For detailed treatment of the processes of weathering, we have to thank van HISE (Treatise on metamorphism. *U.S. geol. Surv. Monogr.* 1904, 47), E. RAMANN (*Bodenkunde,* Berlin 1911), R. LANG (*Verwitterung und Bodenbildung als Einführung in die Bodenkunde,* Stuttgart 1920) who discussed particularly the chemical aspect of the problem. More recent investigations on chemical weathering have been carried out by, amongst others, J. M. VAN BEMMELEN, the founder of modern soil science (Die Verschiedenen Arten der Verwitterung der Silikatgesteine in der Erdrinde. *Zeitschr. anorg. Chem.,* 1910, LXVI, p. 322), H. STREMME (Die Verwitterung der Silikatgesteine. *Landwirtsch. Jahrb.* 1911, XL, p. 326 and elsewhere), P. VAGELER (Physikalische und chemische Vorgänge bei der Bodenbildung. Frühling's *Landw. Zeitg.* 1910, LIX, p. 878), E. BLANCK (Beiträge zur Kenntnis der chemischen und physikalischen Beschaffenheit der Roterden. *Journ. Landw.* 1912, p. 59), H. NIKLAS (*Chemische Verwitterung der Silikate und Gesteine.* Berlin 1912) and others. H. E. BOEKE (*Grundlagen der physikalisch-chemischen Petrographie,* Berlin 1915: D. Die Verwitterung) threw new light upon the physico-chemical side of the question. J. WALTHER (*Das Gesetz der Wüstenbildung,* p. 111, 2. Aufl. Leipzig 1912) was concerned with mechanical weathering in arid regions, B. HÖGBOM devoted an important paper to frost shattering (Über die geologische Bedeutung des Frostes. *Bull. geol. Instn. Univ. Upsala* 1910, IX).

(36) The magnitude of the change in volume depends upon the coefficient of cubic expansion of the rocks and that of the minerals composing them. The data for this, as far as is known at present, have been collected by K. SCHULZ in the *Fortschritten der Mineralogie, Kristallographie und Petrographie* (1914, Bd. IV, p. 337; 1916, V, p. 293; 1920, VI, p. 137). Using MELLARD READE's data as a basis, A. PENCK calculated the surface expansion of a square metre of rock to be 1400 square millimetres for a temperature change of 70° C. (*Morphologie der Erdoberfläche,* Bd. I, p. 203).

(37) With E. PECHUEL-LOESCHE, J. WALTHER attributes the shattering of rock, into fragments of all sizes, to the rapidity with which it has cooled after

U

having been heated by the sun's rays. In deserts, this effect is produced by the sudden downpours of rain which are not infrequent occurrences. In this way cracks develop in the core, as contrasted with the normal result of insolation, the peeling of shells termed desquamation by V. RICHTHOFEN (Das Gesetz der Wüstenbildung, *loc. cit.* [n. 35], p. 131 ff.).

(38) According to P. RANGE, who was able to draw upon a fairly long series of observations for south-west Africa, the variations in the ground temperature for an arid region are 60° [Centigrade] in seven hours in the summer, 50° in five hours in the winter (*Meteorol. Zeitschr.* 1920, Heft 3–4, p. 103. See also J. V. HANN, *Lehrbuch der Meteorologie*, chap. 1, p. 37, 3. Aufl. Leipzig 1915).

(39) Statistics for the conductivity of heat by various rocks are to be found in LANDOLT-BORNSTEIN's *Physikalisch-chemischen Tabellen* (1905) and in WINKELMANN's *Handbuch der Physik*. Experiments by E. LESS show that the conductivity is different not only for different kinds of rock, but also for the same kind of rock from different localities. The following table of conductivities of heat is based upon the conductivity of silver being taken as 1:

Quartz	0·0158	Basalt	0·00673
Granite	0·00757–0·00975	Sandstone	0·00304–0·00814
Syenite	0·00442	Gneiss	0·00578–0·00817
Marble	0·00578–0·00817		

Note that variations in magnitude may be as much as three times the actual value!

(40) W. PENCK, Op. 16, p. 239.

(41) *Zeitschr. anorgan. Chem.* 1912, LXXVII, pp. 384, 435. The pressure in the rock crevices actually remains unaltered and, the volume being constant, ice I appears in addition to ice III. If the cracks widen, as much of modification III increases in volume and changes into I as is necessary for filling up the enlarged space. Thus, there, no frost shattering takes place, but changes of temperature or of space (pressure) are followed merely by an alteration in balance between water, ice I and ice III. Hence R. LANG is incorrect when he considers temperature extremes to be the determining factor in frost weathering also (*loc. cit.* [n. 35], p. 16).

(42) According to BLÜMCKE and S. FINSTERWALDER especially at the bottom of a glacier, where there is rapid alternation between surface moistening and freezing (Zur Frage der Gletschererosion. *Sitzungsber. Kgl. Bayer. Akad. Wissensch., math.-phys. Kl.* XX, p. 435, München 1890). B. HÖGBOM has indicated the extreme geological importance of frost action (*loc. cit.* [n. 35]); J. HIRSCHWALD wrote of his practical experience of frost shattering (*Handbuch der technischen Gesteinsprüfung* 1910).

(43) See, for example, R. LANG, *loc. cit.* [n. 35], p. 10.

(44) *U.S. Dep. Agr. Off. public Roads* 1908, Bull. 28. See also E. RAMANN, *Zentralbl. Min.* 1921, no. 8–9, pp. 233, 266.

(45) In Constantinople, the granite obelisk erected on the Atmeidan by Theodosius the Great (A.D. 346–395) shows how, since his time, lichens have established themselves on the exposed (north-east) side, and have already eaten several millimetres into the rock's polished surface.

(46) Knowledge of this goes back to F. CORNU (Die Bedeutung der Hydrogele im Mineralreich. *Zeitschr. prakt. Geol.* 1909; also *Kolloidzeitschr.* 1909, IV, p. 275). E. RAMANN (*Bodenkunde* 1911) and P. EHRENBERG (*Die Bodenkolloide*, Dresden-Leipzig 1915) gave a detailed account of soil colloids, their properties and their importance.

(47) Not quite true, since all soils from rock reduction are climatic soils, even the rubbly soils of mechanical disintegration. It would be incorrect to speak of soils having a climatic horizon, and to contrast it with the rock horizon below.

(48) The colloidal state is nothing but an uncommonly fine distribution, suspension, of matter. It is not stable, but changes spontaneously, though as a rule extremely slowly, into the crystalline phase. It has been noticed that colloids develop with rapid weathering, crystalloids of a corresponding chemical composition with slow weathering. Adsorption is a phenomenon due to the adhesive force exerted by the surface of each colloidal particle. All these surfaces together form the *inner* surface of the colloid. The smaller the size of the individual colloidal particles, the greater is the inner surface, and the capacity of adsorption increases with this. A. E. MITSCHERLICH gives the following figures:

	Size of the inner surface per gram of the substance sq. metres	Amount of adsorbed water grams
Fine Tertiary sand	1·38	0·034
Loamy sand	56·80	1·40
Sandy loam	84·90	2·09
Mellow loam	121·80	3·00
Strong loamy soil	265·00	6·54
Strong clay from Java	966·70	23·81

On the average about 4 square metres of inner surface will hold 0·1 gram of water, which is in this way prevented from exerting any further chemical or mechanical influence (*Bodenkunde für Land- und Forstwirte*, p. 71, Berlin 1905).

(49) Thus the Mediterranean red earths are by no means the simple residue left from the solution of limestone; see E. BLANCK, Beiträge zur Kenntnis der chemischen und physikalischen Beschaffenheit der Roterden. *Journ. Landw.* 1912 and *G.R.* 1916, VII, p. 57).

(50) E. GULBY, Die 'Humussäuren' im Lichte neuzeitlicher Forschungsergebnisse. *Intern. Mitteil. Bodenkunde* 1915, V, pp. 232, 347.

(51) It is assumed that the sensitive colloidal particles are surrounded by insensitive colloids which are not so easily precipitated. The latter—in our case the humic substances—thus exert *a protective influence* on the former, especially on the hydrated oxides of iron and aluminium.

(52) R. LANG, Versuch einer exakten Klassifikation der Böden in klimatischer und geologische Hinsicht. *Intern. Mitteil. Bodenkunde* 1915, V., p. 312. H. STREMME'S objections (*G.R.* 1917, VII, p. 330) have been met by LANG in

various writings, the last being in his *Bodenkunde* (*loc. cit.* [n. 35]). The dispute does not touch on that aspect of the problem of weathering in which we are interested.

(53) Another part of such substances, leached out under the influence of excessive moisture, goes into the ground water, or is again separated out in the lower horizons of the soil. Iron-pan might be mentioned as an instance of this. H. STREMME calls such zones of enrichment, found beneath the bleached upper layer, *illuvial horizons*; and he considers that in the regions of the earth where precipitation is abundant there are, to be sure, quantitative differences, due to the different mean temperatures, but no qualitative differences in the development of the soil profile (Laterit und Terra rossa als illuvialer horizont humoser Walböden. *G.R.* 1915, V, p. 480).

(54) There seems to be a condition of equilibrium established: $CaCO_3 + CO_2 + H_2O \rightleftarrows Ca(HCO_3)_2$. Such a solution, *saturated* with $CaCO_3$, cannot attack limestone (with which it is in equilibrium) in spite of the presence of free carbon dioxide. A surplus of CO_2 is necessary to make the solution aggressively active again. This is why the solution of calcareous material ceases at the level of the water table even in limestone areas.

(55) K. V. TERZAGHI, Beitrag zur Hydrographie und Morphologie des kroatischen Karstes. *Mitteil. Jahrb. ungar. geol. Reichsanst.* 1913, XX, Heft 6.

(56) Their walls are on the whole smooth, roughened by corrosion in individual cases. A. GRUND earlier reported having made similar observations (Der geographische Zyklus im Karst. *Z.G.E.* 1914).

(57) The preservation of ground moisture is as essential for the process of solution as for that of hydrolytic splitting. This is a second reason why conditions are more favourable in places with a cover of vegetation than where the rock is bare. In the same way, places where the snow lasts for a long time are better off than those where the surface is quickly cleared.

(58) The constantly repeated error that there is no ground water in a desert makes it necessary to stress particularly the fact of its existence, which has been proved on many occasions. (See amongst other references E. KAISER, Die Wassererschliessung in der südlichen Namib Südwestafrikas. *Zeitschr. prakt. Geol.* 1919, XXVII, p. 165.)

(59) E. KAISER, Studien während des Krieges in Südwestafrika. *Z.D.G.G.* 1920, LXXII, Monatsber. no. 1–3 and *Abhandl. Giessener Hochschulgesellsch.* 1920, II.

(60) D. HÄBERLE, Die gitter-, netz- und wabenförmige Verwitterung der Sandsteine. *G.R.* 1915, VI, Heft 4–6, with extensive bibliography.

(61) The way in which the rate of weathering depends upon the area of the inner surface, and its consequential effects on vegetation, is well illustrated in Hawaii. Here the rough vesicular Aa-lava provides a nutritious soil, suitable for plant growth, far more quickly than the non-cellular smooth-surfaced pillow lava of the same chemical composition and of the same age (W. BRIGHAM, The Volcanoes of Mauna Loa and Kilauea. *Mem. Panahi Bishop Mus. Ethnol. and nat. Hist.* Honolulu 1910).

(62) E. DE MARTONNE, *Traité de géographie physique*, Paris 1909.—A.

Rüil, Eine neue Methode auf dem Gebiete der Geomorphologie, *Fortschr. nat.-wiss. Forschung* (E. Abderhalden) 1912, VI.

(63) The increased task can, however, be managed since there is another side to the matter. As the number of divisional planes grows, so does the inner surface, and with it the surface exposed to attack, by chemical agents in particular. Thus in the latter stages of weathering the amount of chemical alteration becomes greater, i.e. more is accomplished in the way of rock reduction, provided the end-product of weathering has not already been developed.

(64) See notes 20 and 22; also WALTHER PENCK, Op. 10.—A. LACROIX, Les latérites de la Guinée et les produits d'altération qui leur sont associés. *Nouv. Arch. Mus. Hist. nat.*, Paris 1914 (5. sér.), V, p. 255.

(65) In the tropics, as in temperate climates, the exceptions seem to be associated with specially flat parts of the country or with places which were, until recently, areas of deposition, not of denudation.

(66) E. RAMANN, *Bodenkunde*, Berlin 1911, p. 313.

(67) E. RAMANN, Die Einwirkung elektrolytarmer Wässer auf diluviale und alluviale Ablagerungen und Böden. *Z.D.G.G.* 1915, LXVII, p. 275.

(68) A. PENCK, Versuch einer Klimaklassifikation auf physio-geographischer Grundlage, *Sitzungber. preuss. Akad. Wissensch., phys.-math. Kl.* 1910, XII, p. 236.

(69) *P.M.* 1878, plate 18.

(70) The colour is connected with the formation of humus, which is favoured by the relatively low annual temperatures, associated with a great deal of moisture. If the humic colloids are adsorptively saturated with mineral salts, they become chemically stable, and are retained in the end-product of weathering, itself yellow, darkening this (the black earths, the calcareous black earths of R. LANG, which with us occur on limestone, and the brown earths of our latitudes). Where there is very thorough soaking, as for example in regions of a somewhat lower annual temperature, the soluble salts are removed from the soil, washed out and even leached from their adsorptive fixation by humic colloids. These latter then become equally soluble, and with them the more sensitive inorganic colloids. Thus part of them goes into the rivers and is lost (bog water, 'black water' rivers). The upper soil horizons become bleached; humus accumulates in the lower ones and frequently the dissolved inorganic colloids, if they have been re-precipitated by salts—especially calcium carbonate—are concentrated there. As a rule this happens near the level of the water table; iron-pan is formed. For the conditions leading to the formation and preservation of humus, see R. LANG, *Bodenkunde, loc. cit.* [n. 35], especially p. 94.

(71) See note 49. In the rainy season, the Mediterranean red earth turns brown, since the red iron oxide takes up water and so changes into the brown hydrated oxide. Also it is in the rainy season that conditions are such as to make the existence of humus possible. It 'dissolves' the sesquioxides of iron and aluminium, which are then precipitated only if there is a plentiful supply of electrolytes, e.g. calcium carbonate. In the dry season the humus is de-

composed, and the sesquioxides remain insoluble. Hence it is particularly on limestone that they accumulate (though they do also occur elsewhere) and form the well-known terra rossa.

(72) M. BAUER showed that this was the origin of the laterite in the Seychelles (Beiträge zur Geologie der Seychellen, insbesondere zur Kenntnis des Laterits. *N. Jahrb. Min. usw.* 1898, LXXXVIII, p. 163 and *ibid.* 1907, p. 33). Not everything which is red and is called laterite in the tropics is a pure hydrated oxide, as is shown by H. BÜCKING, among others, in his analyses (Zur Geologie von Nord- und Ostsumatra. *Beitr. Geol. Ostasiens und Australiens* VIII, Heft I, Leiden 1904). See further F. W. CLARKE, The Data of Geochemistry. *U.S. geol. Surv. Bull.* 330, Ser. E, p. 419, Washington 1908.

The earlier view, still held by H. STREMME (see note 53, also H. STREMME, Die Entstehung des Laterits. *Z.G.E.*, no. 2, 1917, and elsewhere) that laterite is developed under a cover of tropical forest and so is an illuvial horizon beneath an upper layer rich in humus, does not seem tenable. Red lateritic soils have indeed been reported from the forest-clad tropical mountains of New Guinea and the Sunda Islands; but according to R. LANG's recent investigations they are there overlain by brown and black earths, and so developed under climatic conditions different from those of the present day. Laterite and analogous tropical red clays are formations belonging to warm belts with pronounced wet and dry seasons (e.g. the regions of light monsoon forest or tropical savanas). If they are today found in areas of tropical rain-forest nearer the equator, there is reason for concluding that some climatic variation has taken place (R. LANG, *Zentralbl. Min. usw.* 1915, no. 5, p. 148; as to further literature, see *Bodenkunde, loc. cit.* [n. 35]).

(73) R. LANG has rightly stressed this. The literature on tropical humus soils, peat bogs, and 'black water' rivers is listed in his *Bodenkunde*. I, too, have seen only dark humus soils in the tropical rain-forests on the eastern slopes of the cordillera of north-west Argentina and the forested districts of the Hawaian Islands.

(74) Humic colloids are also present where exuding water gives rise to patches of luxuriant vegetation—though not on the cultivated oases. Their presence here is connected with the slowing down of organic decay brought about by the high content of salts (see R. LANG, *Bodenkunde, loc. cit.* [n. 35], p. 83).

(75) E. W. HILGARD was the first to recognise the close connection between climate and type of soil, pointing it out for North America (Über den Einfluss des Klimas auf die Bildung und die Zusammensetzung des Bodens. *Wollnys Forsch. Gebiet Agrikultur-physik* 1893, XVI, p. 82. The same: *Soils*, New York 1906). K. GLINKA attempted the same thing for Russia (*Die Typen der Bodenbildung*, Berlin 1914) and E. RAMANN was able to extend to the whole of Europe the knowledge thus gained (*Bodenkunde*, Berlin 1911, p. 521). Since then attempts have frequently been made to discover similar connections over the world as a whole. The credit for carrying this through successfully belongs to R. LANG, and his findings were ultimately presented in a comprehensive

manner in his *Bodenkunde, loc. cit.* [n. 35]. H. L. F. MEYER also gave a cursory treatment (Klimazonen der Verwitterung usw. *G.R.* 1916, VII, Heft 5–6, p. 193), and H. STREMME showed for Germany in what a sensitive way the soil formation reacts to relatively small climatic differences, and how varied therefore are soil types over even a small area (Die Verbreitung der klimatischen Bodentypen in Deutschland. *Branca-Festschrift*, p. 16, Leipzig 1914).

(76) Red colouration is by no means characteristic of desert formations, as is sometimes thought. In the desert iron, which gives the colour to red products of weathering, is more often in the form of crumbs of limonite which do not affect the colour of the detritus from arid weathering (E. W. HILGARD, Die Böden arider und humider Länder. *Intern. Mitteil. Bodenkunde* 1912, p. 240).

(77) The conclusions of R. LANG (see note 38 [? 35]) and J. WALTHER (*Das Gesetz der Wüstenbildung*, 2. Aufl. 1912, pp. 297, 298) lead in this direction.

(78) 'Premature' here means: before a little piece of rock has, through progressive reduction, become so mobile that it is capable of spontaneous migration.

(79) T. S. HUNT seems already to have noticed this (The decay of rocks geologically considered. *A.J.S.* 1883, XXVI, p. 190), and J. C. BRANNER reported observations on it (Decomposition of rocks in Brazil. *B.G.S.A.* 1896, VII, p. 255).

(80) If the regular arrangement is not disturbed owing to thorough-going transportation by rivulets or rainwash.

(81) He considers the seas of rock to be the result of a 'periglacial facies of weathering' (*C. R. Congr. géol. int.* 1910. Stockholm 1912).

(82) B. HÖGBOM, Über die geologische Bedeutung des Frostes, *loc. cit.* [n. 35].—W. SALOMON, Die Bedeutung der Solifluktion für die Erklärung deutscher Landschafts- und Bodenformen. *G.R.* 1916, VII, Heft 1–2, p. 30. G. KLEMM introduced a vital qualification, well-based upon actual observation; but he, too, considers that the rock seas are on the whole Pleistocene formations. (Über die Entstehung der Felsenmeere des Felsberges und anderer Orte im Odenwald. *Notizbl. Ver. Erdk. usw.* Darmstadt 1917, V Folge, Heft 3, p. 3, 1918.)

(83) Die Blockfelder im östlichen Vogelsberg. *Ber. Versamml. Niederrhein. geol. Ver.* 1916, p. 29. MEYER seems to take the block seas to be fossil formations, since as a rule they cannot have been derived from precipices or crags (*loc. cit.* [n. 75], p. 31). Closer examination of the substratum leads without difficulty to the conclusion that not every accumulation of blocks has originated as scree or can be traced back to it. The further argument, that the formation of block fields is brought to an end if they become forest-clad, is thus invalid (*loc. cit.*, p. 44).

(84) H. SCHMITTENNER, Die Oberflächengestaltung des nördlichen Schwarzwaldes. *Heidelberger Dissertation*. Karlsruhe 1913.

(85) This mistake is obviously traceable to the common confusion (found also in other connections) of mechanical reduction with mechanical weathering.

(86) Thus it is wrong to say, as PASSARGE believed could be done, that there

is now no longer any movement within block seas (Wüstenformen in Deutschland. *G.Z.* 1911, p. 579). Seas of blocks and immobility are, as is shown
by the whole state of affairs, conceptions almost mutually exclusive. As
they move, the components rub one another down, and there may be a
scratching of susceptible rock fragments. The scratched pieces of hornstone,
which O. H. ERDMANNSDÖRFER found embedded in the material of some of the
streams of granite blocks in the Harz Mountains, may be cited as illustration
(Über Blockströme am Ostrand des Brockengranitgebietes. 7. *Jahresberichtd.
Niedersächs, Geol. Ver.* Hannover 1914, p. 53). The scratches are too indis-
tinct to be considered as of glacial origin; and, still more important, the deposit
as a whole shows no connection with any source of supply possessing glacial
forms. Now such a connection is absolutely essential for proving the glacial
origin of a mass of rubble or blocks. Cf. C. CHELIUS (Die Bildung der Felsenmeere in Odenwald. *Z.D.G.G.* 1896, p. 644) who took slopes of moving
material, masses of rubble and block fields to be moraines, and was corrected
by G. GÖTZINGER who recognised their pseudoglacial character (*Geogr.
Abhandl.* 1907, IX, Heft 1, p. 84).

(87) W. PENCK, Op. 10. The same phenomenon is also to be seen, excellently
developed, on the subdued relief of the granitic summits (not on the slopes) of
the Laoshan in Shantung.

(88) It is not entirely superfluous to stress this, since the transporting force
and the transporting medium are occasionally mistaken for one another. See
the views of MEYER-HARRASSOWITZ on the movement of blocks of stone (Die
Blockfelder im östlichen Vogelsberg, *loc. cit.* [n. 83], p. 44: 'Transport by the
force of gravity is in most cases excluded on account of the flatness of the
slopes.' p. 45: 'The greater part was set in motion and slid downwards along
the very slightest of slopes, under the influence of the tjaele. . . .'

(89) *Morphologie der Erdoberfläche*, I, p. 202. Stuttgart 1894.

(90) It is self-evident that Nature shows no sharp distinction between mass-
movement and mass-transport. If, for example, in a gravitational stream of
the first type, the amount of the water assisting the movement is increased,
and if this increase gains the upper hand, then mass-movement changes into
mass-transport. Rainwash by surface run-off, considered by A. PENCK to be
still mass-movement, belongs of course by its nature to the second type of
gravitational stream. It will not, therefore, be discussed till a later chapter.

(91) Therefore, even when at a loss for a better term, we cannot speak of
soil movement when we mean mass-movement. (G. BRAUN, Über Boden-
bewegungen. 11. *Jahresber. geogr. Gesellsch. Greifswld* 1908).

(92) So also, in the Valle del Bove on Etna, the wall-like appearance of
basalt dykes, standing up above the surrounding basalt tuffs and unconsolidated material also of the same composition, is due not so much to a difference
in resistance to weathering as to their very different degree of cohesion.
Greater quantities of loose material than of massive dyke rock move away in
unit time—helped sometimes by rainwash. This is because it is unconsolidated. It is not noticeably more weathered than the basalt, of which only small
amounts are so reduced as to be made mobile in the same interval of time. The

choice of this as a text-book example of differential weathering is not a particularly happy one.

(93) The mobility characteristic of a rock itself is undoubtedly superior to the acquired mobility which comes from reduction. However little it may resist weathering, there always seems difficulty in denuding strong rock, and so this stands out prominently from surrounding material of greater original mobility no matter how resistant to weathering the latter may be. It is incorrect to use the terms hard and soft for rocks which it is respectively difficult and easy to denude, since this does not take into account that what constitutes the difference in resistance to denudation is colloidal content, cohesion and resistance to mechanical or chemical weathering. It does not matter at all whether or not the rock is ?? coherent?? (*aber keinesweg der Kohärenz*).

(94) Increase of friction, brought about by increase in the velocity of the movement, may therefore be neglected in this case.

(95) M. BLANCKENHORN still describes soil movement as slow slumping. Theorie der Bewegungen des Erdbodens. *Z.D.G.G.* 1896, p. 382.

(96) The friction is equal to the product of the coefficient of friction ρ and the pressure exerted at right angles to the substratum: mg cos α, where m = the mass, g = the acceleration due to gravity, α the angle of slope of the substratum. When $\alpha = 90°$, then ρ mg cos $\alpha = 0$.

(97) The downward movement definitely comes to a stop when the friction has the same magnitude as the component of gravity causing the movement. This is g sin α and depends upon the angle of slope α. The angle of slope at which this equality occurs, is called the angle of friction. It is given by the equation ρg cos $\alpha' = $ g sin α' where ρ = the coefficient of friction, g cos α' = the pressure exerted at right angles to the substratum, the inclination of which is given by the angle α'. The condition for the actual cessation of mass-movement follows from this, viz. when $\rho = $ tan α'. Thus the less the friction, and the more effective the factors reducing friction, the gentler will be the slope along which the material can still move.

(98) S. PASSARGE, Physiologische Morphologie. *Mitteil. geogr. Gesellsch. Hamburg* 1914, XXVIII and Geogr. Zeitschr. 1912, Heft 2.

(99) K. SAPPER gives an account of slopes covered with tropical forest which reach an inclination of as much as 70°! (Über Abtragungsvorgänge in den regenfeuchten Tropen und ihre morphologischen Wirkungen. *G.Z.* 1914, XX, Heft I, p. 5).

(100) W. BEHRMANN, Der Sepik und sein Stromgebiet. *Mitteil. deutschen Schutzgebieten*, Ergänzungsheft 12, Berlin 1917 and Z.G.E., No. 1–2, p. 44, 1921.

(101) Such profiles are most likely to be found on slopes which decrease in steepness from above downwards. They show that material, taking its rise from the upper parts of the slope, is moving down more quickly than it can be changed by reduction into a more advanced stage. It then, on the less inclined parts of the slope, forms a facies which not only contrasts with that occurring in the profile of reduced rock developing there, but also ceases to show any correlation with the slope of the substratum. Such ab-

normal profiles make it easy to recognise the slow downward movement of material; and it was through them that this movement was first detected (G. Götzinger, Beiträge zur Entstehung der Bergrückenformen. *Geogr. Abhandl.* 1907, IX, Heft 1). They are almost the rule where slopes are not too gently inclined and have resistant bands outcropping in them above rocks that are reaching the state of mobility more easily. With the more rapid disappearance of the latter, these bands also crumble away, are broken down, and migrate comparatively quickly even under a cover of vegetation. Naturally, the rubble thus developing beneath such a cover shows at the outset but few signs of chemical alteration; these are acquired only during the course of its migration. Thus it may easily be confused with products of mechanical weathering, especially if rock from which it comes is on the whole as little susceptible to chemical weathering as the German Triassic sediments (S. Passarge, *Mitteil. geogr. Gesellsch. Hamburg* 1914, XXVIII). The extreme freshness, occasionally shown by e.g. Muschelkalk rubble beneath a vegetation cover, had been taken as indicating that its origin was Pleistocene frost weathering. This Muschelkalk is one of the most widely distributed materials in Thuringia and south Germany in those formations which are due to mechanical rock reduction (not mechanical weathering). It is still far from showing those changes which lead in one of two directions: either to solution, or to the precipitation in increasing amounts of colloids, both inorganic and humic, especially on limestone. These processes have already, at the present day, caused considerable alteration in Pleistocene limestone rubble; and they could not have failed to mark this also with the imprint of powerful chemical weathering.

(102) Johnston Lavis, The Eruption of Vesuvius in April 1906. *Sci. Trans. roy. Soc.* Dublin 1909, IX, part 8, p. 139.—A. Lacroix, *C. R. Acad. Sci.* Paris 1906, CXLII, p. 1244.—F. Perret, *A.J.S.* 1909, XXVIII, p. 413.

(103) The saggings somewhat frequently mentioned as a special form of slumping are merely early stages of this—where, for one reason or another, the transition from a sliding to a flowing movement, by which the moving system breaks down into a stream, has not occurred or is rudimentary.

(104) The earliest observations on this were communicated by Canon Moseley and Charles Davison (Note on the movement of scree material. *Q.J.G.S.* 1888, XLIV, pp. 232, 825); see A. Penck, *Morphologie der Erdoberfläche* I, p. 221.

(105) The differences in volume between the dry and moist conditions are as follows:

	dry	moist
Sandy soils	1	1·00
Loess soils	1	1·13
Calcareous loams	1	1·29
Soils rich in humus	1	1·34
Peaty soils	1	1·38

F. Haberlandt's results (Frühling's Landw. Zeitg. XXVI, p. 481) quoted by E. Ramann, *Bodenkunde* 1911, p. 327.

(106) The reason for this is that when ice crystals are formed by freezing, their major axes are oriented in the direction of the radiation, that is at right angles to the exposed surface (E. RAMANN, *Bodenkunde*, p. 325). This is very beautifully shown by the ice on ridge crests, which often raises rock particles several centimetres, and, where the upper surface of the soil is inclined, drops them again lower down the slope (see CHARLES DAVISON, On the creeping of the soil cap through the action of Frost. *G.M.*, n.s. 1889, dec. III, vol. VI, p. 255 and A. PENCK, *Morphologie der Erdoberfläche* I, p. 221).

(107) This is due to the high degree of mobility which is also responsible for the fact that, other things being equal, flatter surfaces are formed by wet than by dry material (see THOULET, *C. R. Acad. Sci.* Paris 1887, CIV, p. 1537). In the rainy tropics, material migrating from the steeper slopes is, according to K. SAPPER, often already in a pulpy condition and flows ('flowing soil').

(108) It is not possible to decide whether the higher summer temperatures have any effect. It was found, at any rate in the Atacama Desert, that insolation rubble was as thoroughly mobile in summer as in winter (WALTHER PENCK, Op. 16).

(109) *Morphologie der Erdoberfläche, loc. cit.* [n. 1], I, chap. III. A summary of more recent literature from 1903 to 1912 is given by A. RÜHL, *Geogr. Jahrb.* XXXV, p. 81; XXXVII, p. 315.

(110) *Über Bodenbewegungen, loc. cit.* [n. 91].

(111) See WALTHER PENCK, *Naturgewalten in Hochgebirge*, Stuttgart, 1912.

(112) Following A. HEIM (*Neujahrsbl. naturf. Gesellsch.* Zürich 1874), J. GEIKIE (*Mountains, their Origin and Decay*, Edinburgh 1913) dealt with this.

(113) As a rule, bare dome-shaped mountains are made of granite or similarly massive rock, frequently characterised by a scale-like type of jointing, the result of primary contraction. This seems to be true in the case of the dome-like mountains in Nubia (J. WALTHER, *Das Gesetz der Wüstenbildung*. 2. Aufl. 1912, pp. 108, 135), the granite domes of the arid Namib (e.g. Kainsberg; H. CLOOS, Der Erongo. *Beitr. geol. Erforsch. deutsch. Schutzgebiete*, Heft 17, p. 148, Berlin 1919), the Rhodesian 'Matopos' (A. PENCK, Südafrika und Sambesifälle. *G.Z.* 1906, XII, Heft 11, p. 604) and the domes which keep on recurring in South America, where they are called 'Pan de Azucar'. In Uruguay, for example, their convex profiles afford a marked contrast to the non-granitic inselbergs of the surrounding peneplane (see plate 1, fig. 2 in K. WALTER, *Revista del Inst. N. de Agronomia*, Montevideo 1919, 2nd Ser. No. 3). On the other hand, the anticline-like structure of the domed mountains on the Bay of Rio de Janeiro is interpreted as resulting from some process of folding. The scaling, which makes the domed structure apparent, is in this case attributed by B. BRANDT to slipping of the highly mobile products resulting from the chemical weathering of the gneissose granite. This process, as it works inwards from the outside, follows the structure of successive shells (Die tallosen Berge an der Bucht von Rio de Janeiro, *Mitteil. geogr. Gesellsch. Hamburg* 1917, XXX). The shell-like scaling of the granite domes in the Sierra Nevada may also be attributed, in all probability, to the relief of tension

and so to the tensions themselves, within the rock: the shells also run parallel to the outer surface of the rock in the wall of the U-shaped Yosemite valley which cuts one of these domes in half. Its exfoliation depends upon dynamic conditions in the same way as the exfoliation of rock laminae often noticed in quarries and on the walls of mining galleries (G. K. GILBERT, Domes and Dome Structure in the High Sierra. *B.G.S.A.* 1904, XV, p. 29 and *Bull. U.S. geol. Surv.* 1907, No. 113, p. 42). R. ARNOLD connects the scaling of the small domes of massive conglomerate in California with tensions brought about by an increase in volume as a result of chemical weathering (*J.G.* 1907 XV, No. 6, p. 560). Thus it is not right to speak of climatic conditions being responsible for mountain domes of rock in the sense of their being confined to regions where rock reduction is by insolation. Rather is it the properties of the rock with which the form is connected genetically. The removal of the loosened material generally takes place as migration of individual separate rock particles.

(114) Conditions for the accumulation of scree are the same as for that of loose volcanic products, which have been experimentally followed out by G. LINCK (Über die äussere Form und den inneren Bau der Vulkane mit einem Anhang über die Dünen. *N. Jahrb. Min. usw.* 1907, Festband, p. 91). The superficial slope of the accumulation is not the greatest angle which the loose material in question can support, but is smaller than this and corresponds to the figure of rolling. The steepness of this latter increases as the size of grain decreases; and the shape of the upper surface of scree conforms to this law. See A. PENCK, *Morphologie, loc. cit.* [n. 1], I, p. 220; for the slopes found on talus: Fr. J. BARGMANN, Der jüngste Schutt der nördlichen Kalkalpen. *Veröffentl. Gesellsch. Erdk.* Leipzig 1895, p. 18 and A. PIWOWAR, Über Maximalböschungen trockener Schuttkegel und Schutthalden. *Vierteljahrsschr. naturf. Gesellsch. Zürich* 1903, XLVIII, p. 335; on the relationship of screes to alluvial cones: M. GORTANI, Materiali per lo studio delle forme di accumulamento *I. Mem. Geogr. Suppl. alla Riv. geogr. ital.,* No. 20, p. 339, Florence 1912.

(115) B. HÖGBOM is the latest to point out that sloping rock faces underlie screes (Über die geologische Bedeutung des Frostes. *Bull. geol. Instn. Univ.* Upsala 1914, XII).

(116) A. HEIM, Über Bergstürze. *Neujahrsbl. naturf. Gesellsch. Zürich* 1882, LXXXIV.

(117) A. PENCK and E. BRÜCKNER, *Die Alpen im Eiszeitalter,* pp. 348, 592, 630, 913, 933, 1039, 1118, etc. Leipzig 1909. The same is true for the San Juan Mountains, Colorado: E. HOWE, Landslides in the San Juan Mountains, Colorado, *U.S. geol. Surv. Prof. Paper* 1909, 67.

(118) The smallest inclination that the slip plane must possess, so as just to prevent movement after the removal of cohesion, is that of the angle of friction (see note 97); the greater the mass of overlying rock, the less is this angle. Thus a slope is undermined if the planes of least cohesion are inclined more steeply than the corresponding angle of friction, but less steeply than the surface gradient in the same direction (A. PENCK, *Morphologie, loc. cit.*

[n. 1], I, p. 223). The undermining can be brought about by running water (erosion) or by wave action, but it may also be produced by human interference. Thus it was the working of a quarry that brought the catastrophe at Elm to a head. The explosions in the quarry seem further to have caused a great loosening of the whole rock complex which later slid down (E. Buss and A. Heim, *Der Bergsturz von Elm*. Zürich 1881). Similarly, explosions are said to have contributed to the slumping and caving in that occurred during the cutting of the Panama Canal (E. Howe, Landslides and the sinking of ground above mines. *C. R. Congr. géol. intern.* Canada 1913, p. 775.—D. F. MacDonald, Excavation Deformations. *ibid.*, p. 779).

(119) V. Turnau, *Beiträge zur Geologie der Berner Alpen. Diss.* Bern 1906.

(120) The release of falls of rock and slumping is quite often due to earthquake shocks. Thus the great landslide on Dobratsch was set in motion by the earthquake of 1348 (A. Till, *Mitteil. k.k. geogr. Gesellsch.* Wien 1907, L, p. 534); and on the occasion of the Assam earthquake of 1897, the steep slopes of virgin forest were, for a great distance around, deprived of their cover of vegetation because the underlying mantle of soil had slipped down (R. D. Oldham, Report on the Great Earthquake of 12th June 1897. *Geol. Surv. India*, Mem. XXIX, p. 119, Calcutta 1899). E. Howe, *loc. cit.* [n. 117, 118] and W. Cross traced the landslides in several parts of the western United States of North America back to earthquakes as the essential factor (Geology of the Rico Mountains, *U.S. geol. Surv.* 21. Ann. Rep. 1900, II, chap. V, p. 129).

(121) E. Richter, Der Bergsturz an der Bocca di Brenta. *Mitteil. deutsch. u. österr. Alpenvereins*, LXXXV, p. 72.—E. Howe, San Juan Mountains, *loc. cit.* [n. 117].

(122) On Vesuvius in 1906 (see note 14), at the eruption of Bandaisan (S. Sekiya and J. Kikuchi. *Journ. Coll. Sci. Imp. Univ.* Japan 1889, III, part II, p. 91), at the eruptions of Mont Pelée and the Soufrière, 1902 (A. Lacroix, Paris 1904.—E. O. Hovey, *B.G.S.A.* 1904, XV, p. 566), etc.

(123) P. Gröber, Informe sobre las causas que han producido las crescientes del Rio Colorado (Territorios del Neuquén y la Pampa) en 1914, Bol. No. 11, Ser. B, *Direccion gal. de Minas etc.*, Buenos Aires 1916.

(124) The landslide at Golma in British Garhwal. *Selections Rec. Govt. India. Public Works Dep.*, serial 30, Vol. CCCXXIV, Calcutta 1896. See also Walther Penck, *Naturgewalten im Hochgebirge*. 1912.

(125) A. Heim, Der alte Bergsturz von Flims (Graubündner Oberland). *Jahrb. schweiz. Alpenklub* 1883, XVIII, p. 295.

(126) Tarnuzzer, Geologische Beobachtungen während des Baues der rätischen Bahn bei Chur und Reichenau. *Jahresber. naturf. Gesellsch. Graubündens* 1896, N.F., XXXIX, p. 55. See also A. Penck and E. Brückner, *Die Alpen im Eiszeitalter, loc. cit.*, p. 293 and R. Schwinner, Der Mt. Spinale bei Campiglio etc. *Mitteil. geol. Gesellsch. Wien* 1912, V, p. 128.

(127) Sven v. Hedin, *Durch Asiens Wüsten*, I, p. 76 and elsewhere. Leipzig 1899.—The same, *Im Herzen von Asien*, Bd. II, pp. 352, 453, and illustrations on pp. 440, 442, 444, 446, etc. Leipzig 1903.—The same, *Trans-*

himalaja, Bd. I, p. 80 and elsewhere. Leipzig 1909.—W. RICKMER RICKMERS, *The Duab of Turkestan*, Cambridge 1913. The phenomenon of 'flowing rock' seems to be developed on a grand scale in Tibet, as can be seen from the reports of SVEN HEDIN (*Southern Tibet*, III, p. 301, etc. Stockholm 1917) and A. TAFEL (*Meine Tibetreise*, Bd. I, p. 323; Bd. II, chap XI, and the excellent photographs, e.g. Plate 67, etc. Berlin 1914). Here it is associated with the onset of the monsoon rains and with snow melt. A. V. SCHULTZ presumed that such relationships held for the Pamirs also (*Abhandl. hamburg. Kolonialinst.* 1916, XXXIII, Reihe C, p. 176). It must, however, be pointed out that in Central Asia, too, it is only in belts of limited area that the movement of rock waste coincides with the temporary snow cover and in general with the more copious precipitation which makes 'rock flow' possible. The more usual feature is growing accumulation of dry rubble, especially in the lower-lying parts of the highlands which are formed by the welding together of the Central Asiatic system of mountain chains. This is linked with neither the climatic differences—semi-arid to completely arid—nor the winter snow-line, but with those parts which have slopes of a low average gradient, such as prevail over the whole of Tibet. It follows from this that in Central Asia also, besides the flow of rock waste soaked through with water, there is also slow migration of material in the dry state; and indeed that there this represents the more usual predominant form of denudation. B. HÖGBOM classes the phenomena with polar solifluction. But if the characteristic of that is that it occurs on a constantly frozen, more deep-seated layer of the soil, then most of the semi-arid 'rock flow' is not solifluction (B. HÖGBOM, Die geologische Bedeutung des Frostes, *loc. cit.* [n. 35]).

(128) M. FRIEDERICHSEN, Forschungsreise in den Zentralen Tienschan. *Mitteil. geogr. Gesellsch. Hamburg* 1904, XX.—E. MACHATSCHEK (Der westliche Tienschan, *P.M.* 1912, Ergänzungsh. 176, p. 73) shows a picture of such a stream of wet rubble and describes the blocking of whole valleys by rock waste which has moved in from the sides. This is a feature frequently found in the Atacama Desert also (W. PENCK, Op. 16).—M. CONWAY deals with the filling in of depressions between the mountain ranges of the Asiatic Highlands; and—on the whole quite justifiably—ascribes it almost exclusively to streams of rubble and mud. *G.J.* 1893, II.

(129) See SVEN HEDIN, *Southern Tibet, loc. cit.* [n. 127], pp. 254, 256, 257, 277, 279, etc., especially Vol. III, chaps. 33–36. Also R. W. PUMPELLY, Physiography of Central Asian deserts and oases. *Washington Carnegie Inst. Public.*, No. 73, pp. 243, 253 ff.—The same author, Physiographic Observations between Syr Darya and Lake Kara Kul, on the Pamir in 1903. *Ibid.* No. 26, pp. 123, 130 ff.—E. HUNTINGTON, The Basin of Eastern Persia. *Ibid.* No. 26, pp. 219, 250 ff.—W. T. BLANDFORD, On the nature and probable origin of the superficial deposits in the valleys and deserts of Central Persia. *Q.J.G.S.* 1873, XXIX, p. 493.—E. PECHUEL-LOESCHE speaks of the Damara Highland as of a land drowned in rubble (quoted by S. PASSARGE, *Südafrika*, p. 95. Leipzig 1908). See also the writings mentioned in Note 127.

(130) Wüste und Steppe, *G.Z.* 1916, XXII, p. 129. G. NACHTIGAL draws

attention to the fact that there are often surfaces of serir stretching out at the lower end of the hamada, and it might well be thought that these surfaces are covered with derivatives from the hamada which after migration have been left in their present position (*Sahara und Sudan* 1879, I, p. 53).

(131) SVEN V. HEDIN, *Zu Land nach Indien*, II, p. 325. Leipzig 1910.— Cl. LEBLING, Ergebnisse der Forschungsreisen Prof. E. Stromers in den Wüsten Agyptens, III. *Abhandl. Bayer. Akad. Wissensch.* München 1919, *math.-phys. Kl.* XXIX, Abt. 1.

(132) J. WALTHER, *Das Gesetz der Wüstenbildung*, 2. Aufl. 1912, pp. 189–192.

(133) There is a continuous series of phenomena intermediate between this free mass-movement and mass-transport, which it can be called when the amount of solid matter is less than that of the water, as in the case of 'Muren'.* It is therefore scarcely possible to draw a dividing line, and there is little point in doing so. The disastrous mud streams caused by volcanic eruptions form one special group in the series. They were observed on Vesuvius in 1906, on Mont Pelée and the Soufrière etc. in 1902, and are quite characteristic of Javanese volcanic outbursts (see T. ANDERSON and J. S. FLETT, Report on the eruptions of the Soufrière etc. 1902. *Phil. Trans. roy. Soc.* [A. 200], London 1903.—F. JUNGHUHN, *Java*, Bd. II (translated by J. K. Hasskarl, Leipzig 1859).—R. D. M. VERBEEK and R. FENNEMA, *Description géol. de Java et Madoura.* Amsterdam 1896). They arouse great interest because of the extent of the erosion, the scraping out and the valley deepening which they accomplish (with regard to this, see E. O. HOVEY, *B.G.S.A.* 1909, XX, p. 409).

(134) Observations are extremely numerous. Amongst many others, reference may be made to G. GÖTZINGER, Bergrückenformen, *loc. cit.* [n. 101].— A. PENCK and E. BRÜCKNER, *Die Alpen im Eiszeitalter*, *loc. cit.*—W. BEHR-MANN, Die Landschaften Rumäniens, *Z.G.E.* Berlin 1919, Nos. 1–2, p. 29. —A. PENCK, *Morphologie der Erdoberfläche*, *loc. cit.* [n. 1], I, p. 226.—G. BRAUN, Beiträge zur Morphologie des nördlichen Apennin II. *Z.G.E.* Berlin 1907, p. 464.—R. ALMAGIÁ, Studi geografici sulle frane in Italia. *Soc. geogr. Ital.* Mem. XIII, Rome 1907 and *G.Z.* 1910, XVI, Heft 5, p. 272. Repetition on several occasions at the same place, and continuance of the process over whole decades has been described by A. HEIM amongst others (Die Boden-bewegungen von Campo im Maggiatal, Kanton Tessin. *Vierteljahrsschr. naturf. Gesellsch. Zürich* 1898, XLIII) and H. SCHARDT (L'éboulement du Grugnay près Chamoson, Valais. *Bull. Soc. murithienne Sci. nat. Valais*, XXXIV, p. 205, Sion 1907) etc.

(135) Regular recurrence of various forms of the slumping type of land-slide has, for example in Italy, led to their receiving special names from the inhabitants of the district, such as 'frane', 'lame' (Almagiá, *loc. cit.* [n. 134]). In the semi-arid regions, too, with their scanty vegetation, the widespread occurrence of slumping is shown, for example, by the processes going on in the Mexican Cretaceous and Tertiary areas and in the south-western states of U.S.A. Thus in the Colorado Canyon district, landslides are important and

[* Wet avalanches of earthy material occurring in the Alps.]

characteristic features of the landscape (W. M. DAVIS, An excursion to the Grand Canyon of the Colorado. *Bull. Mus. of comparative Zoology* 1901, XXXVIII, p. 107, Geol. Ser. V, No. 4).

(136) See Notes 99, 100, 107. The significance of slumping in the tropics has been stressed by J. C. BRANNER (Decomposition of rocks in Brazil. *B.G.S.A.* 1896, VII), W. VOLZ (*Nordsumatra*, Bd. I, Berlin 1909; Bd. II, 1912), J. ROMANES (*Q.J.G.S.* 1912, p. 103), B. BRANDT (*loc. cit.* [n. 113]), R. D. OLDHAM (*loc. cit.* [n. 120]) and others in addition to those that have been previously mentioned.

(137) Undercutting naturally brings about slumping on the flatter slopes also. It is not only running water which helps to bring this about; but any interruption of the forest by wind devastation or the tracks of wild beasts, any cutting for roads and railways, is followed in the tropics by landslides. SAPPER, BEHRMANN and J. C. BRANNER have specially drawn attention to this. The difficulties encountered in the construction of the Panama Canal brought this out clearly (D. F. MACDONALD, *Annual Report on the Isthmian canal commission*, Appendix E, p. 205, Washington 1912).

(138) W. PENCK, Op. 13. Whenever there has been a downpour, water runs off rapidly and in great quantities along furrows trenched in the slowly flowing material. These, however, do not persist the whole time; frequently, as the rock waste flows together again, they become closed up, leaving no trace, only to appear afresh in other places. In this way, water trickling in rills promotes and accelerates mass-transport, first by carrying away solid matter, and then by causing more rapid movement of successive fragments of rock down the steep sides of their rain-furrows. This co-operation of running water and mass-movement can be followed specially well on flattish slopes, where there are very great differences between the speed of running water and that of rock waste. It is obvious that the prerequisite for this process is the vulnerability and actual damaging of the vegetation cover.

(139) *Q.J.G.S.* 1904, LX, p. 243.

(140) A preliminary paper on the geology of the Cascade Mountains. *U.S. geol. Surv.* 1900, 20. Ann. rep. II, p. 193.

(141) G. BRAUN, Zur Morphologie des Volterrano. *G.Z.E.* 1905, p. 771.— J. GIRARD, *Les Falaises de la Manche*. Paris 1907. On the Channel coast the undercutting of cliffs is partly due to the direct action of breakers. The scarps which bound the oases of the Libyan Desert and border the valley of the Nile also recede in consequence of slow crumbling away and slipping. Cl. LEBLING considers undercutting by wind to be responsible for this (*loc. cit.* [n. 131], p. 34), but this is certainly not correct in so generalised a form.

(142) WALTHER PENCK, Op. 16, p. 44.

(143) F. X. SCHAFFER, Das Miozän von Eggenburg. *Abhandl. geol. R.-A.* Wien 1914, XXII, Heft 4.

(144) WALTHER PENCK, Op. 10, pp. 46, 47.

(145) J. SÖLCH, Epigenetische Erosion und Denudation. *G.R.* 1918, IX, Heft 7–8, p. 161.

(146) R. SERNANDER, Flytjord i svenska fjälltrakter. *Geol. Fören. i Stock-*

holm Förhandl. 1905, p. 42. J. GEIKIE has already pointed out the possibility of such a kind of movement in frost rubble, and has made use of it for explaining masses of fossil rubble—now apparently motionless—found far from their places of origin (*The Great Ice Age* 1894). He also, in this connection, referred to the masses of limestone rubble in Gibraltar, that have repeatedly and recently been interpreted as relics of Pleistocene rubble which, reduced by frost, is supposed to have flowed in this manner of polar solifluction from the region of supply. Taking into account the latitude and altitude of Gibraltar, both these suggestions seem very hazardous.

(147) J. G. ANDERSON, Solifluction, a component of subaerial denudation. *J.G.* 1906, XIV, p. 91. For detailed investigations we have to thank BERTIL HÖGBOM (Über die geologische Bedeutung des Frostes, *loc. cit.* [n. 35]; Einige Illustrationem zu den geologischen Wirkungen des Frostes auf Spitzbergen. *Bull. geol. Instn. Univ. Upsala* 1910, IX), J. FRÖDIN (Beobachtungen über den Einfluss der Pflanzendecke auf die Bodentemperatur. *Lunds Univ. Årsskr.* 1913, N.F., Afd. 2, VIII, No. 9; Geografiska studier i St. Lule älvs källomrade. *Sverig. geol. Unders. Årsb.* 1913, VII, No. 4, Ser. C, No. 257, Stockholm 1914) and AXEL HAMBERG (Zur Kenntnis der Vorgänge im Erdboden beim Gefrieren und Auftauen usw. *Geol. Fören. Förh.* XXXVII, Heft 5, Stockholm 1915). A general survey of this group of phenomena was given by K. SAPPER (*G.R.* 1913, IV, Heft 2, p. 103).

(148) J. FRÖDIN, Über das Verhältnis zwischen Vegetation und Erdfliessen in der alpinen Region des schwedischen Lappland. *Meddelanden från Lunds Univ. geogr. Inst.* 1918, Ser. A, No. 2.

(149) The sorting of material in the upper rubble horizon seems to be connected with frost action. Separation of the mixed material takes place in such a way that the coarser ingredients often form regular rings enclosing polygonal areas in which the finer components have accumulated. Hence the name polygonal soils or 'structure ground'. See, besides the authors mentioned above: H. RESVOLL-HOLMSEN, Om jordbuntsstrukturer i polarlandene og planternes forhold til dem. Nyt. *Magaz. Naturvid.* XLVII, Kristiania 1909. —W. MEINARDUS, Über einige charakteristische Bodenformen auf Spitzbergen, *Sitzungsber. med.-naturw. Gesellsch. Münster,* Bonn 1912 and Beobachtungen über Detritussortierung und Strukturboden auf Spitzbergen. *Z.G.E.* 1912, No. 4.—G. HOLMSEN, Spitzbergens jordbundsis og de bidrag dens undersøkelse har kunnet gi til forstaaelsen av de i arktiske land optrædende varige isleier i jorden. *Norske geogr. Selskaps Aarbok* XXIV, Kristiania 1914. It may be mentioned that F. KLUTE and F. JAEGER found polygonal soils in East Africa, the former on the Kibo, the latter outside the sphere of any influence by frost (F. KLUTE, *Ergebnisse der Forschungen am Kilimandscharo* 1912, chap. V. Berlin 1920.—F. JAEGER, Das Hochland der Riesenkrater. *Mitteil. deutsch. Schutzgebieten* 1911, Ergänzungsheft 4, p. 173).

(150) Chas. DARWIN was the first to notice, in the Falkland Islands, those low ramparts running together asymptotically in the direction of the gradient and partitioning the surfaces of rock waste. The streams of detritus found

there were described by B. STECHELE (Die Steinströme der Falklandinseln, *Münchner Geogr. Studien* 1906) and studied in detail by J. G. ANDERSON, who also showed illustrations of them (Contributions to the geology of the Falkland Islands, *Wissensch. Ergebn. schwed. Südpolarexpedition* 1901–1903, Bd. III, Lief. 2, plates 8, 9 and figs. 9, 10. Stockholm 1907). See also O. NORDENSKJÖLD's description: *Die Polarwelt und ihre Nachbarländer*, Leipzig 1909. There are no rubble ramparts on the 'rock glaciers' of Alaska which on the whole seems to be a special kind of rubble stream not yet understood (S. R. COPPS, *Journ. Geol.* 1910, p. 359). All that has been established about them is that they are moving.

(151) B. HÖGBOM, Über die geologische Bedeutung des Frostes, *loc. cit.* [n. 35], p. 375. Frost phenomena in rubble are of course also present on high mountains near the summer snow-line. Mention may here be made of the rubble facets in the Alps (Chr. TARNUZZER, *P.M.* 1911, II). It is also quite possible that, in eastern and southern Tibet, the flow of rubble begins on a frozen subsoil with the onset of the spring monsoon. In the end, the subsoil thaws out completely; but the flow of rubble persists right up to the beginning of the dry season. Further, it must be borne in mind that once a year, in winter, the region of solifluction extends equatorwards. Very transitory frost phenomena are also to be expected in the rubble of temperate regions at that time (see F. M. BEHR, Über geologisch wichtige Frosterscheinungen in gemässigten Klimaten. *Z.D.G.G.* 1918, LXX, Monatsber. Nos. 5–7, p. 95).

(152) Beiträge zur Entstehung der Bergrückenformen, *loc. cit.* [n. 101]. Before that Th. FUCHS (Über eigentümliche Störungen in den Tertiärbildungen des Wiener Beckens und über eine selbständige Bewegung loser Terrainmassen. *Jahrb. k.k. geol. Reichsanst.* Wien 1872, p. 309) and M. SINGER (Fliessende Hänge, *Zeitschr. österr. Ing.-u. Archit.-Ver.* 1902, p. 190) had already indicated the importance of the movement of rubble.

(153) Morphologie des Messtischblattes Stadtremda. *Mitteil. geogr. Gesellsch. Hamburg* 1914, XXVIII.

(154) *G.Z.* 1915, XXI, Heft 2, p. 105.

(155) There are also earlier observations available; see G. A. F. MOLENGRAAFF, *Verkennings-Tochten in Zentral Borneo*, Leiden und Amsterdam 1900. Fresh observations have been communicated by F. KLUTE amongst others (*Kilimandscharo* 1912, *loc. cit.* [n. 149]). What W. VOLZ describes as forms of soil displacement in Sumatra are apparently nothing but the steep paths made by game and cattle (*Z.G.E.* 1913, No. 2, p. 1).

(156) See GÖTZINGER, Über pseudoglaziale Erscheinungen (Bergrückenformen, *loc. cit.* [n. 101], pp. 81–100).

(157) Die Entstehung der Stufenlandschaft. *G.Z.* XXVI, Heft 7–8, p. 207.

(158) See also O. LEHMANN's subtly-made observations (Bibl. geog. Handb., N.F., *A. Penck-Festband*, p. 48, Stuttgart 1918).

(159) Besides this, there may often be noticed furrows, arranged beside or behind one another, which are covered in by grassy sod; they begin abruptly, become narrower and deeper up-valley, and end suddenly. They develop after a thorough soaking, wherever water issues at the surface, and so causes

little sub-surface streams of mud to flow from ever higher up the valley. Analogous phenomena play a significant part on alluvial cones and in alluvial regions generally.

(160) W. SALOMON, Tote Landschaften und der Gang der Erdgeschichte. *Sitzungsber. Akad. Wissensch. Heidelberg* 1918, Abt. A, math.-phys. Kl., p. 1.

(161) The view that various climatic conditions give rise to various sorts of denudational forms seems to have been prompted in the first place by comparisons having been made between portions of the earth's crust which were not comparable, having undergone different tectonic movements. For example, blocks of the continental massif type, in the geological sense, such as parts of Africa, were compared with crustal fragments that had undergone more vigorous movement, like the German Highlands or even the zone of [recent] movement. We must postpone till later the detailed consideration of two further points which are apt to be brought forward in this connection, the *activity of the wind* which undoubtedly has a wider scope in arid regions than elsewhere, and the *dependence of the base level of erosion upon climate*, this determining the interior drainage of arid regions. Here the following reference must suffice: The base level of erosion is not a form, but a level; and whether this level is continental or marine, is of no consequence for the modelling of the slopes tributary to it. Conditions with respect to the wind are not dissimilar. There are only two places on earth for which, up to the present, wind action to any considerable extent has been established for certain (the Namib of south-west Africa and the great oases of Libya). The wind does indeed influence the level towards which mass-movement and mass-transport (rainwash) stream down, since it lowers this; but it leaves to them the modelling of the tributary slopes (see p. 45).

(162) See WALTHER PENCK, Op. 17.

(163) See J. W. GREGORY's compilation [on the use of these terms], *G.J.*, p. 189, London 1911.

(164) Following G. K. GILBERT ([see] *Morphologie der Erdoberfläche*, I, p. 245, Stuttgart 1894).

(165) A. GRUND, Karsthydrographie, *Geogr. Abhandl.* 1903, VII, Heft 3; Beiträge zur Morphologie des dinarischen Gebirges, *ibid.* 1910, IX, Heft 3, and elsewhere.

(166) It is no longer true to the same extent when it is a matter of flowing ice, beneath which, since the movement is so slow, erosion does not entirely replace frost action; still less does it hold for currents of air. Because of the extraordinarily low density of the medium these, even when their velocity is high, have not sufficient power to produce any erosional effects worth mentioning. So far as there are any morphological effects at all, denudation (deflation) is far more important in this case.

(167) A. HEIM, *Untersuchungen über den Mechanismus der Gebirgsbildung*, Bd. I, Basel 1878.

(168) See WALTHER PENCK, Op. 16, chap. VI, 2.

(169) Wind activity has thus no relationship to a lower level, analogous to the base level of erosion, such as could be reduced to a law. On the other hand,

denudation and erosion by wind do have an absolute lower limit imposed by the water table, since moisture so increases the cohesion of loose particles that, even when their size is sufficiently small, they can no longer be lifted by air movements.

(170) A. PENCK calls this theoretical end position the 'lower level of denudation' (Über Denudation der Erdoberfläche. *Schriften zur Verbr. naturw. Kenntn.* XXVII, p. 484, Wien 1886–87. Das Endziel der Erosion und Denudation, *Verhandl. VIII deutsch. Geographentages*, Berlin 1889, p. 91. See also: *Morphologie der Erdoberfläche, loc. cit.* [n. 1], I, p. 363). The concept is identical with POWELL's base level of erosion (J. W. POWELL, *Exploration of the Colorado river of the West*, Washington 1875).

(171) For the reasons which forbid us to keep to DAVIS' terminology see WALTHER PENCK, Op. 17, p. 102.

(172) This is especially the case when the three types of relief are preserved side by side as so often occurs in regions of broad folding—peneplanes on the summits, steep relief types on the flanks of the ranges—and when they are delimited one from another by sharp breaks of gradient. See amongst others, W. PENCK, Op. 16, chap. VI, 1.

(173) A. HEIM makes the following contribution as to the influence of stratification: for slopes inclined in the direction of the dip of the strata, the steepness increases with the angle of dip, other things being equal. If the upper edges of the strata outcrop on the slopes, slopes with a mountainward dip are about $5°–10°$ steeper, those with a valleyward dip $10°–20°$ gentler, than if the bedding is horizontal. (*Geologie der Schweiz*, p. 659, Leipzig 1919).

(174) G. GÖTZINGER, Beiträge zur Entstehung der Bergrückenformen, *loc. cit.* [n. 101], chap. V.

(175) R. GRADMANN, Das Schichtstufenland. *Z.G.E.* 1919, no. 3–4, p. 113.

(176) For an excellent illustration of this, note the series of pictures by N. H. DARTON mentioned below: Preliminary Report on the geology and underground resources of the Central Great Plains, *U.S. Geol. Surv. prof. Pap.*, no. 32, plates 47, 51, 54, 48, 50 (A), Washington 1905.

(177) These then are the denudational forms of which A. PENCK said that they imitate, as it were, forms of deposition (Geomorphologische Studien aus der Herzegowina. *Zeitschr. deutsch. österr. Alpenver.* 1900, p. 34).

(178) S. PASSARGE, *G.Z.* 1912, Heft 2.

(179) It must be pointed out that undercutting plays a rather important part in the denudation of every slope, whatever its inclination. This is the way it takes place: if particle y (fig. 3, p. 137) leaves its place of origin, a very small niche is produced, the steep back wall of which cannot be maintained but soon collapses, i.e. it migrates upslope and accelerates the removal of rock from the position $y\,a\,2$. Such niches will develop at many places on the slope, and all move upwards. After unit time, they have set in motion the whole mass $t\,a\,2'–2$, and the new position of the slope $2'–2$ is established.

(180) O LEHMANN has already made observations on the origin of convex breaks of slope, the independent development of the various slope units, especially the way in which they shift back parallel to themselves, and the

typc of maoo movcmont on thom: Dio Talbildung duroh Sohuttgorinno. *A. Penck-Festband*, p. 48. Bibl. geogr. Handbücher, Stuttgart 1918. This is an investigation unequalled for delicacy of observation.

(181) It is necessary to stress this, since the divides between the younger, deeply incised valleys by no means everywhere coincide with the old inter-valley divides. The connections between them can be particularly well studied on the Kösseine in the Fichtelgebirge. Here the steep slopes of the younger watersheds have already in several places worked upwards to the old inter-valley divides. In this way the relics of steeper slope units, the many crags which still exist on these latter, crown the precipitous younger slopes on the one side, and, on the other, the old flattish slopes which belong to them (Hauenstein, Haberstein).

(182) Hence the totally different scenery that is unfolded before an observer standing, for example, at Werenwag, as he looks up valley or down valley. In the former case he sees a deep valley, well wooded, with steep and rounded slopes; down valley—a rocky canyon with a sharply drawn upper edge.

(183) W. PENCK, Op. 17, p. 95.

(184) Specimens of the various types of rounded ridge are to be found in the Badlands: forms pressed down more or less flat, with strongly curved sides (great acceleration of the erosion); and the types more stretched out, with less strongly bent slopes, projecting higher (slighter acceleration of erosion). See plate 45, ill. A in N. H. DARTON's article (Prof. Paper 32, *loc. cit.* [n. 176]) and G. K. GILBERT's figs. 2–4 (Convexity of hill tops. *J.G.* 1909, XVII, no. 4, p. 344). Gilbert, like W. M. DAVIS (*Science*, XX, p. 245), considers convexity to be the normal denudational form, owing to soil creep. His deduction, however, moves in a circle, since he begins from the already completed convex ridges and does not explain how they arose; but—taking for granted the correctness of his assumptions—shows that they are preserved in a similar shape once they have arisen.

(185) WALTHER PENCK, Op. 13, pp. 49 ff.

(186) H. SPETHMANN, *Zentralbl. Min.* 1907, p. 747.

(187) R. GRADMANN, Das Schichtstufenland, *loc. cit.* [n. 175]. See also E. HENNIG, Strukturelle und skulpturelle Züge im Antlitz Württembergs. *Erd-gesch. landesk. Abhandl. aus Schwaben und Franken*, Heft 2, Öhringen 1920.

(188) The broken line *F S* in fig. 11, p. 172, is the vertical from a ridge, crest or peak, and enables us to follow such changes in shape and height, e.g. those of a hill lying in front of an escarpment. Slope position 13, for example, reproduces very closely the profile of the Jail Rocks in N. H. DARTON's illustration (*loc. cit.* [n. 176], plate 48).

(189) Der Erongo. *Beitr. geol. Erforsch. deutsch. Schutzgeb.*, Heft 17, pp. 221–222, Berlin 1919).

(190) This may also be made clear with the help of fig. 7 (p. 158). If the slope unit *c* represents the maximum gradient in a rock of slight resistance, *d* that in a stronger rock, it is obvious that an angle of slope such as *c* is developed and maintained when the general base level of denudation falls by the amounts 3–4, 4–5, and so on; while the steeper slope (corresponding to *d*) in the

stronger rock requires, on the other hand, a greater lowering (in unit time) of the base level of denudation.

(191) See A. HETTNER, Rumpfflächen und Pseudorumpfflächen. *GZ.* 1913, XIX, Heft 4, p. 185.

(192) W. M. DAVIS, An excursion to the Grand Canyon of the Colorado. *Bull. Mus. compar. Zoology,* XXXVIII (Geol. ser. V, No. 4), Cambridge 1901.

(193) W. SCHMITTHENNER, Die Oberflächengestaltung des nördlichen Schwarzwaldes. *Diss. Karlsruhe,* 1913.

(194) E. HENNIG, *loc. cit.* [n. 187], p. 54.

(195) The general arrangement of the geological outcrops is shown in the *Übersichtskarten* by C. REGELMANN, Württemberg und Baden 1 : 600,000 and by C. W. GÜMBEL, Bayern 1 : 100,000, Sheet N., XII, XIII, XIV, XV, XVI, XVII. The morphological relationship can be gathered to some extent from the sheets of the 1 : 25,000 Geological *Spezialkarten* for Baden, Württemberg and Bayern. For the areas considered in the text, see particularly sheets 110, 111, 120, 121, 132, 133 of the Grand Duchy of Baden.

(196) In addition, there is no enclosure by rather steep slopes, since these have been replaced by flattish ones. This means that when precipitation occurs, the surface run-off is lessened with a corresponding gain to infiltration.

(197) R. GRADMANN, Das Schichtstufenland. *Z.G.E.* 1919, p. 113.

(198) E. SCHEU, Zur Morphologie der schwäbisch-fränkischen Stufenlandschaft. *Forsch. deutsch. Landes- und Volkskunde,* XVIII, Heft 4, p. 365, Stuttgart 1909. Just as little consequent in this sense is the drainage system of the Roth-Brenz, diverted by the Kocher. Its origin preceded the carving out of the scarplands. Since that began, i.e. since the main lines of the drainage net found occasion for more intense downcutting, *lateral branches* of the Roth-Brenz (which apparently was not captured by the Kocher till Pleistocene times) have progressively penetrated the intervalley masses and are still doing so. Meanwhile, on the summits of these, there developed and continue to develop the peneplanes (above the Stubensandstein scarp and the Lias scarp) with their own special drainage net. To some extent these lateral branches follow the direction of the main entrenched streams from which they arose, and so run against the slope of the scarpland peneplanes which were being formed in the meantime. Their penetration into the foundation of these does not follow the line of the valley troughs which genetically belong to the peneplanes, but those of their own less deeply sunken earlier stages.

(199) W. BORNHARDT, *Zur Oberflächengestaltung und Geologie Deutsch-Ostafrikas.* Berlin 1900, especially pp. 27, 34. E. OBST, Das abflusslose Rumpfschollenland im nord-österlichen Deutsch-Ostafrikas. *Mitt. Hamburg. geogr. Gesellsch.* XXIX, 1915. W. M. DAVIS, Observations in South Africa. *B.G.S.A.* XVII, 1906, p. 377. S. PASSARGE, *Die Kalahari,* Berlin 1904. *The same,* Die Inselberglandschaften im tropischen Afrika. *Nat.-wiss. Wochenschr.* 1904, p. 657. A large part of the extensive literature has been listed by E. OBST, *P.M.* LX (1), 1914, p. 177.

(200) This state of affairs is considered to be expressed by the term 'Restberg', introduced by A. SUPAN (*Grundzüge der physischen Erdkunde,* 5. Aufl.,

1911, p. 685; as well as in Davis Braun, *Physiographie* II, 1915, p. 11 and elsewhere). Later Supan spoke of 'Rumpfrestbergen' and Obst (Terminologie und Klassifikation der Berge, *P.M.* 1914, p. 245) of 'Rumpfbergen'. We keep to the striking, purely descriptive expression 'Inselberg', understanding by it elevations bounded by denudation surfaces, and rising isolated above the farther denuded surroundings. We do not associate it with any interpretation, especially none as regards the character of the rock (stratified or massive, with disturbed or flat bedding, having a greater or less resistance to denudation). In the course of the investigation it will become quite evident that inselbergs are a form-type belonging to waning development; they do not appear at all with any other kind of development.

(201) S. Passarge at first supported the hypothesis that peneplanes were due to denudation by the wind; but later he gave it up. In view of the slow action of aeolian denudation it was necessary to assume a long desert period during the Mesozoic era within which the African inselberg landscapes were thought to have originated (Rumpfflächen und Inselberge. *Z.D.G.G.* 1904, LVI, Monatsber. p. 193; the same: Physiologische Morphologie, *Mitt. geogr. Gesellsch.* Hamburg XXVI, 1912, p. 133, especially p. 179 ff.; also O. Hecker, *Z.D.G.G.* LVII, 1905, p. 175). Later W. M. Davis (*Die erklärende Beschreibung der Landformen*, 1912, p. 366) and Em. Kayser (*Lehrbuch der allgemeinen Geologie*, 5. Aufl. 1918, p. 288 and p. 578) amongst others seriously considered the idea of aeolian planation of the land. C. Keyes, dispensing with any closer investigation of the processes of denudation in arid regions and of denudation surfaces themselves, put forward the thesis that in such areas denudation by wind surpassed, in its force and significance, all other denudational processes taken together, in spite of the fact that in the Basin Ranges as elsewhere the nature and arrangement of these surfaces, the way in which they slope in a constant direction towards their base levels of erosion contradicts, in a perfectly unambiguous manner, the notion that denudation by wind takes even a noticeable share in the work (Erosional origin of Great Basin Ranges. *J.G.* XVII, no. 1, 1909, p. 31). F. E. Suess followed this up by ascribing to wind action such superiority over erosion and other processes of denudation, as regards its power of peneplanation, that he considers times when the climate was humid to be times when denudation was retarded and hindered, as compared with what happened in periods of aridity (Zur Deutung der Vertikalbewegungen der Festländer und Meere. *G.R.* XI, 1921, Heft 7–8, pp. 372 ff., especially p. 374). Actual *observation*, on the other hand, teaches us quite otherwise. Denudation by wind, where its activity is not exceeded by that of streamlets, leads to just the opposite result from planation of the land. This has been convincingly expounded by H. Cloos (Der Erongo. *Beitr. Erforsch. deutsch. Schutzgebiete*, Heft 17, especially p. 218 and following, Berlin 1919) and E. Kaiser for the Namib of south-west Africa, one of the only two places on earth where it has so far been proved with certainty that denudation by wind has had a share in shaping the major land forms. It is seen as a matter of course and a necessary result, when one studies the long series of observations that have been made on denudational processes in arid regions, and especially

those on the nature and connection of the *slopes* and *their uniform inclination towards the base levels of erosion*. These, in arid lands, are to be found in the tectonically formed depressions, which are usually basins of interior drainage. These slopes can be formed only by such gravitational streams as cling to the surface of the land, and they prove that even in the desert the activity of occasionally flowing streamlets and the effects of mass-movement far surpass the denudational activity of wind (see pp. 24 [?17] and 45).

(202) E. KRENKEL, Über den Bau der Inselberge Ostafrikas. *Nat.-wiss Wochenschr.* XIX, no. 24, 1920, p. 373. See also the following illustrations: S. PASSARGE, *Südafrika*, Leipzig 1908, the upper illustration of the plate opposite p. 88, and plates opposite pp. 112, 272; also K. HASSERT, Beiträge zur Landeskunde der Grashochländer Nordwestkameruns I, *Mitteil. deutsch. Schutzgebieten*, Erg.-H. 13, Berlin 1917, illustrations 16, 19; F. JAEGER, Beiträge zur Landeskunde von Deutsch-Südwestafrika. *Mitteil. deutsch. Schutzgebieten*, Erg.-H 15, Berlin 1921, illustrations 30, 33, 34; H. CLOOS, Der Erongo, *loc. cit.* [n. 113], plate III, illustration 1; plate V, illustrations 1, 2; plate VI, illustrations 1, 2; plate VIII, illustration 1; E. OBST, Das abflusslose Rumpfschollenland, *loc. cit.* [n. 199], illustration 19; K. WALTHER, Lineas fundamentales de la estructura geológica de la Rep. O. del Uruguay, *Rev. Inst. Nat. Agron.*, Montevideo, 2nd ser., no. 3, 1919, plate 1, illustration 3; plate 3, etc.

(203) This can also be followed excellently in the Scarplands, where there are valleys sunk in specially resistant zones of Muschelkalk and Malm (e.g. the valley of the Kocher in Württemberg, the valley of the Wiesent in the Franconian Jura). Below the break of gradient in the longitudinal profile (treated above), the sharply incised V-shaped valleys are narrow, steep and rocky; in the middle course they are wider with the gradient less, canyon-like, accompanied for long distances by walls of rock; in the lower course they become wide trough-valleys, the rocky walls of their flanks having become completely replaced by their basal slopes. These latter lead right up to the convexly curved edge of the scarpland peneplane. The ramifying lateral branches have the same character as that possessed by the main valley at the place where they join it; i.e. along those debouching into the lower course of the main valley, the three sections repeat themselves upstream: trough-valley, canyon, rocky, sharply incised V-shaped valley. Naturally only this last is developed for the whole region of the upper course of the main stream. This arrangement shows that the eroding portion, which now works at the upper ends of the *entrenched* valley system, has successively passed along all parts of the river—first of all the lower course which it left behind it longer ago than the middle course through which it passed only later.

(204) Compare the description of the valleys of the Erongo by H. CLOOS (*loc. cit.* [n. 113]). On a small scale the Erongo, which is perhaps the best known inselberg, affords an excellent opportunity for following the increase in density of the valley net, the disintegration of the intervalley spurs into inselbergs of a lesser order of magnitude, and their demolition—in short, the whole course of waning development.

(205) This still holds true at the present day, without any reservations, for

the inselberg landscape of southern Uruguay, draining to the Atlantic Ocean, as well as for those of Africa with their interior drainage. On the relatively narrow strip of German south-west Africa sloping towards the Atlantic Ocean, typical inselberg landscapes are undergoing more recent dissection, of post Upper Cretaceous age (F. JAEGER, *loc. cit.* [n. 202]). According to H. CLOOS (*loc. cit.* [n. 113]), this becomes noticeable as far as the neighbourhood of the Erongo, taking the form of isolated erosion furrows which are sunk in the peneplane that, over wide stretches, is still completely intact.

(206) H. SPETHMANN, *Zentralbl. Min. usw.* 1908, p. 747.

(207) The similarity in composition between many inselbergs and their peneplanated surroundings, especially in the East African examples, has been stressed several times (F. JAEGER, Geographische Forschungen im abflusslosen Gebiet von Deutsch-Ostafrika. *Verh.* 18. *Deutscher Geographentag zu Innsbruck*, Berlin 1912, p. 26. The same: Das Hochland der Riesenkrater, etc., *Mitteil. deutsch. Schutzgebieten*, Erg.-H.4. Berlin 1911; Erg.-H. 8, 1913. E. OBST, Vorläufige Berichte I–IV der Ostafrika-Expedition. *Mitteil. geogr. Gesellsch. Hamburg* 1911–13. A. HOLMES, The precambrian and associated rocks of the district of Mozambique. *Q.J.G.S.* LXXIV, 1919, no. 293, p. 31, etc.). Closer investigation usually shows that amongst the inselbergs examined monadnocks of resistant rock are the exception rather than the rule. This statement of their nature as resistant monadnocks is generally based on a vicious circle, such as A. HETTNER has already deprecated (*Die Oberflächenformen des Festlandes*, Leipzig 1921, p. 134). Amongst other examples are most of the domes that rise above the peneplanes found on the summits of the German Highlands, such as Feldberg in the Black Forest, the Brocken in the Harz, Ochsenkopf-Schneeberg in the Fichtelgebirge, Fichtelberg in the Erzgebirge etc. Their existence has absolutely nothing to do with the properties of the rocks; it is by the very absence of such a connection that they are to be distinguished from neighbouring resistant monadnocks which are associated with certain types of rock, *and with them only* (in the Harz, for example, definite parts of the metamorphic schists enwrapping the granite, or the Devonian quartzite). Feldberg and its surroundings consist of the same paragneisses, the Fichtelgebirge granite takes as great a share in the build of the inselbergs as in that of the surrounding peneplane, and the granite of the Brocken constitutes the heights as well as the adjoining parts of the peneplane. The granite boss of Thale lies completely below this. We shall return to this group of phenomena and its interpretation. [Section on the Harz, pp. 197 ff.]

(208) K. WALTHER, Lineas fundamentales, *loc. cit.*; P. P. BAUER, Nordwestamazonia, *Dissertation*, München 1919; F. KATZER, *Grundzüge der Geologie des unteren Amazonasgebietes*, Leipzig 1903.

(209) *Das Gesetsz der Wüstenbildung*, 2. Aufl. Leipzig 1912, p. 217.

(210) In addition to the authors named, see F. THORBECKE, Die Inselberglandschaft von Nord-Tikar, Breslau 1921, p. 215 (*Zwölf länderkundliche Aufsätze von Schülern A. Hettners ihrem Lehrer zum 60. Geburgstag*) and F. BEHREND, Über die Entstehung der Inselberge und Steilstufen, besonders in

Afrika, und die Erhaltung ihrer Form. *Z.D.G.G.* 1918, Monatsber. no. 8–12, p. 154. Both come to the conclusion that the inselbergs have certainly arisen under present day climatic conditions. The great importance of rainwash as well as of the retreat of steep slope units has not escaped BEHREND in particular, and he quite rightly points out that the steep scarps at the edges of the rift valley in East and Central Africa need not necessarily coincide any longer with the fault lines along which they originated, but that they may have receded. It is not therefore permissible to conclude without further investigation—as is often done—that steep scarps are fault scarps. The decision as to whether a feature is a fault scarp or a denudation scarp (i.e. a valley slope which has receded) can be made only from detailed geological investigations which so far are lacking for that region.

(211) A. HETTNER, *Die Oberflächenformen des Festlandes, loc. cit.* [n. 9], p. 22.

(212) G. L. COLLIES, Plateau of British East Africa. *B.G.S.A.* XXIII, 1912, p. 297.

(213) Besides the official German map 1 : 100,000 (sheet nos. 335–337, 360–362), a good idea of the country can be obtained from the *Höhenschichtenkarte des Harzes* 1 : 100,000, published by the Prussian Geological Survey, in connection with the geological *Übersichtskarte* of the same scale by K. A. LOSSEN. For what is to follow, see especially sheet Zellerfeld and Harzburg of Prussian geological *Spezialkarte* 1 : 25,000.

(214) In the higher parts of the Harz there are at least *three levels of the intervalley divides*:

(*a*) that of the peneplane which, close to the central mountainland, is somewhat over 600 metres above sea level, and sinks very gradually eastwards to an average height of about 500 metres in the region between Thale and Stolberg. The level plateaus to the east are probably not a direct continuation of the same peneplane but represent a lower peneplane level. Conclusive observations on this point are lacking.

(*b*) The second main level rises towards the Brocken from about 750 metres to an average altitude of 850 metres. It is especially well developed south and west of the highest parts of the country. The lower elevations of the central mountainland belong to it. They extend as broad, extremely flat plateaux which contrast sharply with the steeper slopes leading to the surrounding peneplane, as well as with those of the greater elevation rising above it. Here, undoubtedly, it is a matter of fragments all belonging to a flattish relief which surrounded the highest parts of the country in the same way as it is itself surrounded by the lower peneplane. Valley dissection has long been causing its progressive separation from this peneplane.

(*c*) The highest level that can be distinguished is formed by the Brocken and its neighbours, in so far as they project above the 900 metre datum line.

(215) Where, however, higher projecting parts of the country arise from a peneplane, the concave slopes reach right up to the intervalley divides, provided these do not have on them still older flattish forms belonging to a higher level. They then intersect in sharpened crests on which, in a region of granite, tors are superimposed as relics of steeper slope units.

(216) It must be stressed here that these breaks of gradient are in no way connected with resistant types of rock. *In addition* to the breaks of gradient, which are completely independent of the nature of the rocks, there are others obviously conditioned by the occurrence of strong types of rock. Breaks of gradient of the first kind have a corresponding arrangement as regards the relative altitude of analogous steps and their number, for valleys which are similar in origin. The second type is bound up with local conditions and does *not* fit into the system.

(217) The official German map 1 : 100,000, sheet nos. 533-534, 513-514, 440-441, 467-468, 491-492, in connection with the geological *Übersichtskarte* by C. W. GÜMBELS for the Bavarian 1 : 100,000, sheets XI and XII, and that of H. CREDNER for 1 : 250,000 of Saxony, are adequate for this survey. For the districts in Prussia and Saxony the geological *Spezialkarten* 1 : 25,000 are available. For what is to follow, see especially the following sheets: *Gradabt.* 71, sheets 5, 11, 12, 16, 17, 18, 21, 22, 23, 24, 27, 28, 33, 34, of the Prussian *Spezialkarte* and sheets 133, 134, 142 of the Saxon *Spezialkarte*.

(218) Thus the tors of the Fichtelgebirge—also within the granitic region—are connected not only with a definite and closely demarcated zone which encircles the highest elevations, but also with an accordant level: Haberstein 869 metres, Burgstein 890 m., Platte 883 m., Rudolfstein 866 m., Waldstein 878 m. These tors are set on the top of the intervalley divides of the P_2 surface. Outside the zone of tors there is no clear indication that a higher projecting mountainland ever occupied the place of the P_3 surface which stretches out very much further. The character of an end-peneplane can be ascribed with certainty only to the parts adjoining the highest elevations. For a lower level of tors, see note 220.

(219) Their lay-out makes it possible to distinguish differences of age: the older ones start from the P_3 surface—to be discussed presently; the younger ones from the valleys sunk in that surface. They are steeper, have stretches of greater erosional intensity than their precursors, and where they reach upwards into the track of these, the side branches possess a broken, on the whole convex, longitudinal profile. This is the case, amongst other examples, on the east flank of Schneeberg, up to which there reach directly not only the P_3 surface, but also the incised course of the Röslau.

(220) The tors of this *lower level* are not set on the intervalley divides of the P_2 surface, but are cut out from its main mass, and crown the intervalley ridges of the P_3 surface. The highest tors of this lower level thus lie just *below* the P_2 surface (Matzen 814 metres, Epprechstein 797 m.) and the lowest just above that of P_3, and so at about 700 m. At various places the concave slopes rising from the P_3 surface lead up to the tors of the higher level, so that it looks as if they belonged genetically to them (Grosser Waldstein, Rudolfstein). This is not the case, as can easily be seen at Burgstein and Haberstein near Wunsiedel. Adjoining the tors, there are still, on the one side, flattish slope fragments of the P_2 level, belonging to them, and on the other steep, younger concave slopes reaching up from lower altitudes.

(221) The P_2 surface is bordered above and below by zones similar to those

for the P_3 surface; thus, like the latter, it belongs to the *same class, and is a full member of the piedmont stairway*. This makes it certain that most of those parts lying outside the zone of tors and definitely outside its peripheral continuation —which has since disappeared—are no end-peneplanes but are of the nature of the P_3 surface or the Harz peneplane. It can no longer be directly established that the same holds for the P_1 surface, but it may be deduced from general considerations which will be investigated later.

(222) See sheets Gefell and Lössau (*Gradabt.* 71, nos. 34 and 28) of the Prussian geological *Spezialkarte* and sheets Hauen and Plauen-Pausa (nos. 133, 142) of the Saxon geological *Spezialkarte*.

(223) See sheets Pörmitz, Zeulenroda, Naitschau of the Prussian *Spezialkarte* (*Gradabt.* 71, nos. 21, 22, 23). All statements as to direction 'north', 'northwards', etc., are to be understood in a general and not in a special sense, as also in the preceding and following remarks. The statements as to altitude are the average values for the heights of the intervalley divides.

(224) Sheets Weida, Triptis and Waltersdorf of the Prussian geological *Spezialkarte* (*Gradabt.* 71, nos. 16, 17, 18).

(225) These deposits transgressing over the Elster valley have only recently been recognised as belonging to the Lower Oligocene. The older surveys still give them as early Pleistocene gravels and sand. See sheets Weida, Naitschau, Greiz of the Prussian geological *Spezialkarte* (*Gradabt.* 71, nos. 17, 23, 24) and Plauen-Pausa, Treuen-Herlasgrün, Plauen-Ölsnitz of the Saxon geological *Spezialkarte* (nos. 133, 134, 142).

(226) In the latitude of Plauen the floor of the old valley lies about 100 metres lower than the divides between the *upper courses and headwater branches* of the valley net belonging to the P_4 surface, where it enters the next higher step north-west of Plauen. This difference in height is no greater than is found on an undulating peneplane at the edge of higher country. Towards the north it is reduced to about 60 m. above Weida. The transgression of the Oligocene naturally did not reach as far south or as high up in the region of the divides between the main valleys as in the main valleys themselves. In addition, the superposed Oligocene has since been considerably denuded in the parts away from the main valley. Both these conditions lead to the result that *today* the southernmost relics of the transgression are found on the peneplane itself at a level about 50–60 m. lower and only 35 kilometres further north than within the main valley itself.

(227) E. PHILIPPI was the first to recognise the date of origin and general character of the landscapes under consideration (Über die präoligozäne Landoberfläche in Thüringen, *Z.D.G.G.* LXII, 1910, p. 305); and with him— although he thought that it was a matter of a single uniform peneplane—one can call the land surface generally pre-Oligocene. It is wrong to ascribe an Oligocene age to it, as H. RASSMUS, led by general considerations, has done (Zur Morphologie des nordwestlichen Böhmen. *Z.G.E.* 1913, p. 35). Closer investigation of the morphological relationships and especially of the arrangement, bedding and facies of the Lower Oligocene would very soon have brought

to light the error of that determination of age; but it would also in particular have destroyed the assumption that it was a *single* peneplane which once—as G. BRAUN considered a possible generalisation—extended over the whole of the Central German Rise as a uniform 'Germanic peneplain'* (*Deutschland*, Berlin 1916, p. 18). This reconstruction finds no support from actual observation.

(228) On some of these valley floors away from the Saale valley, fluviatile deposits of great antiquity occur. Thus near Grötenbruck, south-west of Hof, a thick soil profile is to be found on the top of the deeply weathered gneiss. The higher loamy horizons pass into sandy loamy beds with interspersed pebbles and rounded blocks of local rock material (quartz, gneiss, quartzite schist, serpentine). This intimate combination with the soil profile, and its restriction to a valley floor of the T_4 stage, make it very unlikely that the deposits belong to the Pleistocene period.

(229) In this respect the contrast with the upper course regions, e.g. near Seulbitz or Sparneck, is impressive. Here the convex slopes of the younger side branches fall quite into the background; and concavity dominates the sets of land forms seen on the summits and in the valleys, just as in the zones near Hof, which are *above* the younger incisions. The stages of greater deepening have apparently not yet eaten back into the above-mentioned upper reaches of the Saale, but there the river still flows in a valley of the T_4 stage.·

[229a Probably W. Penck: Die Piedmontflächen des südliches Schwarzwaldes. *Z.G.E.* 1925, pp. 81–108.]

(230) A further indication of the existence of intermediate levels seems to be that, in the immediate neighbourhood of the elevations still showing the P_1 surface, tors appear, crowning the intervalley ridges of the P_2 surface. They seem in reality to be remains of an intermediate level; for it is difficult to see how the highest eminences could have, in one place, already completely succumbed to waning development, whilst those in the closest proximity are still very far from having done so. Transitional stages of development are not met with.

(231) For the proof of their existence and the elucidation of the general conditions of their formation see W. PENCK, Op. 16 and Op. 17.

(232) See the geological *Übersichtskarte* of Saxony 1 : 250,000 (H. CREDNER); and for what follows the geological *Spezialkarte* of Saxony 1 : 25,000, sheets 4, 13, 28, 29, 43, 44, 59, 60.

(233) See sheets Colditz and Grimma, nos. 44 and 28 of the Saxon geological *Spezialkarte*.

(234) In addition to white pebbles from the Lower Oligocene gravels, remains of white clays and sands are significant, more particularly the so-called *Knollensteine*, gigantic blocks of quartzite (concretionary indurated sand), which are found in them. So is the kaolinisation of the quartz porphyry, which is restricted to the zones lying underneath the Lower Oligocene and attains a thickness of several metres at the bottoms of the pre-Oligocene valleys, as well as a perfect degree [of kaolinisation] (saggar clays).

* *Rumpfebene*

(235) See sheets Wurzen and Thallwitz, nos. 4 and 13 of the Saxon geological *Spezialkarte*.

(236) Thus in the Hohburger Mountains, the northernmost group of inselbergs in the highland sections considered, one finds above the valleys of the P_5 level (about 120–130 metres) the intermediate level at 150–160 m.; and between this and the highest inselbergs, belonging to the P_4 level (average altitude 230 m.), other inselbergs, the flattish summits of which are at about 200 m. The latter obviously belong to yet another intermediate level.

(237) See sheets Tanneberg, Wilsdruff, Freiberg and Tharandt, nos. 64, 65, 80, 81 of the Saxon geological *Spezialkarte*.

(238) For example, under the basalt of the Landsberg. As in the more western section, so also east of the Granulitgebirge, the P_4 surface rises from north to south. In the latitude of the Granulitgebirge, its intervalley ridges are at an average height of 300–320 m. (the same altitude as is found at the same latitude in the region of the Zwickau trough); southwards, they rise very gradually to 400 m. (region: Langhennersdorf—north of Freiberg) and slightly over 510 m. south of Freiberg; see sheets 63–65, 79–81, and 98–100 of the Saxon geological *Spezialkarte*.

(239) *Erläuterungen zu Blatt Freiberg-Langhennersdorf* by A. SAUER and A. ROTHPLETZ, 2. Aufl., by C. GÄBERT, Leipzig 1906, pp. 37–38.

(240) Sheets Brand and Lichtenberg, nos. 98, 99 of the Saxon geological *Spezialkarte*. At the scarp, the intervalley divides of the P_4 level lie at a mean altitude of 510–520 m., those of the higher level at about 570 m., bearing island-like elevations rising to 620 m.

(241) F. KOSSMAT, *Übersicht der Geologie von Sachsen*, Leipzig 1916. K. PIETZSCH, *Erläuterungen zu Blatt Pirna*, 2. Aufl., Leipzig, p. 69 and elsewhere.

(242) O. v. LINSTOW, Untersuchungen über den Beginn der grossen Kreidetrangression in Deutschland. *Jahrb. preuss. geolog. Landesanst.* XXXIX, Teil II, Heft I, Berlin 1919, p. 1.

(243) J. WEIGELT, Die mitteloligozäne Meerestransgression usw. *Steinbruch*, Heft 17, Berlin 1921.

(244) From the way in which the sedimentation of the continental Tertiary beds ends off, Th. TEUMER (Die Bildung der Braunkohlenflöze im Senftenberger Revier. *Braunkohle* 1920, no. 44) deduced the setting in of instantaneous sudden subsidences following on preceding slow secular subsidences. If this is replaced simply by 'increase in intensity of subsidence', it may in fact provide an explanation for the strikingly similar development of the facies which is to be found in every profile of the continental Lower Oligocene. See also R. LANG, Die Entstehung von Braunkohle und Kaolin im Tertiär Mitteldeutschlands. *Erdmann, Jahrb. Halleschen Verb. Erforsch. mitteldeutschen Bodenschätze usw.*, Heft 2, p. 65.

(245) Part of the relevant literature is to be found collected in Cl. LEBLING, Tektonische Forschungen in den Appalachien II. *G.R.* V, Heft 8, p. 511, 1915.

(246) B. WILLIS, Round about Asheville. *Nat. Geogr. Mag.* I, 1889, p. 291. W. M. DAVIS, The geological dates of origin of certain topographic forms on the Atlantic slope of the U.S. *B.G.S.A.* II, p. 545, 1891.

(247) See illustrations: L. C. GLENN, *Prof. paper* 72, Washington 1911, plates 5, 15.

(248) W. M. DAVIS, The triassic formation of Connecticut. Ann. Rep. 18, *U.S. geol. Surv.*

(249) An exceptionally fine illustration in L. C. GLENN, *loc. cit.* [n. 247], plate 18.

(250) From LEBLING's account one gets the impression that in New York there is an intermediate level, the Highlands, between the piedmont flat and the Cretaceous peneplane.

(251) Of course, this cannot be said positively, so long as the under surface of the Miocene transgression has not been more closely investigated. The overstepping of a complex of beds on to a peneplane still does not determine the geological period of its origin. Here I am having in mind the Lower Oligocene transgression in Saxony.

(252) C. W. HAYES and M. R. CAMPBELL, Geomorphology of the Southern Appalachians. *Nat. geogr. Mag.* VI, 1894, p. 63. Both authors believe that they can establish several axes of doming, of the nature of anticlinal axes.

(253) H. REUSCH, Betrachtungen über das Relief von Norwegen. *G.Z.* IX, 1903, p. 425.

(254) H. W. AHLMANN, Geomorphological studies in Norway. *Geografiska Annaler* 1919, Heft 1–2. A. G. HÖGBOM, Über die norwegische Küstenplattform. *Bull. geol. Instn. Univ. Upsala* XII, 1913, p. 41.

(255) We are here disregarding the cases in which peneplanes have not been proved to be present, but merely assumed to be so from theoretical considerations. Thus G. BRAUN thought he could recognise a post-Miocene peneplane in the plane tangential to the summits of the north facing slope of the northern Apennines (this would stand in the relationship of a piedmont flat to the High Apennines rising above it). He supposed that its continuation was to be found in the extremely hummocky under surface of the transgressing Pliocene. As evidence, he points to some plateau-like heights in the southern parts of the above-mentioned slope, interpreting these as remnants—though scanty ones—of a peneplane which he conceived to have been widely extended, but practically destroyed by the present valley dissection. Further, the clay and marl facies of the Pliocene strata is brought forward as implying a planated area to the south from which it originated, i.e. the peneplane, with streams which were not eroding. The first point, however, merely indicates that in the northern Apennines there occur well-marked forms of waxing development; and the facies of marine Pliocene depends not only upon the altitudinal conditions of the catchment basin, but also upon its petrographical composition and the distance, at that period, of the surfaces that were being eroded from the places where the rivers entered the sea (and so depends on the length of the *graded* reaches). Also, the Pliocene at the northern edge of the Apennines is by no means devoid of thick intercalations of coarse clastic material, as BRAUN himself mentions (Beiträge zur Morphologie des nördlichen Apennin. *G.Z.E.* 1907, nos. 7–8). H. v. STAFF's hypothesis that the present summit level of the Alps is a Pliocene peneplane is even less well founded; it has already

been proved wrong in its essential points, at any rate as regards the Eastern Alps (Morphogenie der Präglaziallandschaft in den westlichen Schweizer Alpen. *Z.D.G.G.* 1912, p. 1).

(256) A. HEIM, *Geologie der Schweiz*, Bd. II, p. 69, Leipzig 1919.

(257) A. PENCK, Die Gipfelflur der Alpen. *Sitz.-Ber. preuss. Akad. Wiss.* Berlin 1919, XVII, p. 256.

(258) O. AMPFERER, Über die Bohrung von Rum bei Hall in Tirol. *Jahrb. geolog. Staatsanst.* Wien 1921, LXXI, Heft 1–2, p. 71.—A. PENCK and E. BRÜCKER, *Die Alpen im Eiszeitalter*, Leipzig 1901–1909, p. 1098.—K. OESTREICH, Ein alpines Längstal zur Tertiärzeit. *Jahrb. geol. R.-A.* Wien 1899, p. 165.—N. KREBS, Die nördlicher Alpen zwischen Enns, Traisen und Mürz. *Geogr. Abh.* VIII, Heft 2, 1903.—H. HÖFER, Das Miozänbecken bei Leoben. Geolog. Führer, IX. *C. R Cong. int. Géol.* Wien 1903, V.—An excellent survey, supplemented by fresh observations, in N. KREBS, *Länderkunde der österreich. Alpen.* Bibl. geogr. Handbücher, Stuttgart 1913.

(259) A. PENCK und E. BRÜCKNER, *Die Alpen im Eiszeitalter, loc. cit.* [n. 258], p. 286 and elsewhere.—A. PENCK, Die Entstehung der Alpen. *Z.G.E.* 1908, p. 5 (see especially p. 15).—A critical discussion of the different views on the pre-glacial aspect of the Alps has been given by H. LAUTENSACH (*Z.G.E.* 1913, p. 1).

(260) H. HESS saw in these pre-glacial elements trough shoulders belonging to the Günz and Mindel Ice Ages, an interpretation which has remained unsupported and is not in accordance with the results of the detailed investigation by A. PENCK, E. BRÜCKNER, H. LAUTERSACH, E. de MARTONNE, W. KILIAN and others. See the discussion by H. LAUTENSACH, who also compiled the relevant literature (*Z.G.E.* 1913, p. 1). The relationships between form and arrangement, set out above, make H. HESS' view untenable (Die präglaziale Alpenoberfläche. *P.M.* LIX, 1913, p. 281). The illustrations published in this show excellently both the convex profiles of the ridge zones, with the subordinate concave interruptions in the profile (plates 47, 48) and also the lower slopes of the intervalley divides, bounded by sharply convex curves, which belong to a longitudinal valley zone (Rhone valley, plates 45, 46).

(261) Eine Frage der Talbildung. Bibl. geogr. Handbücher, Stuttgart 1918. *Festband Albr. Penck*, p. 66.

(262) WALTHER PENCK, Op. 17, p. 71. The change of facies does not take place steadily but, just like the cycles of sedimentation, in progressive periods, a partial phenomenon to which we shall refer later; see the facies profile in Alb. HEIM, *Geologie der Schweiz*, Leipzig, 1916, Bd. I, p. 65.

(263) As to the form of the *longitudinal profile of the* pre-glacial *valleys*, no direct conclusion can be drawn from observation, since naturally the valley floors experienced, and show, the strongest glacial action. A. PENCK, E. BRÜCKNER (*Die Alpen im Eiszeitalter, loc. cit.* [n. 258]) and H. LAUTENSACH (Die Übertiefung des Tessingebiets, *Geogr. Abh.*, N.F. Heft 1, 1912) ascribed a graded longitudinal profile to the pre-glacial valley floors and referred the steps in trough valleys solely to erosion by Pleistocene ice. Indeed, H. LAUTENSACH believed that he could recognise the edges and upper ends of

fluviatile V-shaped valleys, worked over by ice, in the shoulders and heads of glacial troughs. During interglacial periods, rivers would have cut into steps previously produced by overdeepening, and have eaten back along the sections of valley lying above these. This interpretation does not make the relationship quite clear between the shoulder and the first trough to be sunk into the supposedly graded pre-glacial valley floor; and it fails as an explanation for the trough shoulders which continue above the terminal basin of the glacier. De MARTONNE, KILIAN and DISTEL also considered trough shoulders and trough heads to be of fluviatile origin; but they make a similar assumption for the valley steps, since these are not always present where they should be found according to the theory of overdeepening. These writers put the fluviatile origin of those glacial forms back in pre-glacial times, thus ascribing to the pre-glacial valley floor an ungraded, broken, longitudinal profile (E. de MARTONNE, Sur la théorie mécanique de l'érosion glaciaire. *C. R. Ac. Sc. Paris* CL, 1910, p. 135; also *Ann. de Géogr.* 1910, p. 289, 1911, p. 1 and elsewhere; W. KILIAN et M. GIGNOUX, *C. R. Ac. Sc. Paris* CLI, 1910, p. 1023; *Bull. serv. carte géol. de France* XXI, 1911, p. 25; L. DISTEL, Die Formen alpiner Hochtäler, etc. *Landesk. Forsch. geogr. Gesellsch. München.* Heft 13 1912; also *P.M.* 1912, II, p. 328). The question cannot here be pursued in greater detail. Merely this can be pointed out: not only are the convex slope profiles essential features of waxing development, but also the longitudinal valley profiles which are, in accordance with the rule, divided up by convex breaks of gradient working back up-valley. This rule has already been demonstrated for the German Highlands, and will later be proved in detail (see fig. 13, p. 200). The division is brought about by the working up-valley, one after another and one above another, of eroding reaches with different degrees of steepness. At times they leave behind them a graded reach which, dissected by the next lower, backward-working break of gradient, may be preserved for a while as a *terrace with a naturally graded longitudinal profile*. The evidence of waxing development in the Alps makes it impossible not to draw the conclusion that the Pleistocene glaciers found stepped valley floors, stepped in their longitudinal profiles by the steeper, backward-working erosional reaches, and in the transverse profile by terraces, each with a gentle, graded longitudinal slope. I consider it probable that the steps of overdeepening are to be associated with such breaks of gradient in the pre-glacial valley floors (accentuating them), and certain that the trough shoulders are the margins of terraces which have been worked over and remodelled by the ice. But this is far from denying that some shoulders and heads of glacial troughs have in fact been derived from the edges of the sharp interglacial V-shaped valleys which, during the ice-free periods, cut back into the steps of overdeepening that were already present. But one must be on one's guard against taking pre-glacial terraces for valley floors which the Pleistocene glaciers found and used, and concluding from the graded course of the terraces that there was a similar grading of the glacier floor. Should no tectonic deformations have occurred, the pre-glacial terraces continue in the same way as far as, or close to, the neighbourhood of the general base level of erosion at the mountain edge; and there, as trough shoulders, they appear at a greater or lesser height above the terminal basins.

(264) *Geologie der Schweiz*, 1919, Band II, pp. 66-71.

(265) N. KREBS was the first to draw attention to the plateau flats, or plateau regions, and their independence of the fold structure (Die nördlichen Alpen zwischen Enns, Traisen und Mürz, *loc. cit.* [n. 258]). For further detailed investigation we have to thank G. GÖTZINGER (Geomorphologie der Lunzer Seen und ihres Gebietes. *Intern. Revue Hydrobiol. Hydrogr.* Leipzig 1912). F. MACHATSCHEK (Verebnungsflächen und junge Krustenbewegungen im alpinen Gebirgsystem. *Z.G.E.* 1916, no. 9, p. 602; no. 10, p. 675) attempted an analysis of the crustal movements with their help. We are unable to agree with the results. They are influenced by the earlier, generally accepted, but erroneous postulate, according to which forms of medium relief, or peneplanes (these being considered as the final result of denudation on a stationary block), can arise only in periods of tectonic rest. This is not in harmony with the fact that plateau landscapes came into existence just at a time of active crustal movements.

(266) G. GÖTZINGER, Lunzer Seen, *loc. cit.* [n. 265]; the same: Zur Frage des Alters der Oberflächenformen der östlichen Kalkhochalpen. *Mitteil. k.k. geogr. Gesellsch. Wien* 1913, Heft 1-2, p. 39. Weitere neue Funde von Augensteinen auf den östlichen Kalkhochalpen plateaus. *Verh. k.k. geol. R.-A.* Wien 1913, p. 61, and 1915, no. 14, p. 272.

(267) F. MACHATSCHEK, Verebnungsflächen usw., *loc. cit.* [n. 265], p. 605.

(268) Lunzer Seen., *loc. cit.* [n. 265], p. 20 and elsewhere.

(269) F. F. HAHN, Geologie des oberen Saalachgebietes zwischen Lofer und Diesbachtal. *Jahrb. k.k. geol. R.-A.* Wien, LXIII, 1913, p. 1 (especially pp. 19-24). As a third and highest level there occur the sometimes plateau-like summits which, on the plateaux of the High Alpine zone, rise several hundred metres above the valley bottoms (e.g. Hoher Göll, Tennengebirge, 2400-2500 m.). HAHN traces this altitudinal position to the westward directed crossfolding at the end of the Oligocene. It would be better to say: the continued upward movement of the Alps and their individual parts, which brought the plateau regions to great altitudes, and led to their being broken up by deep valleys, steeply incised, was not without horizontal components which, at the end of the Oligocene, were directed westwards.

(270) H. HASSINGER, Geomorphologische Untersuchungen aus dem Wiener Becken und seinem Randgebirge, *Geogr. Abh.* VIII, Heft 3, 1905.—G. GÖTZINGER, *loc. cit.* [n. 265].—N. KREBS places the origin and development of the plateau country between Oligocene and the second Mediterranean stage (*Länderkunde der Österreich. Alpen, loc. cit.* [n. 258], p. 40); but in his recent work he considers these raised beaches of the Vienna Basin to be Mediterranean and not as late as Pontian (*Z.G.E.* 1914, no. 4, p. 234).

(271) In attempting to give a date, the following points must be borne in mind: the plateau country has wide trough-shaped valleys from which concave slopes lead up to a definite average steepness, taking into account only the pre-glacial slopes. Occasionally these very steep slope units have already met in

sharp edges. But often above them the slopes curve convexly again to produce rounded forms, and even plateau surfaces at a higher level (see note 269), a witness to waxing having preceded waning development. The dating may thus refer to two periods of time: to that of waxing development, continuing till the steepest slope units found anywhere along the course of the down-cutting streams had been produced; and to the succeeding period of waning development, lasting till dissection of the plateau began. This involved the final separation of its set of land forms from their former base level of erosion; and since then any further happenings have been only in the direction of waning development. It was probably in the Lower Miocene, if not earlier, that the plateau dissection commenced. As a first rough approximation, we may put the onset of waning development, i.e. the completion of the valley systems peculiar to the plateaux, in the Oligocene. In any case, it becomes evident that the developmental history of the plateau regions of the High Alps, traces of which are to be observed in the forms of *waxing* development, must reach far back into early Tertiary times.

(272) *Länderkunde der Österreich. Alpen, loc. cit.* [n. 258], p. 39.

(273) This dating is completely uncertain, and has apparently been put at too high a horizon in the late Tertiary. See E. BRÜCKNER, *Die Alpen im Eiszeitalter, loc. cit.* [n. 258], p. 992.

(274) For orientation see F. KOSSMAT, Die adriatische Umrandung in der alpinen Faltenregion. *Mitteil. geol. Gesellsch. Wien* 1913, p. 61 (with geol. *Übersichtskarte*), the geol. *Spezialaufnahmen* by F. KOSSMAT 1 : 75,000, Bl. Tolmein (Z. 21, K. IX) and Bischoflack-Idria (Z. 21, K. X) and F. KOSSMAT's accounts in *Verh. k.k. geolog. R.-A.* Wien 1908, p. 81, 1909, p. 85.

(275) F. KOSSMAT, Die morphologische Entwicklung der Gebirge im Izonzo- und oberen Save-gebiet. *Z.G.E.* 1916, no. 9–10, p. 645.

(276) F. KOSSMAT, Geologie des Wocheiner Tunnels. *Denkschr. math.-nat. Kl. Akad. Wiss. Wien*, LXXXII, 1907, p. 41.

(277) N. KREBS, Die Halbinsel Istrien. *Geogr. Abh.*, Wien 1907, IX, 2.— F. KOSSMAT, Der küstenländische Hochkarst und seine tektonische Stellung. *Verh. k.k. Geolog. R.-A.* Wien 1909, no. 4–5, p. 85 (p. 116 ff.). The same: *Z.G.E.* Berlin 1916, no. 9–10, pp. 35 ff. See the profile in N. KREBS, *Länderkunde der Österreich. Alpen, loc. cit.* [n. 258], p. 42. For the following, consult the geological *Spezialaufnahmen* 1 : 75,000 drawn up by G. STACHE and F. KOSSMAT: Sheets Görz (Z. 22, K. IX), Triest (Z. 23, K. IX), Adelsberg (Z. 22, K. X). Sheet Sessana (Z. 23, K. X) is topographical only.

(278) *Loc. cit.* [n. 277], p. 52. F. TELLER, *Erläuterungen zur geolog. Karte* 1 : 75,000, Sheet Rohitsch-Drachenburg [Z. 21, K. XIII]. Wien 1905.

(279) See sheet Cilli und Ratschach of the geolog. *Spezialkarte* 1 : 75,000 (Z. 21, K. XII). [Wien].

(280) F. TELLER, Geolog. *Spezialkarte* 1 : 75,000, Sheet Eisenkappel und Kanker (Z. 20, K. XI) and sheet Prassberg (Z. 20, K. XII); *Erläuterungen sur geolog. Karte Eisenkappel und Kanker*. Wien 1898.

(281) Here this is the surface which the lacustrine Upper Oligocene (Sotzka beds) found and covered over. Its distribution does not coincide with that of

the marine Middle Oligocene, but it transgresses over denudational remains of this; and over wide areas it extends directly on to the older substratum (Trias, Palaeozoics) from which these had already been removed.

(282) E. Brückner, *Die Alpen im Eiszeitalter*, Bd. III, 1909, p. 1037.—A. Grund, Die Entstehung und Geschichte des Adriatisches Meeres. *Geogr. Jahresber. aus Österreich* VI, Wien 1907. Die Oberflächenformen des Dinarischen Gebirges. *Z.G.E.* 1908, p. 468 (pp. 479 ff.).—N. Krebs, Die Halbinsel Istrien, *loc. cit.* [n. 277]. Verbogene Verebnungsflächen in Istrien. *Geogr. Jahresber. aus Österreich* IV, Wien 1906, p. 75.—F. Kossmat, Der küstenländische Hochkarst, etc., *loc. cit.* [n. 277], p. 121.

(283) A. Grund, Die Karsthydrographie. *Geogr. Abh.* VII, Heft 3, Leipzig 1903. Beiträge zur Morphologie des Dinarischen Gebirges, *loc. cit.* [n. 165], pp. 196 ff. Cvijić also describes the finger-like penetration of the lower surfaces into the higher lands which again are topped by peneplanes (J. Cvijić, Bildung und Dislozierung der Dinarischen Rumpffläche. *P.M.* 1909, Heft VI, VII, VIII); but in the end he considered them all to be parts of a single, uniform peneplane.

(284) J. Cvijić, *loc. cit.* [n. 283]. According to the information so far obtained, the peneplanes and piedmont benchlands on the individual ranges of the Dinaric Mountains, which are divided from each other by synclinal zones (with series of polyes, and often also with longitudinal faults) have little or nothing at all to do with one another. They seem in every case to be peculiar to the chains on which they occur. The same thing has been noticed in the tectonic and morphological continuation of the Dinarids in the western Taurus. Here, as in other regions of broad folds, it is not a uniform peneplane, nor even an ancient uniform set of land forms, warped into undulations in such a fashion that they extend into the floors of the broad synclines—in which faults or overthrusts may ultimately appear; but the form associations on the ranges came into existence whilst these were rising, and are therefore confined to them. Their geological equivalents are to be found within the broad synclines as form associations of a different type, or as correlated deposits [see glossary]. One might assume analogous conditions for the Dinaric Mountains; yet it is not possible to form an opinion so long as views differ so widely not only as to the interpretation of the features, but even as to their characteristics.

(285) Good illustrations of the peneplanes, piedmont benchlands, and inselbergs of the Dinaric Mountains may be found, amongst other places, in J. Cvijić (*P.M.* 1909, *loc. cit.* [n. 283], plate 13), A. Grund (*G.Z.E.* 1908, illustrations 99–104), O. Maull (*Geogr. Jahresber. Österr.* XI, plates II, III).

(286) Where the substratum is impermeable, the piedmont flat persists in its function of local base level of erosion for the eroding reaches working back from it, even though it becomes itself dissected by valleys. This holds until this same function is taken over by the convex breaks of gradient which form the upper ends of the new eroding sections (those dissecting the piedmont flat), and migrate upstream with them. Important differences occur in the Karst. The process which gives rise to the dissection of a piedmont flat—

uplift—also produces a relative lowering of the ground water level; and where the terrain is limestone, this leads to a disappearance of the streams. Whole valley courses thus become functionless and further normal dissection of the higher-rising land is impeded. In this way earlier conditions of valley dissection become, as it were, fixed, and for a long time remain pretty well intact— see, for example, the high valleys of Čepovan, Godowitsch, Radek, etc., described by F. KOSSMAT, all presumably of Pontian age (*Z.G.E.* 1916, nos. 9–10, pp. 650 ff.). They last until obliterated by the formation of dolines, a process of dissection which then replaces fluviatile erosion (see the progressive dissection by doline stairways of the high-lying limestone areas which rise up in the western Taurus: W. PENCK, Op. 10).

(287) A. PENCK, Geomorphologische Studien aus der Herzegowina. *Zeitschr. d. und ö. Alpen-Vereins* XXXI, 1900, p. 25.—O. MAULL, Geomorphologische Studien aus Mitteldalmatien. *Geogr. Jahresber. aus Österreich* XI.

(288) A. AIGNER, *Jahrb. geol. R.-A.* Wien LXVI, 1916, p. 293.—A. WINKLER, *Mitteil. geolog. Gesellsch. Wien* III–IV, 1914, p. 256.—J. SÖLCH, *Verh.* 18. *deutsch. Geographentag* Innsbruck, 1912, p. 218.—H. SL NAR *Mitteil. k.k. geogr. Gesellsch. Wien*, 1916, p. 281.—H. MOHR, Geologie der Wechselbahn, *Denkschr. k.k. Akad. Wiss. Wien*, math.-nat. Kl. LXXXII.— F. MACHATSCHEK. *Z.G.E.* 1916, no. 9, p. 602 (pp. 608 ff.).—E. de MARTONNE, *Bull. géogr.-histor. descr.*, no. 3, 1911, p. 387 (pp. 405 ff.), etc.

(289) A. AIGNER, *loc. cit.* [n. 288], considers the old flattish form associations on the mountainous margin of the embayment of Graz to be of Pliocene age (Pontian). But the valleys had already been invaded by lacustrine Lower Miocene! Further investigation is necessary.

(290) Apart from the fact that, *other things being equal*, the old form associations on the limestone intervalley divides are more likely to be preserved than on impermeable material.

(291) Established by F. KOSSMAT for sheet Stein 1 : 25,000 (oral information). Part of the basal transgressive formations of the Lower Miocene on sheet Cilli-Ratschach (F. TELLER, *loc. cit.* [n. 278] might also probably be marine Aquitanian (part of the lower Nullipore limestone).

(292) Amongst the works named see especially: W. PETRASCHEK, *Verh. k.k. geol. R.-A.* Wien, 1915, Heft 17–18, p. 310.—J. SÖLCH, Das Grazer Hügelland, *Sitz.-Ber. Akad. Wiss. Wien* math.-nat. Kl. CXXX, Heft 8–9, 1921, p. 265.—A. WINKLER, *Jahrb. geolog. Staats-Anst.* Wien, LXXI, 1921, Heft 1–2, p. 1; *idem.* 1913, LXIII, p. 617 and elsewhere.—V. HILBER, Das Tertiärgebiet um Graz. *Jahrb. k.k. geolog. R.-A.* Wien, 1893; *idem.* 1894, XLIV, p. 389.— R. HÖRNES, *Bau und Bild der Ebenen Österreichs.* Leipzig 1903.

(293) WALTHER PENCK, Op. 10.

(294) P. OPPENHEIM, Das Neogen in Kleinasien. *Z.D.G.G.* LXX, 1918, p. 1. My earlier view, that the *youngest* divisions of the Neogene *generally* belong to the Levantine stage, does not seem to be correct.

(295) It is also because of this that the Neogene, which throughout possesses either a shallow water (marine, brackish or lacustrine) or a fluviatile

character, also attains an exceedingly great thickness. From this, A. PHILIPPSON, who published numerous individual observations on the facies and bedding of the Tertiary, had already deduced deposition on a sinking substratum (Reisen und Forschungen im westlichen Kleinasien. *P.M.* Erg.- Hefte 167, 172, 177, 180, 183, 1910–15).

(296) The assumption that the Anatolian broad folds might have arisen by compression from outside (W. PENCK, Op. 10, p. 116) is erroneous, and has already been withdrawn as untenable on other grounds (W. PENCK, Op. 16, p. 345, note 1).

(297) The same relationship has been established in the north of the Argentine Pampean sierras on approaching the Puna de Atacama (W. PENCK, Op. 16), and is, as I have stressed elsewhere, the fundamental mechanical feature for the development of this kind of faulting (*Geol. Zentralbl.* XXV, 1920–21, pp. 392 ff.). It sets in with *increase in the intensity* of the crustal movement, which leads to overstepping the limit of elasticity proper to the block that is being moved. Increase in amplitude is due to similar causes. In the Argentine, however, the depressions are not as a rule traversed by two long tudinal faults, but only by one. They cannot here be called rift valleys (trough faulting). According to my observations, the same thing holds for the longitudinal depressions of north-west Anatolia which, in spite of the faults, have by no means lost their synclinal character. A. PHILIPPSON, on the other hand, stresses the trough-faulted character of many depressions in western Asia Minor. Further investigation is required.

(298) See W. PENCK, Op. 10, pp. 21–42, profile on p. 26. Geol. map by A. PHILIPPSON 1 : 300,000, sheet 2 (*P.M.* Erg.-Heft 1913).

(299) The western Pleistocene corries are sunk in this set of slopes.

(300) This is the case particularly in the western part of the 'upper terrace'. Thus two levels are present: on the broad divides between the minor valleys there are flattish form associations, widespread fragments of the piedmont surface, and the level of the flat floors themselves scarcely 100 metres lower. At the headwaters of the valleys, both levels almost or quite merge into one another (here the peneplane has no sharp V-shaped incisions, or merely slight suggestions of them); on the other hand they *converge* downwards towards the edge of the 'upper terrace' (coincidence of both levels at the point where the minor valleys issue on to it, e.g. in the western section of the 'upper terrace'). In between lies the zone of the strongest downcutting, where V-shaped valleys, often still narrow, are enclosed by low, steep convex slopes. It follows indubitably from this that dissection is still continuing, that it has a *modern* character. Some of the minor valleys are of pre-Pleistocene origin (glacial modification is to be seen near Kirkbunar, corries being sunk into the slopes in the district east of it), others are younger; all have portions where down-cutting is active at the present day. But—and here is the essential point—this finds its lower surface of reference, not at the mountain foot, but more than 1000 metres higher at the edge of the 'upper terrace' or close below it. The minor valleys are not parts of the steep relief, which is similar in nature (though its altitudinal differences are immensely greater) and reaches up from

the foot of the mountain chain into its flanks; but they end high above it. In a word, they are nothing but the result of the still persisting deformation of the piedmont surface and of the steepening thus produced.

(301) W. PENCK, Op. 10, p. 36 and elsewhere.

(302) W. PENCK, Op. 10, pp. 163 ff.

(303) *Atti della Soc. Toscana di Sc. nat.* IX, Pisa 1894–95, Proc. verb., p. 141.

(304) This is a pure assumption. For the present all attempts at dating in this area are still utterly uncertain. There are, however, adequate grounds for ascribing a post-Levantine age to surface II (which I had distinguished, together with the central mountainland (I), as 'Relief I'). A. PHILIPPSON has pointed this out (Zur morphologischen Karte des westlichen Kleinasien. *P.M.* 1920, p. 197); but, on the other hand, he has overlooked the fact that I did not discover anything corresponding to the configuration of piedmont surface II in the coarse basal conglomerates of the Neogene on the south side of Olympus. These were rather to be correlated with contemporaneous dissection of the mountainland rising above. This even today strews coarse granite blocks over the 'upper terrace' lying in front of it, and right away from the Pleistocene corries. My previous identification in date of surface II with the Levantine peneplane in Thrace, rested partly on the fundamental error that similarity of form, which signifies merely similar development, was taken to mean contemporaneous development, as is customarily done (A. PHILIPPSON also adopts this usage in the work just quoted). To assume a parallel development in age for peneplanes, or other form associations of a similar kind, occurring on different ranges, is absolutely inadmissable, even if they have similar or exactly the same altitudes, unless their similarity in age has been proved *stratigraphically*. It is possible, but by no means certainly established, that the peneplane (corresponding to surface III) which can be traced at least fragmentarily in all the Anatolian depressions and cuts across the Neogene filling, is a uniform formation, since in several places it has been found to pass over without interruption from one depression to another; and according to PHILIPPSON it also passes over into the peneplane of Inner Anatolia, which occupies the same position over the Neogene beds, there but little distorted. In every case this undoubted primary peneplane signifies a change from deposition to denudation in the broad synclines and central basins of sedimentation as well. It is a change which naturally cannot owe its origin to the broad folding, but which is due to the regional uplift of the whole system of broad folds (W. PENCK, Op. 10, pp. 38, 116, and elsewhere).

(305) W. PENCK, Op. 10, pp. 15–21.

(306) R. A. DALY, The accordance of summit levels among alpine mountains. *J.G.* XIII, no. 2, 1905.—A. PENCK, Die Gipfelflur der Alpen, *loc. cit.* [n. 10], pp. 257 ff.

(307) On the south side of the Gulf of Gemlik (somewhere between the Kavakli liman and the mouth of the Susurlu) the Neogene dips uniformly northwards towards the sea, to emerge again on the north side of the drowned broad syncline with an equally regular southward dip (island of Emir Ali

[Imrali]). Here, in the thick beds of sandy conglomerates, I collected *Dreissensia* of presumably Pontian age. Work still remains to be done.

(308) Quite often the gipfelflur condition has not been reached. Instead, over wide areas, there are still—between the sharply sunk V-shaped erosion valleys—old flattish form associations. These immediately give one an insight into the fact that there has been abrupt anticlinal warping. (Op. 10, pp. 19, 72, etc.)

(309) Oral communication.

(310) Grundlinien der Geographie und Geologie von Mazedonien und Altserbien. *P.M.* Erg.-Bd. XXXIV, Heft 162, 1908, pp. 85–86, 167, 185, 334.

(311) *Georgr. Abhg.* X, Heft 3, Leipzig 1921.

(312) See note 284. The longitudinal depressions between the Dinaric chains were originally, i.e. during their formation, also areas of deposition, even if not to the same extent as in Anatolia. Oligocene, early and late Miocene, perhaps even Lower Pliocene, basin deposits have been recognised in them. In the majority of cases, those broad synclines have (as in Anatolia) later become areas of denudation. Peneplanes, acting as piedmont flats for the ranges on either side, extend over their floors and over the superimposed Tertiary. Here, series of polyes are sunk in the peneplanes of the broad synclines, and are analogous to the river valleys in Anatolia. They are a species of dissection which owes its development and its peculiar features to the special denudational processes that occur in the Karst; but fundamentally their causation is no different from the valley dissection of the Anatolian depressions. Here, as there, the sequence of phenomena: sedimentation—primary peneplane—downcutting or karsting (polyes) as the case may be, signifies the onset and the *intensification of the causes* leading to the destructive invasion of the region of subsidence by meteoric waters. Here, as there, these causes have originated from the broad folding, on account of which the synclines sink with respect to the anticlines. For that, naturally, would not promote downcutting. If anything, it could only impede it, so leading rather to lateral erosion or to deposition in the depressions. Any consequences of broad folding would appear as *an interruption* of that outstanding process of development which is known from observation. The (Pliocene?) gravels occasionally transgressing over surface III (and its analogous Anatolian surfaces), the present deposition and lake formation at the bottom of the zones of denudation within the Anatolian depressions, the stabilisation of some of the polye lakes in the Lycian Taurus, may be cited here. The progressive dissection of the depressions by streams, and the equivalent polye formation can, on the other hand, be induced only by progressive uplift of the whole broad fold system. Obviously this applies to the Dinaric Mountains as well as to Asia Minor.

(313) G. K. GILBERT, *Geographical and geological explorations and surveys west of the one hundredth meridian*, Washington 1874, and Vol. III, *Geology*, 1875.

(314) G. K. GILBERT, Lake Bonneville, *U.S. Geol. Surv. Monogr.* 1, 1890. —I. C. RUSSELL, Geological history of Lake Lahontan, etc., *U.S. Geol. Surv. Monogr.* 11, 1885.—A. C. LAWSON, The recent fault scarps at Genoa, Nevada.

Bull. Seismological Soc. Am. II, no. 3, 1912, p. 193. A. KNOPF, A geological reconnaissance of the Inyo range and the eastern slope of the southern Sierra Nevada, Cal. *U.S. geol. Surv. prof. Pap.* 110, 1918 and elsewhere.

(315) W. M. DAVIS, The Mountain ranges of the Great Basin. *Bull. Mus. comparat. Zoology*, XLII, 1903, p. 129. The Wasatch, Canyon and House ranges, Utah. *Ibid.* XLIX, 1905, p. 15. Even when using the cycle theory for the morphological treatment of the question, it is obvious that the decisive geological premise is whether the faults are actually present. DAVIS takes them for granted, adducing as evidence a feature already used by the earliest investigators of the Basin Ranges (see S. F. CUNNANS, *Report of the Geological Survey of the Fortieth Parallel*, II. Descript. Geol., Washington 1877, p. 345). Today, too, it is pretty generally accepted as a direct indication, free from all ambiguity, of the faulted nature of the mountain edges, when other methods, geological and incontrovertible, cannot be used. This feature is the simple straight line course of the mountain foot, i.e. the boundary between the zones of denudation and deposition; the way in which this line runs, independent of the mountain structure; and the steep drop of the mountain side towards it. Yet this group of features proves nothing at all. The base of the mountain in the above definition is the outcrop of the lower surface of the youngest of the correlated strata. It is an unconformity, the outcrop of which is, of course, likewise *independent* of the mountain structure. It can intersect the strike of the mountain at any angle whatsoever, in the same way as it intersects the exposure of any other older and more or less distorted unconformity. Nor could recent deposits be expected to border on the base of the range any differently from the way in which the older correlated layers border on the folded or otherwise disturbed sedimentary strata of the mountain mass, viz. by abutting against the upper surface of the layers upon which—beneath the present surface—they are superposed. These unconformities at the edge of growing ranges, particularly the older ones, exhibit a graded form, i.e. they are almost level. Continued arching of the range naturally leads to varying degrees of tilting of the unconformity or, in more general terms, of that part of the mountain flank which, through the downwarping as it becomes covered by the accumulating material, corresponds to such an unconformity. The foot of the range then possesses—like many steeply arched broad anticlines which are entirely unfaulted in their structure—a simple straight course against which the steep relief of the flexed mountain flank rests, provided that there are the requisite general causes for producing steep relief (and note that these have nothing in the least to do with fault dislocation). Thus, by themselves, the above mentioned features in no way possess the value of a clear cut proof that the mountain mass is bordered by anything in the nature of a fault.

(316) Thorough geological surveys have brought home the unreliability of these morphological characteristics, even to observers who were otherwise perfectly convinced of their validity as a tectonic proof (of dislocation by faulting). Thus A. KNOPF (*loc. cit.* [n. 314]) attempts to deduce the trough-faulted nature of Owens Valley and the neighbouring depressions, as W. LINDGREN had done before him (Tertiary gravels of the Sierra Nevada of

California. *U.S. geol. Surv. prof. Pap.* 73, 1911) from the steep drop of the ranges that enclose it (Sierra Nevada in the west, Inyo Range in the east), and from the facetted spurs along the foot of each. But he finds that the 'steep drop' of the Sierra Nevada is a slope having a maximum inclination of 25°, characterised by a roughly dissected steep relief. He takes it to be the out-cropping of the marginal fault, since that steep relief meets the gentle forms of medium relief, on the summit of the range, in a sharp break of gradient. Herein lies the great illusion, to which very many observers in other places have even more thoroughly succumbed, which causes the steep forms (of vigorous downcutting) found on a slope to be taken for the steepness of the slope itself. The same kind of steep drop, where steep relief below is linked to medium relief forms above, occurs on the flanks of broad folds where it has been proved that they have been formed without faulting (see, for example, illustration 6 and the profiles belonging to it in WALTHER PENCK, Op. 16, and for the same region illustrations 7–8 in WALTHER PENCK, Topographische Aufnahmen am Südrand der Puna de Atacama. *Z.G.E.* 1918, no. 5–6, p. 193). Further, the facets which, too, KNOPF considered to be undoubted fault sur-faces, have shown themselves to be quite a fickle characteristic, absent where faults could be stratigraphically proved, appearing where they could not be established, visible along the mountain foot for short stretches with long inter-ruptions, and penetrating into valleys (*loc. cit.* [n. 314], pp. 78, 88, 89, plate XV, A). As a result, KNOPF considers Owens Valley to be a fault-trough, but he admits that the marginal faults can only be surmised, not discovered (*loc. cit.*, p. 80). On the other hand, there are recent faults present in the alluvium near the middle of the depression.

(317) Examine, for instance, the profiles drawn to scale on plate IX and pp. 102, 293 in WALTHER PENCK, Op. 16, and the illustrations 1, 16, 22, 29 belong-ing to them, as well as illustration 1, plate 1 in *Geologische Charakterbilder*, Heft 24, 1921, which morphologically show nothing of the strike faults that traverse the section illustrated by the picture. Similarly with plate III and the profile on p. 58 in A. KNOPF, Inyo range, *loc. cit.* [n. 314], and elsewhere.

(318) C. KING, *Report of the Geological Survey of the Fortieth Parallel*, III, Mining Industry, Washington 1870, and I, Systematic Geology, 1878.

(319) *J.G.* XXI, 1913, p. 273.

(320) See, amongst others, the profiles by G. D. LOUDERBACK through the Humbolt Lake Mountains (*B.G.S.A.* XV, 1904, p. 289). Outside the Basin Ranges proper we may mention the broad anticline of the Bighorn Mountains (N. H. DARTON, *U.S. geol. Surv. prof. Pap.* 51, Washington 1906).

(321) A general idea of the geology is given by the geological map of the Argentine Republic 1 : 1,000,000 of L. BRACKEBUSCH (Gotha 1891, *Actas Acad. Nac. Ciencias Cordoba*, VII). See also the short discussion by H. GERTH (Die pampinen Sierren Zentralargentiniens. *G.R.* IV, Heft 8, 1913, p. 577) and the more recent supplements by H. RASSMUS (*Minist. de Agricultura Dirección General de Minas etc.*, Bol. 13, Serie B, Buenos Aires 1916).

(322) WALTHER PENCK, Op. 16. L. BRACKEBUSCH had already assumed the, presence of broad anticlines and synclines in the ranges and depressions.

(323) A. STELZNER, *Beiträge zur Geologie und Paläontologie der Argentinischen Republik*, I. Kassel-Berlin 1885.—G. BODENBENDER, La Sierra de Cordoba. *Anales Minist. de Agricult. Sección Geología*, I, no. 2. Buenos Aires 1905.

(324) R. BEDER gives illustrations of the greatest drops on the western side of the Sierra de Cordoba: Estudios geologicós etc., Villa Dolores, *Minist. de Agricult., Dirección General de Minas etc.*, Bol. 14, Serie B, Buenos Aires 1916, plate IV, lower illustration, and plate V.

(325) O. SCHMIEDER, Apuntes geomorfológicos de la Sierra Grande de Cordoba. *Bol. Ac. Nac. de Cienc. Cordoba*, XXV, 1921, p. 183, profile p. 189.

(326) O. SCHMIEDER, *loc. cit.* [n. 325].—H. GERTH, *loc. cit.* [n. 321], p. 587. The same: Constitución gelóogica, hidrogeológica etc. de la Provincia de San Luis. *Anales Minist. Agricult. Sección Geología*, X, no. 2, Buenos Aires 1914, p. 33.—H. RASSMUS, La Sierra del Aconquija. *Soc. Argentina de Cienc. naturales*, Buenos Aires 1918.—E. RIMANN, Estudio geológico de la Sierra Chica. *Bol. Acad. Nac. de Cienc. Cordoba*, XXIII, 1918, p. 129.

(327) WALTHER PENCK, Op. 16, pp. 137, 365.

(328) Figs. 6, 8, 9 of E. RIMANN's treatise show this as clearly as could be desired.

(329) I am here following the information given by H. SCHMIEDER, *loc. cit.* [n. 325], pp. 188–191. The general situation may be gathered from G. BODEN-BENDER's small generalised geological map (*loc. cit.* [n. 323]).

(330) Their convex form and slight average gradient can be recognised in illustration 3 of SCHMIEDER's paper (*loc. cit.* [n. 325], p. 190)—in other respects the illustration is not very good; next to it, p. 191, is an inselberg belonging to the highest level.

(331) G. BODENBENDER, Constitución geológica de la parte meridional de La Rioja y Regiones limitrofes. *Bol. Ac. Nac. de Cienc. Cordoba*, 1911, XIX, Entr. 1, pp. 131 ff.

(332) E. RIMANN, *loc. cit.* [n. 326], p. 58.

(333) G. BODENBENDER, La Sierra de Cordoba, *loc. cit.* [n. 323], p. 63. Cf. the map. The Sierra del Norte is not a continuation of the Sierra Chica, but begins, with its trend along a more easterly meridian, approximately at the place where the Sierra Chica comes to an end northwards. The ends of the two chains are separated from each other by a depression.

(334) WALTHER PENCK, Op. 16, chap. IV and V, 3, especially pp. 346–348.

(335) WALTHER PENCK, Op. 16, chap. IV. The basis for what follows is contained in chap. III, 2–5 and chap. VI; see also the profile and the geological map 1 : 200,000.

(336) An example of this type is the range which rises up from the basin of Tinogasta along the meridian of the Sierra de Fiambalá, south of Tinogasta itself, and continues along the western side of the longitudinal depression of Copacabana, through which the Rio Abaucan flows (see the map by BRACKEBUSCH and WALTHER PENCK, Op. 16, pp. 18–19, sketch map p. 15).

(337) It must be borne in mind that the absolute amount of the limiting value must be very different for individual kinds of rock, since these reach

their maximum slope gradients, which normally cannot be exceeded, at very different angles of inclination. Such diversities are shown in illustrations 6 (crystalline rocks) and 1 (Cretaceous-Tertiary) in WALTHER PENCK, Op. 16, plates 1 and 2.

(338) The intensity of erosion is a function of the intensity of uplift. It increases with this so long as a limiting value, dependent upon the amount of water available, has not been reached—it being assumed that the character of the rocks is the same. More details will be given in later sections. Further increase in the intensity of uplift will then no longer be counterbalanced by an equally rapid sinking-in of the stream beds; but these are raised with the block, and so, in spite of the most intense downcutting, they are moved to greater absolute heights above sea level. This again naturally brings about an increase in the absolute altitude of the gipfelflur, though not of its relative height.

(339) See illustration 29, WALTHER PENCK, Op. 16.

(340) III is not everywhere present, since in several places the younger steep relief already abuts directly upon II. The same is true for II, e.g. it is absent from the east side of the Tolar. Here relief types I and III are in direct contact. And this may be connected with the fact that ranges at this latitude do not drop to deep bolsons on both sides; but on the east they drop to a secondary longitudinal depression which rises to a great altitude and possesses in its upper parts a medium relief, as yet completely undissected (Lajas depression). See fig. 20 B.

(341) WALTHER PENCK, Op. 16.

(342) WALTHER PENCK, Op. 16, pp. 377 ff., p. 399. For the same feature in Anatolia see pp. 280–281 and Note 300.

(343) W. PENCK, Op. 16, pp. 200–202.

(344) A glance at fig. 20 shows that the arrangement of form associations typical of type A 2 does not occur at all on the older ranges (B). The sections a, b, c (fig. 20 B) across the Sierra de Fiambalá have been so arranged that form types ever younger in origin are shown successively on the summits (I → III). The sections might just as well be transverse profiles through the highest parts of three chains of different ages, which originated one after another in the sequence a → c, and have [taken] the same developmental *direction* as the Sierra de Fiambalá. It is immediately evident that a cross section through the plunging end of the Sierra de Fiambalá (e.g. at the position g) which would correspond to a section through one of the youngest ranges, has the form of fig. 20, A 1 and *not* that of A 2.

(345) WALTHER PENCK, Op. 16, chap. III, 2–4, VI, 1.

(346) See sections 9–18 of the plate of profiles and the diagrammatic profile on p. 367, W. PENCK, Op. 16.

(347) Owing to the absence of fossils it is not possible to determine exactly the age of the vast continental sequence of strata. We are here keeping to the age classification which in a wider connection has, up to the present, proved to come nearest to the truth: Lower Calchaqui beds, only red and brown sandstones; Upper Cretaceous; Upper Calchaqui beds, sandstones transgressing

over conglomerates at the mountain edge: Lower Tertiary Lower Puna beds; sandstones with pityoxylon and, at the edge of the ranges, thick beds of transgressing gravels: Middle Tertiary; Upper Puna beds, pebble-bearing sandstones, gravels at the edge of the ranges: Upper Tertiary.

(348) In a traverse taken a little further south (latitude of Tinogasta) this transitional facies is missing. Obviously the sections of the Famatina chain that are concerned (C. Negro de los Andes) had already appeared by the Lower Tertiary, and there was a gap between them and the parts of the range, also very old, at the edge of the Puna (C. Palca), a gap which was afterwards filled by the 'Sierra Narvaez', part of the range that arose later.

(349) See plate 26, illustration 1, WALTHER PENCK: Hauptzüge im Bau des Südrandes der Puna de Atacama, N. Jahrb. Min. B. B. XXXVIII, 1914, p. 643. The exposure of the surface that was unaffected by denudation of the strata above (re-exposed) is—at the place in the illustration as well as elsewhere—associated with zones of more powerful tilting. Wherever the surface and the bed above it are little inclined, it has not been bared by later denudation, but has—like the bed above—been merely dissected.

(350) See the detailed observations on facies development and damming-up in WALTHER PENCK, Op. 16, pp. 41 ff., Chap. III. 6, and pp. 389 ff. Here, too, features are reported which have to do with the thickness and facies of deposits, as influenced by the geological composition of the areas of supply. Since they are of a local nature, no account has been taken of them in the preceding pages.

(351) All three between the Sierra de Fiambalá and the Calchaqui valleys; see BRACKEBUSCH's map.

(352) See plate 5, illustration 2, Geologische Charakterbilder, Heft 24, 1921.

(353) Geologische Charakterbilder, Heft 24, plate 2, illustrations 2 and 4.

(354) WALTHER PENCK, Op. 16, illustrations 3, 11; Geologische Charakterbilder, Heft 24, plate 3, illustration 2, and plate 2, illustration 1.

(355) See illustrations 3, 11, Op. 16, and Geologische Charakterbilder, Heft 24, plate 7, 2.

(356) Geologische Charakterbilder, Heft 24, plate 1, illustration 3. WALTHER PENCK, Op. 16, illustrations 9, 24.

(357) It is similar in the case of the flanks, sometimes of considerable steepness, of the high ranges that originated earlier, as e.g. the Nevados de la Laguna Blanca. A number of higher, majestic chains, originating later, rear up above the west side of this very old granitic chain. In contradistinction to the broad folds of the southern Puna, of the same age but lower, they are dissected by rocky steep relief into sharp jagged crests, between which there run deeply incised erosional valleys. Farther to the north of this system the superposed volcanic beds, still preserved there, make it evident that the rocky crests have been sculptured out of quite simple anticlines, and that the longitudinal valleys are sunk into similarly simple synclines.

(358) Geologische Charakterbilder, Heft 24, plate 4, illustration 4. For the geological conditions see WALTHER PENCK, Op. 16, pp. 72–73, 212–215, 300–302, 308–310. Illustration 3 shows the range at an acute angle to the strike.

The range west of the Chaschuil depression belongs to the same series, illustration 10.

(359) But it does not show that denudation began only after the completion of the folding. Obviously the two were absolutely simultaneous. It is therefore wrong, without further information, to conclude from a peneplane which extends over folded strata little older than itself, that it is of a later age than the folding. It is younger than the strata, but not younger than the deformation.

(360) Mountain ranges of the Great Basin, *loc. cit.* [n. 315], p. 742.

(361) For literature, see Notes 127–131.

(362) See A. TAFEL, *Meine Tibetreise*, 1914; for peneplanes (and piedmont flats) and their breaking up into convex intermediate forms: Band I, illustrations on plates 57, 60, 67, 68, Band II, plates 6, 10, 17; for steep forms of the highest central mountainlands: Band I, plates 54, 70, Band II, plates 39, 45, etc.

(363) See A. TAFEL, *loc. cit.* [n. 362], Band II, plate 30.

(364) See H. STILLE, Geologische Studien im Gebiet des Rio Magdalena, *v. Koenen-Festschrift*, 1907.—W. SIEVERS, *Z.G.E. Geogr. Abh.* III, Heft I, 1888 and elsewhere.

(365) W. M. DAVIS, The mountain ranges of the Great Basin, *loc. cit.* [n. 315].—A. C. LAWSON, Geomorphogeny of the upper Kern Basin, *California Univ. Dept. Geology Bull.* III, No. 15, 1904, p. 291.—J. A. REID, Geomorphogeny of the Sierra Nevada north-east of Lake Tahoe, *ibid.* VI, 1911.—A. KNOPF, Inyo range and the eastern slope of the southern Sierra Nevada, Cal., *loc. cit.* [n. 314].

(366) A profile through the Sierra Nevada, etc. *Am. geogr. Soc. Transcontinental Excursion*, Memorial Vol. 1915, p. 313.

(367) *U.S. geol. Surv. prof. Pap.*, no. 19, Washington 1903.

(368) The Rocky Mountains also belong to this series. W. M. DAVIS, The Colorado Front Range, *Ann. Assoc. Am. Geogr.* I, 1912.

(369) For the Pamirs see R. W. PUMPELLY, Physiographic observations between Syr Darja and Lake Kara Kul on the Pamir, in 1903. *Carn. Inst. Publ.*, no. 23, p. 122.—A. SCHULTZ, Landeskundliche Forschungen im Pamir. *Abh. Hamburger Kolonialinst.* XXXIII, Series C, 1916.—For the morphology of the Tien Shan: M. FRIEDERICHSEN, Forschungsreise in den zentralen Tienschan. *Mitteil. geogr. Gesellsch, Hamburg* XX, 1894.—R. W. PUMPELLY, Physiography of central Asian deserts and oases. *Carn. Inst. Publ.*, no. 73, 1908, p. 243.—W. M. DAVIS, A journey across Turkestan. *Ibid.*, no. 26, 1905, p. 23.—E. HUNTINGTON, A geologic and physiographic reconnaissance in central Turkestan. *Ibid.*, no. 23, p. 159.—H. Keidel, Ein Profil durch den nördlichen Tienschan. *Abh. k. Bayr. Akad. Wiss.* II Kl. XXIII, Abt. 1, München 1906, p. 91, and *N. J. Min. B. B.* XXII, 1906, p. 266.—K. LEUCHS, *Abh. k. Bayr. Akad. Wiss.* II Kl. XXV, p. 95, München 1912.—F. MACHATSCHEK, Der westliche Tienschan. *P.M.* Erg.-Heft 176, 1912.—P. GRÖBER, Der südliche Tienschan. *Geogr. Abh.* X, Heft I, Leipzig 1914. See also the discussion of recent literature by F. MACHATSCHEK (*G.Z.* XX, Heft 5, Leipzig 1914, p. 257), the general account of the geology in K. LEUCHS, Zentralasien,

Handbuch Regional Geol V, Abt. 7, Heidelberg 1917, and M. FRIEDER-
ICHSEN's topographical *Übersichtskarte* (*Z.G.E.* XXXIV, 1899).

(370) B. WILLIS, *Research in China*. Washington 1907.—F. MACHATSCHEK,
Über epeirogenetische Bewegungen. Bibl. geogr. Handbücher, *Festband
Albrecht Penck*, 1918, p. 1 (18).

(371) K. LEUCHS thinks that they are always directed from the high-lying
parts towards the depressions. *G.R.* V, Heft 2, 1914, p. 81.

(372) What MACHATSCHEK cites in opposition to this is irrelevant; it has no
connection with the principal issue, which cannot be settled by pointing to
existing faults—which nobody doubts if they have been proved to exist
(*Mitteil. k.k. geogr. Gesellsch. Wien* 1915, LVIII, Heft 7–8, pp. 398 ff.). It is,
however, an entirely different question whether, as GRÖBER thinks, the Tarim
Basin and Tien Shan as a whole represent fold elements. We confine the term
broad folding to the elements which compose a system of ranges.

(373) Les formes du relief dans l'Altai russe etc. *Fennia*, XL, no. 2,
Helsingfors 1917.

(374) E. NOWACK, *Zentralbl. Min.* 1921, nos. 6–7, p. 175. *Z.D.G.G.
Berlin*, LXLII, 1920. Monatsber. no. 8–10, p. 241. *G.R.* XII, Heft 1–2, 1921,
p. 35.

(375) See illustrations 5 and 8–10 of the paper by GRANÖ that has been
quoted [n. 373].

(376) G. A. F. MOLENGRAAFF, Folded mountain chains etc. in the East
Indian Archipelago. *C. R. XII intern. geological Congress*, Toronto 1913, p.
689. Modern deep sea research in the East Indian Archipelago. *G.J.* 1921, p. 95.

(377) See the compilation by MACHATSCHEK, Über epirogenetische Bewegungen, *loc. cit.* [n. 370].

LIST OF PUBLICATIONS BY WALTHER PENCK

(compiled by Albrecht Penck)

A. *Books and Journal articles*

1. Geologische Beobachtungen aus den Euganeen. *Zentralbl. Min. Geol. Paläont.* 1910, pp. 575–581, 597–608. 3 figures in the text.
2. Der geologische Bau des Gebirges von Predazzo. (Auch als Heidelberger Dissertation erschienen). *Neues Jahrb. Min. Geol. Paläont.* 1911, Beilage Bd. XXXII, pp. 239–382. Plates IX, X. 10 figures in text.
3. *Naturgewalten im Hochgebirge.* Strecker & Schröder, Stuttgart 1912, 122 pages. 6 illustrations in the text, 30 as plates.
4. Studien im Eruptivgebiet von Predazzo. Vortrag. *Mitteil. Wiener geol. Gesellsch.* 1912, V, pp. 8–12.
5. Die Melaphyrausbrüche von Buffaure. *Ibid.* 1912, pp. 20–86. With maps, 3 profiles, 5 figures in the text.
6. Studien am Kilauea (Hawai), *Zeitschr. Gesellsch. Erdkunde. Berlin*, 1912, pp. 1–24.
7. Hauptzüge im Bau des Südrandes der Puna de Atacama (Kordilleren Nordwestargentiniens). (Auch als Leipziger Habilitationsschrift). *N. Jahrb. Min. Geol. Paläont.* 1914, pp. 643–684. Beil. Bd. XXXVII. Plates XXIV–XXVII, 2 figures in text.
8. Der Anteil deutscher Wissenschaft an der geologischen Erforschung Argentiniens. *Zeitschr. Gesellsch. Erdk. Berlin*, 1915, pp. 1–28.
9. Bau und Oberflächenformen der Dardanellenlandschaft. *Ibid.* 1917, pp. 30–49.
10. *Die tektonischen Grundzüge Westkleinasiens.* Beitr. z. anatolischen Gebirgsgeschichte auf Grund eigener Reisen. Engelhorns Nachf., Stuttgart 1918. 120 pages, 11 figures.
11. Topographische Aufnahmen am Südrande der Puna de Atacama (Nordwestargentinien). *Zeitschr. Gesellsch. Erdk. Berlin*, 1918, pp. 193–212. 1 map.
12. Zur Landeskunde von Thrazien. *Ibid.* 1919, pp. 358–370.
13. Grundzüge der Geologie des Bosporus. *Veröffentlichungen des Instituts f. Meereskunde, Berlin*, 1919, N.F., Heft 4, pp. 1–71. 3 illustrations, 1 plate.
14. Reisen in den Kordilleren Nordwestargentiniens. Vortrag. *Mitteil. Verein Erdkunde*, Leipzig 1919, pp. 80–87.
15. Aufgaben der Geologie in der Türkei und ihre Förderung während des Krieges. *Naturwissenschaftl. Wochenschr.* 1919, N.F., Bd. XVIII, pp. 493–498.
16. Der Südrand der Puna de Atacama (Nordwestargentinien). Ein Beitrag zur Kenntnis des andinen Gebirgstypus und zu der Frage der Gebirgs-

bildung. *Abhandl. math.-phys. Kl. sächs. Akad. Wissensch.* Leipzig 1920, Bd. XXXVII, no. 1. 420 pages, 9 plates, 1 map, 17 figures in the text.

17. Wesen und Grundlagen der morphologischen Analyse. *Bericht math.-phys. Kl. sächs. Akad. Wissensch.* Leipzig 1920, Bd. LXXII, pp. 65–102.

18. Die südliche Puna de Atacama (Kordilleren Nordwestargentiniens). *Geol. Charakterbilder, published by Andrée,* Berlin 1921, Heft 24. 19 pages, 22 illustrations on 7 plates.

19. Die Entstehung der Gebirge der Erde. *Deutsche Revue,* Berlin 1921, 46. Jahrgang, Bd. III, pp. 265–276, Bd. IV, pp. 30–44.

20. Zur Hypothese der Kontinentalverschiebung. *Zeitschr. Gesellsch. Erdk. Berlin,* 1921, pp. 130–143.

21. Die geographischen Regionen Südamerikas. *Lateinamerika,* Berlin 1922, pp. 726–728.

22. Morphologische Analyse. *Verhandl. deutsch. Geographentages,* 1921, Berlin 1922, pp. 122–128.

   Appearing after the author's death:

23. Über die Form andiner Krustenbewegungen und ihre Beziehung zur Sedimentation. *Geolog. Rundschau,* Bd. XIV, pp. 301–315.

24. Anteil der Schmelzflüsse an den Bewegungen der Erdkruste, *Die Naturwissenschaften* XII, Berlin 1924, pp. 847–851.

25. Die morphologische Analyse. Ein Kapitel der physikalischen Geologie. *Geographische Abhandlungen.* 2. Reihe, Heft 2, Stuttgart 1924, J. Engelhorns Nachf. 283 pages with portrait, 12 plates and 21 figures in the text.

[Published after No. 25, so not in A. Penck's list:

26. Die Piedmontflächen des südlichen Schwarzwaldes. *Zeitschr. Gesellsch. Erdk. Berlin,* 1925, pp. 83–108.

27. Über den Gang der Abbragung. *Mitt. geogr. Ges. Wien,* 71. Bd., 1928, pp. 200–218.]

B. *Shorter Papers and Notices*

(a) Eine Besteigung der Latemartürme. *Mitteil. deutsch. österr. Alpenvereins,* 1905, no. 21, pp. 247–248.

(b) Das Eggentaler Horn im Latemar. *Ibid.* 1917, no. 13, pp. 157–158.

(c) Büsserschnee. Notice of *H. Keidel:* Über den Büsserschnee in den argentinischen Anden. *Zeitschr. Gletscherkunde. Geol. Rundschau* III, 1912, pp. 512–514.

(d) Notice of *Bodenbender*: Constitución geológica de la parte meridional de la Rioja. *Ibid.* 1913, IV, pp. 121–124.

(e) *A. Philippson*'s Reisen in Anatolien. *Zeitschr. Gesellsch. Erdk. Berlin,* 1917, pp. 175–180.

(f) Geologische Aufgaben in Anatolien. *Deutsche Levantezeitung,* 1917, no. 22, p. 775.

(g) Das geologisch-mineralogische Institut der Universität Konstantinople. *Zeitschr. Gesellsch. Erdk. Berlin,* 1918, pp. 344–345.

TABLE OF CRETACEOUS AND TERTIARY FORMATIONS
(to show the position of beds mentioned in the text)

ERA	PERIOD	EPOCH	AGE		
			S.E. Europe	Italy etc.	Other Correlations
TERTIARY	Neogene	Pliocene Upper	Upper Levantine	Sicilian Calabrian Astian	Crag etc. (England)
		Lower	Upper Dacian	Plaisancian	Lenham (Eng.)
		Miocene Upper	Lower Levantine (= Lower Dacian) Pontian Mœotian Sarmatian	Sahelian	Upper Fresh-water Molasse (Switzerland)
		Middle	Vindobonian (= 2nd Mediter-ranean) Schlier	Tortonian Helvetian	Marine Molasse
		Lower	1st Mediter-ranean	Langhian Aquitanian	Burdigalian (France)
	Palæogene	Oligocene		Castel-Gomberto	Stampian
		Eocene Palæocene	(sub-divisions omitted)		
	PERIOD	EPOCH	AGE		
SECONDARY	Cretaceous	Upper	Danian Senonian Turonian Cenomanian		
		Lower	Albian Aptian Barremian Hauterivian Valanginian } Neocomian		
	Jurassic		(sub-divisions omitted)		

SUMMARIES

(*by* K. C. B.)

CHAPTER I

INTRODUCTION

1. NATURE OF THE PROBLEM

Geomorphology* is the concern of both geography and geology. However, its real significance is not so much the description and explanation
of the visible land forms as the solution of problems of crustal movement
—a matter of geology. The development of the forms is a problem of
physics. The earth's surface separates the spheres of action of the internal
(endogenetic) forces, expressed by crustal movement, and the external
(exogenetic) ones causing denudation. The resultant land forms depend
upon the relative intensities of these two sets of processes, which act in
opposition to one another.

2. BASIS, NATURE AND AIM
OF MORPHOLOGICAL ANALYSIS

The three elements concerned are internal or endogenetic processes,
external or exogenetic processes, and the land forms developed from
their interaction.

Two exogenetic processes may be distinguished: weathering, or the
preparation of rock material for removal; and the transport of this
'reduced' material [W. Penck uses the term 'Aufbereitung', here translated 'reduction', apparently to stress the idea that disintegration is
preparatory to the next stage—as when an ore is 'reduced']. Transport
is brought about by the force of gravity, both when weathered material
slips down by its own weight [what Penck calls 'spontaneous' move-
ment], and when it is moved along by some outside agent such as water
or ice. Denudation is the result of such removal, and is conditioned by
the law of gravity. Differences of rock material or of climate merely
modify the details of the processes. The study of soils has taught us
much about the processes of weathering; but, though open to direct

* Walther Penck never uses this term.

355

observation, there has been little exact measurement of the movement of the 'reduced' material.

Investigation of the denudational forms should include the stratigraphical relations of the deposits formed by the material that has been removed from them [what W. Penck terms the 'correlated' strata]. These throw light on the history of the denudation at the place in question. It must be borne in mind that the morphological features themselves do not conform to a single general law. They are individual in character, being dependent also upon local crustal movements.

Since direct observation can be made of exogenetic processes, and of land forms, it should be possible to deduce the course of the third element, the endogenetic processes, which cannot be seen (except in their by-products, earthquakes). Studies in morphology and tectonics supplement one another, and can be used together to find out the causes of crustal movements, the main problem of general geology.

3. CRITICAL SURVEY OF METHODS
(a) Cycle of Erosion

Davis was the first to attempt the analysis of land forms from the point of view of development, using the method of deduction. All applications of his concept of an erosion cycle, however, have been based upon the special case of a rapidly uplifted block which came to rest before its denudation began. Even opponents of the Davisian school of thought have done this. But the fact that deductions have so far all been made from an inadmissible premiss does not discredit deduction as a means of investigation. It is an essential, without which geomorphology cannot become an exact science.

(b) Relationship between Endogenetic and Exogenetic Processes

Earth sculpture depends upon the ratio of the intensity of endogenetic to that of exogenetic displacements of material. The existence of any elevated land shows that the external activity has been less than the internal. Hence the resulting land forms must show the influence of crustal movement. The rate of denudation increases with the gradient, and so usually with the height. Thus the ratio changes in favour of the exogenetic processes; and instead of an indefinite increase in altitude, conditions approach closer and closer to equilibrium. Therefore in studying how denudational forms have arisen and developed, it is essential to find out the ratio of uplift to denudation, and how this has altered with time. Writers on this subject have usually considered cases in which uplift is taken as ended before denudation begins. A similar device is used in school physics to obtain the resultant of processes acting concurrently. But this is permissible only if dealing with forces acting uniformly, i.e. producing equal results in successive units of time. It is not permissible in the case of uplift and denudation.

(c) The Differential Method

If the simultaneously acting forces are not uniform, it is necessary to follow their course continuously, by infinitely small steps, i.e. by the method of the differential calculus. Not one, but an infinite number of evolving series of forms may have led to any particular land form. The differential method must be used in working out the interdependence of crustal movements, erosion acting along a line, and denudation over a whole surface.

(d) Present Method of Approach

This will be the study of denudation and its preparatory processes, with the object of discovering what laws control it. Only those processes will be considered which are dependent upon the surface gradient, and so upon movement of the crust. Weathered material may move under the influence of gravity alone [what W. Penck terms 'spontaneous' movement] or with the help of moving agents. The movement of these latter may, like ocean currents, be due to differences of pressure, and so have no bearing upon crustal movement. Wind action may determine the base level of erosion for slopes draining to an inland basin, but it cannot excavate below the level of the water table; and so the resultant gradient is dependent upon climate, not crustal movement. Neither do the effects of moving ice give the desired information. Here the lower edge depends upon the position of the snow-line (a matter of climate), and upon the mass of the ice stream. Uplift or depression alters the position of the mountain summits with relation to the snow-line, not of the snow-line in relation to sea-level. It is possible to decide whether the relative shift of this line is due to climatic change or to crustal movement; but not to deduce anything about the nature of the latter. Coastal development also lies outside the scope of this work. Even if eustatic movement can be excluded, evidence as to vertical displacement of the coast line tells only that there has been movement, when it began, and its direction—practically nothing about changes in intensity. In this it resembles stratigraphical evidence. Oscillations of sea-level must, however, be given some consideration, since they affect the base level of erosion for running water, and so the modelling of the land by both denudation and deposition.

SUMMARIES

CHAPTER II

THE EARTH'S CRUST

For the detailed sculpturing of denudational forms, the determining factor is the rock, its cohesion being of great importance. [The author uses the term 'rock conditions'—*Gesteinsverhältnisse*—to cover mineralogical properties, structure (e.g. divisional planes, porosity, cementation, stages in metamorphosis) and bedding. For want of a better expression, this is translated as *the character of the rock* wherever the term occurs in this book.] This adaptation of form to the character of the rock must be carefully traced out before the part played by crustal movement can be distinguished.

In addition to the dynamic side of endogenetic processes—the movement, there is the static side—the results. These comprise (*a*) the composition of the crustal material, (*b*) its structure, and (*c*) its altitudinal form.

1. COMPOSITION AND STRUCTURE OF THE CRUST

Substructure and superstructure differ. Folding is the characteristic of the substructure. Increasing compression may put a limit to folding and lead to metamorphism, such as is found in the depths of fold-belts. [The author does not use the term *Metamorphose* or *metamorphische Gesteine* though he here writes of *Umprägung*—reconstitution.] The material is predominantly siliceous, consisting of reassorted sedimentary material and of igneous rocks. Vast areas of substructure are visible at the earth's surface, since the superstructure, of unfolded strata, forms an incomplete cover, much having been removed by denudation. What remains is largely composed of the chemically stable end-products of weathering.

In Archaean times, no part of the earth's surface seems to have escaped folding. With each recurrence of this, the affected parts have been successively narrowed, so that the most recent zone of folding consists merely of two curved strips, the Pacific belt and the Mediterranean belt. The areas withdrawn from folding form rigid continental masses, and here the superstructure rests undisturbed upon the metamorphosed and now stable substructure. But within the fold-belts, the lower parts of the superstructure, folded to incompetence, become part of the substructure. This remains unstable, capable of sinking to form further

358

geosynclines. But the rigid continental masses grow at the expense of the zones of instability.

2. THE ALTITUDINAL FORM OF THE EARTH'S CRUST: HOW IT IS BUILT UP

There are two major types of relief: (1) the simple relief formed by warping of the stable regions, and (2) the very varied relief, based on mountain chains and elongated depressions, found in the two zones of instability.

In the stable continental areas, the youngest folded structures are of late Palaeozoic age. The continental upwarpings usually cut across them. Even when they show mountain features at the present day, these are unconnected with the folding, being due to comparatively recent arching (e.g. the Appalachians and the Urals). In the zones of instability, the mountain relief and the lines of folding do coincide. For the European-Himalayan belt it was possible to uphold the concept that the folding caused the uplift. But for the Pacific fold lines of the two Americas, such a causal connection cannot be maintained. Two sets of facts provide evidence against the view that the uplift was produced by the folding. (1) Intensity of folding by no means always corresponds with mountain relief. In several places (e.g. the Dinaric Alps, the western Taurus Mountains and western Argentina) transgressing strata pass from conformably bedded strata on to violently folded beds, along an almost level surface. This indicates that the latter never had any other relief, since the unconformities pass into bedding planes, and also there could not have been a sufficiently long time interval for peneplanation. (2) The mountain belts of the world are far more extensive than the zone of Mesozoic-Tertiary folding; and sometimes, even within it, the mountain ranges cross the lines of folding at an acute angle (e.g. Inner Armenia). At times the superstructure of the mountains is unfolded, and lies upon a substructure folded at some distant geological period. This is true of the Andes and of what were taken for fault blocks in North America.

The ridge and furrow effect is due to broad folding (*Grossfaltung*), an undulatory upwarp accompanying regional arching. Faults may occur as minor phenomena associated with its increased intensity. Probably such uplift (as contrasted with the folding due to compression) is caused by the entry of magma into the crust. Especially in arid regions, deposition often takes place in the broad synclinal depressions, and the strata in them become distorted as the broad folds rise on either side.

3. CONNECTION BETWEEN ALTITUDINAL FORM AND THE STRUCTURE OF THE EARTH'S CRUST

In the zones of Mesozoic-Tertiary folding there has often been an overlap in time between the compressional folding and the uplift due to broad folding. This latter effect seems to come into play when the original folding has brought the rocks to the phase of incompetence and they are becoming incorporated in the substructure. Structure and relief are thus different effects of the crustal movement. They may belong to crustal movements of different age, as for instance the Variscan folding of the Harz massif and its later uplift. The records of that are to be found in the distortion of the strata of the superstructure lying in and at the side of the old folded material. The structural features will be preserved after denudation has levelled the relief.

Thus from a combined study of structure and relief it becomes possible to deduce the course of crustal movements. The structure is seen as the total result of the crustal movement; and so, given a constant intensity, is a function of time. The relief, given a certain duration of time, is a function of the intensity of the uplift. The study of land forms is complementary to the study of structure. But so far too much attention has been devoted to the adaptation of forms to structure as revealed by the outcrops of different rocks, and too little to the crustal movements which produced the gradients necessary before denudation could begin. In the Swiss Jura, for instance, the development of land forms, as they became adapted to structure, has been influenced by further growth of the structures.

CHAPTER III

REDUCTION OF ROCK MATERIAL

A surface of solid rock is usually more or less smothered in rock derivatives, varying from fragments of relatively fresh rock, through all degrees of comminution and chemical change, to chemically stable or unalterable end-products. These are prepared by a process of progressive reduction (*Aufbereitung*), the essence of which is to bring about ever increasing mobility in the crustal material.

1. THE NATURE OF WEATHERING. EXPOSURE

Weathering brings about physical and chemical changes, and can occur only where the rock material is exposed to atmospheric conditions. Unless this exposure is preserved, weathering comes to an end. Though exposure is originally the same on every surface, more rock material is reduced the greater the area of surface exposed. Since a high mountain has a greater surface than a low hill of equal base measurements, steep slopes reaching high altitudes are more rapidly demolished than gentler ones with lower elevations. Exposure is of immense importance in preparation for denudation and in the process itself.

2. WEATHERING PROCESSES AND THEIR PRODUCTS

The processes are (1) mechanical disintegration, (2) chemical alteration, which is accompanied by disintegration, and (3) solution, which may be separated from (2) because, acting alone, it may affect large areas. These three processes work simultaneously, but their relative importance varies in different parts of the world.

(a) MECHANICAL REDUCTION
Effect of Insolation

Rapid changes of temperature lead to tensions between the outer parts of the rock, which are most affected and respond by changes in volume, and the inner parts which suffer less change. It is only under the clear skies of arid regions that the strong insolation and subsequent radiation by night cause sufficiently rapid temperature changes for rock shattering to occur. The process comes to an end when the fragments are too small for there to be any perceptible lag between changes at the surface and in the core. The worse the rock conducts heat, the smaller the fragments before this occurs. Insolation rubble begins as coarse fragments, but in its later stages has a large admixture of fine particles.

Frost Weathering

Frost shattering is due to the expansion of water as it freezes in the rock fissures. Freezing takes place downwards; and so the ice stopper causes pressure to be passed hydrostatically downwards as well as in other directions. Thus mechanical loosening takes place even below the actual zone of freezing; but this effect never goes deeper than a few metres. It is essential that the rock should be porous, or fissured, and for the geographical distribution to be near the snow-line or on the colder side of it.

There is also mechanical breaking up by the roots of plants. It occurs, too, as an accompaniment to chemical weathering, and to solution which generally acts along special planes of weakness, loosening the unaffected lumps of rock between them. This is the principal way in which mechanical loosening of rock fragments takes place in the moist tropics and in the temperate regions.

(b) CHEMICAL WEATHERING

This requires the presence of water. For the weathering of silicates, its ionisation—twice as great in the tropics as in temperate regions—is far more potent than the presence of dissolved carbon dioxide, or other acids, in causing the decomposition. Below 0° C., chemical weathering ceases. It is of greatest importance in a humid, warm temperate climate. It is aided by the action of bacteria and by a covering of vegetation. Not only do life processes lead to the excretion of acids, but the plant cover stores the water required and allows it to pass slowly into the substratum, lengthening the period of chemical attack upon the rock surface. Even more important, the dead plants decompose into chemically active substances, like carbon dioxide and the humus which plays such a great part in soil reactions.

The end-products of weathering are usually colloids, consisting of a series of clays and loams. What differences exist, depend not upon the rocks from which they are derived but upon the climatic conditions under which they were produced, so that they are sometimes termed climatic soils. Because of their capacity for adsorption, the presence of these colloids has an important effect upon denudation. When they have taken up water, they are highly mobile. On drying, they become hard clods, unless there has also been adsorption of dissolved salts, when they become crumbly. Calcium carbonate is the commonest of these, and the terra rossa on limestone is an instance of such precipitation of colloids from the soil condition. The acid humic substances, also colloidal, are far less sensitive to the effect of electrolysis. When present, they hinder flocculation of the inorganic colloids also. Neutral humus does not have this effect.

In studying denudation, the distribution of humus must therefore be considered. This depends upon the rain factor, a relation between precipitation and temperature. Humus occupies only a narrow girdle within each of those three strips of the world (separated by arid belts) that are covered by vegetation; and these themselves lie within the wider zone of chemical weathering.

(c) SOLUTION

The solution of limestone is a reversible chemical change. In the tropics, there is less carbon dioxide dissolved in the water, but the acids excreted by the vegetation are important. Not even deserts are entirely waterless, and solution may be effected by dissolved salts, e.g. silica is soluble in a solution of sodium carbonate. Thus slight hollows, in which water lingers, are deepened by chemical action aided by the wind which blows away the crumbling residues. Similarly salt solutions within a rock lead to internal decay, though solutions reaching the surface will crystallise out. Honeycombing of sandstones by solution of the cementing material is not confined to arid or semi-arid regions.

3. RATE OF WEATHERING AND DIFFERENTIAL WEATHERING

The rate of weathering, for an attacking force of given intensity and the same degree of exposure, depends upon the resistance of the rock concerned. This is due partly to the method of its formation, partly to characteristics acquired later. The inner surface, or extent of pore space and parting planes, is of great importance, since percolating solutions can here reach and attack the rock, destroying it from within. Certain rocks, like quartzite and clay, the composition of which approximates to that of the end-products of weathering, are very resistant to chemical weathering. The rate is also affected by climatic conditions.

Differential weathering (1) loosens fragments from the solid rock, by attacking it along lines of less resistance. Especially when carried along by running water, these fragments do mechanical work upon the materials over which they pass. (2) It produces relief features as less resistant rocks wear down to form depressions, leaving the more resistant ones upstanding. It is the relative resistance that matters; and the same igneous dyke may give rise to a wall in one place and a trench in another.

Unresistant rocks are those in which there is rapid reduction to a state of mobility, sufficient to allow of denudation. The adaptation of land forms to different rock materials is a matter of time—a mathematical function of time if the differences in resistance to weathering are constant and other conditions similar.

4. UNIFORMITY IN THE PROCESS OF ROCK REDUCTION. THE SOIL PROFILE

The complete soil profile, where there has been both mechanical and chemical weathering, shows (from the surface downwards): the end-products of weathering (clay or loam); a mixture of these with more or less altered rock fragments, increasing in number, size and freshness till a definitely rubbly horizon is reached; between this and the merely loosened parent rock, a zone of special importance to denudation, where rearrangement of the loosened fragments occurs. Below the loosened rock is the untouched solid rock. As each horizon becomes more weathered, the whole series pushes down further into the parent rock. The amount of weathered material determines the amount of denudation; the degree of reduction (which includes alteration as well as comminution) decides the onset of denudation and how it proceeds.

No absolute times are known; but rock reduction takes progressively longer to produce each higher horizon, since more and more divisional planes are required in the change from rock loosening to rubble, rubble to very fine fragments, and these to dust or colloids. Thus the degree of reduction is not directly proportional to the duration of the reduction, but decelerates (so long as exposure is unaltered). However, for a given rock and given exposure, the total quantity of rock waste, the depth of the soil, does depend directly upon time. By uniformity of rock reduction is meant that (on similar rock, with similar exposure and similar climatic conditions) if profiles have the same topmost horizon, they must have had equal periods of time for their formation—because the same number of divisional planes will have been required. Denudation, on the other hand, does not act uniformly with respect to time.

5. UNEQUAL EXPOSURE

(1) Plant cover: This reduces exposure to mechanical weathering, but increases exposure to chemical weathering.

(2) Rubble and soil cover (not always stationary): This also hinders mechanical weathering by lessening the exposure, though it may favour

chemical weathering since it retains water, especially in its lower parts. Sometimes this chemical change may even eat into the solid substratum, though rearrangement of loosened fragments is prevented. Thus at the upper surface of the parent rock, exposures beneath a soil cover of varying thickness may differ, although the upper surface of the soil has the same exposure in each case. Where the soil thickness gradually decreases to nothing in a horizontal direction, mechanical weathering takes place far more rapidly on the bare rock, so that this tends to 'catch up' as regards depth of soil and degree of rock reduction (or preparation for denudation). This is particularly important in the case of inclined surfaces.

6. MOBILITY OF REDUCED MATERIAL

Mobility is the essential feature in the preparation for denudation, and making crustal material mobile is a matter of uniform progress (uniformity of rock reduction, p. 51).

Moisture lessens mobility when the dry substance is (like insolation rubble) less cohesive than water; but increases it for colloidal matter which when baked dry is more cohesive than water.

Rounding of fragments, as well as decrease in size, increases mobility.

In very cold regions, salts are less soluble and so there is less electrolysis of the water and colloids remain unprecipitated. This increases the mobility of moist rubble, thus aiding rock-flow and solifluction.

In arid regions, the colloidal material is crumbly from adsorptive saturation with salts. This reduces friction. Also, in the mixture of grit, sand and dust formed by insolation, the coarser grains exert unequal pressure on the finer ones, which then slip away.

7. WORLD CLIMATIC AND SOIL ZONES

Everywhere the action of weathering is to increase the degree of reduction of the rock material, so increasing the mobility of the rock waste. But the rate of reduction differs from one climatic region to another. Under polar climatic conditions, the material is mobile at snow melt, immobile when frozen. In humid regions, temperate and tropical, chemical weathering is important, and the constant moisture leads to all the material, even the rubble, being perpetually in a mobile state. A dark colour is imparted to the soil by humic weathering. In the semi-humid regions (which include monsoon areas) there is alternation of wet and dry seasons. When dry, the colloids have a binding effect, rendering the material immobile. The soils are red. In arid belts (and continental interiors), the reduced material is always mobile (see section 6). In semi-arid regions, there is least mobility at time of transition from rain to drought and vice versa.

In every climatic region there are optima for the mobility of reduced rock material, and these are at the places where moisture is to be found all through the year.

[There follows an enumeration of the soil belts of the world.]

8. LIMITS OF WEATHERING

The depth of weathering is dependent upon the position of the water table. For below it, inadequacy of oxygen, and increase in the content of carbon dioxide and dissolved minerals leads to cementation in place of weathering. If the whole soil profile consists of stable end-products of weathering, reduction of course ceases, and the depth of soil should depend solely upon that of the water table. But since the depth of the actual soil cover often differs greatly from that of the water table (as calculated from a knowledge of the climate, rock materials and surface relief), it follows that denudational processes must play an important part in hindering the formation of an ideal zone of soil.

9. RELATIONSHIP OF WEATHERING TO DENUDATION

The water table is not a fixed level even if climatic and rock conditions remain unchanged. It sinks as the exposed surface is lowered by denudation, and with it the lower limit of weathering, and thus each horizon of the soil profile sinks also. This means downward movement of the border zone between rock loosening and the rearranged fragments in the rubble horizon, or *Renewal of Exposure*, which is dependent upon the intensity of denudation. This in its turn is affected by the rate of rock reduction. Renewal of exposure is most rapid when denudation removes the merely loosened material from the bare rock before the complete soil profile has had time to form. At the other end of the series, is the condition when denudation is so slow that end-products are formed right down to the water table, the soil increasing in depth till this brings it to a halt. In between is a state where the speed at which reduced material is removed by denudation from the top of a complete soil profile just equals the rate at which fresh rock is weathered into the end-product. In this case the soil thickness remains constant.

For any given gradient, removal of material is related to the length of time which the process of reduction requires in order to produce the degree of mobility required for migration along that gradient.

Intensity of denudation is measured by the *quantity* of reduced material removed in unit time. The rate at which the reduced material moves on is measured by the distance it travels in unit time; and this depends upon both the type of denudation and the type of material transported. For 'spontaneous' movement, i.e. migration of the reduced material by the force of gravity alone, the intensity of denudation may be measured by the time taken to produce the requisite mobility. It is greatest on bare rock. If the reduced material cannot move away freely, but accumulates, *exposure is decreased*, and so intensity of denudation diminished until equilibrium is attained between preparation of material and its removal. This removal is dependent upon the *gradient* of the slope; and in general, the thickness of the soil cover increases with decrease of gradient; and on steep slopes only the lower horizons of the normal soil profile appear at the surface. This is true for moist and arid climates.

Seas of Rocks or Block Seas are illustrations of the above relationships between weathering and denudation. They are common in the German Highlands and have been considered to be the result of frost action in the Pleistocene period. But they also occur in Uruguay and south Brazil where such an explanation is not possible. Here, too, they are associated with specific rock types (e.g. granite, syenite, quartzite, basalt) and on definite gradients ($15°$ to $30°$). Observation shows that there are two sets of accumulations of blocks:

1. Screes of angular fragments, found on very steep slopes usually near a rocky source of supply, e.g. precipitous crags.

2. Those supplied from the rocky substratum itself, but found only where there is a definite gradient (though some blocks may slip down on to gentler slopes below). In this case the blocks tend to be rounded, and to be embedded in fine material which has undergone chemical decomposition. Where the gradient lessens, the blocks project less and even disappear, being buried in gritty loam when the inclination is less than $10°$. On steeper gradients, the fine material slips down and may carry blocks with it.

These two types may merge into one another as the slope of the substratum alters. The blocks begin to appear as the slope becomes sufficient for the fine material to migrate; when it is so steep that they themselves slip down before chemical reduction has had time to take place, the result is scree.

Summary. Seas of blocks correspond to definite horizons in the profile of reduction, which reach the surface on certain gradients, because of the 'spontaneous' migration of the reduced material, this being more intense and more rapid the steeper the slope. Thus, for transport by denudation, there is needed (a) a slope, (b) mobility of the material. The steeper the gradient, the less the mobility needed for denudation. The ratio of gradient to mobility determines the intensity of denudation. *Weathering* is responsible only for the mobility of the material, i.e. rock reduction, and this depends upon the kind of rock and the climate. The nature of the rock determines the quantity reduced to mobility in unit time; the climate influences the composition of the result. But no one climatic region specially favours denudation over the whole surface; nor —provided the endogenetic conditions are identical—do different climatic regions lead to different denudational forms arising from a different course of development.

CHAPTER IV

MASS MOVEMENT

It is denudation, i.e. the removal of weathered material from its place, which produces land forms. *Gravity is the driving force*, often through the agency of a moving medium, such as water or ice. The flow is along definite lines of motion, tending to produce linear results, whether river bed or glacier bed—though in the case of air movements the 'bed' may be a wide stretch of land. *Mass-transport* of loosened solid material is thus *restricted to the paths of the moving media*. Outside them, there is *mass-movement*, 'spontaneous' migration under the force of gravity alone. The two together give rise to *denudation of the whole surface*, or sheet denudation, in which the movement is determined by the gradient of each individual slope. (Contrast the action of wind, which may move material up the land gradient.) The full force of gravity is effective only where there is free fall from a vertical precipice. Elsewhere the effective component is proportional to the sine of the angle of inclination. Mass-movement can neither start nor continue unless the opposing resistance has been overcome.

1. RESISTANCE TO DENUDATION

The connection between denudation and crustal movements is that denudation tends to bring the material it moves into a position of stable equilibrium, whilst crustal movements disturb such a state of rest.

Resistance to denudation depends in the first place upon the property of cohesion in a rock.

COHESION IN ROCKS

Some rocks have practically no cohesion, even in the unweathered state: examples are recent unconsolidated matter and, most important of all, rocks containing colloidal clay and thus becoming mobile if wetted. Clay is far more resistant to weathering than an igneous rock; and the so-called 'weathering out' of a dyke from clayey sediments round it is a matter of differential denudation (not of differential weathering). Clayey intercalations, as in flysch, render the whole mass mobile, should moistening take place; and highly coherent rocks may slide over wet clay which is dipping valleywards. Thus streams of rocky fragments and steep-walled niches may result from the presence of naturally mobile rocks, although such forms owe their characteristic features to the coherent rock overlying them.

The impermeability of clayey rock also makes it susceptible to denudation by rainwash.

FRICTION

This hinders the continuance of mass-movement (as cohesion hinders the start). It is so great as to make mass-movement very slow and thus difficult to observe. There is *internal friction* between the components of a moving mass of rock waste, and *external friction* against the substratum, with sliding and rolling in both cases. Internal friction decreases with the size of the grains, and with their rounding. It is less in the upper horizons than where there is a weight of material above, and diminishes where a slope becomes steeper. Also it is less after movement has once begun. Thus both in the rapid descent of a landslip and in the slow movement downslope of weathered material, the topmost parts move over those below with a rolling motion analogous to flowing.

Where intersecting slopes are mantled with the products of rock reduction, the thickness of which diminishes upwards, the slighter friction beneath the smaller load leads to more rapid movement, and so increase of exposure. Hence, denudation is more intense above than below and the *crests become rounded*. The effect is increased if the slope is steeper above than below, since the magnitude of the friction (due to the weight of the downpressing material) acts at right angles to the plane of friction. Thus on a steep slope material can begin to move whilst it has less mobility than would be required for a gentler one (cf. p. 65 'as slopes become steeper, only the lower horizons of the normal soil profile are developed at the surface'). Mass-movement, however, does not cease till a gradient of just under 5° is reached. For as the rock waste gradually descends, not only does rock reduction (by weathering) continue, increasing the colloidal content; but the rolling grains rub one another into smaller as well as more rounded granules, thus diminishing friction. Frequently it is only the upper layers which move, since the increasing weight of accumulated material may make friction in the lower parts too great to allow of any further motion. The above statements are true for all climatic regions.

ROOT SYSTEM OF PLANTS

The effect of roots in obstructing mass-movement of rock waste has been exaggerated. The sieving action which impedes the movement of large fragments is offset by the increased chemical action beneath a plant cover, and by the fact that on very gentle slopes, and in the wet tropics where there is a thick layer of highly reduced rock, some of this lies below the zone of the root mesh. The same correlation between steepness of slope and thickness of soil cover is found in forested as in treeless regions. Moreover, even in forested areas, examples are found of less reduced material from higher up the slope covering that of the normal horizon.

2. MOTIVE FORCES CONCERNED IN MASS-MOVEMENT

Observations on the 1906 ash avalanches down the slopes of Vesuvius have shown that the force of gravity is the prime cause of mass-movement; but that the movement cannot start until there is sufficient weight from accumulated material to overcome the resistance of friction (especially great at this change from rest to motion).

INCREASE OF WEIGHT

The weight of reduced rock material on a slope undergoing denudation is increased in the following ways:

(*a*) By increased thickness, as reduction attacks ever deeper.

(*b*) By rock derivatives arriving from higher up the incline. This increase is greatest at the slope foot. It leads to movement of the whole mass of waste, instead of that of the highest horizons only. The angle of friction—that inclination of the substratum at which movement of material, resting directly upon the solid rock, comes to an end—is less than it would be were there no mass-movement, no denudation, and so no accumulation of rock derivatives on the lower-lying parts of the land. Thus it is that there is movement along the very gentle foot-slopes on both sides of a valley trough, leading to the 'cicatrisation' or complete covering-in of disused stream-beds.

(*c*) By the absorption of water. This is extremely important, especially in loose material and in rocks rich in colloidal clay. This often accounts for the release of landslips.

FLUCTUATIONS IN VOLUME

These lead to frequently repeated fine movements, which further the spread of rock waste to slopes inclined at less than $5°$. The causes for such fluctuations are (*a*) temperature variations, and (*b*) swelling and shrinkage of colloids with variations of moisture content.

PERIODS OF MOVEMENT

In most climatic regions there are seasonal periods when mass-movement is most active, (though there seems to be no interruption of its course in the wet tropics or in deserts). Thus the smallest unit of time for its measurement is the year.

3. WAYS IN WHICH MASS-MOVEMENT TAKES PLACE AT THE EARTH'S SURFACE

The velocity of mass-movement depends not only upon the gradient but also upon the weight of the moving material. This latter may move freely or may be impeded by vegetation binding it together.

(a) MIGRATION AS INDIVIDUAL LOOSE FRAGMENTS

Observations in the Atacama Desert show that on bare rock, weathered fragments move (without the help of rainwash) when the gradient reaches about 25°. Above 30°, slopes are always rocky. The movement is a rolling tumble. Fragments collecting at the foot of a steep rock face form scree, the upper surface of which is concave [in longitudinal profile]. The under surface, which has a slope less than that of the rock face above, is here termed the basal slope (*Haldenhang*). It is not always buried beneath talus. The rubble moves as a whole, in addition to the motion of its individual fragments. It receives further material from disintegration of the basal slope which it covers.

In *Landslides* also there is generally movement of individual fragments rolling over one another, especially when they are *of the type of rock-falls*. The three areas typical of mass-movement can be seen at a glance: the denudation scar, the path of the moving material, and the area of deposition.

(b) MOVEMENT WHERE MATERIAL IS ACCUMULATING

(α) *Free Mass-Movement*

This may occur not only within screes and in rock falls, but also in the dry rubble which often occupies valley-like depressions where slopes are inclined at less than 25° continuing till 2° or 3° is reached. In semi-arid regions the rock waste, when sodden with water, may spread out to form great sheets that are almost level.

Slumping is often the chief type of movement where there is plenty of moisture and a considerable amount of colloidal matter. A cover of vegetation hinders this, but need not prevent it entirely, for the increasing weight of dammed-up material may gash open even forest-clad slopes (usually the steep declivities of the wet tropics). The formation of such landslide niches may be an important method of denudation. In semi-humid regions the grass sod may tear. In the wet season, streams of waste move along, becoming corrugated as they do so. Frequently these are in definite valleys, but they may spread out over wide plains inclined at only 2° to 3°.

Slumping at the level of the water table is of special importance. It may merge into the rock-slide type of landslide where a resistant permeable bed overlies a saturated impermeable stratum rich in colloids.

Solifluction is common in high latitudes at the time of snow melt. The superficial rock waste often 'flows' over what is still unfrozen (the tjaele) The part played by frost action is not yet fully understood, but seems to be associated with changes of volume consequent upon alternations of freezing and thaw. Solifluction also takes place on slopes with an inclination of scarcely more than 3°. The 'stone rivers' of the Falkland Islands have probably had their finer matrix washed away. Their occurrence in valleys is explained by the fact that water would collect here, so changing mass-movement into mass-transport for at least the fine-grained constituents, whilst on the side slopes the moisture would be completely absorbed in the debris and all the components would continue to move as a whole. The 'stone rivers' are most likely still forming and moving, at an extremely slow rate; just as the block seas of temperate regions are probably not mere fossil relics of the Pleistocene period, but are even now continuing to move downwards.

(β) Bound-down Mass-Movement

Mass-movement goes on even beneath a cover of vegetation. It often arches this up, where it is insufficient to tear it. Tree trunks may show a 'stilt effect' (p. 109); the beds of small streamlets are closed up by what moves in from the sides. Movement occurs on slopes of less than 5° (though more than 0°). It is more rapid if assisted by flow of ground water.

(γ) Corrasion and Corrasion Valleys

Corrasion is the mechanical action by means of which fragments of rock are pressed off or chiselled away, before the rock is sufficiently reduced to allow of 'spontaneous' migration. Slowly moving rock waste corrades its substratum when the weight of the whole mass is sufficient, as near the foot of a ridge. The waste frequently moves along definite lines as 'mass-streams'. Wide shallow valleys floored with detrital deposits but without any definite water-course, (or even traces of a former channel), are probably in a large measure due to corrasion. So are narrower furrows with a steeper gradient and sometimes several metres' thickness of rock waste. Corrasion valleys often show considerable headward ramifications, and may form the uppermost parts of normal valley systems, e.g. on the gently inclined upper regions of the German Highlands and on the peneplanes of the German Scarplands.

CHAPTER V

GENERAL CHARACTERISTICS OF DENUDATION

1. RETROSPECT. RELATIONSHIP TO CLIMATE

No climatic region is without denudation over the whole surface, provided that the mean gradient of the land is above a minimum (somewhere between 5° and 0°). The same land forms can therefore appear under all climatic conditions (p. 119), though the rate at which they develop may be different. They depend upon the gradients, which are determined in the first place by endogenetic factors. The character of the rock determines only the minor features. Climatic changes may alter the relationship of mass-movement to mass-transport, but do not produce any fundamental change in the denudational forms.

2. THE PRINCIPLE OF FLATTENING

Denudation can never make a slope steeper; it always flattens it (or diminishes the gradient). A slope may, however, be replaced by the development of a new, steeper slope [due to erosion].

3. THE CONCEPTS: DENUDATION, CORRASION, EROSION

Exposure is renewed by the removal of small pieces of loosened rock. In denudation, this latter takes place at the same rate as the rock is reduced. With corrasion and erosion, it takes place more rapidly, under the influence of the moving material, whether it be water, ice or rock waste.

The sculpturing of land forms depends upon the relationship between what is occurring over the whole surface and what is occurring along watercourses. The former is denudation. Erosion is here understood as the mechanical action produced by linear movement within a moving substratum (e.g. wind, water, ice) and brought about by it; corrasion, the similar action beneath rock waste migrating 'spontaneously', i.e. solely under the force of gravity.

4. CLASSIFICATION OF THE REGIONS OF DENUDATION

All the processes, by which rock waste is removed, begin with denudation over the whole surface, develop into linear removal and then into definitely directed courses.

Regions of pure denudation occur on the upper parts of slopes. Lower down, corrasion and erosion are combined with the denudation, and finally erosion predominates. This can be so intense that there is no time for rock reduction to occur—in contrast to corrasion which essentially depends upon the presence of reduced rock before it can begin to act. Denudation occurs over the surface of slopes; erosion and corrasion in incised furrows. Transitional forms link them, especially near valley heads. Lines of erosion, or of corrasion, have tributary surfaces of denudation. Increased dissection by valleys causes dismemberment of the areas of denudation; but there is no lessening of the superficial area, since the number of inclined surfaces increases. The amount of denudation accomplished in unit time thus increases, since the amount of surface exposed to denudation is increased. Corrasion prevails where a cover of vegetation impedes erosion, in arid regions where running water is rare, and also in upland regions of low relief where infiltration may be in excess of run-off.

5. BASE LEVELS OF EROSION AND OF DENUDATION

The absolute lower limit below which erosion cannot take place, *the base level of erosion*, is the level at which running water can no longer flow, and so no longer remove material. The *absolute base level of erosion* is sea level, or else the lowest part of an inland drainage basin. However, the work performed by rivers is often controlled, not by this, but by the *general* or *immediate base level of erosion*. This is usually where the stream leaves a tectonically uniform block of the earth's crust to enter one which has undergone some different endogenetic movement. Several of these may occur in a river's course; and all ultimately recede upstream to the headwaters. Occasionally the general base level of erosion may coincide with the absolute base level, as where a tectonically uniform block drains directly to the sea. Though each point in a river bed is a base level of erosion for that immediately upstream from it, there are also more specific *local base levels of erosion* at (*a*) the confluence of a tributary with the main river, for the tributary cannot erode below this, (*b*) breaks of gradient in the course of the stream itself. These latter also recede upstream. They may arise from a variety of causes.

Not only running water, but all gravitational streams, have analogous base levels. For moving ice, it is the lower limit of ablation, or else where the ice is lifted from its substratum by a body of water which it has entered.

For mass-movement, the corresponding levels may be called the *base levels of denudation*. As the slope leading down to a watercourse cannot be denuded below the level of the stream bed, the *general base level of denudation* for it is this, i.e. the longitudinal profile, or gradient curve, of the stream. When the watercourses have (on a stationary block) reached their final gradient curves, the base levels of denudation are fixed. The slopes can be worked down to these levels only where they actually meet the streams; but, above these lowest edges, extremely gentle slopes of minimum gradient develop, along which no further denudation is possible. These form a final peneplane (Davisian peneplain) with slight undulations and a general fall towards the base level of erosion.

The general base levels of denudation may coincide with those of erosion—e.g. where the slopes of broad anticlines lead directly to the broad synclines (Asia Minor, etc.). The resulting effect is seen to be quite different from that where the influence of the base levels of erosion is exerted indirectly through the drainage net (e.g. on the slopes of the erosional valleys within such broad anticlines).

But the base levels of denudation are functionally independent of, and may be quite different from, the lines of eroding streams and their base levels. The outcrop of a resistant band of rock, far above the river, may form a base level of denudation for a ledge above it, or for a summit peneplane, separated from the former base level of erosion by the interpolation of younger, steeper relief. These are *local base levels of denudation*, conditioned by structure; and the slopes above them continue their development with reference to these breaks of gradient. They may coincide with concave or convex elements in the land forms. Such a local base level, and the slope related to it, form a single system, and may be termed a form system. Thus breaks of gradient separate *form systems* [or *slope units*, a term conveying a clearer impression to an English reader when it is used later, in Chapter VI].

CHAPTER VI

DEVELOPMENT OF SLOPES

1. GRADIENT AND FORM OF SLOPES

Slopes of almost identical maximum gradients tend to be characteristic of particular natural regions. Thus it is possible to speak of *uniformity of relief for a district*, this implying the total effect of the arrangement and combination of all the slopes with approximately the same angle of inclination. Instead of using the common expressions Alpine relief and Highland relief, more general descriptive terms are here used for the *relief types*: steep forms and steep relief, where the land forms show what is about the maximum gradient for resistant types of rock; intermediate forms and medium relief, for those with inclinations comparable to their basal slopes, and similar to the relief found in the valleys in the German Highlands; flattish forms and peneplanes, where the gradients are slight throughout. There are, however, an infinite number of transitions in the series. Also, within any one relief type, there will be minor diversities associated with differences in rock resistance and attitude.

A problem is presented, not only by this association of slopes of more or less uniform gradient in definite limited regions, but also by the *form of the slopes*. This may be convex, concave or straight (rectilinear) in profile; and these forms, too, are arranged in definite groupings. Convex or straight profiles are usually associated with vigorous erosion; concave profiles with old landscapes, often upraised (e.g. the summit area of the German Highlands and of the German Scarplands). Form associations with convex slopes are typical of the two high mountainous belts of the world, and are less frequent on continental masses, where concave slopes are the general rule. Straight profiles are commonest with steep relief, but are not confined to this. They occur also with medium relief, being the rule where valleys are sharply incised; and they are quite frequent at ridge crests where these have been formed by the intersections of retreating slopes. All three types are excellently exhibited in Badlands.

Theoretically, slopes meeting in these upper extremities should always give rise to sharp linear edges (or pointed peaks). Actually, these edges are always somewhat rounded or blunted, the more so the gentler the intersecting slopes. The width of the zone of blunting decreases with increasing steepness. It is present when the intersecting slopes are concave or straight, as well as in the case of convex slopes which would naturally meet with a rounded effect.

Some have imagined an initially sharp edge which became flattened. But this conflicts with what has been observed in valley excavation, where the gentler slope develops at the base (basal slope or *Haldenhang*), and works upward—not vice versa; while the convex curvature would imply more rapid denudation on the flattish ridge summits than on their steeper flanks. This is not possible [except to the very limited extent due to increased exposure there (because there is less rock debris) which is discussed on pp. 78, 142–143].

2. FLATTENING OF SLOPES

Concave Base Levels of Denudation

Here we have, worked out with the aid of diagrams (figs. 2 and 3) the way in which a cliff, rising from the edge of a non-eroding stream, retreats by the process of denudation; and the development and (slower) retreat of a gentler basal slope (*Haldenhang*) below it, and of slopes of diminishing gradient (*Abflachungshängen*) below that.

3. UNEQUAL EXPOSURE: ROUNDING OF HEIGHTS

The accumulation of rock waste, which increases from above downwards, brings about inequality of exposure. This lessening of exposure on the lower parts of a slope system may retard the rate of development (if corrasion is absent), but does not alter the forms described in the previous section. Where slope units intersect—along ridge crests or in peaks—if the exposure is greater at the top, rock reduction is more rapid there than lower down where there is a mantle of rock waste. This means flattening of the uppermost part of the slope unit. The process reaches downwards until renewal of exposure is taking place at the same rate on the flattened part (where it is now becoming retarded) as lower down the slope where the rate has not changed. The gentler the gradient, the sooner will this limit to flattening be reached.

It is thus impossible for *broad* rounded ridges and, from them, flattish form associations, to have been derived from sharp crests by a process working from above downwards.

The rounding takes place more quickly if climatic conditions allow of plant growth, which assists in the accumulation of soil, so producing inequality of exposure on the slope unit. The character of the rock also exerts an influence.

4. STRAIGHT SLOPE PROFILES.
UNIFORM DEVELOPMENT

In VI. 2, it was assumed that the base level of denudation remained unchanged, i.e. the river was neither incising nor depositing, merely transporting its load. In such a case, the whole system of slopes moves back further and further from the edge of the stream; and, one after another, the uppermost slope units disappear. The only one that continues to gain in area is the lowest of all, that of minimum gradient.

If any slope unit other than this is to remain adjacent to the base level of denudation, the river must erode it. With the aid of fig. 4 (p. 145), it is shown that a slope unit can maintain itself (with unaltered gradient) at the edge of the stream only if the intensity of erosion is constant or bears a constant ratio to the intensity of denudation on the adjoining slope unit. The latter depends upon the gradient and this upon the character of the rock. Hence, if the adjoining slope is steep, greater erosional intensity is necessary to maintain equilibrium than if it is gentle. The limiting case is equilibrium between a slope with the smallest possible gradient and a non-eroding river (the case of the theoretical peneplain or end-peneplane). Fig. 5 (p. 146) is used to show that the gradient of the slope unit which rises up from the river's edge is determined by the intensity of erosion (though details of the inclination depend upon the rock material). If this intensity remains constant, the inclination of the slope unit developing at the margin of the stream must also remain constant, i.e. the form of the slope is rectilinear in profile. The *development* is said to be *uniform*, and the characteristic is a straight slope profile which may have any gradient.

The cliff face in fig. 5, if produced upwards, would meet an analogous slope unit in a sharp edge. It has been shown that a slope of uniform gradient develops below each original steep slope, with a single concave break of gradient. As this works backward and upward, the steep face is shortened to the same extent. The arête is lowered by the corresponding vertical amount. In course of time, the original slopes are replaced by the gentler slopes of uniform gradient, which meet in a blunter edge. Up to this time, the vertical distance between the zone of intersection and the general base level of denudation (which is sinking uniformly) has been lessening. In other words, the relative height has been diminishing. But from now on, this is not so. The uniform straight slope is being shortened from above at the zone of intersection; but it is also being supplemented from below, at the river's edge, by the same amount. It can be seen from the diagram that, in unit time, the zone of intersection is lowered by the same amount as the river cuts down. This is regardless of the angle of inclination of the intersecting slopes of uniform gradient, and irrespective of the rounding of the summit ridge (since this 'flattening from above', incident upon unequal exposure, is rapidly brought to an end, p. 142).

Thus, with uniform intensity of erosion, if the uniform development lasts sufficiently long, straight slopes are produced. As soon as these intersect, the relative heights remain constant.

5. CONVEX BREAKS OF GRADIENT

By reference to fig. 6 (p. 149) it is shown that a convex break of gradient is produced if the intensity of erosion is increasing. It arises at the edge of the stream and works upwards at a rate depending upon the intensity of denudation on the steeper (lower) slope unit. The development of the higher, flatter slope unit depends upon the position of the break of gradient, and so becomes independent of the base levels of erosion.

ADDITIONAL NOTES ON THE ORIGIN OF CONCAVE BREAKS OF GRADIENT

Convex breaks of gradient thus correspond to concave base levels of denudation as far as their origin, their behaviour and their function are concerned. Both originate at the general base level of denudation, both recede upslope at a rate determined by the intensity of denudation (which equals the rate of development of the steeper slope unit); both are local base levels of denudation and thereby remove the slopes above them from the influence of the drainage net and the base level of erosion.

By analogy from VI. 5, it follows that concave breaks of gradient will develop not only with a fixed base level of denudation (stream neither eroding nor depositing), but whenever the intensity of erosion is diminishing. A sharply concave curve indicates rapid deceleration of the erosional intensity, and less strong curvature a slower rate.

6. DEVELOPMENT OF RELATIVE HEIGHT. WAXING DEVELOPMENT AND WANING DEVELOPMENT

Development of relative height is discussed with reference to figs. 2 to 6. Lowering of the zone of intersection depends solely upon the development of the slope units which meet there; and the rate of lowering decreases with the gradient of the intersecting slopes.

But relative height depends also upon the position of the general base level of denudation. This is constant only at the end of a series of developments characterised by decreasing erosional intensity. Such a

course of development is here termed WANING DEVELOPMENT (*Absteigende Entwicklung*). Its characteristic features are concave breaks of
gradient, concave slope profiles, and decreasing relative heights.

Waning development may succeed uniform development, or be
followed by it (as was assumed for fig. 6). With UNIFORM DEVELOPMENT,
the relative height becomes constant as soon as the straight slopes intersect (p. 148).

WAXING DEVELOPMENT (*Aufsteigende Entwicklung*) is the name given
to that course of development which is due to increasing erosional intensity. Its characteristic features are convex breaks of gradient, convex
slopes and increasing relative heights, even though there is lowering of
the zones of intersection.

Variations in relative height depend upon the differences between
what is happening at the zone of intersection and in the eroding channel,
the edge of which forms the base level of denudation. If intensity of
erosion becomes less, relative height diminishes (this being associated
with concavity of the slopes, and the intersection of slopes of gentler
gradient). If it increases, so does the relative height; but again not until
the new slopes of the convex slope system have established themselves.

7. RATES OF GROWTH AND AREAS OF SLOPE UNITS

As concave or convex breaks of gradient recede upslope (regularly, if
the rock material is homogeneous), the slope unit immediately above the
break is shortened. But that immediately below it is lengthened. This
growth of slope units varies in its rate with the intensity of denudation,
and so with the gradient of the slope.

When development is uniform (straight slopes), there are no breaks
of gradient, and the amount of shortening at the zone of intersection is
compensated for by an equal lengthening at the general base level of
denudation, i.e. the area of the slope unit remains constant (as does the
gradient).

With waning development, since the steeper slopes are above, each
higher break of gradient recedes upslope more quickly than the next
below it. Thus the area of the slope unit between them increases. The
increase is small since differences of gradient on adjoining slope units
are slight, except those between the original cliff and its basal slope.
Also the increase is not unlimited; and it is only the slope of minimum
gradient which increases continuously at the expense of the rest.

With waxing development the situation is reversed. The more rapidly
receding breaks of gradient (which are convex) are found at the lower
margin of each slope unit. Thus they all decrease in area except that
adjoining the general base level of denudation. Slope units may vanish

before they reach the zone of intersection (see fig. 7, p. 158). They are replaced by sharper breaks of gradient. Hence it eventually happens that the lower limit of an uplifted flattish landscape is a sharp break of gradient above steep slopes which may even be slopes of maximum gradient, e.g. Black Forest. This is demonstrated with the aid of fig. 7 The slope which 'eats up' the others always has a straight profile; so that from its shape it is impossible to tell whether the water-course at its base has had uniform, accelerated or decelerated erosion, i.e. whether the slope has had uniform, waxing or waning development, provided the intensity of erosion more than balances the 'spontaneous' denudation on a slope of maximum gradient. Where such undercut slopes intersect to form a ridge, the relative height becomes constant. This then no longer indicates uniformity of development.

CONTINUITY OF THE CURVATURE OF SLOPES

In the above diagrams, erosional intensity has been assumed to increase intermittently. But this is not necessary for the accentuation of convex breaks of gradient by the removal of intermediate slope units. Actually the intensity of erosion changes, not discontinuously, but steadily—although by comparison with the very slow processes of sheet denudation the increase may seem to be intermittent. The general base level of denudation is being lowered continuously by erosion, by a very small amount at each instant of time. So that very minute slope units are perpetually developing at the edge of the eroding stream, each increasing in steepness with the increase in erosional intensity. They combine to form a continuously curved slope. This is shown in fig. 8 (p. 159), where the more rapid rate of erosion in (B) is seen to produce a stronger curvature than in (A).

When, in a continuously curved slope of medium gradients, a steeper slope unit (e.g. that of maximum gradient) overtakes these, a markedly curved section of the slope is developed; and this recedes upwards, acting like a convex break of gradient. Such a break in the general change of gradient is a discontinuity in the slope. But it has been brought about by a continuous increase in erosional intensity, i.e. *a continuous cause has produced a morphological discontinuity*.

Similarly, the concave profiles of waning development are also continuously curved. Even the transition from cliff face to basal slope is not a sharp angle but curved; although this curve may be hidden by the accumulation of detritus making a sharp nick in the profile where it joins the cliff.

8. RISE IN THE GENERAL BASE LEVEL
OF DENUDATION

A relative rise in the general base level of denudation does not lead to any alteration in the type and shape of the associated slope units unless the rise is continually changing. The result is then a special case of waning development. Unless the base level rises as rapidly as a cliff face is receding by denudation, it cannot continue to adjoin it. If the rise lags behind, a basal slope develops which separates the cliff from base level, even if the lower part of the basal slope becomes buried. If the rise in base level is decelerating, the slope of diminishing gradient may also appear. Slope units, that are being drowned, or buried, preserve their gradient only when the rate at which the base level is rising keeps pace with, or surpasses, the rate of development of the slope unit concerned. When base level rises more rapidly than the adjoining slope unit recedes, this slope is preserved unaltered at base level. But there develops below it, being covered as it develops, a gentler slope, which is however steeper than the normal slope of diminishing gradient associated with a fixed base level of denudation. With a decelerating rise of base level, the slopes, which are being buried as they form, produce a convex profile. Above them, concave slopes of waning development will appear; and often below them also, as erosion ceases. Profiles of this type occur near Istambul in Devonian beds that have been covered over by Neogene beds.

9. INFLUENCE OF HETEROGENEOUS ROCKS UPON
THE DEVELOPMENT OF SLOPES

STRUCTURAL BASE LEVELS OF DENUDATION

If a belt of more resistant rock, e.g. an eruptive dyke, outcrops on a slope, two types of break of gradient develop. These are the two types: (a) on the downhill side, the steeper slope of the resistant band is separated from the gentler one below by a concave angle; on the uphill side, a convex break of gradient separates it from the gentler slope above. These breaks do not migrate upslope, but merely follow the shifting of the rock boundaries as denudation proceeds. They are independent of the base level of denudation. (b) The breaks of gradient of the second type occur within the individual rock outcrops, originating at the structural base level of denudation, and migrating upslope in the normal manner.

Where there are rocks of differing resistance, the intensity of denudation on a lower slope unit is one of the factors determining the development of those sections of slope that lie above it.

Waning development is not fundamentally disturbed when a more resistant type of rock outcrops on a slope. The concave profile appears, though it is interrupted by a convex break of gradient at the upper boundary of the more resistant bed. Waxing development has its convex profile interrupted by a concave break of gradient at the lower boundary of the more resistant rock.

For given differences in rock resistance, the difference in gradient between the slope units in the two rocks increases as the mean gradient of the slope increases. And as this mean gradient depends upon intensity of denudation, adaptation of denudational forms to crustal structure depends not only upon the duration of the denudation but also upon its intensity. That is, the influence of various rocks is far more noticeable where there is steep relief than on peneplanes. On moderately inclined slopes, the adaptation of individual forms to crustal structure is more pronounced the greater the difference in rock resistance.

To consider the special case of *scarplands*—formed in tilted beds of alternately resistant and less resistant rock. Those between the Fichtelgebirge and the Black Forest have been very fully studied. Gradmann has shown that the steps are not tectonic, being unconnected with faults or flexures. The peneplanes, generally upon impermeable and mobile sediments, between the upstanding ridges of resistant permeable material, are not (Davisian) peneplains. He considered them to have been formed by the denudational lowering of ridge crests between deeply incised valleys during a period when erosion was at a standstill, so that the base level of denudation was in a fixed position. With the help of fig. 11, it is shown that it is impossible for scarpland peneplanes to have arisen in this way, the ridge crests becoming flattened whilst the scarp steps were preserved. Surface denudation is by itself inadequate for this. There must have been an active drainage net on the less resistant beds, during their peneplanation. This is necessary to account for the preservation of steepness in the scarp ridges; and it would have acted as general base level for denudation on the less resistant beds. But the location of the water courses on the weaker strata presupposes an original surface on which these outcropped between the resistant beds (as Gradmann shows in his profile). Fragments of such a surface—which was not a (Davisian) peneplain—are still clearly recognisable.

Since cuesta ridges and intervening peneplanes exist side by side, different parts of the drainage net must have had different values as general base levels of denudation: (*a*) the main branches, directly connected with the general base level of erosion for the whole area, were able to cut through the ridges; (*b*) the ramifications on the peneplanes were held up by more resistant beds and so eroded but slightly, if at all. Recession of the scarps, and further modelling of the peneplanes, took place in relation to these.

Such flattish forms or peneplanes are found not only in scarplands, but in other areas where resistant beds lie below less resistant ones, particularly at the edges of such regions, where the outcropping of a resistant bed forms a structural base level of denudation. But more often they are related to a drainage net (general base level of denudation), the downcutting of which is impeded by the resistant beds. These relationships are exhibited on Erongo, a South-west African inselberg.

If the more resistant and the less resistant beds are arranged side by side (instead of below one another), the valley cross section changes noticeably, widening out in the weaker beds, even when the erosional intensity is constant.

When slope units at the same stage of development intersect to form a ridge crest, then the relative height is greater in the more resistant rocks (other things being equal). The argument is developed with reference to fig. 11.

At certain stages of development, there may also be a change of form associated with that in rock material—e.g. with waning erosional intensity, concave slopes appear first in the more resistant material whilst the weaker bed is still able to maintain *its* slope of maximum gradient (with straight profile). This may be seen where the stream follows a rock boundary; or where the rock beds, though differing in their resistance to denudation, are similar as regards resistance to erosion.

But more often the change in erosional intensity with a difference in rock material is similar to that in denudational intensity. A bank of specially resistant rock may check the erosional intensity above it, so that the denudational forms become concave (waning development). The concave slopes work back from the edges of the river, which meanders because of impeded erosion; and thus easily removed beds may be cleared away, e.g. the Neogene beds that have been removed from the broad synclines of western Anatolia (where the frame round the broad synclines is of resistant material). Denudational terraces (e.g. Grand Canyon of the Colorado, scarplands, etc.) are also due to differences in the resistance of the rocks.

The nature of the rocks and their arrangement are of immense importance in determining individual land forms and their groupings. But these are merely details of land sculpture, modifications of the fundamental laws of denudation; and adaptation to rock material is only part of the feature, a fact that has often been overlooked.

SUMMARY

[not further summarised.]

CHAPTER VII

LINKING OF SLOPES, FORM ASSOCIATIONS AND SETS OF LAND FORMS

1. OCCURRENCE AND COMBINATIONS OF CONVEX AND CONCAVE SLOPES

Concave slopes predominate all over the earth and may be considered the normal type. This is because denudation, which acts everywhere on a surface and the whole time, can produce only this kind. Straight and convex profiles develop only where erosion also comes into play, and this varies from place to place, and from one time to another.

But though now predominant, concave slopes cannot be the original type. They cannot be parts of the earth's surface as it was uplifted, since they are always found rising up from streams incised in it. But erosion (by rivers) must have begun and suffered acceleration before it could decrease in intensity—and it is found that the concave slopes of waning development do usually lead upwards to convex ones of waxing development (unless these have been removed by the working back of the later concave forms). Good examples may be seen in the German Highlands, but it is a world-wide feature. The problem is: what are the causes that have led, in these places, to periods of increasing erosional intensity followed by periods when the intensity was decreasing?

Moreover, terraced deposits, remnants of former valley floors, often divide up the slopes. In the German Highlands they occur particularly along the main lines of drainage. The problem is complicated by the fact that frequently these terrace steps are closer and closer together as the valley floors are approached, and that they often vanish where the deeply entrenched rivers leave the highlands. The alternately convex and concave sections of the valley side are then replaced by convex slopes, or straight slopes of the steepest angle possible for that type of rock. The usual explanation is quite inadequate.

Concave and convex slopes may also be associated horizontally in a valley, as the shifting current undercuts a bank or slips away from it. Such undercutting by meanders may lead to occasional convex profiles where the valley slopes as a whole show waning development with concave forms; and vice versa. But these divergences relate merely to local

erosional changes (modifying the denudation here and there) and throw
no light upon the development of the district as a whole.

What matters to the solution of our problem is the characteristic, constantly repeated form. Quite often, the main valleys have the concave
forms of waning development whilst the tributary streams, developed
later, are still actively eroding so that their valley sides are convex.
Their immediate, practically constant, base levels are the floors of the
main valleys, and they have a long way to go before catching up in their
stage of development. It is these convex forms which give its characteristic appearance to the district, since the density of their tributary network is increasing by headward erosion and ramification. In other places
there may be equally great vertical dissection, but slopes are concave and
the valley net is no longer increasing in the density of its mesh.

*Thus the core of the problem is found in the development of the valley net-
work.* A fact worth noting is that in areas quite separate from one another,
we find examples of a still developing net of tributary valleys with convex
slopes dominating the landscape, in spite of the concave slopes of the
main valley sides, as well as examples of an already fully developed net
with concave slopes everywhere.

2. SCARPLANDS (CUESTA LANDSCAPES)

The watershed region between the Danube and the Wutach shows
two units: (*a*) the gentle eastern slope of the Black Forest (more or less
uniform), and (*b*) the Malm scarp (a continuation of the Swabian Alb).
Although the Triassic and Jurassic strata lying between these seem
suited to scarp production—as in the Neckar basin to the north, and
even on the sides of the deeply entrenched Wutach—there is no scarpland
here. The reason for this is the absence of a rapidly eroding drainage
system, which would lead to the uncovering and constant renewal of
structural base levels of denudation—an essential preliminary for scarpland formation.

On the scarplands, which begin east of Donaueschingen and extend to
the Franconian Jura (and even beyond, to the edge of the Bohemian
massif), two contrasting types of drainage can be distinguished. (*a*) The
principal rivers—the Main, the Neckar and their larger tributaries—
with an abundant water supply, have entrenched their valleys, which cut
through the scarp-forming horizons. (*b*) At the top of each scarp step,
there is subdued relief, often forming a peneplane. On this are the headwater ramifications of the above tributaries, only scantily supplied with
water. However, they work back to the edge of the next higher scarp,
dissecting it into lobes. Downstream, this type ends with a break of

gradient in its longitudinal profile where the edge of the scarp-forming stratum is reached. For example, the very resistant Upper Muschelkalk gives the sharpest breaks of gradient, and bears the most extensive and most level of the peneplanes, which spread over on to the Lettenkohl and Lower Keuper beds lying above it.

The main lines of drainage show alternations of reaches with vigorous downcutting and others where erosion has almost ceased, but will recommence as soon as the eroding sections below them have worked up to those points. The valley sides are convex, straight or terraced, often with concave slopes at the base. At the top is the scarp-forming horizon through which the river has cut.

Lateral tributaries work back into the high land between the main valleys, progressively dissecting the scarps which overlook these, and so reach up to the peneplanes on their summits. Where they join the main valley, their cross sections may be canyon-like entrenchments (if the main valley is of that type); higher up, they are V-shaped. They suddenly become wide and shallow as they reach the peneplane (above a break of gradient).

Sometimes the contrast is less obvious, as when the headwater tributary, or even the upper part of a main stream itself (like the Tauber above Rothenburg), lies wholly on the top of a step. In such a case the break of gradient separates (a) the mixed forms of the incised valley from (b) the concave flattish forms on the intervalley divides and on the scarpland peneplane, which leads to the next higher scarp face with its forms of medium relief. The general base level of denudation for this receding scarp (where landslips may play an important part) is formed by the chief streams on the peneplane at its foot. For them the local base level of erosion is the outcrop of the resistant beds (at the break of gradient above the lower, incised part of the stream). This may be considered fixed, relative to its tributary slopes; so that the peneplane and scarps above it develop without reference to any endogenetic occurrences [such as might be affecting the lower courses of the main rivers.]

Each scarp is dissected by watercourses which often begin along corrasion furrows or where springs issue. Although frequently intermittent, they erode vigorously, since the gradient is steep, and work their way back by headward erosion. The sharp V-shaped valleys unite below with the wide shallow valleys of the peneplane lying in front of the scarp. As each streamlet cuts down its bed, the lower reaches—towards the peneplane—become more or less graded, so that only its uppermost, newest, and still steep sections are eroding. They dissect the scarp face into lobes, and each intervalley spur becomes itself similarly dissected by streamlets tributary to those which issue on to the peneplane. Thus the scarps recede, as first leaving residual hills in front, and are replaced below by slopes of diminishing gradient, so that the peneplane extends farther and farther backwards.

The preservation of the peneplanes between the scarps is dependent upon the structural base levels of denudation. These are renewed in two ways:

(1) The main streams which cut through the scarps, and flow along the peneplanes, are still connected with the general base level of denudation and so affected by endogenetic factors [i.e. if the land is rising relatively, their eroding power is increased]. The upper peneplanes—on the interfluves between these rivers—are further and further dissected and flattened as denudation works the slopes back from the rivers. Hence the lower peneplanes extend at the expense of the scarp steps, and so of the upper peneplanes on these.

(2) Rising from the peneplanes, which are controlled by their structural base levels of denudation, and so unaffected by endogenetic factors, are the scarps. These are preserved as typical forms, since they are always being worked back by vigorously eroding streams, cutting headward as well as down.

It is often difficult to trace the erosional history of the watercourses on the peneplanes, since mass-movement of rock waste tends to mask it. The absence of stream channels in the wide shallow valleys is due partly to this, and partly to choking by what has been brought down by flood waters from the intermittent streams dissecting the scarps. A very important factor is that these streams, in their lower courses, trench through the scarp-forming horizon to the less resistant strata below; and this looser, finer material, even on the lessened gradient, creeps down to the stream channels, filling them in from the sides (see chapter IV, pp. 109, 113, 116).

The scarpland peneplanes have a general inclination in the same direction as the drainage on them. This is because the streams cannot erode below the local base level of erosion, the break of gradient at the scarp edge; and all upstream from this, denudational slopes as well as erosional curves, are controlled by this level. Sometimes the peneplane valleys are drained in the direction of the dip of the strata, e.g. from Steigerwald eastward to the Regnitz and Franconian Jura. Sometimes the streams flow against the dip, e.g. the Neckar tributaries coming from the Swabian Alb. Those tributaries of the Jagst, Kocher and Murr which flow with the dip have been considered consequent. But actually they have extended headwards along a water-bearing horizon at the base of the Lias (which, though often reduced to mere scattered residual hills, shows this feature in parts of the Jagst basin).

3. INSELBERG LANDSCAPES

Here the characteristic feature is island-like projections from a pene-plane; in contrast to the way in which an uplifted portion of the earth's crust derives its special character from the pattern and depth of the excavations—the valleys and the modelling of their flanks. *The slope profile of all inselbergs is concave*, including the slopes by which they are linked to the surrounding peneplane with *its* concave forms. *The inselberg landscape is characteristic of waning development.*

The minimum extent of the vertical dissection, during the preceding period of waxing development, is shown by the maximum height of the inselbergs. When these are flat-topped, they are generally all about the same altitude, and their relative height is approximately the maximum ever attained by dissection of the original landscape. When the inselbergs are pointed and on the way to demolition, their heights vary more; and the slopes are gentler the lower the heights. Gradually they diminish to mere faint suggestions of intervalley divides before they are entirely lost in the peneplane.

The development of inselberg landscapes is due to the weakening and final loss of erosive activity in the drainage net. This cessation does not occur simultaneously everywhere. It is first of all to be noticed along the main streams, accompanied by concave slope profiles and the movement upwards of flatter and flatter slope units towards the intervalley divides. The valleys are widened as meanders increase in size; and the distances between the upper edges of the valleys also become greater as denudation causes the steep slope units to recede, being replaced below by those of diminishing gradient until the minimum is reached. Meanwhile, in the uppermost reaches, erosion is still active. Headward erosion lengthens the streams which are working back into higher ground and have steep valley sides. This process continues as long as there is any land left standing above the curve of erosion.

The intervalley divides are at the same time being eaten into by the tributaries of the main streams, and the lateral ramifying branches of these. They, too, work backwards and upwards into the flanks of the main valleys, forming fresh steep-sided erosion cuts. The last and youngest of these are the gashes that furrow the slopes of the inselbergs. The steepness of the sides here shows that the erosional intensity is transmitted, without loss, right up to the furthest ramifications of the valley system, and is seen in isolated branches of it when the greater part of the system has reached the stage of waning development and appears as wide shallow valleys on the peneplane. The inselbergs have been formed from dissection of the intervalley divides, as the headwaters of ramifying backward-working tributaries meet from opposite sides and eventually break up the ridge into separate peaks.

Just as the phase of intense erosion and waxing development spreads backwards up-valley, and up the tributaries and their branches, so does that of waning development. The progress is unaffected by further changes downstream. Thus waning development may be only reaching the headwater areas whilst a fresh impulse of waxing development may have begun to spread up-valley. Under such circumstances, the waning development will not have reached completion in the lower courses, and so cannot reach completion in the uppermost central areas. For the renewal of activity in the lower parts means that new, steeper slope units develop and pass upwards, overtaking and swallowing up the waning forms before they have attained their greatest possible degree of flattening.

A characteristic of the inselberg landscapes of continental areas is that they extend over immense regions of tectonically uniform parts of the earth's crust; and that the form associations of waning development stretch from the lower courses of the main drainage lines (where the development is quite complete) to the most centrally lying parts (where it is nearing completion). This implies a relatively long period with base levels of erosion constant. This is a fundamental, deep-seated difference from the regions where such forms of waning development are confined within narrow limits, e.g. in areas of broad folding (on mountain tops, especially in arid and semi-arid regions) and on the summits of the German Highlands and Scarplands. In these latter, a zone of renewed erosion, and steep slopes, separates the narrow zone of waning development from its present general base level of erosion, and peneplanation is effected only in the uppermost, headwater areas.

Suppose there are sections of a valley where erosion has ceased. The steep slope units will recede from the river, being replaced below by slopes of diminishing gradient till the minimum slope is reached. The intervalley ridges—already divided up into peaks—will be narrowed; and the gentler slopes will first meet in the depressions between the peaks, which will remain as inselbergs. Downstream the whole area will have become a peneplane—upstream is still mountain. The zone of inselbergs is comparable to the belt of residuals in front of a retreating escarpment. It works its way upstream, and ultimately the central mountain region is disintegrated into inselbergs.

Where the rock material is resistant, inselbergs last longest; and some have thought that such 'monadnocks' are always associated with specially durable rock. But inselbergs are also found where the whole area is of homogeneous rock. All that is necessary is undisturbed waning development, i.e. constant base levels of erosion. The inselbergs are the relics of what was the highest part of the district. Eventually they also are flattened until the result is an end-peneplane or (Davisian) peneplain.

Waning development is independent of climate—all that is necessary is the weakening of erosion; and, if the development is to reach completion, endogenetic influences must be eliminated, for they would lead to fluctuations in the general base levels of erosion. The absence of such influences may be either because the base levels actually remain stable for a sufficiently long time, or because local base levels of erosion are interposed (i.e. breaks of gradient in the longitudinal profile are working back sufficiently slowly). The result is a wide peneplane with inselbergs standing up from it. Genetic relations show that inselberg formation is unconnected with climatic conditions—and actual facts bear this out, for typical inselberg landscapes have been found in almost every climatic region. *They are distinctive features, not of any special climatic region, but of the continental masses*, areas long withdrawn from orogenic movements.

Climate does, however, affect some details of the form, e.g. in climates where vegetation is sparse, it is found that the soil is very thin not only on the slopes of the inselbergs, but also over the peneplanes. This leads to the development of sharper concave curvature in the foot-slopes of the inselbergs.

4. PIEDMONT FLATS AND PIEDMONT BENCHLANDS

There is a striking similarity between the forms characterising inselberg landscapes and those of other form associations, also upon tectonic units. The German Highlands exemplify this. Valley forms will not be considered here, only the subdued land forms on the heights between the entrenched valleys. In some cases dissection has advanced so far as to remove these entirely, e.g. on the steep western slope of the Black Forest. But its eastern slope, especially in the south, is almost intact and shows the older form associations upon its intervalley divides. The same is true for the northern slope of the Fichtelgebirge, and remnants are also visible on its western side.

(a) THE HARZ

The original northern and southern slopes have been almost entirely removed by dissection, but a larger proportion of the summit area remains. Valleys (such as those of the Oder and Bode) penetrate far into the mountain mass; and between their steep slopes and the gentle forms on the summit, there is just as sharp a break of gradient as that from the summit to the short sharply incised valleys at the edge of the massif It is the number and closeness together of these latter which give the semblance of mountains.

Except for occasional recent gashes on the sides of the inselbergs rising above it, all forms on the summit peneplane show the concave slopes of waning development, with wide shallow valleys. The central mountainland rising above it consists of the Brocken and its associated summits. These are not due to the occurrence of specially resistant rock, since the Brocken and Bode granites, for example, help to compose both the summit peneplane and the mountain tops rising from it. There are, however, some lower, less steep elevations which are definitely associated with resistant rock material; but they are found only where this outcrops at or just above the general level of the land between the dissecting valleys, a level which has been determined by other factors.

The summit peneplane is clearly developed to the north of the central mountainland, though there it is narrower than to the south. On the east, it stretches from the northern to the southern edge of the mass. Here there is similarity to the inselberg landscapes of the vast continental areas. But it is not quite like even a pocket edition of these; for it is only in the headwater regions that waning development has reached its completion, not also in the lower courses of the drainage net, where there has not been prolonged fixity of the general base level of erosion.

On the other hand, the forms indicate a succession of periods of intenser erosion, each more vigorous than the preceding one. For the longitudinal profile of the valleys shows a succession of eroding sections, separated by breaks of gradient from sections having a much gentler profile; and as one passes upstream, the eroding sections become in turn less steep (and also shorter) until the low relief of the summit peneplane is reached. That is, the whole longitudinal profile is convex, although each unit is concave (see fig. 13, p. 200).

The cross sections correspond to these divisions, being narrow with convex valley slopes where the longitudinal profile is steep, more open with concave foot-slopes where it is gentle. The valleys on the summit are shallow and wide.

These sections that are now eroding must have arisen successively from the general base level of erosion, and worked upstream. When waning development supervened, the break in the longitudinal profile of the stream formed a local base level of erosion for the part above it. Thus the central mountainland has become separated from the general base level of erosion by these local base levels above each of the more steeply inclined sections of the river bed. The peneplane surrounding it is therefore different from that of an inselberg landscape on a continental mass. It is not an end-peneplane, and may in contradistinction be termed a *piedmont flat*.

A preliminary survey of the Black Forest and the Fichtelgebirge shows similar features to those of the Harz. But in these cases there is not one piedmont flat but a series, which may be termed *a piedmont stairway*, or *piedmont benchlands*.

(b) PIEDMONT BENCHLANDS

The northern slope of the Fichtelgebirge shows this development particularly well.

The central mountainland has two types of summit: sharp crests, often surmounted by granite tors; and dome-shaped mountains. The almost level tops of these latter, with their wide, shallow valleys, are in some cases (e.g. Hochhaide) at heights of about 900 metres; and they are fragments of the same peneplane P_2 which elsewhere surrounds other dome-shaped mountains that reach an altitude of 950 m. (e.g. Ochsenkopf). In recognising these as parts of the same peneplane, even more important than accordance of heights is the fact that each is bounded, both above and below, by a belt of convex slopes, separating the flattish, concave form associations. The higher domes bear on their summits what seem to be fragments of another peneplane, P_1. This is an endpeneplane of almost completed waning development; though even there a few crags are perched on the flattish ridges between the wide shallow valleys.

Only the highest elevations on the P_2 surface still bear traces of the P_1 level. In the peripheral parts, steeply rising concave slopes already intersect, at lower elevations, to give pointed summits (e.g. Kösseine).

Shallow, but fairly steep-sided erosion furrows score the slopes of the higher domes, and debouch on to the P_2 surface. V-shaped valleys, with steeper sides, start at lower levels and cut back, the more vigorously the lower their local base levels of erosion. Examples of such local base levels are the flattish interfluves between the Eger and the Röslau, parts of a P_3 peneplane at c. 370 m.; and also these rivers themselves. This P_3 surface penetrates the central mountainland in the form of wide valleys, which themselves have younger, narrower valleys sunk in their floors. North of the central mountainland it is the dominating feature, sloping northwards and ending in the steep convex slopes of a lobed scarp, in front of which lie residual hills. At its southward edge, concave slopes lead up towards the P_2 level, sometimes meeting in sharp crests crowned by crags (where the side valleys coming down to this peneplane are sufficiently close together).

The following general relationships are now evident:

(1) Each peneplane of a piedmont stairway continues in the form of valley floors into the region rising above it.

(2) Each lower peneplane was thus the level at which dissection started for the zone having a higher peneplane for its upper surface.

(3) Each lower peneplane must thus be younger in origin than the next higher one.

(4) The highest parts of the country are the oldest of the denudations areas.

(5) Dissection by valleys is due to erosion. These erosive incisions are associated with the steeper slopes connecting two peneplane levels. Their headward cutting tributaries show convex profiles both in longitudinal and transverse sections; so that zones of convexity separate the peneplane levels.

(6) The nearest base level for such erosion is the next lower peneplane.

(7) Each eroding section of a stream leaves behind it a zone of decelerated or of completed erosion, i.e. waning development starts on each lower peneplane and spreads upslope from it.

A piedmont stairway (or piedmont benchlands) is thus characterised by zonal alternations of the features of waxing and waning development (convexity and concavity). The uppermost peneplanes are the oldest; and on the others those parts nearest the next step above (the proximal part) are closest to being end-peneplanes. This part is continuously growing, whilst its peripheral edge is constantly being encroached upon from below by the next lower one, as the steep convex slopes separating them are worked back by stream action and denudation of the slopes. Peneplane P_3 corresponds to the Harz peneplane.

As regards the age of any peneplane belonging to a piedmont stairway, it must be remembered that the surface is always increasing in size at the expense of the higher land, so that even peneplanes of very ancient origin may have a part which is geologically recent. The transgression of Tertiary beds on to the P_4 peneplane (e.g. near the embayment of Leipzig) helps to date this, combined with the fact that it truncates beds ranging from Cambrian to Mid-Bunter.

As regards valley dissection, identical stages in different areas may be recognised by the similarities of their longitudinal and transverse profiles. Following the valleys and their tributaries upstream, zones are reached where the valleys are increasing in width, decreasing in depth, and have gentler slopes in cross section. These show the first and oldest stages of valley dissection. Such zones are separated from similar ones below by steep sections; and these eroding portions are steeper, and have a greater difference in altitude between any two breaks of gradient, the lower the level to which they belong, i.e. the later they have arisen at the base level of erosion (cf. fig. 13 for the Harz). This makes it clear that those parts of a piedmont flat lying out beyond the zone of inselbergs (or tors) cannot be an end-peneplane, since its forms are growing steeper with waxing development.

There are also intermediate levels to be discerned, especially in the neighbourhood of the Saale near Hof (between P_3 and P_4). They are not separated phases in the process of dissection, but members of a continuous developmental series, which points to the steady nature of the course of natural events.

The inselbergs diminish in height away from the step between the P_3 and P_4 peneplanes—i.e. the P_3 and P_4 flats converge away from the central mountainland, and must have originally merged into one another. This is true for all the lower peneplanes of the piedmont stairway. That a similar connection cannot be traced between P_3 and P_2, P_2 and P_1, in the Fichtelgebirge, is because denudation has wrought greater destruction there, so that it cannot even be determined whether or not there were intermediate levels between those peneplanes now visible. But the fact that the scarps between the older, higher surfaces are of greater altitude than those between the lower ones [contrast the relationship between the steep drops in the longitudinal sections of the valleys] does suggest that the upper peneplanes also converged, and united in one surface, outwards from the mountain.

Thus the scarps between the peneplanes are not an original feature, but have been produced by valley dissection, commencing at a lower level of the peneplane—which is not an end-peneplane. The scarps are valley slopes, or have originated from such slopes; and their steepness and trend are completely independent of the nature and arrangement of their rock material. The original border zone between two peneplanes is the first part to be destroyed. It is replaced by inselbergs and the spreading lower peneplane (fig. 16). The whole of this becomes an end-peneplane only when it has worked far back—like P_1 and P_2 in the Fichtelgebirge—and its peripheral part has been consumed by the next lower peneplane. Such a step-like arrangement of one end-peneplane above another can be formed only by piedmont stairway development.

Erosional intensities between zero and a very small limiting value occur twice in those reaches of the streams which are directly tributary to the general base level of erosion—viz. at the beginning of each period of erosion, and at its close, i.e. at the onset of what causes erosion, and as this ceases. The end-peneplane is associated with the second case, and its course has been characterised by progressive flattening. This is not true for the piedmont flats, which are continually being replaced, at their peripheral ends, by steeper forms. This indicates increasing intensity of erosion. Such peneplanes, which are not developing into peneplanes, but are undergoing dissection, may be termed primary peneplanes. Their formation is associated with the gentle erosion occurring between the original onset and a small upper limiting value.

This takes the problem of the piedmont benchlands back to the causes of the erosion, and of its variations. Erosion came into play in one zone after another, each further down the general slope of the mountain mass, and it increased slowly in intensity. Meanwhile, in successively higher zones, erosion was increasing to what was a definite maximum for each. These maxima became successively greater, and meanwhile the edge of the mountain mass extended further and further northwards (as seen from the position of the Oligocene transgressional beds, and from where the P_4 peneplane has been preserved below them).

Examination of the surfaces below the transgressing Oligocene beds, in the neighbourhood of the Mulde, shows the P_4 surface, its northward extension dissected into inselbergs, an intermediate level similarly dissected by the P_5 level, and valleys in P_5 itself. This puts P_5 back to the Eocene period. The P_4 surface is older; but not older than the Cenomanian which it truncates near Freiberg (in Saxony). The under surface of the Cenomanian transgression probably corresponds to the peripheral part of the P_3 level which has its crystalline surface weathered deeply. The uppermost, P_2 and P_1, surfaces must therefore have originated far back in the Mesozoic era; so that we may be seeing Jurassic form associations, which have continued to develop till the present day, preserving the same characteristics throughout.

The seas of the Upper Cretaceous and Lower Oligocene were merely episodes, associated with the sinking area to the north (as shown by the transgression of Cretaceous horizons over one another with retrogression in Danian times—and similarly for the Oligocene). This area of fluctuation separated that of continuous sedimentation to the north from that of continuous denudation to the south.

Similar piedmont benchlands are to be seen on the Atlantic slope of the Appalachians. They have heretofore been interpreted as end-peneplanes—Davisian peneplains. Here, too, there was marine transgression (Senonian to Miocene), and upwarping of the 'Cretaceous' peneplane. Here, too, the direction of movement did not alter, either in the area of uplift and denudation (Appalachians) or in that of subsidence and deposition (edge of Atlantic Ocean); but the latter area increased and diminished in size during the periods of time considered. The Hudson submarine channel is associated with recent subsidence in this region.

Scandinavia seems also to show a central mountainland (in south Norway—a Caledonian relic) surrounded by stepped peneplanes of which the lowest, the strand-flat, bears many inselbergs. The absence of strata containing the detritus of denudation is a hindrance to exact inter-pretation of the features.

No piedmont stairways have so far been found in the mountain belts of crustal instability.

5. BROAD FOLDS

Peneplanes occur quite frequently in the mountain belts, variously combined with other form associations. Till recently no satisfactory ex-planation has been given for them, since it had been assumed that they were associated with periods of 'tectonic rest'.

The first thing to be done is to describe them.

(a) THE ALPS

The remodelling effected by the Pleistocene glaciation makes it diffi-cult to characterise the special aspect of relief being considered here, especially as it has also masked the connection between pre-glacial forms and the deposits derived from their denudation. In addition, complica-tions are introduced because folding continued into early Tertiary times, extending into the foreland and involving the deposits of denuded material that had been laid down there.

Well-marked forms of waxing development may be seen where the extension of folding caused antecedent rivers to pass through gorges, the convex walls of which rise to flattish forms on the summits of the ranges. But not only there. They occur also well within the Alps, even though here dissection has gone further. They are clearly visible in the zones of the great longitudinal valleys, which run parallel to the trend of the mountain chains. Here the intervalley spurs do not rise so high as in the mountain belts at either side. These zones seem to have developed from longitudinal undulations in the rising mountain arch, probably far back in Tertiary times. Between these depressions were what now form the zones of ridges, where, at the present day, the valley slopes intersect in edges reaching higher altitudes. The forms are usually steep-sided, recti-linear in profile. But even here, especially on the spurs, there is often convexity. This is true well above the limit of glacial rounding. Sculp-ture by glaciers has notched them with concave sections in the general convexity of slope. It is more difficult to recognise the pre-glacial form of the valley floors. But these do appear to show breaks of gradient of very ancient origin.

There seems no doubt that the present steep relief was preceded by gentler slopes, preserved—to differing extents—in both the zones of longitudinal valleys and those of the ridges. Confirmation is found in the correlated deposits of the foreland. For from Stampian to Sarmatian stages, the grain of these increases in coarseness upwards, until conglomerate is reached. The Alpine area was increasing in height from early Tertiary times to that of the Pleistocene glaciation, its valley slopes and the long-profiles of the valleys becoming steeper. This also explains the narrowing of the valley cross-sections downstream, as was found to be the case in the German Highlands.

Differences in rock material are not the deciding factor here. For the same Triassic limestones, which give rise to sharp peaks and ridges around the Lech valley, form rounded bosses near that of the Inn (longitudinal valley zone); and the same differences hold true for the crystalline rocks belonging to the Silvretta and Ötzal nappes. Variations in rock material are very important as regards any individual features in the Alps, especially the lines of small valley ramifications. But even here the shape of the slopes is unaffected by the type of rock.

The gipfelflur (or imaginary surface tangential to the peaks and ridges, which show an extraordinary accordance of summit levels) is independent of glacial remodelling and shows a notable connection with the distribution of forms of slope. Its shape is that of an undulating arch, sinking longitudinally to the main trend of the mountains in the region of the great longitudinal valleys, and sinking transversely where there are passes or sections of the principal river courses which cross the strike of the folding. Where the gipfelflur sinks, flattish slope units are to some extent preserved on the summits; where it rises, any flattish precursors of the steep slopes have vanished. But their former existence is proved by the convexity which can still be traced on the slopes. This association with the undulations of the gipfelflur explains why it is that the great Alpine valleys are, on the whole, independent of the arrangement of folds and nappes. These undulations cannot well be the result of later warping, since its risings and fallings are associated with the preservation of different types of slope, indicating differences of erosional development in the two cases, and so of the causes leading to the erosion.

A peneplane, of post-Sarmatian origin, cuts across the Neogene strata of the Alpine Foreland. Its surface is slightly uneven, and it is covered by outwash gravels of the first Ice Age. It looks as if it might be a piedmont flat in front of its associated mountainland. But it cannot be one of the usual type, since the Alpine area and its foreland are separate tectonic units, which have generally moved in opposite directions.

However, piedmont flats are found within the Alpine region itself—

in the eastern part, where the endogenetic development has been differ
ent from that in the west, where also there was less glaciation, and where
there are massive and extensive deposits of limestone. Ancient form
associations, of medium relief, are found on the limestone plateaux of
both northern and southern Calcareous Alps, and show the concave
forms of waning development. Sharp breaks of gradient separate these
from the steep slopes of the valleys reaching up into this mountainous
country. In the northern Calcareous Alps there is a general slope northwards, and a lessening of relative relief in this direction so that the forms
approximate to a peneplane. For the Saalach region (Salzburg Calcareous Alps) two different levels have been established for the plateau
surfaces. In a southern group, they show a rise southwards from c.
1600 m. to c. 2700 m., the summits of the peaks (of moderate height)
rising similarly. A northern group has its surfaces at about 1500 m. and
its peaks at c. 1700 m. In two places this lower plateau is interlocked
with the higher one in embayments. Elsewhere the two levels are separated by a low-lying belt containing the Saalach. This is like a longitudinal
valley zone, and slopes down to the north-east. It also is probably a
downward undulation of the gipfelflur, the plateaux corresponding to
the ridge zones. On them, there have been preserved the gentler slopes
which have been replaced by steeper ones in the zones of ridges in the
west.

The date of origin of the plateaux of the High Calcareous Alps seems
to be Oligocene. Some of the (lower lying) plateaux of the Fore Alps may
be younger, and possibly the lower plateau of the Saalach district.

In the southern Calcareous Alps, the Dolomite plateaus, continuing to
the Julian Alps, form the upper level. The marginal chains of the Val
Sugana—Bellunese lines are lower.

(b) The Eastern Slope of the Alps and its Boundary against the Karst

Between the Julian Alps and the Karst three plateau levels can be distinguished: (a) Triglav-Krn, from c. 2500 m. in the north-west to c.
1800 m. in the south-east, and the tops of mountain ranges, between the
uppermost tributaries of the Wocheiner [Bohinjska] Save, Bača, etc., at
the same level; (b) a peneplane below this, continued as piedmont flats
into the valley floors of the higher level, altitude c. 1500–1300 m., e.g.
Jelovka Plateau; (c) broad, flat areas, often sunk valley-like in (b), at c.
1000 m., followed by, e.g., the Wocheiner Save.

There has not yet been enough investigation to date these levels geologically. But it is known that:

(1) The Wochein [Bohinj] (at the eastern end of the Julian Alps) is a synclinal region, containing Oligocene beds. The surrounding district bears the uppermost plateau, the origin of which cannot therefore be later than pre- Middle Oligocene.

(2) The second level (Jelovka) is younger, and seems to stretch over the (disturbed) Oligocene of the Wochein—perhaps of Mediterranean age (that of the beds in the Save embayment).

(3) This *may* be a continuation, in the form of valleys, of the peneplane which extends over much of the mountain area between Trieste and the Save. This latter is the main peneplane of the transitional region between Alps and Karst. On the Adriatic side it is dislocated by fractures, parallel to the trend of the Dinaric folds. It has been considered to be of Pontian age. But even the common generalisation of Miocene cannot be verified, though it is certainly later than the main Oligocene folding.

All that seems certain is that there are, at several levels, one above the other, ancient form associations, of a subdued character, related to one another in the same way as piedmont flats; and that the approximate date of their formation is between Eocene and Upper Miocene. This was a time when vigorous crustal movements were in progress, making it most unlikely that these are end-peneplanes (Davisian peneplains) associated with tectonic rest. Some of the most nearly graded peneplanes to be found anywhere are in the Dinaric Karst; and the lower ones continue as valley floors into higher ones, just as with a piedmont stairway. The manner of development has been influenced by the soluble nature of the limestone composing them; but here, as elsewhere, piedmont flats have grown at the expense of the land rising above them. The grandeur of the scale of these successive plateau steps in the Dinaric Mountains has attracted attention. Convex slopes, or convex breaks of gradient, separate them from one another. The plateau surfaces slope towards the main lines of drainage, from which the steps work back. The intervalley divides of level II disintegrate into inselbergs standing 400–500 m. above level III, and south-eastwards they merge into a higher plateau surface. South-east Tschitschenboden [Monti dei Vena] corresponds in altitude to level II on the eastern slopes of the Julian Alps; and, like it, is on the mountain strip between the downfaulted zones of the Save and the Adriatic. Schneeberg of Carniola [M. Nevoso] seems to be an inselberg of level I.

(*a*) Discounting the undulations of the gipfelflur, its absolute height diminishes not only towards the northern and southern edges of the mountain system of the Alps, but also towards the eastern end of its general trend. On the summits of even the centrally lying ridge zones, flattish and intermediate form associations are better preserved in this eastern part. They are analogous to the plateaux of the Calcareous Alps. The main relief features are independent of both structure (folds and nappes) and rock material.

(*b*) A further difference at the eastern end is that the undulations of the gipfelflur become sharper. The zones of longitudinal valleys are very ancient in origin—as is shown by the Middle or even Early Tertiary strata in them. These have invaded zones which were relatively subsiding, and mantled a denudational relief. Continued crustal movement has distorted these beds. The eastern end of the mountains, especially in the Save valley, shows repeated alternation of sedimentation and denudation from Middle Oligocene to Lower Pliocene; but on the whole the deposits recede further and further from the mountains, and the areas of denudation expand.

(*c*) This oscillation of the area of sedimentation is not confined to the Save embayment but is characteristic of the whole eastern end of the Alps as they plunge towards the Pannonian Plain. That is, as in the zones of the continental massifs, the mountainland (here occupying the western part) is separated from an area of continuous sedimentation (to the east) by a zone of unconformities.

(*c*) ANATOLIA

The great undulations along the strike, found in the east part of the Eastern Alps, are comparable to the tectonic type of broad folds. Research in Anatolia first provided information about this structure.

Two regions may be distinguished there: (*a*) the western part of the peninsula within the Dinaro-Tauric festoon; (*b*) the festoon itself. In (*a*), the broad folds, running east-west, are entirely independent of the way in which the strata are folded (the folding being of various ages from Palaeozoic to Oligocene). In (*b*), the strike of the broad folds coincides with that of the folded strata. In the western and Lycian Taurus, the age of folding is Eocene to Middle Oligocene; that of the broad folding seems to be from Upper Oligocene to the present day.

The deposits, laid down as the broad folds rose, are found mainly within the troughs of the broad synclines. Their ages vary, in the individual regions, from Aquitanian to Levantine. These Neogene beds were laid down in areas of relative subsidence; but the latter do not everywhere coincide with the present synclines, having occupied a greater area in the Miocene period. Fresh anticlines, with east-west strike, have arisen in the older broad synclines. The regions of deposition were divided up and also their area was decreased. Thus some ranges (the earlier ones) were never covered by Neogene beds, which occur only at their foot. Others were arched up beneath them, but have lost the greater part of them by contemporaneous denudation. Younger Neogene beds are found at the sides of these ranges, as strata correlated with their uplift and denudation.

Earlier Neogene strata have often been distorted by later movements, and covered unconformably by later beds. The unconformities within the Neogene sequence are not all at the same stratigraphical level, so cannot be used for determining age. Several, one above another, may even occur in the same range.

The anticlinal character of the mountain chains and the synclinal nature of the longitudinal depressions are shown by the facies and bedding of these Neogene strata. In general, the older horizons seem to have been pushed together more strongly than the younger ones. This must have been due to tangential forces situated within the system of broad folding. Longitudinal faults are found in the west, where the broad folds have increased in amplitude (or relative height between ridge crest and trough floor). They die away towards the high land of the interior, horsts giving place to anticlines, downfaulted troughs to synclines.

The Bithynian Olympus (Keshish Dagh, now Ulu dağ) is typical of an east-west range of rather early origin. It shows several levels. Level I, on the summit, is the oldest, and is hill country of subdued relief, with concave slopes and trough-like valleys. It does not stretch far in an east-west direction, but is soon replaced by a ridge formed from the intersection of younger, steeper slopes, the continuation of those leading down from summit level I to a lower level which, on the north side of the range, forms an undulating piedmont surface ('the upper terrace') with its own system of shallow valleys. On its lower side is a convex break of gradient leading to further steep slopes. Sometimes (north-east part) these are associated with the present-day valleys, which are working upwards. Elsewhere (north-west) they end below in a lower piedmont flat (surface III—the 'lower terrace', preserved mainly on intervalley divides), which penetrates as valley floors into the upper region. Surface III has certain features in common with surface II:

1. Due north and south of the central mountainland (I), surface III is not present—either it has never been formed or has been replaced by a younger steep relief. Westwards, it widens as surface I becomes lower and disappears, surface II then occupying the summit of the range at a lower altitude. Surface II is also found on the ridges between the valleys which issue on to surface III.

2. Surfaces II and III are both strongly warped in a direction at right angles to the strike of the mountain range. The recent steep-walled

valley incisions are confined to the upwarped parts, and end above the convex break of gradient leading downwards.

Surface III at the edge of the range stretches over on to the Neogene strata filling the Bursa-Apulyont syncline. The present-day valleys form surface IV.

Thus the higher eastern section of the range (east of the Ülfer Chai) shows the whole of the piedmont benchlands. Westward, as the range becomes lower in altitude, the upper surface vanishes; the uppermost piedmont flat of the east becomes the summit level in the west, and the steep relief does not reach to as great an altitude. The causes of erosion have affected the eastern and the western parts to a different degree. Erosion set in first where the piedmont flats are now most numerous, i.e. where the area of denudation has been increasing. The range has grown much less in width than in length and height.

There are not yet sufficient data for accurate geological dating. But it is *possible* that surface III originated at the Levantine stage, surface II at some time in the Miocene period, and surface I as far back as the Oligocene.

The western part of the Keshish Dagh belongs, like the coastal range between 'Little Phrygia' and the Sea of Marmora, to the more recent type of broad anticline. The gipfelflur, formed from the dissection of the ancient form associations of surface I, often reflects the brachyanti-clinal structure of the broad folding. Surface II is found on both the wide depressions of the range crest (separating brachyantinal summits) and the later Tertiary beds in the broad synclines, showing how individual mountain uplifts grew together, by elongation along the strike, into a single range.

It seems certain that broad folding is a characteristic of the Graeco-Balkan Dinarids also; and probable that, in the north-western continuation towards the Alps, the morphological differences between the inner and the marginal parts are due merely to differences in the date of origin of broad folds.

(d) THE ANDINE SYSTEM OF RANGES

The chief characteristic of these is the alternation of more or less closely ranged chains and depressions, similar to the Basin and Range structure of the western United States. The general explanation has been that of faulting, giving rise to tilted blocks.

Although strike faults are present in the Cordillera of North and South America, it has never been proved that it is the rule for the ranges to be bounded by faults; and too often these have been assumed from morphological criteria alone. For flexures can produce the same effect of a steep,

straight edge; and when the presence of strike faults of great throw has
been geologically proved, often there is no associated relief feature. The
formation of the ranges is not primarily due to faulting; though, under
certain conditions, faults may accompany their formation.

In some parts of the Argentine Andes, strata have been preserved
which are correlated with denudation of the rising chains. They date
from Upper Cretaceous to the present day. These help to show the
broad fold nature of the basin and range structure, though morphological
investigation is still at an early stage.

The complex of the Sierra de Cordoba (rising from the Pampas)
shows asymmetrical ranges, each steeper on the western side, which has
been dissected into steep relief forms giving the impression of a steeply
inclined fault. But the actual mean gradient is generally less than $11°$—
the average being $5°$. The steep relief forms are due to more vigorous
dissection as contrasted with the longer (and gentler) eastern slope, which
is less cut up and shows vast fragments of peneplane between its precipitously incised valleys. The series of scarps are steps between piedmont flats. Nevertheless, the interpretations offered have given an important place to faulting. Peneplanes at different levels have been assumed to be dislocated parts of a single re-exposed Palaeozoic peneplane—a theory which has now been disproved for the German Highlands. The variations in thickness within the Gondwana beds, and the
way in which Permian, Triassic, and Rhaetic strata transgress directly
on to the old folded substratum, seem to indicate that the Palaeozoic
surface was no peneplane but mountainous in relief. The peneplanes
of the Pampean sierras, like those of the German Highlands, are not
ancient relics, but causally connected with the formation of the Andine
ranges.

In the Sierra de Cordoba complex, the highest and oldest peneplane
levels are confined to the Sierra de Achala (part of the Sierra Grande).
The uppermost has an altitude of over 2000 metres, and above it rise
inselbergs, the remnants of a disintegrated central mountainland. Their
flanks and those of the valley troughs on the peneplane show the concave
slopes of waning development. This surface (II in fig. 19) is probably an
end-peneplane. It is separated by concave slopes from the far more extensive peneplane (III), 500 metres below it. In both cases the most
extensive development is along the trend of the mountains and on the
eastern slope. On the west, a narrow depression separates it from the
Sierra de Pocho. On its eastern flank is a peneplane (IV, about 1000
metres above S.L.) having an upturned western edge, and sinking northward beneath the Pampa. Similarly, the Sierra Chica (east of the Sierra
de Achala) has an eastward sloping peneplane (II) on its summit and a

steeper western side. Surface III, between it and the Sierra de Achala, functions as a piedmont flat to both ranges. As it sinks north-westwards beneath the Pampa, it may merge into that over the northern end of the Sierra Grande (which is somewhat south of it). If so, it shows arching, since that occupies a lower level at this latitude.

The deposits at the foot of the Sierra Chica seem to be of Upper Cretaceous and Tertiary age, and are thought to have formerly covered the range. Thus it appears likely, as fits in with more detailed investigation of the Sierras to the north-west, that the present surface forms belong to early Tertiary or even late Cretaceous times.

By comparison with the higher ranges to the north-west, it seems as if the ridges of the Sierra de Cordoba are still at a relatively early stage of broad folding; and that they are of the type which increases in length and in phase as they grow in amplitude.

In those parts of the mountain mass which adjoin the High Cordillera and the Puna de Atacama, and are attached to them, strike faults are characteristic structural elements over wide areas of the younger parts, but do not give rise to conspicuous relief features. They are often overthrusts; and the Bolson of Santa Maria (Calchaqui Valley—Catamarca) is a broad syncline overthrust from both east and west. Further west, all the chains make for the rise of the Puna, which they cross as unfaulted anticlines. There are, however, abrupt morphological changes when the Puna is entered. For its depressions lie higher, at about 2000 m. above sea level; whilst on the other side of the 4000 to 5000 m. summits the bolson floors lie at 1000 m. The majestic broad folds have here an even crest-line and bear peneplanes or the forms of medium relief on their summits (i.e. on the ranges of earlier origin). But the flanks and the ends, which sink beneath the alluvium of the lowlands, are dissected into steep relief, the plunging ends showing a gipfelflur of individual peaks. Such steep relief is found all over the ranges which have been proved to be of later origin, and convex curves are characteristic. The form association here (e.g. on the lower parts of the San Salvador Range dropping east to the Basin of Andagalá) is in sharp contrast, however, to that of the steep relief forms found on straight slopes of maximum gradient (e.g. the uppermost slopes of the same range). Sometimes these two types occur in widely separated areas; sometimes within the same zone of steep relief but well marked off from each other. The intervalley divides of the 'convex zone', though a surface tangential to them would be humpy and not even, belong to a definitely lower level than that of the sharp edges in the crest region and on the western side. Since there is no difference in climate or rock materials, the explanation must be that in the former case the causes tending to replace convex curves by straight slopes of maximum gradient (i.e. increased erosional intensity) have not been in operation for so long as in the latter.

Straight slopes, meeting to give a gipfelflur, do not necessarily mean uniformity of development. For after the maximum inclination has been reached (differing in different rocks), further increase in erosive intensity cannot alter it; and it remains the same while the intensity is decreasing to that value which first produced it. The slope development is, therefore, only pseudo-uniform. The gipfelflur does not lie at the level of the earlier, gentler forms, now removed. On the older ranges, where this has been preserved, it is seen to be separated from it by a perceptible difference in altitude. Still less is it removed from it by an unlevelled fault line, as has been assumed for similar cases in other parts of the world. But its altitude depends upon the character of the rock, as this influences the valley incisions. Its relative height increases with the steepness of the intersecting slopes of maximum gradient; and with the increase in distance between adjacent valleys. What decides the absolute altitude is left for later consideration.

The following form associations characterize the *older type of broad folding* (exemplified by the Sierra de Fiambalá—c. 5000 m. high where it enters the Puna). They are elongated in the direction of the trend of the mountain ranges, but are limited to narrow strips, or are even absent, at right angles to this.

(*a*) A peneplane of more or less extensive remnants—relief type I in fig. 20 B. It forms a summit peneplane with gentle slopes. These lead by convex curvature to the wide valleys surrounding it (waxing development). Occasionally it is crowned by tors. The part near these is an end-peneplane, developed from a piedmont flat (cf. p. 214). On some ranges, e.g. Famatina and Aconquija, there rise rounded, individual summits bearing the remains of a yet higher peneplane (Nevado Famatina—6000 m., Cerro Palco—5300 m., and Nevado Aconquija—over 5300 m.).

(*b*) Medium relief. This includes II and III of fig. 20 B. II comprises forms with the concave slopes of waning development which replace the lower parts of I. The valleys are broad troughs, but may be 500 m. deep.

III is a zone of steeper, convex forms, leading to deeper, narrower valleys (still high-lying), with concave foot-slopes showing the penetration of waning development from below.

(*c*) Steep relief—IV in fig. 20 B. It extends from the mountain foot to a sharp break of gradient (at 3500 m. on the Sierra de Fiambalá), separating it from III. Maximum gradients have not been reached in III because development has been interrupted by the appearance of this break of gradient. It is associated with increased erosional intensity leading to the development of slopes of maximum gradient which spread upwards from the general base level of erosion.

Towards the ends of the ranges, relief type III forms the summit level, surfaces II and I having both disappeared (fig. 20 C).

Peneplane I, in relief type I, fig. 20 B, has the character of a piedmont flat, though it may form the summit of ranges of later origin. It is a primary peneplane (see pp. 212–215). The medium relief (II and III) below it shows clear signs of warping, as seen in the alien forms of the gorges which traverse it, high above the young, steep relief IV. They seem to peter out on to old bolson floors which have been dragged up as the ranges increased in altitude, becoming tilted, and often worn into terraces by the encroachment of the steep relief IV from below. That this intensified doming of the broad anticlines persisted, during the stage when steep relief was developing, is shown by the way in which valley terraces of uplift converge towards the mountain foot.

The form associations show a time sequence from above downwards, the characteristic feature being the increase in steepness of their slopes; flattish relief is succeeded by medium relief and that by steep relief. As each steeper set of slope units and slope systems appeared, convex breaks of gradient developed, separating the form associations above them from their general base level of erosion, and so inducing the waning development which has dominated them up to the present day. It has gone furthest in that form association which has been longest separated from the general base level of erosion, i.e. the oldest and highest stage. The flattish (primary) surface of the central mountainland is rarely left. Its piedmont flat (I) and even relief II show the concave slopes of waning development with wide valley troughs. Waning development is only just beginning at the outer edges of relief III and is absent from relief type IV.

A comparison of *different stages of development* shows that in later stages the central mountainland has been surrounded by a piedmont flat, stretching out along the trend of the range. This means that *as the ranges of earlier origin grew in height* (amplitude), *they were also increasing in both length and width* (phase). The Sierra de Cordoba, in a primitive state as compared with the high ranges of the Puna edge, exhibits this stage today. But younger and lower piedmont flats cannot be detected on the flanks of these ranges of earlier origin. So it follows that *during the later stages of development, they continued to increase in length and amplitude* (height), *but not also in phase* (width). *Instead, warping of the existing relief zones took place.*

This is not altogether true of the *later formed ranges*, e.g. San Salvador (fig. 20, A 2), where very young piedmont flats (small-scale stairways of them) are found in front of the mountain-foot proper. They have been terraced by streams flowing down the mountain slope; but the terraces are marginal to the range as a whole and their longitudinal scarps are the work of longitudinal streams. They show that there has been increase in phase during a late stage of development, the marginal stream having become pushed ever further towards the adjacent depression as the edges of this region of deposition became an area of denudation.

The very *youngest ranges of all* have no piedmont flats, this showing that they *have not yet begun to increase in phase*. As contrasted with older chains which are *no longer* increasing in phase, their form association of convex slopes is below, instead of above, the zone of steep relief (see fig. 20, A 2, as contrasted with B b).

Uniformity in development is proved when various ranges show similarity in the formation and arrangement of their slope units; but this does not mean simultaneity in the production of the corresponding forms. This has usually been assumed for the summit peneplanes found all over the world which, when at different altitudes, were assumed to be differently uplifted fragments of a single immense end-peneplane, the lower parts of which were at the bottom of areas of sedimentation. This preconception (associated with the erosion cycle as generally applied) prevented the recognition on the peneplanes of form associations peculiar to the mountain ranges on which they occur. But whenever strata, that can be correlated with the denudation, have been preserved (e.g. in the broad synclines of arid regions), it can be demonstrated that these assumed connections do not exist.

In the Puna itself these strata are of volcanic materials; at its southern edge, of continental formations (Upper Cretaceous to present day). Their extraordinary thickness (up to ten kilometres), shows that they have been deposited on a relatively sinking substratum. The facies arrangement (coarse clastic mountain-foot material to fine sand) corroborates this. It shows that the areas of sedimentation became narrowed and were divided up. This means that fresh ranges appeared one after another, or that previously existing ranges grew in length, entering what had been zones of sedimentation. The attitude and facies of the correlated strata are a sure means of distinguishing the relative age of a range or its parts.

It is found that the peneplanes of the range summits pass over into unconformities, with a peneplanated appearance, when they reach the edges of the adjoining broad synclines; and they pass into stratification planes as the actual basin is approached. This proves that they are primary peneplanes, never having had any other form. It also gives the geological age.

On account of uplift, these primary peneplanes have been exposed to denudation. The unconformities have also been arched with them, and are more steeply tilted the older they are. The stratigraphical age of the deposits, and that only, gives the age of such peneplanes, and shows whether or not it is the same for those on the summits of different ranges.

Fig. 21 A illustrates this diagrammatically for the neighbourhood of the Sierra de Fiambalá. The section passes through four ranges. The oldest is the Sierra de Fiambalá, this being shown by the fact that the Lower Tertiary Calchaqui beds contain fragments of the rock type found here. The conglomerates (c k) of these strata surrounded the rising range. Westwards, they pass into formations of fine sands, lying conformably on the Upper Cretaceous sandstone. This is seen at the foot of the Sierra Narvaez, proving that it had not yet risen as a mountain range. These Calchaqui beds lie on what is seen (wherever accessible) to be an almost level surface of denudation. It is not possible, however, to decide with any certainty as to which elements of the present mountain surface are of Lower Tertiary age. The piedmont flat I, derived from a central mountainland, seems to be correlated with the Tertiary Calchaqui beds; and the fact that the Upper Cretaceous sandstones east and west of the Sierra de Fiambalá taper off towards the range itself, implies that at that period it was already separating two areas of deposition. Its fine grain indicates that the relief was but slight. Thus it seems likely that it was an Upper Cretaceous peneplane which formed the primary peneplane at the surface of the original summit of the range (now represented only by tors). Then, in Lower Tertiary times, a piedmont flat was formed round a central mountainland, the dissection into valleys providing the material for the Calchaqui conglomerates.

The under surface of the Puna strata (Middle Tertiary) is a parting plane which extends from the Bolson de Fiambalá to near the Famatina Range. Here gravels of Lower Puna age, derived from the then rising Sierra Narvaez (Famatina Range) lie conformably upon the Lower Tertiary Calchaqui sandstone. Between the Sierra de Fiambalá and the Sierra Narvaez was a wide depression, for the now folded beds consist of Puna *sandstone*, which must have been deposited at a distance from the mountains, lying conformably on the Tertiary Calchaqui conglomerates (as well as on the Lower Tertiary Calchaqui sandstone). But at each side of this zone of conformability, the Puna beds transgress in a sharply marked unconformity over the disturbed substratum which had been levelled by it. This unconformity passes over into the summit peneplane of the present Sierra Narvaez; and, on the other side, into the hummocky level of relief III on the Sierra de Fiambalá. This connection is shown by the overlying strata, the Upper Puna beds. Between the Calchaqui

Mountains (west of the Sierra de Fiambalá) and the Famatina Range (Sierra de Narvaez), the under surface of the Upper Puna beds can be traced as a parting plane; and here there later arose the youngest ridge of all (the Anchoca anticline). At the edge of the Famatina (Sierra Narvaez) range also, the coarse Upper Puna gravels transgress on to a surface with definite relief features, which indeed cannot be distinguished from the valley floors of the so-called High Terrace (of relief type III). This same surface is quite smooth on the flanks of the Calchaqui Mountains, showing it to be a peneplane. This [primary] peneplane would have continued as the upper surface of the Calchaqui Mountains, though it is only here and there that any summit peneplane is now visible.

The repeated alternation of facies, coarse to fine and back again, in one and the same vertical section, is of importance (e.g. eastern edge of Calchaqui Mountains—fig. 21 A). It might be thought at first sight to imply alternations of uplift and standstill. But the strata show superposed facies with different source regions, belonging to different ranges in differing states of development. As a range first appears, its denudational derivatives are predominantly fine-grained; then, with greater uplift, a coarse mountain-foot facies is laid down above them, and stretches out further and further into the area of deposition. This is to be seen in the Calchaqui beds to the west of the Sierra de Fiambalá. The coarse conglomerates extend further west in the upper layers. The same is true for the Lower Puna beds, extending inwards from both the Sierra de Fiambalá and the Sierra Narvaez, and for the Upper Puna beds also (if the presence of the Calchaqui Mountains is neglected). Once a range has begun to produce coarse material, it continues doing so, up to the present time. Thus sections through the present Calchaqui Mountains show, from Lower Tertiary to Upper Puna strata, nothing but coarse derivatives of the Sierra de Fiambalá; and this facies is now forming huge alluvial cones at the base of this Sierra. Fragments from the Sierra Narvaez, of increasing coarseness from Lower Puna times to the present day, extend further and further into areas where the Lower Tertiary beds are of fine-grained material; while the fine-grained facies of Lower Puna times has not only been narrowed in extent, but has been pushed eastwards (towards the Sierra de Fiambalá), so that it lies above the Lower Tertiary mountain-foot facies of the Calchaqui beds (fig. 21 A—p_1s over $c\,k$, beside the Calchaqui Mountains). The Upper Puna beds show corresponding features, their fine-grained material having been shifted westward as the Calchaqui Mountains rose. Finally, fine-grained Quaternary material occurs only in the central strip of the Bolson de Fiambalá. It is bordered by coarsely clastic talus and overlies coarse Upper Puna gravels.

Thus, in successive periods there has been a horizontal displacement of the facies regions. The facies laid down at a distance from the mountains is restricted to that part of the trough which is lowest at the time; and, as fresh chains arise, this is not only narrowed down but also shifted east or west. Conditions along the present watercourses illustrate this.

There is nothing in the facies arrangement to suggest alternations of uplift and tectonic repose. Each individual range has gone on rising continuously, from its first appearance to the present day. Its gradients have therefore increased, leading to increased erosional intensity. Hence the grain size of the detritus has always been increasing.

Somewhat different features are shown by the ranges which join the Sierra de Fiambalá eastwards and stretch into the Puna. In places their summits bear extensive remains of a peneplane, and downwarped portions of it now and then form broad surfaces on the mountain flanks. As a rule, however, it has been replaced by a medium relief with convex slopes (type III) on its lower side. It is obviously later than the Lower Tertiary, since it passes over small scattered remnants of Upper Cretaceous sandstones and Calchaqui conglomerates. In the depressions (e.g. San Fernando and Lampacillo) it seems to continue to the base of the Puna beds (of which only the upper division has been found here). The bordering ranges do not seem to have appeared, between the much older Sierras of Fiambalá and Aconquija—Cerros de los Animos, until the beginning of the Upper Tertiary. (At present this has been found true only for the parts south of the Puna.)

The summit peneplane is of the same type as in the older ranges, though it is younger (corresponding to the under surface of p_2 in the Calchaqui Mountains, in fig. 21 A). There is not enough information to tell whether it is part of a very large surface which has been arched on the ranges and bent down in the depressions. This is not so where the ranges continue into the southern Puna (Laguna Blanca—Laguna Grande district) for there the summit peneplane passes across the volcanic deposits in the troughs instead of lying below them, and so must be younger than the floor of the depression.

The southern Puna de Atacama is also divided meridianwise by ranges and depressions. No longitudinal faults have been found here, the morphological features being due to simple anticlinal folding which includes the superimposed volcanic material. In the Laguna Grande region the *ranges, of* rather *youthful origin,* have preserved the summit peneplane. On the flanks, this is replaced by medium relief with convex slopes, which become concave (though just as steep and as deeply divided) towards the mountain-foot. Sometimes this waning development has reached to the summit. However, the very youngest of the form associations consists of steep slopes (convex or of maximum inclination) appearing along the watercourses, in the few cases where these are powerful enough to remove the rock waste. It penetrates from the edge of the sediments in the adjoining depression up to the sharply incised ravines and even to the flat floors of the trough valleys within which it produces a sharp break of gradient. Thus the prevalence of forms of waning development along the lower parts of the mountain flanks is not due to lack of relative height, but to the lack of constantly flowing water in this desert region. It is only in the higher parts and on the steeper slopes that transport seems able to catch up with the formation of rock waste.

It is characteristic for these ranges of more youthful origin to have the summit peneplane passing on to a lower disturbed stage of volcanic accumulation (perhaps equivalent to the Lower Puna beds). But sometimes the flat surface seems never to have existed, e.g. the low ranges near the Salt Lake of Pairique (extending from the northern edge of the Bolson de Fiambalá towards the very high Nevados de la Laguna Blanca (an old range)). Of very recent origin, they are completely disintegrated into a *steep* mountainland (though not of maximum gradient) with concave forms (fig. 21, C3). When there is no summit peneplane, its former existence is shown by scattered rounded eminences, with accordant heights, rising above a mountain landscape of concave slopes; or the whole summit is made up of flattish domes. On the whole, steepness of slope and valley depth increase from above downwards, becoming respectively gentler and shallower at the mountain-foot. In the Puna, it is on the lower parts of the sides of the ranges that steep relief (or the impression of it) is found.

In the southern Puna (as in the Pampean sierras) the *older ranges* are characterised by greater height and breadth and by more denudation levels, e.g. the Nevados de la Laguna Blanca, with broad dome-like shapes appearing as if built up one above another. This is because they are peneplane levels separated by clearly marked convex slopes.

Fig. 21, C and D, shows the central mountainland (I) surrounded by an elongated piedmont flat (II), its valleys having convex slopes. The lower piedmont flat (III) was overwhelmed by andesitic lavas flows. Together with the overlying beds, it was flexed into ranges and troughs of more recent origin. On the flanks of the older ranges, surface II is also anticlinally arched. In consequence of the bending, the outer edge of the zone of convex slopes, between II and III, has therefore undergone an interesting transformation. It is slight towards the sinking ends of the range; but on the flanks, its increased gradient led to more rapid denudation; so that on the eastern flank of the Nevados de la Laguna Blanca it has been replaced by steeper slopes which join surface II in a sharp break of gradient, and on the lower side pass down with a concave slope into piedmont flat IV. The effect of these steep slopes, overlooking the Laguna Blanca basin, is that of facetted spurs—such as has, in North America, been taken as evidence of faulting. But there is no fault here.

Piedmont flat IV is equivalent to the summit peneplane on the younger ranges, extending over the (older) andesitic formation and its substratum.

(e) GENERAL SURVEY

All the mountain chains examined in this book have, in spite of diversities, shown agreement in fundamental features:

(1) Division into ranges and longitudinal depressions; taken as a whole, these represent elongated domings of the crust;

(2) Arrangement of form systems (slope units) and form associations —the flattest above, the steepest below;

(3) Great extension of the form associations along the trend of the ranges, small extension at right angles to this;

(4) The longitudinal (strike) depressions between parallel ranges contain strata which are correlated with denudation on the ranges.

There are great quantitative differences in regard to deposition, faulting and dissection by valleys; but these are not differences in type. They are found in various parts of the same mountain system, as well as in different systems of ranges.

Folding is particularly important in the Eastern Alps; and an intimate, though obscure, connection may be presumed to exist between the folded structure and the broad folding that caused the height of the present ranges. Several of the nappes of the central Western Alps, and also the Aconcagua nappe of the Andes, seem to have resulted from broad anticlines; whilst the more recent ranges at the edge of the southern Puna show imbricated structure. Where there is sufficient thickness in the complex of strata, the correlated beds have also shared in the folding, as in the area just south of the Puna de Atacama. Since here the primary peneplane surface passes over the pile of recumbent folds, it indicates that the formation of the range began with the folding of the strata.

Where there is a suitable substructure, broad folding begins by compressing this, and it outlasts the compression. It is related to true folding in that it is the result of tangentially directed forces. In all stages of their development, broad folds grow predominantly in length and height, and in their advanced stages cease altogether to grow in width. In this, as in the narrow longitudinal form of the piedmont flats, they differ from the more evenly spreading continental uplift of areas such as the German Highlands.

Dissection by valleys often makes it difficult or impossible to find evidence for peneplanes and piedmont flats. It seems as if these were always present on ranges of early origin, but not on recently formed ranges. These latter are normally characterised by steep and medium relief forms. W. M. Davis considered their counterparts in the Basin Ranges and Mexico to be the remnants of tilted blocks which are approaching peneplanation. However, they show waxing development on their intervalley ridges.

If the younger ranges in the southern Puna are compared with the lower of the Tibetan ranges, both agree in showing the roundish forms of medium relief. In the same way, the older ranges of the Puna and the higher ones of Tibet both show summit peneplanes; and where these are replaced by intermediate form associations of medium relief, show the same change from convex intervalley ridge tops to concave foot-slopes. Central mountainlands are present in both.

At the eastern end of the Tibetan Highland, the longitudinal depressions take the form of deep inaccessible river gorges between broad flattish ridges. They are comparable, though on a far grander scale, to the longitudinal valleys of the Eastern Alps, in contrast to the flatter depressions between the ranges at the southern Puna edge. This is partly related to the moister climate with drainage to the ocean, like the greater dissection into sharp ridges of the Eastern Alps as contrasted with the Pampean sierras. But it is not entirely due to this; for the essential factor in the differing degrees of dissection is differences in the causes leading to erosion in the various systems of ranges and their individual parts. This explains such anomalies as these: some of the bolsons of north-west Argentina (Fiambalá and Calchaqui Valley) show continuous sedimentation even though drained by rivers; whilst the Anatolian type of broad syncline had repeated alternations of scouring and infilling. The high valleys of the 'Inter-Andine Highland', draining to the Amazon, have streams dissecting immense thicknesses of fluviatile and lacustrine deposits presumably laid down when this highland was not at such a great altitude above sea-level; whilst deposition is taking place now, as in Tertiary times, in the low-lying depressions of the Columbian-Venezuelan humid tropical region.

In North America also there are found ranges with even crest lines, flattish or intermediate form associations on the summits, and steep forms on the slopes—a complete contrast to the customary idea of a 'sea of Alpine peaks'. They have been assumed to be tilted blocks, e.g. Wasatch Mountains, Sierra Nevada. But they are very similar to the

Pampean sierras and also to the Tien Shan of central Asia. In spite of Pleistocene glaciation, the Cascade Mountains still show remnants of a central mountainland, an extensive piedmont flat, intermediate forms below it, and then steep forms in the most recent valleys.

The same holds for central Asia, where the piedmont steps used to be considered as parts of one gigantic faulted peneplane. The unconformity below the Gobi sediments (dating back to the Upper Cretaceous) passes into a parting plane of stratification between the Tien Shan and Kashgar Mountains—this being comparable to what has been observed at the southern edge of the Puna. The Tien Shan summit peneplane seems to be equivalent to this, and so is a primary peneplane; and there are repetitions of such levels on the heights and unconformities within the Gobi strata.

In the central Asian depressions, as in those at the southern edge of the Puna, it can be seen, from the arrangement of coarse (mountain-foot) and finer deposits, that sedimentation occurred on a subsiding floor; and also that the strata at the edges have been dragged upwards and folded. As in the Anatolian broad syncline, the basin deposits often bear a low-level peneplane into which the valleys have been sunk.

Folding has been able to occur, in connection with range formation, only where the sediments are present over considerable areas, and in suitable stratigraphical relationship to the rising chains (apparently the Tertiary deposits are unfolded in the interior of the western Tien Shan). It indicates tangential forces, and strike faults often become overthrusts (e.g. Tarim and Ferghana depressions. Cf. also the southern edge of the Puna).

The growth of the mountain system as a whole differs somewhat from that of the individual ranges. Its general growth in height is shown not merely by increased elevation of the separate chains, but by the dissection of the longitudinal depressions which have also been raised high up; by increasing coarseness of grain in the Gobi strata; and by the lifting of Lower Eocene marine strata to 4000 metres above sea level (western Tien Shan). The correlated strata are themselves folded and form independent chains. The mountain system links fresh ranges to itself and pushes its periphery outwards. The same feature has also been noticed on the eastern side of the Andes in north-west Argentina. Growth in phase is shown by the appearance on their outer flanks of very recent, wide, piedmont flats, a very fine example occurring at the edge of the Russian Altai. Mountains of Alpine structure also show this widening by the addition of fresh folded elements and imbricated slices. Sometimes the old substructure itself is included in the disturbance (seen where stratified deposits are relatively thin). Systems of ranges behave differently from individual ranges in that they increase in phase as well as amplitude even in their most advanced stages of development.

Descriptions of the Altai system of ranges show that here, too, it is a matter of broad folding, and dissection into central mountainlands and piedmont flats.

Less is known about eastern and south-eastern Asia. But it seems likely from descriptions of the Sunda region and New Guinea that similar features occur there also.

It has not yet been proved geologically that all mountain systems of the world are associated with broad folding. But there is great similarity in their configuration; and, in the systems that have been closely examined, this corresponds to similarity in development, both where broad folds have been proved to exist and where there is still uncertainty as to the tectonics. Thus uniformity has been established at least in the posing of the problem presented to us by crustal movements.

The following papers contain important assessments of Walther Penck's work:

WURM, A., Morphologische Analyse und Experiment, Schichtstufenlandschaft (pp. 1–24), Hangentwicklung, Einebnung, Piedmonttreppen (pp. 57–87). (*Zeitschrift für Geomorphologie* (Leipzig) 1935/36 Bd. IX).

SPREITZER, H., Die Piedmonttreppen in der regionalen Geomorphologie (*Erdkunde*, Bd. V, Heft 4. 1951) (pp. 294–304).

GERMAN-ENGLISH GLOSSARY

(of some of the words used in translating W. Penck's
Die Morphologische Analyse)

Abdachung, f., slope
Abflachung, f., flattening (lessening of gradient)
Abflachungshang, f., slope of diminishing gradient
absteigende Entwicklung, f., waning development (lit. descending)
Abtragung, f., denudation (lit. 'carrying away', not 'laying bare' as in the English term)
Aufbereitung, f., reduction. *Aufbereitung* is a mining term for which the best equivalent seems to be the English mining term 'reduction', in its sense of the preparation or dressing of ores by reducing them to fine particles (*not* the chemical sense of the removal of oxygen). H.C., however, is thoroughly dissatisfied with this as a translation, and prefers 'working up' (which has been used to translate *Aufarbeitung* on the one occasion when this occurs).
Aufbereitung is defined on p. 4. It is practically the same as 'weathering' and 'disintegration'. But it differs from 'weathering' (see p. 40) in that mechanical reduction may be brought about by chemical weathering; and from pure disintegration in that it alters composition as well as texture (p. 4). W. Penck seems deliberately to have chosen an unusual word so that it may specially denote the way in which fragments of rock material are reduced in size until they are so small that they move collectively under the force of gravity alone (what he calls 'spontaneous' movement (p. 64), 'spontaneous migration' and 'mass-movement' (p. 74)
Auffaltung, f., upfolding
Auflösung, f., breaking up (of mountain masses)

aufsteigende Entwicklung, f., waxing development (lit. ascending)
Aufwölbung, f. doming, arching

Bankwasser, n., reserves of water
Bergland, ein zentrales, n., a central mountainland
Bergschlipf, m., rock-slide
Bergsturz, m. (general term for) landslide, landslip; (specifically) a fall of rock, as contrasted with slumping
Blockfeld, n., block field
Blockgipfel, m., tor
Blockmeer, n., sea of rock, block sea
Blockstrom, m., block stream, stone river
Böschung, f., slope, declivity

Deckenschotter, m., outwash gravel
Delle, f., dell (used in a special sense, see p. 113)
Denudation, f., denudation

'Ecken', f., (term used by J. Sölch), steps on intervalley ridges
Eigenschaften, f., properties (of rocks)
Eindeckungshang, m., slope developed beneath a covering (of water or alluvium)
eingelassen (valleys), sunk in (peneplane)
eingesenkt (*einsenken*), entrenched (of drainage net); worked down into (of denudation features); let down into (of faulting)
eingesunken (*einsinken*), downsunken; entrenched
einschneiden, incise
eintiefen, deepen, incise
endogen, endogenetic (originating from within)
Endrumpf, m., end-peneplane (p. 144)
Endrumpffläche, f., end-peneplane (produced at the end of a cycle of erosion); final surface of truncation (p. 144)

Erdfliessen, m., flowing soil
exogen, exogenetic (originating from without)
Exposition, f., exposure

Fastebene, f., peneplain (p. 153)
Felsenmeer, n., rock sea
Felssturz, m., rock-slide
Felswand, f. rock wall, cliff, precipice
fest, strong (rock); H. C. would prefer 'solid' (as on p. 1). *Gesteinsfestigkeit* is equated with *Kohäsion* (p. 176)
Flachform, f., flattish form
Formen, f., (land) forms
  Flachformen, flattish forms (defined on p. 131)
  Mittelformen, intermediate forms (defined on p. 131)
  Steilformen, steep forms (defined on p. 131)
Formenschatz, m., set (wealth, collection) of land forms; land forms
Formsystem, n., slope unit (defined on p. 129). This term, used by J. Kesseli, is prefered (by K.C.B.) to 'form system', esp. in Ch. VI, because it instantaneously conveys the requisite picture, whilst the other expression does not do so.
Fusshang, m., foot-slope (a more general term than *Haldenhang* (basal slope), one which seems to include both the basal slope and all the slopes of diminishing gradient)

gebundene (*Bewegung*), bound-down (movement)
Gehängeschutt, m., scree material, talus
Gestaltung, f., modelling, sculpturing, shaping, form
Gesteinsaufbereitung, f., rock reduction (see *Aufbereitung*)
Gesteinsbeschaffenheit, f., nature of the rock
Gesteinscharakter, m., characteristics of the rock
Gesteinsnatur, f., (*Anpassung an*), rock material (adaptation to)
Gesteinsverhältnisse, n., character of the rock (lit. rock conditions), (defined on p. 19)
Grat, m., arête
Grossfaltung, f., broad folding
Grossmulde, f., broad syncline

Grosssattel, m., broad anticline
Grundaufdeckung, f. (term used by J. Sölch), basement stripping (uncovering the ancient folded or crystalling rocks beneath a stratified cover)

Halde, f., talus; scree (p. 67)
Haldenbewegung, f., dumping movement
Haldenhang, m., basal slope (the less steep slope found at the foot of a rock wall, usually beneath an accumulation of talus. Defined on pp. 93, 135. It is the top part of the *Fusshang* or foot-slope, which includes all the slopes of diminishing gradient)
Haldenscheitel, m., the top of the basal slope (where it meets the steeper rock wall)
Hang, m., slope
Hangsystem, n., slope system
Härtling, m., residual (or monadnock) of resistant rock
Hochgebirgsrelief, n., Alpine relief
Höhengestaltung, f., altitudinal form, altitudinal modelling, altitudinal configuration, modelling of the height

Kerbe, f., sharply V-shaped valley
Klippe, f., crag, (granite) tor
Kohärenz, f. coherence (note 93)
Kohäsion, f., cohesion
Korrasion, f., corrasion (definition of W. Penck's usage on p. 112)
korrelaten Schichten, f., correlated strata (formed from the products of denudation and so correlated with the period at which the denudation took place. Throughout the book W. Penck uses the term in this sense)
Kuppe, f., dome, rounded summit
kuppig, hummocky

labile Zonen, f., (der Erdkruste), zones of instability
Landstufe, f., cuesta scarp

Massen, f. pl. (often translated), material
Massenbewegungen, f., mass-movement
Massenstrom, m., mass-stream
Massentransport, m., mass-transport

Massenverlagerung, m., transference of material

Mittelform, f., intermediate (relief) form

Mittelgebirge (*deutsche*), n. (German) Highlands

Mittelgebirgsrelief, n., highland relief

Mittelrelief, n., medium relief

Mosor, m., mosor (see English-German)

Mulde, f., trough, syncline

Muldental, n., trough-shaped valley

Mure, f., wet avalanche of earthy material, occurring in the Alps

Oberbau, m., superstructure

Piedmontfläche, f., piedmont flat

Piedmonttreppe, f., piedmont bench-lands, piedmont stairway

Primärrumpf, m., primary peneplane (defined p. 215)

Quetschschlammstrom, m., (term used by Albert Heim), flow of squeezed mud

Relieftypen, f., relief types (p. 131)
Hochgebirgsrelief, Alpine relief
Mittelgebirgsformen, Highland (relief) forms
Mittelrelief, medium relief
Rumpfflächen, peneplanes
Steilrelief, steep relief

rieselndes Wasser, n., water in tiny streamlets, trickling water

rinnendes Wasser, n., streamlets, rivulets; trickling water (p. 123)

Rücken, m., ridge, broad ridge

Rumpfebene, f., peneplain (note 227, p. 333)

Rumpffläche, f., peneplane (W. Penck uses *Rumpffläche* purely to express relief, with no implication as to position in the cycle of erosion. To distinguish it from the Davisian peneplain, which W. Penck writes as *Peneplain*, the spelling 'peneplane' is used) since 'peneplane (R)' seemed unnecessarily clumsy); surface of truncation

Rutschung, f., slumping (type of landslide); landslip (sometimes, to avoid verbal repetition)

Sattel, m., anticline

Scheide, f., divide (watershed)

Scheitelrumpffläche, f., summit peneplane

Schichtstufenland, n., cuesta landscape, scarplands

Schneide, f., ridge, sharp ridge, knife-edge

Schneidenzone, f., zone of ridges, ridge zone

Schubfläche, f., slip plane (for landslide)

Schutt, m., rubble, detritus, rock waste, debris

Schuttfliessen, n., flowing rock waste

Schutthalde, f., scree

Schuttstrom, m., stream of detritus

Schuttwälle, m., rubble ramparts

Schwelle (mitteldeutsche), f., (central German) rise

Solifluktion, f., solifluction

Steinschlag, m., rock-fall (on a small scale)

Stockwerklandschaft, f., storeyed landscape

Streichen, m., strike, trend

Struktur, f., (petr.) texture, (earth's crust) structure

Stufe, f., step, scarp

Tagesoberfläche, f., visible surface (of rock)

Tallichte, f., distance apart of the upper edges of a valley, measured at right angles to its trend

Textur, f. (petr.), structure

Trogtal, n., trough valley

Umprägung, f., reconstitution (of rock, in the substructure)

Unterbau, m., substructure

Verband, m., (rock) fabric

Wand (for *Felswand*), rock wall, cliff, rock face, precipice

zentrales Bergland, n., central mountainland

zerfallen, disintegrate

Zeugenberg, m., residual

Zungenbecken, n., terminal basin (of a glacier)

ENGLISH-GERMAN GLOSSARY

(of some of the words used in translating W. Penck's
Morphological Analysis of Land Forms)

Alpine relief, *Hochgebirgsrelief*, n. (p. 131), *alpines Relief* (p. 230)
altitudinal form, altitudinal modelling, *Höhengestaltung*, f.
anticlinal, *antiklinal*
anticline, *Sattel*, m.
arching, *Aufwölbung*, f.
arête, *Grat*, m.

basal slope, *Haldenhang*, m. (defined on pp. 93, 135). The less steep slope found at the bottom of a steep rock face, usually covered by an accumulation of talus
basement stripping, *Grundaufdeckung*, f. (see German word)
block field, *Blockfeld*, n.
block sea, *Blockmeer*, n.
block stream *Blockstrom*, m.
bound-down (movement), *gebundene (Bewegung)*, f.
breaking up (of mountain masses), *Auflösung*, f.
broad anticline, *Grosssattel*, m.
broad folding, *Grossfaltung*, f.
broad syncline, *Grossmulde*, f.

central mountainland, *zentrales Bergland*, n.
character of the rock, *Gesteinsverhältnisse*, n. (defined on p. 19). (As 'rock conditions' is not a normal English expression for all that is included in this term, 'character' has been used wherever it occurs, as having a wider implication than 'nature of the rock', which is used throughout for *Gesteinsbeschaffenheit*)
characteristics of the rock, *Gesteinscharakter*, m.
cliff, *Wand*, *Felswand*, f.
cohesion, *Kohäsion*, f.
coherence, *Kohärenz*, f.
corrasion, *Korrasion*, f.
correlated strata, *korrelate Schichten*, f. (used by W. Penck to denote beds correlated in time with the denudation which has produced the material for them)
crag, *Klippe*, f.
cuesta landscape, *Schichtstufenland*, n.
cuesta scarp, *Landstufe*, f.

debris, *Schutt*, m.
dell (in the special sense of a depression up-valley from the source of a stream), *Delle*, f.
denudation, *Abtragung*, f., *Denudation*, f. (*Abtragung*, lit. means 'carrying away', whilst *Denudation* means 'laying bare')
detritus, *Schutt*, m.
diminishing gradient (slope of), *Abflachungshang*, f.
disintegrate, *zerfallen*
divide (watershed), *Scheide*, f.
dome (-shaped mountain), *Dom*, m., *Kuppe*, f.
doming, *Aufwölbung*, f.
downsunken, *eingesunken*

endogenetic, *endogen*
end-peneplane, *Endrumpffläche*, f., *Endrumpf*, m.
entrenched, *eingesenkt* (rarely *eingesunken*)
exogenetic, *exogen*
exposure, *Exposition*, f.

fabric (of rock), *Verband*, m.
fault trough, *Graben*, n.
flattening, *Abflachung*, f.
flattish forms, *Flachformen*, f.
flowing rock waste, *fliessender Schutt*, m.
foot-slope, *Fusshang*, m. (apparently including both basal slope and the slopes of diminishing gradient)
form, *Form*, f. (a smaller feature than) *Gestalt*, f., *Gestaltung*, f.
steep forms, *Steilformen*, f.
intermediate forms, *Mittelformen*, f.
flattish forms, *Flachformen*, f.

gipfelflur, *Gipfelflur*, f. (imaginary surface touching accordant summits)

highland relief, *Mittelgebirgsrelief*, n.
Highlands (German), *Mittelgebirge* (deutsche), n.
hummocky, *kuppig*

incise, *einschneiden*, sometimes *eintiefen*
instability, zones of, *labile Zonen*, f.
intermediate (relief) forms, *Mittelformen*, f.

knife-edges (ridges), *Schneiden*, f.

land form, *Landform*, f. (rarely used)
land forms (set of, wealth of), *Formenschatz*, m.
landslide, landslip, *Bergsturz*, m.

mass-movement, *Massenbewegung*, f.
mass-stream, *Massenstrom*, m.
mass-transport, *Massentransport*, m.
material, (often used to translate) *Massen*, f. pl.
medium relief, *Mittelrelief*, n.
modelling of the height, *Höhengestaltung*, f.
monadnock (of specially resistant rock), *Härtling*, m.
mosor, *Mosor* (residual mountain, named after Mosor Mts. in Dalmatia)
mountainland, central, *zentrales Bergland*, n.

nature of the rock, *Gesteinsbeschaffenheit*, f.

outwash gravel, *Deckenschotter*, m.

peneplain, (reserved for) *Peneplain*, f., *Fastebene*, f. (W. Penck equates this with his 'end-peneplane', *Endrumpffläche*; although, as C. A. Cotton points out (*Landscape*, p. 185, note 1, 1st ed. 1941) Davis' peneplain is a penultimate actual form, not a theoretical final one)
peneplane, (here used for convenience, to translate) *Rumpffläche*, f., (to distinguish it from the Davisian term 'peneplain')
piedmont benchlands, *Piedmonttreppe*, f.

piedmont flat, *Piedmontfläche*, f.
piedmont stairway, *Piedmonttreppe*, f.
precipice, *Felswand*, f. (occasionally translated thus)
primary peneplane, *Primärrumpf*, m.
properties (of a rock), *Eigenschaften*, f.

reconstitution (of rock, in the substructure), *Umprägung*, f.
reduction (of rock), *Aufbereitung*, f. Defined on p. 4 (see note on the German word)
relief types, *Relieftypen*, f. (see p. 131)
    steep relief, *Steilrelief*, n.
    medium relief, *Mittelrelief*, n.
    peneplanes, *Rumpfflächen*, f.
reserves of water, *Bankwasser*, n.
residual (mountain), *Zeugenberg*, m.
residual of specially resistant rock, *Härtling*, m.
ridge (broad), *Rücken*, m.
ridge (sharp), *Schneide*, f.
ridge zones, *Schneidenzonen*, f.
rift valley, *Graben*, m.
Rise (central German), *Schwelle* (mitteldeutsche), f.
rivulets, *rinnendes Wasser*, n.
rock face, (sometimes used to translate) *Wand*, f.
rock-fall, *Steinschlag*, m. (small); *Bergsturz*, m. (considerable size)
rock glacier, '*rock glacier*'
rock material (adaptation of forms to), *Gesteinsnatur*, f. (*Anpassung an*)
rock sea, sea of rock, block sea, *Blockmeer*, n.; occasionally *Felsenmeer*, n.
rock-slide, *Bergschlipf*, m., *Felssturz*, m.
rock stream, '*rock stream*'
rock wall, *Felswand*, f.
rock waste, *Schutt*, m.
rounded summit, *Kuppe*, f.
rubble, *Schutt*, m.
rubble ramparts, *Schuttwälle*, m.
running water, *fliessendes Wasser*, n.

Sauzei beds, *Sauzeischichten*, f. (zone of *Ammonites Sauzei*)
scarp, *Stufe*, f.
scarplands, *Schichstufenland*, n.
scree, *Schutthalde*, f., (rarely) *Halde*, f.
scree material, *Gehängeschutt*, m.
set of land forms, *Formenschatz*, m.
sharply incised V-shaped valley, *Kerbtal*, n., *Kerbe*, f.

slope, *Abdachung*, f., *Böschung*, f., *Hang*, m.

basal slope, *Haldenhang*, m.

slope developed beneath a covering (of water or alluvium), *Eindeckungshang*, m.

slope of diminishing gradient, *Abflachungshang*, m.

slope system, *Hangsystem*, n.

slope unit, *Formsystem*, n. (defined on p. 129. 'Slope unit', when used in later passages, at once conveys the mental image in a way that the English 'form system' does not)

slumping, *Rutschung*, f.

solifluction, *Solifluktion*, f.

spontaneous (migration), *spontane* (*Abwanderung*, f.), (defined on p. 64)

squeezed-mud flows, *Quetschschlammströme*, m.

steps on intervalley ridges, '*Ecken*', f. (J. Sölch's nomenclature)

stone river, *Blockstrom*, m. (*Steinströme* as title of book, n. 150)

streamlets, *rinnendes Wasser*, n.

storeyed landscape, *Stockwerklandschaft*, f.

strong (rock), *fest*

structure (petr.), *Textur*, f.

substructure, *Unterbau*, m.

summit peneplane, *Scheitelrumpffläche*, f.

sunk in (a peneplane), *eingelassen*

superstructure, *Oberbau*, m.

syncline, *Mulde*, f.

synclinal, *synklinal*

talus, *Halde*, f., *Gehängeschutt*, m.

terminal basin (of glacier), *Zungenbecken*, n.

texture (petr.), *Struktur*, f.

top of basal slope, *Haldenscheitel*, m.

tor, *Blockgipfel*, m., *Klippe* (Granit), f.

trickling water, *rieselndes Wasser*, n.; *rinnendes Wasser* (p. 123)

trough, *Mulde*, f.

trough-faulted nature, *Grabennatur*, f.

trough-shaped valley, *Muldental*, n.

trough valley, *Trogtal*, n.

truncation, surface of, *Rumpffläche*, f.

visible surface (of rock), *Tagesoberfläche*, f.

waning development, *absteigende Entwicklung*, f. (lit. descending)

waxing development, *aufsteigende Entwicklung*, f. (lit. ascending)

weathering, *Verwitterung*, f.

INDEX

(This index covers pp. 1–354 only and does not include the summaries,
pp. 355–417)

424

PRINTED IN GREAT BRITAIN
BY ROBERT MACLEHOSE AND CO. LTD.
THE UNIVERSITY PRESS, GLASGOW